Abnormal or Exceptional: Mental Health Literacy for Child and Youth Care

Deborah M. Gural
Red River College

Dawne MacKay-Chiddenton

PEARSON

Toronto

Editorial Director: Claudine O'Donnell
Acquisitions Editor: Kim VeeVers
Marketing Manager: Michelle Bish
Program Manager: Madhu Ranadive/John Polansky
Project Manager: Rohin Bansal
Developmental Editor: Cheryl Finch
Production Services: Jogender Taneja, iEnergizer Aptara®, Ltd.
Permissions Project Manager: Kathryn O'Handley
Photo Permissions Research: Dimple Bhorwal
Text Permissions Research: Phyllis Padula
Art Director: Alex Li
Cover Designer: iEnergizer Aptara®, Ltd.
Cover Image: shutterstock

Credits and acknowledgments for material borrowed from other sources and reproduced, with permission, in this textbook appear on the appropriate page within the text.

Original edition published by Pearson Education, Inc., Upper Saddle River, New Jersey, USA. Copyright © 2016 Pearson Education, Inc. This edition is authorized for sale only in Canada.

If you purchased this book outside the United States or Canada, you should be aware that it has been imported without the approval of the publisher or the author.

5   17

Library and Archives Canada Cataloguing in Publication

Gural, Deborah M. (Deborah Mary), 1967-, author
  Abnormal or exceptional : mental health literacy for child and youth care / Deborah M. Gural, Dawne Mackay-Chiddenton.

Includes bibliographical references and index.
ISBN 978-0-13-287967-5 (paperback)

  1. Child psychopathology.   I. MacKay-Chiddenton, Dawne, 1953-, author   II. Title.

RJ499.G87 2015   618.92'89   C2015-904671-8

ISBN 978-0-13-287967-5

Brief Contents

Contents

Preface

> Good child and youth care isn't brain surgery—it's much more difficult. No educational courses, training programs or textbooks can give you what you need in order to be with, understand and guide a young person through the fear, pain, chaos and anger once these demons are at work. We are not dealing with theory and strategic intervention here. Being in relationship means that we have what it takes to remain open and responsive in conditions where most mortals and professionals quickly distance themselves, become "objective," and look for the external "fix." (Fewster, 2004, p. 3)

Notwithstanding the truism that no single book, or even many courses and books, could possibly teach you everything you need to know to be "good" at child and youth care (CYC), it is our hope that this text will help you understand and more fully appreciate the importance and some of the nuances of good mental health for all young people, particularly for those vulnerable youth we hope to guide through their fear and pain.

The World Health Organization (2001b) defines *mental health* as a state of emotional and psychological well-being in which individuals are able to use their cognitive and emotional capabilities to function in society and meet the ordinary demands of everyday life. For the vulnerable children and youth we engage with, the demands are usually not ordinary; they're often quite extraordinary, and the chaos and anger these young people endure can easily become normalized. Their coping strategies may look like emotional and behavioural dysfunction and mental health difficulties, but they once served an important purpose for most at-risk youth—survival.

CYC and psychology are distinct disciplines, and as such, they view these coping strategies from very different perspectives. Is it ADHD? Or is it trauma? Is it ODD? Or is it attachment? The CYC perspective is strength-based and traditionally avoids the use of the medical model and the diagnostic labels that pathologize youth behaviours. Accordingly, we stress that child and youth care practitioners (CYCPs) see the world through an ecological lens, whereby the context of *all* behaviour has significant meaning for the development of mental health issues. From a psychological perspective, the focus is on the description, assessment, diagnosis, and treatment of abnormal child and youth behaviours. Thus, although there are similarities in the language and frameworks used in both fields, CYCPs have a unique view of what psychologists refer to as *disordered behaviour*.

The foundational assumption of this textbook is that CYCPs have an ethical and professional obligation to be knowledgeable about child and youth mental health issues and concerns. According to this approach, known as *mental health literacy*, members of society ought to have at least a minimum basic knowledge about mental health, as this will aid in the recognition, management, and prevention of mental health issues. As CYCPs, you'll need to understand and appreciate all aspects of young people's mental health and know how to intervene and where to refer. You'll need to act as an advocate for youth to access services, reduce stigma, promote youth voice, and develop youth-friendly mental health programs.

CENTRAL THEMES

The aim of this text—to enhance mental health literacy in CYC students and practitioners—stems from a collaboration between two faculty members at Red River College: a CYC instructor and a psychology instructor. The psychology instructor, Deb Gural, taught a course titled *Abnormal Psychology* to CYC students; the CYC instructor, Dawne MacKay-Chiddenton, taught a course titled *Exceptional Children and Youth*. Together, we determined that an appropriate text for our courses would be one that presented both the CYC and psychological perspectives; the result of that partnership is this textbook. And in the process of developing a vision for this text, specific themes emerged.

Multidisciplinary. In 2009, as editor-in-chief of *Child and Youth Care Forum*, Carl Weems called for a multidisciplinary focus in the journal's future publications. A primary goal in child and youth care, he contended, is the utilization of information from diverse domains of knowledge "to foster what is best for the child and adolescent's development and functioning" (Weems, 2009, p. 2). Consistent with that vision, this text considers emotional and behavioural disturbances of childhood and youth from both a psychological and a CYC perspective.

CYC Focused. The typical abnormal psychology text includes a wealth of information about disturbances in child and youth behaviour from a psychological perspective. This text emphasizes the CYC perspective and uses language that is congruent with a CYC approach. It also emphasizes the role of trauma, resilience, context, and relationship as a means for understanding youth behaviour. When we look beyond the symptoms to the strengths and the needs of the child, that child's mental health will improve. The field of neuroscience offers increasing evidence that traditional Indigenous healing, mindfulness, meditation, relationship, caring, and connectedness all work in therapeutic healing. Good child and youth care is healing.

Practice Oriented. CYCPs work with children who are at risk of not reaching their developmental potential or have already experienced difficulties in development as a result of social disadvantage. This text emphasizes a practice-oriented approach that doesn't merely summarize key theories and research findings, but also outlines specific recommendations for action and interaction in language that is in keeping with CYC training and practice. This integration of relevant theory with guidelines for practical strategies can help CYCPs choose appropriate approaches in working with children and youth and facilitate their communication with other professionals (e.g., psychiatrists, clinical psychologists).

ORGANIZATION OF THE TEXT

Abnormal or exceptional? Disorder or trauma? Mentally ill or in pain and despair? Is the medical model antithetical to good CYC practice? At first glance, it would seem that these are black-and-white questions with straightforward, black-and-white answers. But the reality of living with a diagnosed (or an undiagnosed, for that matter) mental health issue can be excruciatingly painful for an individual youth and his or her family. We have structured this text to provide the learner with both the psychological and CYC viewpoints on each child and youth disorder as it appears in the *Diagnostic and Statistical Manual of Mental Disorders*, Fifth Edition (DSM-5). The DSM-5 provides detailed descriptions of all major psychological disorders currently recognized. Its categorical system is based on the medical model, in that mental disorders are viewed as being similar to physical illnesses and diseases—meaning that they're associated with specific symptoms and require treatment. The DSM-5 describes each disorder in detail, summarizing the symptoms that must be present in order to warrant a diagnosis; clinicians use the DSM-5 as a reference to guide in their assessment and diagnosis of those experiencing mental health issues.

Thus, every chapter in this text (1) outlines general definitions of important concepts; (2) summarizes the relevant diagnostic categories and criteria as defined in the DSM-5; (3) summarizes the incidence, comorbidity, and developmental issues of the disorder; (4) describes the major psychological paradigms of causation; (5) describes the relevant CYC conceptual and causal models; and (6) outlines a selection of the most commonly used psychological and CYC intervention approaches.

Acknowledgments

No duty is more urgent than that of returning thanks.

—Unknown

We would first like to acknowledge, honour, and thank the young people and their families whose stories and struggles have inspired us to write this text. It is our hope that this book will encourage and motivate child and youth care practitioners to be the very best they can be in their relationships with children, youth, and families. We also want to thank all our colleagues in the Child and Youth Care and Nursing programs at Red River College who have supported us in various ways during the course of this project. We owe special thanks to our colleagues across the country who reviewed early drafts of the text and provided us with thoughtful feedback and helpful recommendations: Kristina Arena, Sheridan College; Aurrora De Monte, Fleming College; Kim Ducharme, Confederation College; Stephanie Griffin, Algonquin College; Mary Harber-Iles, Thompson Rivers University; Karen Marr, St. Clair College; and Katherine Sloss, Humber College.

We would like to thank members of the Pearson production team (particularly Cheryl Finch) for their ongoing support, especially when the times got tough (and they did get tough). We greatly appreciate Cheryl's contributions to the manuscript and how she was always there for us in so many ways (despite the physical distance between us!). We are grateful to Joel Gladstone, Madhu Ranadive, and Kim Veevers for the strong support they have given this project. We also thank Karen Alliston for her fine copyediting, Jogender Taneja for shepherding the text through production, and the team in Creative Services for their skillful design of the text.

We are also deeply grateful to Duncan MacKinnon for his early encouragement to submit our proposal to Pearson. In addition, we extend our sincere thanks to friend Barb Arnal for her valuable assistance in the preparation of references and key terms. And finally, we would like to express tremendous gratitude to all our family and friends, especially Mark, Eryn, Kathleen, Jackie, Kevin, Steve, Marlene, Sharon, Kathryn, and Stacie, for always being there for us and cheering us on when we needed it most. We thank you for your patience and support during the many months we had to ignore everyone and everything else in order to complete this project.

To you all: Thank you, Merci, Meegwetch.

About the Authors

Deb Gural is an instructor in both the Nursing and the Child and Youth Care programs at Red River College (RRC) in Winnipeg. She completed her graduate work at the University of Manitoba in the area of Personality and Social Psychology. Her doctoral dissertation, "Choice making and difference making in the perception of control, responsibility, and blame" (2001), reflects her ongoing interest in the areas of perceived control, coping, and stress management. Since 2001, Deb's teaching responsibilities for the Child and Youth Care program have included Introduction to Psychology, Child and Adolescent Development, and Emotional and Behavioural Disorders of Youth. While teaching these courses she became passionate about enhancing mental health literacy in Child and Youth Care students. In 2008, together with her friend and RRC colleague Susan Claire Johnson, she received a Research Innovation Fund Award from RRC for her international evaluation of Child and Youth Care student volunteer efforts post–Hurricane Katrina. As instructor for Cross-Cultural Psychology in the Nursing program, she is dedicated to promoting strategies that increase cultural competence and minimize prejudice and discrimination in students who are future social service and health care providers.

Dawne MacKay-Chiddenton was the academic coordinator and an instructional faculty member of the Child and Youth Care Diploma Program at Red River College in Winnipeg from 1998 to 2015. Before this she was a long-term front-line child and youth care practitioner and supervisor working with vulnerable youth residing in out-of-home care. After retirement, she was a co-researcher on a project promoting youth-in-care voice with her RRC CYC friend and colleague Diane Parris: "Live my life: see what it's like." Dawne was Métis, and was passionate about improving the cultural competence of social service providers working with Aboriginal client populations. She was a longtime board member of Manitoba's Child and Youth Care Workers' Association and an advocate for accountability, program evaluation, service quality, ethical practice, improved standards, and certification in CYC work in Manitoba for many years. Among her committee and organization work, Dawne was a member of the Child and Youth Care Accreditation Board of Canada and of the Children and Youth in Challenging Contexts committee.

Perspectives: Abnormal or Exceptional?

MKrilyn Barbone/Fotolia

One important question in the area of abnormal psychology is how to distinguish "normal" from "abnormal" behaviour. But as these two doors suggest, this is often interpreted as distinguishing between "normal" and "abnormal" people. Which door would fit for you?

Case Example: *Troy*

Thirteen-year-old Troy had never had a problem with separation, nor had he suffered from anxiety. But when the new school year started he began feeling tense and uneasy, and soon he refused to go to school altogether. Consequently, his mother stopped going to work in order to stay home with him. Troy began to have panic attacks characterized by the sudden feeling that he was going to die, along with palpitations, shortness of breath, trembling, and restlessness. He began refusing to leave his mother for any reason, and would follow her everywhere through the house. Finally, he began sleeping with his mother while his father went to sleep in Troy's bed. The panic attacks became almost continuous.

Source: Excerpt from "Father–Child Hospitalization in a Severe Case of Separation Anxiety Disorder with Panic Attacks" by H. Chabrol and R. Fouraste in Clinical Psychology & Psychotherapy 3(4): 288–290, December 1996. Copyright © 1996 by John Wiley & Sons, Inc. Used by permission of John Wiley & Sons, Inc. via Copyright Clearance Center (CCC).

Learning Objectives

1. Identify, define, and provide examples for the four elements of abnormality. Explain how cultural and societal norms play a role in definitions of abnormality.

2. Describe the field of abnormal psychology. Distinguish between mental health, mental illness, and abnormality. Summarize the DSM approach to abnormality.

3. Summarize key elements of a CYC conceptual model and highlight those elements that are particularly relevant in CYC work with young people experiencing mental health concerns. Define mental health literacy.

4. Summarize the CYC perspective on diagnostic labelling. Identify the strengths and limitations of using the DSM-5 in CYC practice.

5. Compare and contrast the psychological paradigms (both historical and modern) of abnormal behaviour.

6. Summarize ways in which CYC professionals may use the major psychological paradigms in their CYC practice.

7. Identify and describe the major psychological approaches to treatment for mental disorders.

8. Describe strength-based assessment processes and the general types of intervention approaches for child and youth mental health concerns.

9. Summarize the pros and cons of using psychotropic medications with children and youth.

Chapter Overview

Abnormal or *exceptional? Disorder* or *trauma? Mentally ill* or *in pain and despair?* In this chapter we examine the major differences between psychological and child and youth care (CYC) perspectives. This distinction is important, because in many ways a CYC approach to understanding young people's emotional and behavioural disturbances or mental "disorders" is based on an alternative to the mainstream societal view of "aberrant," "disturbed," or "deviant" behaviours.

Consider the following statistics. According to Kessler et al. (2005), at least 18 percent of children and adolescents display serious *mental disturbances* and are in need of clinical treatment. And according to Health Canada's (2002) *Report on Mental Illness in Canada*, the onset of most *mental illnesses* occurs during adolescence and young adulthood. It is estimated that, at any given time, approximately 15 percent of children and youth in Canada experience *mental disorders* that interfere with healthy development (*British Columbia, Provincial Health Officer*, 2008). What is a *mental disturbance?* Does the term *mental illness* mean the same thing as *mental disorder?* Do you think Troy's behaviour qualifies as an example of any of these? This chapter will clarify these familiar, but often misused, terms. It will also summarize the major paradigms used by both psychologists and CYC professionals to better understand the behaviour of those they work with. As you'll see, although there are similarities in the language and frameworks used in both fields, child and youth care practitioners (CYCPs) have a unique view of what psychologists refer to as "disordered behaviour."

The CYC perspective is strength-based; it avoids the use of the medical model and diagnostic labels, which pathologize youth behaviours. Accordingly, in this chapter we stress that CYCPs see the world through an *ecological* lens, whereby the context of all behaviours has significant meaning for the development of mental health issues. The major approaches to the various intervention modalities that CYCPs can use in their practice will be briefly introduced as well.

Each of the following chapters focuses on a particular group of disorders, or "exceptional behaviours," while following the same format throughout. For each group, we outline (1) definitions of important concepts; (2) relevant criteria as defined and categorized in the *Diagnostic and Statistical Manual of Mental Disorders* (DSM-5); (3) incidence, comorbidity, and developmental issues; (4) major psychological paradigms of causation; (5) CYC conceptual and causal models; and (6) the most common psychological and CYC intervention approaches.

WHAT IS ABNORMAL BEHAVIOUR?

Generally, psychologists agree that disordered behaviour involves disrupted emotions, behaviours, and/or thoughts. Mental health practitioners also recognize that disordered functioning results in the experience of personal distress and can interfere with one's ability to achieve important personal goals. Everyone experiences periods of sadness, confusion, anger, and so forth, but these are typically normal, expected, short-term responses to challenging events or experiences. For example, consider someone who's been diagnosed with a serious illness or has recently experienced the death of a loved one. We would likely expect sadness, distress, and perhaps anger, as well as behaviours consistent with such emotions. Under what circumstances would psychologists consider such distress or behaviour "abnormal"? As you'll see, there is no simple way to define or identify abnormal behaviour.

Elements of Abnormality

Abnormality is that which is considered the opposite of normal. Defining and identifying what is normal versus abnormal is not an easy task. Most definitions of "normal" include what is expected, usual, or typical, including the idea of conforming to a standard. This standard is associated with the concept of **norms**, socially based rules that define appropriate behaviour in specific situations. One example of a norm in Canada is to shake hands when you're introduced to someone for the first time. Another is to arrive at scheduled appointments on time. Behaviours that conform to these standards are considered normal; behaviours that violate these standards (e.g., not extending a hand to shake when being introduced or arriving an hour late for a lunch date) might be referred to as abnormal.

When it comes to defining any particular behaviour as normal or abnormal, however, abnormality is not always an easy concept to characterize. Although there may be disagreement regarding definitions of abnormality, most would agree that there is no single element or condition that defines abnormality. Instead, several characteristics are considered to be *possible* indicators; it is the co-occurrence of these elements that increases the likelihood that a specific behaviour or condition will be defined as abnormal. Thus, psychologists consider various indicators or elements of abnormality when distinguishing between normal and abnormal. What are the specific elements of abnormality?

Deviance. Infrequency and social undesirability have been associated with abnormality and are related to two different forms of deviance: *statistical deviance* and *social deviance*. If a behaviour or emotional state is unusual or rare, some may consider it to be abnormal. This indicator of abnormality is referred to as **statistical deviance**. Specifically, if behaviour is unusual or not observed very often in the population, such infrequency may be used to define that behaviour as abnormal. Consider the case of Troy, and the fact that he sleeps in his mother's bed while his father sleeps in another room. In North America, most children are encouraged to sleep in their own beds from an early age (Cortesi et al., 2008); few 13-year-olds share a bed with their parents. Statistically, then, this behaviour is rare or unusual and some may define it as abnormal as a result.

Notice that not all rare behaviours or characteristics are defined as abnormal from a psychological perspective. For example, extremely high levels of intelligence (i.e., genius) are rare, but few would label these as abnormal. Similarly, although few people give up all their belongings and move to Africa to devote their life to helping those in need, such behaviour might be viewed with respect and admiration rather than as qualifying for consideration in the field of abnormal psychology. Thus, infrequency alone is not sufficient to define a behaviour or characteristic as abnormal in the psychological sense. In fact, some statistically deviant behaviour is actually considered desirable (e.g., extreme intelligence, athletic abilities, creativity) rather than requiring assessment and change. Therefore, although statistical deviance may be one element useful in defining abnormality, something else in addition to infrequency must be present in order to define a particular behaviour or characteristic as abnormal in the psychological sense.

Another indicator of abnormality is whether the behaviour and/or emotional experience is considered *socially or culturally unacceptable*. In other words, behaving in ways that violate social standards or deviate from the norms of society can result in a behaviour being labelled abnormal. This is referred to as **social deviance**. Norms tell us what is valued in a particular society and specify expected behaviour for particular situations. For example, Troy's refusal to attend school and his need to sleep with his mother are both examples of behaviours that deviate from what most Canadians might define as normal or from what most would expect in the behaviour of a 13-year-old male. However, different societies often have different norms or definitions of appropriate behaviour. For instance, other cultural groups consider "co-sleeping" to be expected and even encourage such behaviour; in Japan and Korea, it is acceptable and not unusual for children to sleep with their parents until adolescence (Yang & Hahn, 2002). This highlights an important aspect of social deviance as a criterion for abnormality. Specifically, definitions of abnormality are *relative to the social and cultural context* in which they occur. We've noted that norms provide guidelines for acceptable behaviour. In doing so, they reflect what is valued or considered important in a culture. For example, in North America, where independence is greatly valued, children are encouraged to separate from their parents early in order to foster a sense of autonomy. Consistent with this value, children are expected to sleep alone at an early age. By comparison, in some collectivist cultures (e.g., those found in Asia and Africa; the Inuit of northwestern Canada), interdependency of the family unit is especially valued and co-sleeping in childhood is believed to support the development of strong bonds to others in the family (Cortesi et al., 2008). Thus, when considering definitions of abnormality in relation to social deviance, we must consider the values and beliefs of the larger social context or society in which we are observing a particular behaviour or characteristic. Definitions of *abnormal* and *normal* will depend on the values and beliefs that are predominant in the larger society.

Similar to our earlier discussion of infrequency, then, just because a behaviour or characteristic violates a social norm doesn't mean that it's labelled as abnormal or negative. As we've seen, different cultures have different definitions of what is valued and considered desirable. Thus, behaviour considered abnormal in one society may be considered normal in another. What is considered abnormal is *relative*, or considered in relation to the context or culture in which it is observed. Moreover, social norms reflect not what is *true* in an objective sense, but rather that group's most current definition of acceptable behaviour. Thus, definitions of normalcy and abnormality not only differ across cultural groups but also change within any one cultural group. For example, consider same-sex orientation. Until 1973, the American Psychiatric Association (APA) classified homosexuality or same-sex orientation as a mental disorder and "abnormal." As a result of changes in North American societal views regarding same-sex relationships, however, homosexuality was eliminated from the list of classified mental disorders and, therefore, is no longer considered abnormal in psychological terms. Thus, changing societal values and beliefs have resulted in changes with respect to definitions of abnormality in relation to same-sex orientation.

Even within a culture and a particular time period, different situations may have different norms. Accordingly, what is normal in one situation may be abnormal in another. For instance, we might consider acts of physical aggression to be normal if they occur between members of a football team on the playing field, but if the same physical acts occurred at a family barbecue, we might label them as deviant or abnormal. Thus, appropriateness to the situation is also an important consideration and, as such, definitions of abnormality are also *relative to the situation*. Is the behaviour expected in the specific circumstance? And, as we discuss later, definitions of abnormality are also relative to one's stage of development.

Personal Distress or Suffering. A second indicator of abnormality is personal distress or suffering. Specifically, does the behaviour or emotion result in the individual experiencing significant personal pain? Distress is often what motivates an individual to seek treatment for symptoms. For example, if one is experiencing painful anxiety or depression, it's not unusual to seek assistance in order to decrease such painful emotions. In Troy's case, his symptoms of palpitations, shortness of breath, trembling, and feeling he was going to die are all associated with significant anguish. Notice how this example highlights the importance of the distress in relation to the appropriateness of the situation. For example, significant distress at the loss of a loved one would be expected, but such distress in the absence of a major life stressor or event is unexpected. It should be noted, however, that not all patterns of abnormal behaviour cause the individual distress. The behaviour viewed as abnormal may not create discomfort for the actor but rather for those around him or her. For example, a child exhibiting high levels of activity and difficulties inhibiting inappropriate behaviour in a classroom may not be experiencing distress himself, but these behaviours are experienced as problematic by others who work or live with the child (e.g., teachers, parents, and peers).

Impairment or Maladaptiveness. A third indicator of abnormality is impairment or *maladaptiveness*. If behaviour or emotions interfere with an individual's ability to achieve important personal goals or to fulfill everyday responsibilities, or if the individual acts in ways that don't contribute to personal well-being, this would indicate impairment of functioning. Specifically, emotional experiences or behaviours that interfere with educational or occupational goals, or with the development and maintenance of personal relationships resulting in isolation from others, are considered abnormal in the psychological sense. For example, in order to be diagnosed with Attention-Deficit/Hyperactivity Disorder (ADHD), there must be "clear evidence that the symptoms interfere with, or reduce the quality of, social, academic, or occupational functioning" (American Psychiatric Association, 2013, p. 60). In Troy's case, the fact that his feelings of anxiety and panic are interfering with his ability to attend school and are resulting in isolation from his peers would be considered important aspects in defining his behaviour and emotional experiences as abnormal.

Risk to Self and Others. A fourth indicator of abnormality is *risk to self and others*, or dangerousness. One obvious example of risk to self is suicidal thoughts or behaviours. Another is violent actions directed toward others. Does the individual behave in ways that create discomfort in others by making them feel threatened or distressed? This might also be associated with a definition of abnormality. For example, in the case of Conduct Disorder (discussed in Chapter 5), a youth demonstrates aggression toward people or animals, destruction of property, theft, and/or serious rule violations. If a behaviour or emotional experience puts the safety of the actor or others at risk, it's likely to be of particular concern for mental health professionals, and also very likely to be considered abnormal from a psychological perspective.

When you consider these elements of abnormal behaviour, it's clear that "abnormality" is a vague label. As we noted earlier, no one element of abnormality is consistently or solely used to define any one behaviour or emotional experience as abnormal from a psychological perspective. Instead, in order for a behaviour or emotional experience to be considered "abnormal," it usually reflects several of these elements. Distress, impairment, and risk are considered to be particularly significant in defining abnormality from a psychological perspective. And different elements may be more or less emphasized in different situations depending on the behaviour of interest. Thus, not all of these elements are equally relevant in each case of abnormality. And because abnormality is also a *relative concept*, definitions of abnormality change in relation to what constitutes abnormal behaviour at a particular time or within a particular culture. Our definitions of abnormality, then, change over time and are subject to cultural differences. Even within a particular culture or historical time period, people may disagree as to what constitutes an *abnormal behaviour*. Can you think of specific examples? Because abnormality is a relative concept, there's often disagreement as to whether a particular behaviour or set of emotions constitutes abnormality. Thus, consistent with the position of the World Health Organization (2001b), discussions of abnormality and mental health and illness must consider cultural differences, the role of subjective or personal judgments, and competing professional theories.

Definitions of abnormality are relative to the situational context in which they occur. Would this behaviour be considered "normal" in a classroom?

Michael Chamberlin/Fotolia

Based on this discussion, it's obvious that defining any one behaviour or characteristic as normal or abnormal is not an easy task. It's also clear that, despite popular belief, it's not possible to draw a clear distinction between "normal" and "abnormal." In fact, the differences between what is normal and abnormal more often relate to a difference in *severity/intensity*, *frequency*, or *duration* of behaviour rather than a difference in the quality or type of behaviour. For example, if Troy had experienced a single panic attack that resulted in his being significantly distressed and staying home from school one day and sleeping with his mother one night only, he may never have been referred for treatment. The fact that his experience was severe, occurred frequently, and lasted for a long period or duration of time increased the likelihood that it would create significant distress and impair his functioning. So rather than thinking about normal and abnormal as a *dichotomy* in which a behaviour is either normal or abnormal, it's more appropriate to think of abnormality as being a *continuum* or a matter of degree. Thus, the behaviour, feelings, and thoughts associated with abnormality don't always differ from normal ones in their nature, but rather in how often they occur or how impairing they are to functioning. As a result, each of us can relate to emotions and actions that are associated with disordered behaviour. It's important to keep this in mind as you read about the various psychological disturbances. It's not unusual to see yourself or others you know reflected in some of these behaviour patterns!

Having identified the major elements of abnormality, we now turn to a discussion of how such behaviours have been explained throughout history. Before going on, however, consider the examples in the *Think About It!* exercise. Which of these behaviours would you consider to be abnormal? Which of the basic elements of abnormality would you use to define any one of these as abnormal?

In order to explore your own views of abnormality, consider the following list of behaviours. Which of these would you consider to be "abnormal"?

1. Refusing to share an idea because you think others will disagree with you.
2. Cheating in order to pass an exam.
3. Playing video games for 10 hours a day.
4. Hitting someone after he or she insults you.
5. Believing that other people can read your mind.
6. Being unable to sleep because you have a presentation the next day.
7. Intentionally cutting your arm with a razor blade.
8. Getting a tattoo that covers your arm or one that covers your face.

WHAT IS ABNORMAL PSYCHOLOGY? THE PSYCHOLOGICAL PERSPECTIVE

Psychology is generally defined as the scientific study of behaviour and mental processes. *Behaviour* includes outward, observable actions (e.g., yelling, crying, and hugging). *Mental processes* refers to the workings of the mind (e.g., internal activities such as thinking, problem solving, feeling, and interpreting). The primary goals of psychology are to *describe*, *explain*, *predict*, and *control* various behaviours. **Abnormal psychology** is a branch of psychology that focuses on the scientific study of *disorders* of behaviour, mood, and mental processes. Therefore, abnormal psychology focuses on describing, explaining, predicting, and controlling (or changing) patterns of *disordered*, *disrupted*, *disturbed*, or *abnormal* behaviour or functioning (from a psychological perspective, we will use these terms interchangeably throughout the text). See Table 1.1 for examples of these goals in relation to the panic attacks discussed in Troy's case.

How do psychologists define and view disturbances in behaviour, mood, and mental processes? In order to better understand definitions of such disruptions, we need to

Table 1.1 Goals of Abnormal Psychology

Goal	Examples
Describe behaviour: What is a panic attack? What happens during an attack?	Individual feels intense fear and apprehension and may experience sweating, shaking, chest pains, dizziness, accelerated heart rate, fear of dying, chills, and nausea
Explain behaviour: Why do panic attacks occur?	Genetic predisposition, severe stress, major life transitions, chemical imbalances
Predict behaviour: Who is most at risk for experiencing a panic attack? When are panic attacks most likely to occur?	Those with a family history of the disorder, significant stress, loss of a loved one, history of childhood sexual or physical abuse, significant trauma
Control/alter behaviour: How can we reduce the occurrence of panic attacks?	Cognitive behavioural therapy, behavioural (exposure) therapy, medication (antidepressants, anti-anxiety)

consider a definition of *mental health*. The World Health Organization (2001b) defines **mental health** as a "state of well-being in which an individual realizes his or her own abilities, can cope with the normal stresses of life, can work productively and fruitfully, and is able to make a contribution to his or her community" (p. 1). **Mental illness**, in contrast, is a general term associated with behaviours and/or states that *interfere* with mental health (i.e., interfere with participation in productive activities, fulfilling relationships, and an individual's ability to adapt to change and cope with challenges).

Based on these definitions, should we consider Troy's behaviour "disordered"? What would a psychologist conclude? When it comes to understanding mental disturbance and disrupted behaviour from a psychological perspective, the concept of abnormality is particularly relevant. However, it's important to note that *abnormal behaviour* does not equal *mental disorder*. Let's examine the difference between these two terms.

The DSM-5 Categorical System

As we've seen, *abnormal behaviour* is a general term that relates to actions or emotions that violate societal norms, create distress, and interfere with functioning (the indicators of abnormality). By comparison, **mental disorder** is defined as a significant behavioural or psychological syndrome or behaviour pattern (associated with the indicators of abnormality) that relates to a very specific group of behaviours, emotions, and impairments. Examples include *Bipolar Disorder*, *Obsessive-Compulsive Disorder*, and *Conduct Disorder*. Each of these disorders is defined by a particular *pattern* of behaviour (rather than a single behaviour or characteristic) that comprises many different actions or emotional experiences that interfere with the individual's ability to function (socially, academically, emotionally, etc.) and/or results in significant distress for the individual. Thus, although certain behaviours can be possible *indicators* of a specific disorder, the two terms are not interchangeable.

The fifth edition of the ***Diagnostic and Statistical Manual of Mental Disorders (DSM-5)***, a publication of the American Psychiatric Association (2013), provides detailed descriptions of all major psychological disorders currently recognized. The DSM-5 is used as a reference guide by mental health professionals around the world. Specifically, the manual is used to guide professionals in their work with those experiencing behavioural and/or emotional challenges. The manual identifies 22 groups or categories of disorders, each summarized in its own chapter. The specific disorders included in any one category/chapter are grouped together on the basis of similar symptoms and similar causes. Box 1.1 presents the 22 groups of disorders along with examples of specific disorders for each category.

How do mental health professionals use the DSM-5 in their work with people experiencing significant distress and/or impairment? Let's take a closer look at what's included in the DSM-5 for any mental disorder and how that information is used by psychologists, psychiatrists, and other mental health professionals.

DSM-5 Disorders: Diagnoses and Criteria

For any specific mental disorder identified in the DSM-5, there is a detailed summary of the *symptoms* that must be observed in order for someone to be *diagnosed* with the disorder. You may be surprised by the use of medical terms (*symptoms*, *diagnosis*) in a discussion of

Box 1.1

DSM-5 Categories and Examples

DSM-5 Category/Chapter	Specific Disorder Examples
Neurodevelopmental Disorders	ADHD, Autism Spectrum Disorder, Learning Disorders
Schizophrenia Spectrum and Other Psychotic Disorders	Schizophrenia, Schizoaffective Disorder
Bipolar and Related Disorders	Bipolar I Disorder, Bipolar II Disorder
Depressive Disorders	Major Depressive Disorder
Anxiety Disorders	Specific Phobia, Panic Disorder, Social Anxiety Disorder
Obsessive-Compulsive and Related Disorders	Obsessive-Compulsive Disorder, Hoarding, Trichotillomania
Trauma- and Stressor-Related Disorders	PTSD, Acute Stress Disorder, Adjustment Disorder
Dissociative Disorders	Dissociative Amnesia, Dissociative Identity Disorder
Somatic Symptom and Related Disorders	Somatic Symptom Disorder, Conversion Disorder
Feeding and Eating Disorders	Anorexia Nervosa, Bulimia Nervosa, Binge Eating Disorder
Elimination Disorders	Enuresis, Encopresis
Sleep-Wake Disorders	Insomnia Disorder, Narcolepsy, Parasomnias
Sexual Dysfunctions	Erectile Disorder, Female Orgasmic Disorder
Gender Dysphoria	Gender Dysphoria
Disruptive, Impulse-Control, and Conduct Disorders	Oppositional Defiant Disorder, Conduct Disorder
Substance-Related and Addictive Disorders	Substance Use Disorder, Gambling Disorder
Neurocognitive Disorders	Delirium, Major and Mild Neurocognitive Disorders
Personality Disorders (PDs)	Antisocial PD, Borderline PD, Narcissistic PD
Paraphilic Disorders	Pedophilic Disorder, Voyeuristic Disorder
Other Mental Disorders	Unspecified Mental Disorder Due to Another Medical Condition
Medication-Induced Movement Disorders and Other Adverse Effects of Medication	Tardive Dyskinesia, Antidepressant Discontinuation Syndrome
Other Conditions That May Be a Focus of Clinical Attention	Relational Problems, Abuse and Neglect

mental disorders. However, because the DSM categorical system is based on the **medical model**, mental disorders are viewed as being similar to physical illnesses and diseases that are associated with specific symptoms and require treatment. The specific symptoms of any disorder are referred to as *diagnostic criteria* and outline the major features of a disorder. For example, Box 1.2 presents the diagnostic criteria for Gender Dysphoria, a disorder identified and summarized in the DSM-5.

You might also be surprised (and perhaps offended) to see Gender Dysphoria included in the DSM. As we saw in our discussion of the relative nature of definitions of abnormality, societal views regarding gender, sexual orientation, and sexual identity have changed significantly in recent decades, and the DSM criteria have changed in relation to shifts in these views. Did you know that in the past, having an identity as an LGBTT person was

Box 1.2

DSM-5 Criteria for Gender Dysphoria

A. A marked incongruence between one's experienced/expressed gender and assigned gender, of at least 6 months' duration, as manifested by at least two of the following:

1. A marked incongruence between one's experienced/expressed gender and primary and/or secondary sex characteristics (or in young adolescents, the anticipated secondary sex characteristics).

2. A strong desire to be rid of one's primary and/or secondary sex characteristics because of a marked incongruence with one's experienced/expressed gender (or in young adolescents, a desire to prevent the development of the anticipated secondary sex characteristics).

3. A strong desire for the primary and/or secondary sex characteristics of the other gender.

4. A strong desire to be of the other gender (or some alternative gender different from one's assigned gender).

5. A strong desire to be treated as the other gender (or some alternative gender different from one's assigned gender.)

6. A strong conviction that one has the typical feelings and reactions of the other gender (or some alternative gender different from one's assigned gender).

B. The condition is associated with clinically significant distress or impairment in social, occupational, or other important areas of functioning.

Source: From DIAGNOSTIC AND STATISTICAL MANUAL OF MENTAL DISORDERS. Reprinted with permission from the Diagnostic and Statistical Manual of Mental Disorders, Fifth Edition, (Copyright ©2013). American Psychiatric Association. All Rights Reserved.

included in the *Diagnostic and Statistical Manual of Mental Disorders*? For example, homosexuality was defined as a psychiatric "disorder" that needed treatment. In 1973 and 1974, due to growing protest, the APA removed homosexuality from the manual. And yet, although homosexuality was declassified in the 1980 edition (the DSM-III), variations of the listing remained until 1986. In 1980, "Ego-Dystonic Homosexuality" was listed in the DSM-III as a disorder characterized by distress associated with homosexuality. This listing was removed from the DSM-III-R in 1987 in light of the argument that any distress associated with homosexuality was more the result of societal reaction to the behaviour pattern (i.e., homophobia) rather than of one's subjective experience of homosexuality. The fifth edition of the DSM introduces the term *Gender Dysphoria* to replace these earlier terms and emphasizes that the critical element in the definition of this "disorder" isn't the gender identity itself, but rather the psychological distress and impairment that might be associated with the incongruence between one's experienced/expressed gender and the gender one was assigned at birth.

By providing such a detailed description of each disorder and its symptoms, the DSM is used as a reference to guide *assessment* and *diagnosis* of those experiencing mental health issues. **Assessment** involves collecting relevant information about a person using a variety of means (e.g., observation of their behaviours, questionnaires, interviews) in order to provide an overall picture of that person's behavioural, cognitive, emotional, and overall functioning. By gathering this information, the mental health professional can identify behaviours, emotions, or thoughts that are interfering with functioning or creating significant distress (i.e., symptoms) and compare these to the diagnostic criteria in the DSM. If there is a match between the criteria outlined and the symptoms expressed by the individual, the person's behaviour pattern can be assigned to a specific category of the DSM

After carefully examining all the information gathered about Andi, a 12-year-old girl living in care, Dr. Balan assigns her behaviour to a specific category of the DSM and writes *Major Depressive Disorder* in Andi's chart.

Seventeen-year-old Carol is a high-school student. Although her parents are recently divorced and she's had to move, she continues to do well academically. She turns to her friends regularly for comfort, and overall, she's managing stress very well.

Dr. Allen interviews Chris, asking a variety of questions. Next, he speaks with Chris's parents and teachers about his behaviour, grades, and social interactions. He also contacts Chris's physician to obtain a summary of his current medical conditions.

classification system. This process of assigning one's behaviour pattern to a category of the DSM is referred to as **diagnosis**. Thus, the manual *specifically describes* each disorder in detail, summarizing the symptoms that must be present in order for someone to be diagnosed with that disorder.

Note that Criterion B in Box 1.2 requires that the individual be experiencing significant distress or impairment in relation to the symptoms summarized in Criterion A. This requirement (associated with our earlier discussion of the major elements of a psychological view of abnormality) is included in the diagnostic criteria for every disorder in the DSM-5.

Before moving on to a consideration of a CYC approach to abnormal behaviour, test your understanding of some of the key concepts (i.e., the bolded terms) associated with a psychological approach to emotional and behavioural disturbances in the *Test Your Understanding* exercise. Can you identify the specific concept associated with each example?

A CYC APPROACH TO ABNORMALITY: UNDERSTANDING EMOTIONAL AND BEHAVIOURAL DISTURBANCES

Given the preceding discussion on the difficulties in defining *abnormality*, it's fitting to re-examine our choice of terms used to describe concerning behaviours related to mental health using a strength-based approach. For example, in CYC practice, one of the terms we might suggest using to describe young people's "abnormal" behaviours or the emotional and behavioural disorders is **exceptional**. This term was developed through the study of learning disabilities in the field of children's special education (Winzer, 2005). The term is philosophically consistent with a CYC perspective in that it avoids the negative labelling inherent in such words as *psychopathology*, *abnormal*, *disturbed*, and *disorder*. A child or youth with an exceptionality displays differences in his or her physical, intellectual, communicative, social, or emotional domains (Winzer, 2005).

Mental Health Literacy. The notion of **mental health literacy** (Jorm et al., 1997) is based on the assumption that in order to aid in the recognition, management, and prevention of mental health issues, members of society ought to have at least a basic knowledge of mental health. Such knowledge also helps to de-stigmatize mental health difficulties.

Children and youth practitioners (CYCPs) have an ethical and professional obligation to be knowledgeable about young people's mental health issues and concerns.

That is, they need to be able to recognize the symptoms and signs of potential mental health difficulties and to respond to these appropriately and effectively. Well-informed helping professionals know how to obtain mental health information; they have a basic knowledge of risk factors, causes, and treatments; and they know where to access appropriate professional help. Indeed, CYCPs, as direct service professionals working with children, youth, and families, "are in an excellent position to recognize and respond to mental health emergencies" (Ranahan, 2010, p. 15).

There are many approaches to the assessment of, and intervention in, emotional and behavioural disorders in children and youth. These are articulated in CYC, counselling, behaviour management, and special education literature. The journal *Reclaiming Children and Youth*, for example, is an excellent resource for researching CYC approaches to exceptional behaviours.

The Context of CYC Work. CYCPs work in a wide variety of agency and program settings within many major systems: child and family services, health (including mental health), justice, community-based, and education, to name just a few. CYCPs could also be doing street work or prevention work with homeless youth or sexually exploited young people. (We use the term *child/youth sexual exploitation* instead of *juvenile prostitution* to highlight the fact that adults having sex with minors constitutes child sexual exploitation/sexual abuse.) You might be a crisis worker responding to calls from the community to assist with a youth or family in crisis, or a family support worker teaching parenting skills and providing support to a young mother. You might be working with youth who are struggling with addictions in all these various systems. Your learning needs, how you approach your learning, and your perspective on the mental health concerns of the children, youth, and families with whom you're engaged will vary and be influenced by the predominant ideologies of each system or setting. The expectations for your treatment approach, your level of involvement in case planning, and the ways you assist young people experiencing mental health concerns will vary as well. For example, if you're working in a child and adolescent inpatient psychiatric facility, its predominant ideology will be based on the bio-medical conceptual model—one that provides a diagnosis and a plan for a cure or treatment of the mental illness (Stuart, 2009a). The first line of treatment and the predominant intervention in this milieu will very likely be *psychotropic medication*—medication that alters perceptions, thoughts, emotion, and/or behaviour. There will likely be little choice in the conceptual model or treatment approach.

If you're a CYCP working in a group home or residential treatment centre, you may have staff psychiatrists, psychologists, social workers, clinicians, or therapists giving you clinical advice about which therapeutic approaches to use with young people experiencing emotional and behavioural difficulties. The CYC staff team work with these youth during what's been termed "the other 23 hours"—the hours that youth who live in managed care programs, residential care, or out-of-home care spend outside the therapist's office (Trieschman, Whittaker, & Brendtro, 1969).

If you're working in a community-based mental health program, you may be responsible for developing the treatment plan for a youth's seven-days/week, 24-hour care, and for reporting changes or concerns to an interdisciplinary team of doctors, psychiatrists, occupational therapists, nurses, and psychologists. If you're a street outreach worker, you'll need to provide advocacy, support, and referrals for youth experiencing mental health concerns. Whatever your role or level of responsibility and in whatever system you may be working, as a CYCP you must be able to recognize signs and symptoms of youth mental health difficulties, and respond accordingly. Although you're not qualified to make diagnoses (and this is not your role), you must be able to engage in a meaningful dialogue with collateral professionals, parents, and the young people themselves. Thus, you need to be familiar with paradigms or conceptual models, theories, interventions, referral sources, psychotropic medications, signs and symptoms, and so on. That is your professional responsibility.

CYCPs must also be knowledgeable about the Mental Health Act in their respective jurisdictions. They need to be well informed about all the services offered in the local mental health system. This includes the Canadian Mental Health Association (CMHA), community-based programs, self-help and support groups, addiction services, crisis response services, emergency services, mental health assessment services, and all in patient and outpatient child and adolescent psychiatric services. CYCPs need to understand how all the various systems (e.g., justice, health, community, child welfare, and education) respond and intersect with regard to child and adolescent mental health issues. Knowledge of referral sources for these services, and of private mental health practitioners who provide ongoing therapy and support to young people and families experiencing mental health issues, is also key to effective CYC practice in the area of child and adolescent mental health.

CYC Domains of Practice. According to Carol Stuart (Stuart, 2009a; Stuart & Carty, 2006), seven domains of practice or competencies are involved in child and youth care practice: self, professionalism, communication, normal and abnormal child and adolescent development, systems context, relationships, and interventions.

The first three domains (self, professionalism, and communication) are *foundational* (that is, the remaining four domains build on these and relate to the specific skills and knowledge required for CYC practice). The first foundation is the **self**, where the CYCP uses self-awareness to guide all interactions with others and ensures that personal values are congruent with professional values; the second is **professionalism**, where the CYCP identifies and resolves ethical dilemmas based on CYC values and strives to maintain a professional presentation and identity; and the third is **communication**, where the CYCP uses communication skills to express self and professionalism toward others, primarily clients and colleagues.

Your treatment approach is significantly influenced by your *self*; that is, your personal and professional experiences and opinions about the mental health concerns of the youth in your care. When considering the domain of self, you need to be mindful of your own life story (Bellefeuille & Jamieson, in Bellefeuille & Ricks, 2008). It's important to explore your own conceptual model or set of beliefs about what causes mental health issues in young people—a process that will help you, as the practitioner, clarify your understanding of how or why mental illnesses develop and affect some children and youth so profoundly. You must also recognize how your story influences your choice of preferred conceptual model. This process is sometimes called *meaning making* (Garfat & McElwee, 2007), which refers to how we make sense of what we observe based on our own context.

The competency domains of professionalism and communication are also critical to mental health literacy in CYC practice. Can you provide examples that illustrate their relevance?

The four remaining competencies required for effective CYC practice (normal and abnormal child and adolescent development, systems context, relationships, and interventions) overlap with each other. CYCPs must be able to assess the status of a child's development and identify areas of competence and areas of developmental delay. They must then be able to apply this knowledge to the systemic context of the young person's life. The assessment is applied to the planned interventions, which are executed by the practitioner. Most importantly, relationships are the foundation of the entire process from start to finish: from assessment through to interventions. "Children and youth as well as their families must trust and feel safe in their interpersonal interactions with CYC practitioners, [and] such safety and trust is developed through relationships" (Stuart & Carty, 2006, p. 26).

Refer to Figure 1.1 for a summary of these seven domains.

It's evident that the domains of CYC practice are all highly interrelated. As Stuart and Carty (2006) point out, the central focus of CYC practice is first the child, youth, and/or family, and second (but also critically important) the quality of care and service CYCPs provide to help them attain optimal mental health. The authors note that the domains of professional CYC practice in child and youth mental health are no different

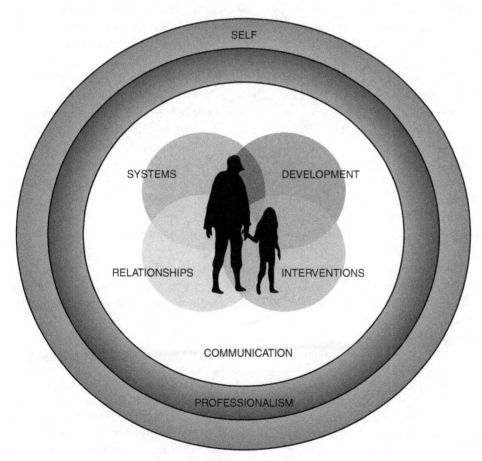

Figure 1.1 The Seven Domains of CYC Practice

The seven domains of practice or competencies involved in child and youth care practice.

Source: Stuart & Carty, 2006.

from those in any other sector that provides care for children, youth, and families. The emphasis may vary slightly and the interdisciplinary team will probably vary significantly in various settings, but competent CYC practice requires knowledge, skills, and abilities in all the domains, regardless of the context (Stuart & Carty, 2006).

CYC and Diagnostic Labelling. The use of diagnostic labels grew out of the special education field in the United States and is based on the medical model, or the biological–psychological paradigm (Winzer, 2005). In special education, diagnostic labelling is used to classify children in order to place them in appropriate settings and to secure funding. Labels can be seen as cues that help organize our knowledge of, and responses to, children's and youth's exceptional behaviours. All labels carry with them certain expectations, some good, and some bad (Winzer, 2005).

The research on the use of diagnostic labels is inconclusive. Although there are always concerns about labelling bias, the research shows that stigma typically exists already, before the formal diagnostic label is applied, and that the label itself does not add appreciably to the stigma (Winzer, 2005). Moreover, the "mentally ill" or "mental disorder" label may help a child and family access help or services. Diagnostic labels, while they can be stigmatizing, can also lead to proper treatment and recovery. Currently, however, in the special education field and in the CYC literature there is much distrust of the use of labels.

As Lavin and Park (1999) note, CYCPs need a good basic understanding of what the DSM diagnostic labels mean and how to distinguish between them—not only in order to understand the signs and symptoms of exceptionalities (a professional obligation in mental health literacy), but also to help "determine the modality, intensity and duration of the interventions" to use in treatment. Nonetheless, they also note, with strong criticism, that diagnostic labels tend to focus on the "child's aberrant behaviour rather than the emotional turmoil that produces it" (Lavin & Park, 1999, p. 5). These authors identify this focus on the behaviour of the child as a pivotal issue for treatment: without an understanding of the context or background issues and/or by viewing behaviours from a strictly conceptual model, CYCPs run the risk of overlooking or minimizing the emotional elements that may be causing and perpetuating the behavioural difficulties (Lavin & Park, 1999). Larry Brendtro (1988) suggests that diagnostic labels are seldom helpful to CYC practitioners—that they're antithetical to a CYC approach in that they stigmatize young people, which in turn negatively influences our responses to their behaviour and to them as individuals.

> We point our finger, then control, treat and fix, as if we're dealing with a disease. . . . ADHD, ODD, PDD, and so on: we have all of the "technical" labels, but are we trying to apply medicine and science where they do not belong? How can these diagnostic labels represent such unique, special and colourful minds? Confining children to categories constricts and changes our beliefs about them, and, consequently, our interactions with them. To understand each child for whom she/he is, we need to embrace "normalcy" rather than "pathology," to be fluid instead of rigid and in our interventions we need to be simply genuine and caring human! (Brendtro, 1988, p. 1)

Indeed, many CYC writers and clinicians (e.g., Fewster, 2002) argue that diagnosing and labelling children has serious and undesirable consequences. Clearly, there is great

Table 1.2 Pros and Cons of Applying Labels to Children and Youth

Arguments for the Use of Labels	Concerns About the Use of Labels
Can't discuss or identify problems without using labels	Labels permanently assign a diagnosis
Labels provide a common language for professionals	Labels don't reflect an individual child's needs
Labels help to access services and funding	Labels don't reflect an individual child's needs
Labels can simplify information for professionals and parents	Parents and professionals may disagree about the use of labels
Labels assist in diagnosis and in insurance coverage	Labels exclude things that are different and divide the normal from the deviant
There is no connection between labels and service delivery	A label only describes problems and deficits
Labels help others become more tolerant of a disability	People expect deviant behaviour from labelled individuals
Labels result in increased viability for those with special needs	People view a labelled individual differently
Labels are helpful to parents; they give a name to the disability and thus an explanation and control	An oversimplified label suggests an unhealthy child
Children suffer damage to self-esteem because of behavioural problems, not because of labels	Labelling negatively affects children's self-esteem
Labels help us identify those who need help	Categorizing encourages professionals to treat children as labels
Stigma precedes the label	Labels result in stigma

Source: From Children with Exceptionalities in Canadian Classrooms 7E by Margret Winzer. Published by Pearson Canada, © 2005.

debate regarding the utility of labelling associated with diagnoses of children and youth. A summary of the advantages and disadvantages of the use of diagnostic labels is presented in Table 1.2. Consider the literature and then decide for yourself. Where do you stand on this important issue?

Person-First Language. A person is not a disorder; CYCPs use **person-first language** when working with young people with exceptionalities. For example, we don't refer to the *FASD child* or the *ADHD youth*, but rather to *a young person affected by FASD* or the *adolescent diagnosed with ADHD*.

> Person first language is the appropriate way to talk about disorders or disabilities. In talking about children with disabilities, we may hear or say things like, "He's ADHD," or "He's a Down's kid." We have all heard and probably said these things without much thought. Person first language is the respectful way to talk about children's disabilities that places the focus on the person and not the disability. To use person first language, simply say the person's name or use a pronoun first, follow it with the appropriate verb, and then state the name of the disability. (Logsdon, 2015)

LoSa/Fotolia

Being sensitive to an individual's cultural identity is fundamental to CYC practice. Aboriginal Peoples in Canada burn sage in smudging ceremonies to cleanse the body and spirit.

Cultural Respect. In the CYC approach to understanding child and youth exceptionalities, "helpers recognize that they need to develop an understanding of each individual they are working with, including that person's personal, family, community and national history and how that history affects the present" (Hart, 2002, p. 107).

In **culturally competent** practice, CYCPs are knowledgeable about the culture of the young people with whom they are working. Cultural competence is a journey (not a destination) of learning about the cultures of the individuals they serve. The term *cultural safety* is similarly defined as "the state of being in which a child or young person experiences that her or his personal well-being, as well as social and cultural frames of reference, is acknowledged—even if not fully understood by the worker(s) claiming to be there to help him or her" (Fulcher, 2001, p. 2).

In Manitoba, for example, the majority of the children in the care of child and family services or involved in the justice system are of Aboriginal descent. To be effective in the justice or managed care system in this province, then, CYC practitioners ought to, at minimum, learn as much as they can about Aboriginal culture, and to acknowledge and address any biases they may have. They need to understand the present-day consequences of colonization and the consequent oppression and intergenerational trauma faced by Aboriginal people. They ought to have knowledge of traditional methods of healing where appropriate, including the sweat lodge and traditional medicines used in smudging, and to have access to Elders and cultural advisers.

Indigenous people have been particularly susceptible to cultural racism in both the allocation of resources for responsive health and social services and in the way services are delivered. Simply trying to understand where people from a different culture are "coming from" can be in itself a huge undertaking. Child and youth care workers seeking to pursue cultural safety in their own practice are encouraged to think about how each encounter is conceptually framed by a cultural context. (Fulcher, 2001, p. 152)

There is a lack of culturally relevant services for Aboriginal mental health needs. There are also concerns about the use of Western labels for many mental illnesses, including depression, and the use of culturally inappropriate questions to assess mental illness in Aboriginal young people. Awareness of these cultural issues is essential to CYC practice.

Distinguishing between First Nations and Western understandings can be problematic and foster the process of othering. However, an understanding of distinguishing features from these two standpoints is essential to effectively address the priority Aboriginal peoples give to mental health and illness. Othering may marginalize Aboriginal peoples or render Aboriginal knowledge as a commodity to exploit, appropriate, or potentially misinterpret. Distinctions between Aboriginal and Western worldviews of mental health also run the risk of generalizing Aboriginal culture without considering individual and tribal differences or appreciating the dynamic nature of cultural worldviews, values, beliefs, and understandings. Nevertheless, to ignore Aboriginal worldviews about mental health and illness is unethical and immoral as Aboriginal peoples fight the legacy of colonization to regain a sense of balance and harmony within their collective historical identity. (Vukic et al., 2011, p. 660)

Explanation and Intervention. In our work with young people, the way we understand the development of their exceptional behaviour ought to guide our choice of intervention. For example, if an ADHD diagnosis includes a biophysical explanation for the development of ADHD's classic triad of behaviours (impulsivity, inattentiveness, and hyperactivity), we would look to a biophysical intervention, such as physician-prescribed medication or diet modification. Although a biological paradigm doesn't usually fit well with the CYC approach, the use of psychotropic medications (as prescribed for ASD, ADHD, FASD, and so on) may indeed be warranted in some cases.

Evidence-Based Practice. CYCPs need to be accountable for the interventions they use in their practice. For most, this means providing evidence that the interventions have resulted in positive and measurable outcomes for youth. True **evidence-based practice** is supported by scientific evidence showing that it works. Many CYC interventions aren't evidence based per se but have much anecdotal evidence of their success; the Life Space Crisis Intervention is one such approach (Stuart & Carty, 2006).

In an Ontario investigation of CYC and mental health, Stuart and Carty (2006) delineated several treatment models recognized by CYCP focus groups as evidence-based; the 10 most frequently identified were cognitive behavioural therapy; therapeutic crisis intervention; COPE; SNAP: Stop Now and Plan; CPI: Crisis Prevention Institute; NVCI; solution-focused therapy; Positive Parenting Program; TAP/C: Arson Prevention; Goldstein's social skills; and pharmaceutical intervention.

Carol Stuart (2009b) notes that she's sometimes uncertain about whether the CYC field should fully adopt an evidence-based philosophy. Our interventions are intuitive and relational, and as such ought not to be strictly evidence based. Moreover, it's difficult to determine whether an approach can be defined as evidence-based treatment, as this requires total consistency and control over the environment. Stuart explains that although we as a profession understand the importance of developing an evidence base about what we do, we need to retain the legitimacy of professional discretion, judgment, and individualized stories about approaches to our CYC work (Stuart, 2009b).

To further consider the way labelling and language can alter our perceptions, read *Troy's Case: Revisited*. Notice how the language we use to describe patterns of behaviour can alter our perceptions of that behaviour as well as our ideas about the person exhibiting it.

Troy's Case: *Revisited*

Reread the opening case of Troy. What pathology- or deficit-based words might be used to describe him? What strength-based words might be used? Now ask yourself how you felt when reviewing each description of Troy. How might young people feel if they were to read some of the descriptions in their logs or case files?

Try this out by describing yourself in 25 words or less using pathology- or deficit-based terms: for example, *I'm a procrastinator; I can't lose weight; My car is a mess; I eat too much junk food*; and so on. Now describe yourself in 25 words or less using strength-based terms: for example, *I'm a good mother; I'm a caring person; I'm good at math; I'm a good friend*. How did you feel when reviewing each description of yourself?

HOW MANY YOUNG PEOPLE STRUGGLE WITH MENTAL HEALTH DIFFICULTIES?

Mental illness will directly or indirectly affect all Canadians at some time in their lives, whether through a family member, friend, or colleague's experience. Twenty percent of Canadians will personally experience a mental illness in their lifetime. Mental illness affects people of all ages, educational and income levels, and cultures.

According to Statistics Canada (2013), adolescents and young adults aged 15–24 experience the highest incidence of mental disorders of any age group in Canada. As illustrated in Figure 1.2, the number of people affected by any particular mental disorder varies significantly. For example, while schizophrenia affects 1 percent of the Canadian population, anxiety disorders affect more than 5 percent, causing mild to severe impairment. Of great concern is the fact that suicide accounts for 23 percent of all deaths among 15- to 19-year-olds (Statistics Canada, 2012).

Studies suggest that as many as 14–25 percent of children and youth in Canada experience significant mental health issues (Waddell et al., 2005). Most mental health problems can be detected prior to the age of 24, and 50 percent of these difficulties surface before the age of 14. Mental health difficulties contribute to problems with achievement and relationships at school. In severe cases, they prevent students from regularly attending class, but more often students simply struggle with these problems on a daily basis, leading to further social and academic functioning concerns. The problem is that most of the

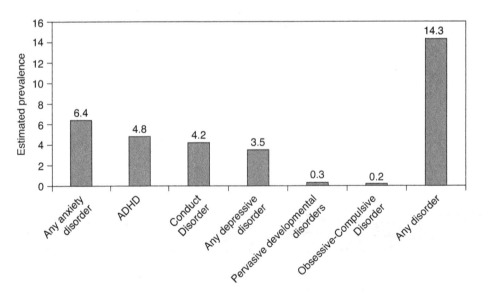

Figure 1.2 Estimated Prevalence of Mental Disorders in Canadian Children Under 15, 2001

The prevalence of mental disorders in Canadian children varies significantly depending on the disorder.

Source: From The State of Public Health in Canada 2009. Copyright © 2009 by the Public Health Agency of Canada. Used by permission of the Public Health Agency of Canada.

children and youth who are struggling with mental health concerns will not say anything to anyone, and thus *will not receive any support or intervention*.

In each chapter of this text we provide statistics regarding current rates of the relevant disorder in Canada. Be aware that estimates vary significantly depending on the source, and that these estimates are constantly changing.

MENTAL HEALTH DISTURBANCES AND DEVELOPMENT

Definitions of abnormality are relative to the *developmental norms* for each age group. Thus, a behaviour or characteristic can be outside the norm within a particular developmental stage. This is especially relevant when considering definitions of abnormality for children and adolescents.

From a CYC perspective, when considering what is normal and what is not, we must recognize that almost all children and youth experience significant emotional and behavioural instability during pre-adolescence and adolescence (Winzer, 2005). CYCPs need to know how the various mental health concerns might manifest differently at the different developmental stages. For example, depression may be manifested as failure to thrive in infants, as defiance in preschoolers, and as anger, acting out, risk taking, and/or substance abuse in adolescents (Wilmshurst, 2004b). CYC students and practitioners need a good understanding of developmental theories to use in their assessments.

As well, knowledge of child and adolescent development is a critically important domain of CYC practice. The sub-domains (Stuart & Carty, 2006; Stuart, 2013) included within the major domain of "normal and abnormal child and adolescent development" are the following competencies:

i. Knowledge of developmental theories

ii. Knowledge of patterns of growth and development

iii. An understanding of learning theory

iv. The ability to link developmental theory to pathology

v. Knowledge of medication and pharmacology

Let's consider the case of Troy once more. As we discussed earlier, sleeping with one's mother might be considered more acceptable and less abnormal for a 3- or 4-year-old than it would be for 13-year-old Troy. Accordingly, definitions of abnormality also consider the norms or expected standards of behaviour as they exist for particular age groups and what we might expect from those within a particular developmental stage. Refer to Table 1.3 for an overview of the age ranges that will be the focus of this text and the terms that will be used to refer to each age group.

We also need to recognize that the characteristics or symptoms of adult mental health issues are different when manifested in children and youth. The DSM-5 acknowledges these differences on occasion as well. For example, the diagnostic criteria for Posttraumatic Stress Disorder are different for those aged 6 and under, and the DSM

Table 1.3 Developmental Age Ranges (as referred to in this text)

Chronological Age Range	Developmental Group and Associated Terms
Birth to 2 years	infants, toddlers
2 to 11 years	child, childhood
11 to 18 years	adolescence, adolescent, teen, youth
Birth to death	individual *(this term is used to refer generally to anyone from any age range)*

includes a specific set of criteria for this age range. In addition, the DSM includes a separate section on **personality disorders**, long-standing patterns of behaviour that are present continuously from childhood, adolescence, or early adulthood into adulthood. In order to be diagnosed with a personality disorder, there must be evidence of the behaviour pattern in earlier stages of development. For example, Antisocial Personality Disorder is characterized by frequent violations of the rights of others, including criminal acts. In order to be diagnosed with this disorder in adulthood, there must be evidence that the adult had a pattern of similar behaviour in childhood and/or adolescence, often being given a previous diagnosis of Conduct Disorder.

COMORBIDITY

As we've discussed, psychological disorders and their symptoms are not clearly separated from normal functioning. In the same way, psychological disorders themselves aren't neatly separated from one another. Similar symptoms (e.g., sleeping difficulties, impulsive behaviour) are included in the diagnostic criteria for many disorders. It's not unusual, then, for one person to meet the criteria for more than one disorder. **Comorbidity** refers to the co-occurrence of two or more disorders in one person. For example, an adolescent might meet the criteria (and be diagnosed) with both Major Depressive Disorder and ADHD.

Comorbidity represents a challenge both for the DSM as a categorical system and for practitioners. For the DSM, the fact that many symptoms are associated with various diagnostic categories (e.g., impulsivity is a criteria for ADHD, Antisocial Personality Disorder, Borderline Personality Disorder, and others) challenges the idea that mental disturbances fall easily into distinct categories. For the practitioner, comorbidity presents challenges regarding which pattern of disturbance (e.g., anxiety or depression) should be the priority of treatment.

Regardless of the challenges associated with comorbidity, and the fact that this term doesn't fit with a CYC approach to conceptualizing youth behaviour, understanding this concept is an important component of CYCPs' mental health literacy. Specifically, knowing how to recognize the most common coexisting disorders in children and youth can facilitate a practitioner's work with youth and their supports.

Before examining the psychological explanations for what causes mental illness, consider the common myths about mental disorders presented in Box 1.3. Are you surprised by any of these myths? Are your beliefs about mental disorders consistent with the facts?

Common Myths About Mental Disorders

MYTH: *Mental illnesses aren't real illnesses.*

FACT: The words we use to describe mental illnesses have changed greatly over time. What hasn't changed is the fact that mental illnesses are not the regular ups and downs of life. Mental illnesses create distress, don't go away on their own, and are real health problems with effective treatments. When someone breaks her arm, we wouldn't expect her to just "get over it." Nor would we blame her if she needed a cast, sling, or other help in her daily life while she recovered.

MYTH: *People don't recover from mental illnesses.*

FACT: People can and do recover from mental illnesses. Today, there are many different kinds of treatments, services, and supports that can help. No one should expect to feel unwell forever. The fact is, people who experience mental illnesses can and do lead productive, engaged lives. They work, volunteer, or contribute their unique skills and abilities to their communities. Even when people experience mental illnesses that last for a long time, they can learn how to manage their symptoms so that they can get back to their goals. If someone continues to experience many challenges, it may be a sign that different approaches or supports are needed.

MYTH: *Personality weakness or character flaws cause mental health problems. People with mental health problems can snap out of it if they try hard enough.*

FACT: Mental health problems have nothing to do with being lazy or weak, and many people need help to get better. Many factors contribute to mental health problems, including biological factors (e.g., genes, physical illness, injury, brain chemistry), life experiences (e.g., trauma, history of abuse), and family history of mental illness.

These myths—and many more—exclude people with mental illnesses from our communities and create barriers to well-being. To reduce the impact of mental illnesses on our communities, we need to learn the facts and start with our own assumptions and behaviours.

Source: Adapted from "Myths about mental illness," n.d.; "Mental health: Myths and facts," n.d.; "Top 11 myths about mental illness," 2014.

EXPLAINING MENTAL DISTURBANCES: PSYCHOLOGICAL PARADIGMS

Why do some people develop mental disorders while others do not? Various explanations for the development of mental disturbances have been offered throughout history. As in the case of defining abnormality, explanations of the causal factors, or **etiology**, of mental disturbances are relative to both the time and context in which they are observed.

Historical Views of Abnormality

While definitions of abnormality have changed throughout history, there have always been attempts to try to understand and explain abnormal behaviour. Early explanations for abnormal behaviour were based on ideas derived from philosophy, medicine, and religion. Following the emergence of the field of psychology around 1879, psychologists developed their own explanations for abnormal behaviour. We begin with a brief overview of historical explanations for abnormal behaviour, and then we'll examine more current approaches to understanding abnormality.

Demonology, Early Philosophers, and the Middle Ages. Early views of abnormal behaviour are believed by some to have been based in *demonology*, which involved the idea

Early explanations for abnormal behaviour involved the belief that evil spirits or demons had possessed the person. Cutting holes in the skull was thought to allow the release of the spirits and help the person return to normal functioning.

that evil spirits or beings resided in or possessed the affected individual. Consistent with this early explanation for deviant behaviour, archaeologists have found Stone Age human skeletons with egg-sized holes in their skulls, and have interpreted these holes to be consistent with prehistoric views that abnormal behaviour was an indication of possession by evil spirits. This *trephining* (or *trepanning*)—cutting a hole in a person's skull—is viewed by some as an assumption that such treatment would allow the release of demons that had possessed the person and were causing the abnormal behaviour. This treatment appears to have been widespread around the world (Kidd, 1946), and Aboriginal specimens with holes in the skulls have been found in British Columbia.

In ancient Greece, those exhibiting abnormal behaviour were often sent to temples for treatment by Aesculapius, the god of healing, who was believed to visit them while they slept, providing suggestions for cures in their dreams. Exercise, nutrition, and rest were also recommended. Those who weren't cured were stoned and driven from the temple, highlighting the negative reactions to deviant behaviour.

But different explanations of abnormal behaviour were evident even in ancient Greece. Hippocrates disagreed with the demonological model and argued that illnesses of the body and the mind were a result of imbalances in bodily fluids, or *humours* (phlegm, black bile, yellow bile, and blood). For example, high levels of yellow bile were believed to result in irritability and anxiety. Although his original explanation for emotional disturbances has not been supported by scientific evidence, Hippocrates marked the beginning of a more natural explanation for abnormal behaviour in a time when supernatural explanations prevailed.

During the Middle Ages (476 c.e. through 1450 c.e.), belief in supernatural causes returned to the forefront when it came to explaining deviant behaviour and emotional disturbance. In relation to the teachings of the Roman Catholic Church, the belief in possession was revived, and behavioural disturbances were believed to be best treated by exorcisms, which included praying, beating, and other extreme treatments of the affected individual. In the later years of the Middle Ages, explanations for abnormal behaviour involved witchcraft and the belief that Satan was responsible for unfortunate events in society (e.g., drought, floods, illness) as well as emotional and behavioural disturbances in particular individuals (Zilboorg & Henry, 1941).

Despite this focus on supernatural explanations, natural causes (e.g., brain trauma, physical disease) were still used to explain many instances of disturbed behaviour. Asylums or mental hospitals were established for the mentally ill. The conditions in these hospitals were dreadful, and treatment of the patients was typically inhumane and not particularly effective. For example, Benjamin Rush, often considered the founder of American psychiatry, believed that a helpful approach to curing mental disturbance was to create significant fear in the patient; treatments involved convincing individuals that they were about to die, placing them in a box with holes and then lowering the box into a tank of water.

A Humanitarian Approach. The work of Philippe Pinel (1745–1826) marked the beginning of the humane and moral treatment of individuals exhibiting abnormal

Geza Farkas/Fotolia

behaviour and emotional disturbances. Pinel took charge of a Paris asylum (La Bicêtre) and began treating the patients as ill rather than as less than human. He allowed them to walk freely through the hospital and grounds (they had previously been shackled to walls with chains) and proposed the idea that they were normal people who would benefit from compassion and humane treatment. Unfortunately, however, this emphasis on humane treatment was more readily available for individuals of higher social classes. Nevertheless, it marked the start of humanitarian treatment of those classified as mentally ill.

Modern Psychological Approaches

Early demonological explanations and methods of treatment for abnormal behaviour seem very different from our current views. However, even early explanations considered the role of more natural, physical factors in explaining such phenomena. How do we currently explain abnormal behaviour? What is now believed to be the best way to help the individual suffering from symptoms of mental illness? The answers to these questions vary in relation to the paradigm one adopts. As illustrated in our discussion of historical views, abnormal behaviour can be considered from multiple paradigms.

A **paradigm** provides a conceptual framework or *conceptual model* that identifies relevant questions for scientific examination, specifies the best way to study these questions, and provides the assumptions that guide the development of acceptable explanations for a particular phenomenon (Kuhn, 1996). Any one paradigm or worldview can be associated with numerous **theories**: tentative, broad statements that explain a particular observation. For example, the *biological paradigm* views abnormal behaviour as arising from atypical biological processes. Numerous theories have been developed in relation to this paradigm, including the theory that low levels of the brain chemical serotonin explain depression, or that high levels of the brain chemical dopamine explain hearing voices or seeing things that are not actually present. Specifically, paradigms identify what should be observed, the kinds of questions to be asked, how these questions are to be structured and assessed, and how the results of scientific investigations should be interpreted. In examining various paradigms relevant to understanding abnormal behaviour, notice that each paradigm has its own major assumptions, explanations of typical/normal development and atypical/abnormal development, and clinical implications for assessment and intervention.

From a psychological perspective, predominant explanations include those offered from the biological, psychodynamic, behavioural, cognitive, and sociocultural paradigms. Although each of these paradigms or approaches is considered independently in our discussion of the psychological perspective, it is generally believed that no single paradigm can explain all instances of abnormal behaviour. Instead, a combination of biological, psychodynamic, behavioural, cognitive, and social factors interact with one another to produce and sustain the symptoms associated with various behavioural and emotional disturbances. This **biopsychosocial perspective** views abnormal behaviour in the context of factors in the body (biological), the mind (psychological), and the social context (sociocultural). *Biological causes* relate to genetics and physical functioning, *psychological causes* relate to experiences (learning) and related thoughts (cognitions) and feelings within an individual, and *sociocultural causes* relate to aspects of one's social environment. This biopsychosocial approach prevails in Health Canada's view of causal factors of abnormal behaviour, which acknowledges that "a complex interplay of genetic,

Table 1.4 Overview of Major Paradigms

Paradigm	Theories of Cause	Approach to Treatment
Supernatural	Demonic possession, evil spirits	Exorcism, trephining
Biophysical or biological	Physiological malfunction (genetics, nervous system biochemistry)	Physiological interventions (drugs, surgery, etc.)
Psychodynamic	Repression of unconscious childhood conflict, painful memories, and trauma	Increase awareness of unconscious conflicts and content
Behavioural	Faulty learning experiences (lack of reinforcement, overly punished)	Replace with new behaviours/ experiences
Cognitive	Inaccurate cognitive structuring of experiences	Change thinking processes, reduce negative thoughts
Sociocultural	Impact of social and cultural factors on individual	Assess and modify impact of environmental aspects

biological, personality and environmental factors causes mental illnesses" (Health Canada, 2002, p. 7).

Consistent with this view, and from a psychological perspective, the best approach to treatment involves utilizing a combination of strategies based on multiple paradigms. Thus, although the paradigms described below might be perceived to be competing and independent frameworks of abnormal behaviour, they are best considered as contributing one or more elements to the overall understanding and treatment of any disordered pattern of behaviour or emotion. Before turning to a discussion of modern paradigms, see Table 1.4 for an overview and comparison of the explanations and treatments associated with some of the historical views we've discussed as well as the major paradigms we will examine in the remainder of this chapter.

Biological Paradigm As discussed in our summary of historical perspectives, the belief that natural or physical factors might explain unusual behaviour and emotional experience is not a new one. This idea is also the basis of the **biological paradigm**. Since Hippocrates, there have been many renowned theorists, researchers, and physicians who have emphasized the relationship between mind and body. In the seventeenth century, Descartes proposed that the body and mind were separate entities, a position referred to as *dualism*. Recently, however, the limitations of this dualistic approach have been emphasized and made apparent in hundreds of scientific investigations. Specifically, countless examples illustrating the interaction of body and mind have been documented, resulting in a great emphasis on the role of biological factors in mental health and illness. Given this history, it's not surprising that the current approach to understanding disturbed behaviour is very much based on a *medical model*, a perspective that views abnormal behaviour as a symptom of an underlying illness or disorder. In fact, **psychiatry** is an area of specialization in medicine that is committed to the study and treatment of mental disorders. Therefore, a *psychiatrist* is actually a physician (not a psychologist) specializing in the treatment of behavioural and emotional disturbances. **Psychopathology** is a field of study that focuses on identifying the characteristics, causes, and treatment of mental distress and abnormal behaviour. Although it's often used interchangeably with the term *abnormal psychology*, some view *psychopathology* as more of a psychiatric term with a greater emphasis on *pathology* or disease and thus on the biological factors associated with mental distress and behavioural disturbance.

The influence of a biological approach to understanding mental disorder is reflected in the language often used to describe disrupted emotions and behaviour. In fact, referring to such disruptions as *illnesses* that are reflected in specific *symptoms* that can be reduced through *treatment* clearly illustrates the relevance of the medical model, the traditional approach to diagnosing and treating physical illnesses. This model emphasizes identification of dysfunction or deficiencies in the individual and treatment of these defects through various methods that alter biological or physical factors.

The relationship between biological processes and mental disorders has been investigated extensively. Research based on this biological approach to understanding abnormal behaviour has focused primarily on the role of genetic, biochemical, and neurological factors in disrupted behaviour.

Heredity and Genetics. Heredity plays a central role in determining various physical and psychological characteristics. **Genetics** is the science of heredity. The basic building blocks of heredity are *genes*, which are sections of *deoxyribonucleic acid* (*DNA*) along the *chromosomes* (rod-shaped structures found in all the cells of the human body). Figure 1.3 illustrates the relationship of these components. Each of us inherits this genetic material from our biological mother and biological father. Because genes contain codes that determine the development and structure of cells in the body (including those in the brain), they have the potential to influence not only physical characteristics but also psychological characteristics. Throughout this text, we'll see that numerous studies have shown that genes play a role in determining anxiety, depression, aggression, and other characteristics associated with abnormal behaviour.

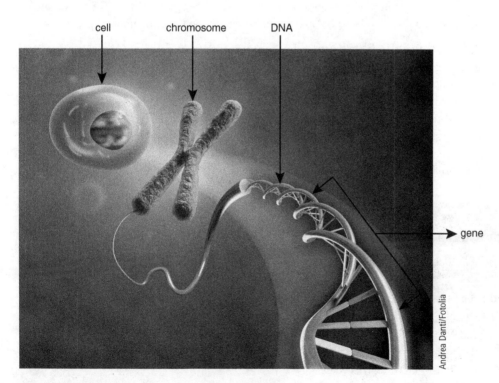

Figure 1.3 Chromosomes, Genes, and DNA

The basic building blocks of heredity are *genes*—sections of *deoxyribonucleic acid* (*DNA*) along *chromosomes* (rod-shaped structures found in all the cells of the human body).

Brain Structures. Various areas and structures of the brain play a role in regulating emotion and thought. For example, a structure deep within the brain called the *amygdala* has been found to be related to the experience of fear as well as rage. From a biological perspective, abnormalities in the size or activity of various structures (e.g., amygdala, thalamus, hypothalamus) might explain the abnormalities in emotional disturbances. The brain images presented in Appendix 2 show the location of various brain structures and areas that have been found to be important in the experience of thought and emotion.

Appendix 2 also shows the areas of the outermost part of the brain, the **cerebral cortex**, which includes the frontal, parietal, temporal, and occipital areas, or lobes. Different levels of activity in some locations of the cortex have been associated with disrupted emotional experience. For example, higher levels of activity in one location of the frontal lobe have been related to thinking repeatedly about negative events, creating feelings of sadness for the individual (Davidson, Jackson, & Kalin, 2000). In the following chapters we'll discuss specific mental disorders and consider the specific brain areas and structures that have been found to be associated with each condition; refer to Appendix 2 to see where these areas and structures are located.

Neurotransmitters. From a biological approach, another explanation for abnormal behaviours and emotional disturbance is an atypical level of certain neurotransmitters. *Neurotransmitters* are chemicals in the nervous system/brain that are responsible for communication between **neurons**, cells in the nervous system that send messages from one location to another. It has been suggested that particularly low or high levels of certain neurotransmitters (including norepinephrine, serotonin, and dopamine) might explain disturbances in emotion, perception, and behaviours. See Box 1.4 for a list of neurotransmitters often found to be associated with abnormal mood or behaviours.

Psychodynamic Paradigm In the **psychodynamic paradigm**, a major assumption is that psychopathology is the result of unconscious conflicts experienced by the individual. This approach was originally developed by Sigmund Freud (1946), a physician who proposed a dynamic model of the human psyche to explain emotional and behavioural experiences. In Freud's **topographic model**, he identified three levels of awareness: (1) the *conscious*, consisting of memories, thoughts, and feelings of which we are currently aware (e.g., that you are hungry); (2) the *preconscious*, consisting of memories, thoughts, and feelings that can easily be brought to mind (e.g., what you had for dinner yesterday), and

---

Box 1.4

Neurotransmitters Involved in Emotion and Behaviour

Neurotransmitter and Examples of Function

Dopamine: Associated with sensations of pleasure, reward; high levels associated with hallucinations (e.g., hearing voices, seeing things that aren't present)

Serotonin: Regulates sleep and emotion; low levels associated with depression

Norephinephrine: Regulates emotions and arousal; low levels associated with depression

GABA (gamma-aminobutyric acid): Regulates sleep, reduces activity levels; related to sensations of relaxation; low levels associated with feelings of anxiety and panic

(3) the *unconscious*, those thoughts, memories, and feelings that can't be easily called to mind but still exert significant influence on one's behaviour. Freud considered the unconscious to be the most significant level of awareness. For example, there are cases in which a person has experienced a significant trauma (e.g., being witness to a bank robbery) but can't recall any details about the event. According to Freud's topographic model, this information isn't easily brought into one's awareness but may emerge into one's consciousness at a later time. More importantly, even though the individual is unaware of the event, he or she may experience anxiety in relation to the unconscious memory.

In addition to his topographic model, Freud proposed a **structural model** that identified three major components of the mind: the id, ego, and superego. The *id* is the only structure that is present at birth and is associated with providing the energy for the basic biological motives of hunger, thirst, warmth, affection, aggression, and sex. As such, the id operates according to the *pleasure principle*, seeking immediate gratification for its impulses. For example, a newborn is highly motivated by the hunger drive. Accordingly, it will cry and experience significant distress if this need is not gratified. The id, then, is instinctual or inborn, entirely unconscious, and primarily concerned with satisfying personal desires as immediately as possible, regardless of the consequences.

During the first two years of life and out of interaction with the environment, the *ego* develops. The ego operates largely at the level of conscious awareness and according to the *reality principle*. Specifically, it attempts to satisfy the demands of the id while considering the constraints of the realities of the situation. For example, although an infant may express a desire to be fed by crying loudly, the reality of the situation may be that the mother has to address the more immediate need of another child who has fallen and is hurt. In this case, the infant must wait for food, and gratification of id impulses is delayed. Through these continual experiences in the environment, the ego develops and becomes able to manage both the selfish demands of the id and the demands or constraints of the environment.

The final structure of the psyche to develop is the *superego*. According to Freud, the superego is the moral branch of personality that represents the values and standards of society that have been internalized over the course of the individual's interactions with parents and other socializing agents. The superego provides guidance with respect to standards to strive toward via the *ego ideal*, the ideas we have about what constitutes good behaviour and admirable characteristics. The superego also places restrictions on behaviours, thoughts, and feelings via the *conscience*, which creates feelings of guilt if we violate or think about violating the rules of right and wrong that we've learned from those around us.

What role do these structures play in psychological health? According to Freud, the healthy individual has a strong ego that doesn't allow the id or superego too much control over the personality. The healthy ego is able to effectively manage the demands of both the id and the superego and consider the constraints of the social environment. If an individual has an overly powerful id that dominates the ego, the result is selfishly driven behaviours that violate the rights of others and prevent the individual from successfully delaying gratification when necessary. By comparison, a superego that dominates the ego results in high levels of guilt and anxiety that are out of proportion to the reality of the situation.

If it sounds as though the three components of Freud's model of the psyche are in a constant state of struggle with one another, then you have an accurate understanding of his view of human personality. Freud believed that anxiety arises from this confrontation between

Table 1.5 Examples of Common Ego Defence Mechanisms

Defence Mechanism	Specific Example
Displacement: releasing or expressing feelings toward a substitute object because releasing these toward the real target would be dangerous	After being scolded by his teacher at school, Jeffrey pushes down another child in the playground
Denial: refusing to accept the reality of an unpleasant or threatening situation	Jan says, "I don't care what you say, my cat will come back to me" after her pet dies
Regression: returning to earlier, less mature ways of behaving in order to cope with distressing events	Five-year-old Brian begins to suck his thumb again after his parents get divorced
Rationalization: creating acceptable but inaccurate excuses for one's own unacceptable behaviour	A student says to herself, "It's not a big deal if I cheat on this test; everyone else is doing it!"
Repression: pushing unacceptable content (memories, thoughts, impulses, desires, etc.) into the unconscious and out of conscious awareness	Fran, the victim of a crime and witness to her brother's death, remembers nothing of the event or what she observed

personality components. A key job of the ego is to keep unacceptable id impulses out of conscious awareness: if we were to experience these, we'd feel extreme guilt or distress. Accordingly, if direct expression of id impulses is unacceptable or dangerous in the real world, another key function of the ego is to use **defence mechanisms**, the ego's protective methods for reducing or avoiding anxiety by unconsciously distorting reality. See Table 1.5 for a summary and examples of important ego defence mechanisms that will be considered throughout this text.

Based on Freud's theory of human personality, people are assumed to be irrational, naturally aggressive, anxious, self-centred, and typically unaware of the real motives that underlie their behaviour. Often criticized as maintaining a pessimistic and negative view of human nature, Freud's theory remains controversial yet influential in discussions of abnormality. Despite a lack of scientific support for many of Freud's original concepts and processes, his early emphasis on the parent–child relationship in the formation of character and the role of early experience in the development of disrupted emotions and personality has served as the inspiration for other theories that have been more consistently supported by research, including attachment theory and object relations theory, to which we now turn.

Attachment Theory. John Bowlby (1969) is well known for his development of attachment theory. Like Freud, he emphasized the great importance of the emotional bond that was formed between mother and infant, not only in humans but in other species as well. More recent psychodynamic theories also view **attachment**, the bond between mother and infant, to be one of the most significant events in one's development. Generally, attachment theories emphasize how this early relationship between infant and mother serves as the basis of later emotional and social adjustment.

Karen Horney (1973) emphasized the relevance of early infant–parent relationships in the later development of abnormal behaviour and emotional disturbance. Specifically, when caregivers are insensitive and uncaring, the child may develop *basic anxiety*, which is associated with feelings of isolation and helplessness. If the child feels anger toward her caregivers, that child may develop *basic hostility*, a form of anger that is pushed into the unconscious (because the thought is associated with fear that she may be punished if her anger was to be discovered by her parents); this repression is associated with feelings of anxiety and insecurity.

Object-Relations Theory. A second modern approach associated with traditional psychodynamic theory is **object-relations theory**. This theory emphasizes the importance of the *symbolic representation* (i.e., our thoughts and mental images) of significant others in our lives, particularly parents. Based on early emotional ties with others, the child forms long-lasting internalized beliefs about himself and other people. If a caregiver (usually the mother is emphasized) is rejecting or insensitive to her child's needs, disrupted emotions and behaviours may be the consequence. As the child observes how his caregivers treat him and view him, he begins to view himself in the same way. This **introjection** or incorporation of the view we believe significant others have of us then serves as the basis for future interactions with others. For example, if a child has been treated by his parents as though he is incapable and unintelligent, the child will also think of himself as stupid or incompetent, acting as though the original attachment object or caregiver was still present and sending those messages. The consequence is the development of specific beliefs about oneself that will influence the child's behaviour and social interactions with others. Thus, if the child believes his parents view him as incompetent, he will see himself as incompetent, and he may be drawn to relationships with those who also view him as incompetent because their view is consistent with his own. It's easy to imagine how such a view of oneself might result in distressing emotions and unhealthy relationships with others.

Behavioural Paradigm   As we've seen, psychodynamic theories emphasize the role of the unconscious, conflict between unseen components of the mind, irrational behaviour, and early attachment relationships in explanations of abnormal behaviour. In contrast, the **behavioural paradigm** emphasizes the importance of observable actions, immediate environment, and learning experiences in determining behaviour. According to this approach, the same learning processes that result in normal behaviour are also responsible for shaping abnormal behaviour. Three forms of learning are particularly relevant to understanding behaviour: classical conditioning, operant conditioning, and social or observational learning.

Classical Conditioning. Russian physiologist Ivan Pavlov and American psychologist John B. Watson are the two individuals most associated with the development of early **behaviourism**, the division of psychology that emphasizes the role of observable behaviour and learning in explaining behaviour. Pavlov (1926) was investigating salivation responses of dogs to the presentation of food. During his investigation, however, he ran into a problem: the dogs would begin to salivate as soon as the researcher entered the room, even before they had been presented with food. What was happening? Based on his later investigations, Pavlov discovered that the dogs had learned to *associate* the researcher with the food. Prior to their experience in Pavlov's laboratory, the dogs would salivate at the presentation of the food (it is an inborn, biologically based reaction to do so). But because the researcher had been paired with the food on repeated occasions, the dogs had learned to associate the sight of the researcher with the food, so began salivating at the sight of the researcher. This form of learning discovered by Pavlov is now referred to as **classical conditioning**, the process by which paired presentations of two *stimuli* (objects or conditions) in the environment result in a response or reaction to one stimulus occurring also in response to a new or previously neutral stimulus. Such classically conditioned associations can help us better understand many of our automatic reactions to various stimuli in the environment. For example, imagine a child who has visited the dentist several times, and on each occasion has experienced painful procedures that result in fear and distress. As a result of the pairing of dentist and pain, the sight of the dentist alone (or even the dental office waiting room) will result in feelings of distress and fear. We'll examine more specific aspects of classical conditioning in greater detail in our discussion of anxiety disorders in Chapter 6.

Operant Conditioning. Harvard psychologist B. F. Skinner (1953) emphasized a different form of learning, **operant conditioning**, in explaining human and animal behaviour. According to this form of learning, people and animals engage in various behaviours, but it's what follows the behaviour, the *consequence*, that influences the likelihood of that behaviour occurring again in the future. Some consequences, referred to as *reinforcers*, increase the likelihood of the behaviour occurring again. For example, if a child throws a tantrum and the caregiver gives a cookie to soothe the child, the child will likely exhibit similar outbursts in the future because such behaviour was followed by a desirable consequence. Other consequences, referred to as *punishments*, decrease the likelihood of the behaviour occurring in the future. If the same child throws a tantrum and the caregiver scolds the child or takes away something the child enjoys (e.g., a favourite toy), such consequences will likely decrease the likelihood of the behaviour occurring again.

Most people use various types of reinforcers and punishers in day-to-day life. Giving a dog a treat for performing a trick, giving a child a time-out for disruptive behaviour, or giving a friend the "silent treatment" because he or she has upset you in some way are all examples of how each of us might use consequences in an attempt to alter others' behaviour. Such consequences can also be used to alter our own behaviour, as in taking a 20-minute break after 30 minutes of studying.

How might operant conditioning explain abnormal behaviour? Consider our previous example—after a child throws a tantrum, a parent gives him a treat or toy to soothe him. Such consequences serve to strengthen or increase the likelihood of this behaviour occurring again, resulting in repeated instances of disruptive behaviour. The role of punishments and reinforcers will be considered throughout the remaining chapters both as explanations of abnormal behaviour and in approaches to managing such disturbances.

Observational Learning. Albert Bandura conducted early experiments demonstrating that individuals acquired new behaviours not only through associations and consequences but also via *modelling*, in which we observe and then imitate the actions of those around us. In the classic Bobo Doll experiment, Bandura, Ross, and Ross (1961) had individual children watch a video of an adult model playing with an inflatable doll. Bandura found that those children who observed a model behaving aggressively toward the Bobo Doll (i.e., hitting, kicking, and punching the doll) were

Diego Cervo/Fotolia

Scolding a child is an example of punishment that's used in hopes of decreasing the likelihood of a behaviour occurring in the future.

more likely to behave aggressively toward the Bobo Doll themselves when they were given the opportunity to play with it. You can probably think of several examples of behaviours you have acquired based on your modelling the actions of others. A child may pretend to "smoke" a pencil after watching her caregiver smoke a cigarette or push down her sibling after watching a wrestling match on television. In each instance, the child makes an observation first and then imitates this action. In later chapters we explore how observational learning may serve as the basis for the development of abnormal or disruptive behaviours.

Cognitive Paradigm   You may have noticed that the behavioural paradigm tends to view people as relatively passive in their learning experiences. Behaviours are assumed to result from experiences in the environment over which one may have little or no control. From a cognitive perspective, however, thoughts and beliefs are considered to be important factors in influencing emotional states. Therefore, rather than actual events being central to understanding the cause of abnormal behaviour and disrupted emotions, how we think about events and assign meaning to our experiences is vital in understanding abnormal behaviour. Specifically, if one seeks to understand behaviour, the thoughts, interpretations, expectations, beliefs, and attitudes of the individual must be examined.

One of the most influential cognitive theorists is psychologist Albert Ellis (Ellis & Harper, 1997). According to Ellis, feelings of anxiety, depression, and distress are not a function of events themselves but rather a result of our irrational beliefs about what these events signify. For example, consider a child who forgets to take his homework to school and says to himself, "See how stupid you are! You can't even remember to take your homework in. You'll never amount to anything!" Ellis would emphasize that such statements are irrational and that it's unreasonable to interpret such an instance as evidence of such extreme deficits. Thus, although the actual event won't necessarily lead to distress, it's the *interpretation* of the event that is most relevant to the emotions and behaviours that follow.

Psychiatrist Aaron Beck (1979) also emphasizes the role of thought in disruptive emotions and distress. According to Beck, *dysfunctional schemas* and *beliefs* help to explain distressing emotions. A **schema** is a general cognitive framework that helps us organize and interpret information. For example, your schema for *classroom* might include desks, chairs, whiteboards, windows, and an instructor. Having this cognitive framework helps you interpret information and guides your behaviour: if you arrive at the room indicated on your class schedule for your first day of lectures and there are no desks, chairs, or whiteboards, you might assume you have the wrong room! Despite their function, however, schemas can result in a biased interpretation of circumstances and events around us and may fuel dysfunctional beliefs. Such schemas are formed as a function of our personal experiences. For example, if a child has been told repeatedly, "You're so stupid!" or "You'll never amount to anything!," a schema of inadequacy may develop where the individual now assumes that he is insufficient and a failure. Associated with this general assumption, the individual develops specific beliefs such as "I don't know how to talk to others" or "I'm ugly." Even in the context of successes (e.g., receiving praise from a teacher for good performance), the individual will tend to focus on those events that are consistent with the schema (e.g., he did poorly on a sample quiz) and ignore those events that are inconsistent with the schema. This bias in perception and interpretation of events continues to support the irrational beliefs.

Once formed, these dysfunctional schemas are maintained through consistent and automatic use of various **cognitive distortions** in which the individual alters his

magnification is when an event is exaggerated beyond its actual significance

perceptions of events and other self-relevant information to make them consistent with underlying negative assumptions and beliefs. One example of a cognitive distortion associated with distress is *magnification*, where the importance of a particular event is exaggerated beyond its actual significance) For example, consider an adolescent who's had an argument with a friend. Interpreting this event as a sign that he'll never be able to resolve the disagreement or assuming that he'll never have another friend again illustrates such magnification. It's easy to imagine how such thoughts might create painful emotions. Additional cognitive distortions will be considered in later chapters.

Sociocultural Paradigm   The paradigms from the psychological perspective we've considered tend to assume that individual characteristics (i.e., biological abnormalities, unconscious conflicts, personal learning experiences, and ways of thinking) serve to explain the occurrence of abnormal behaviour and emotional disturbances. According to the **sociocultural paradigm**, however, social and cultural factors must be examined in order to understand and explain abnormal behaviour. From this perspective, explanations for abnormal behaviour must consider conditions *outside* the individual exhibiting such disturbances.

Culture. We've discussed how norms or societal standards for behaviour relate to the concept of abnormality (Cultural ideas about sex, gender, ethnicity, and race can also influence behaviour and may result in differences in abnormality across various groups in a society)

> For example, the rate of death by suicide in rural regions in China is higher among young females than males. This has been attributed to the difficulties faced by young women in Chinese society; suicide attempts in rural areas often use agricultural poisons with high lethality. This example is a clear illustration of the profound impact of social factors on suicide. (Kirmayer et al., 2007, p. 24)

In Canada, there are also variations with respect to abnormal behaviour in relation to social characteristics.

> For Aboriginal people, suicide is an affliction of the young. From the ages of 10 to 19, Aboriginal youth on reserves are 5 to 6 times more likely to die of suicide than their peers in the general population. (Kirmayer et al., 2007, p. 1)

What social and cultural factors might explain such differences in suicide between different groups within the same society? Throughout this text we'll examine various explanations for group differences in specific abnormal behaviours, including the role of poverty, abuse, education, and prejudice and discrimination. For now, it's important to acknowledge that the sociocultural paradigm recognizes that abnormal behaviour isn't solely a function of disturbances that reside within the individual. (According to this approach, abnormal behaviours may be more a function of dysfunctional environments, and as such are best "treated" by changing conditions in the social context)

Family. Clearly, biological and psychological factors aren't the only factors associated with increased risk for developing a psychological disorder. Various family factors, including conflict, communication strategies, discipline approaches, and neglect and abuse, have been found to increase the likelihood of developing specific emotional and behavioural disturbances.) For example, families of children diagnosed with ADHD demonstrate significantly higher levels of parenting stress and lower levels of perceived parenting competence (e.g., Anastopoulous et al., 1992). Lack of parental supervision, marital conflict,

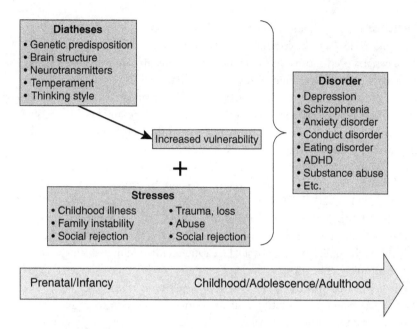

Figure 1.4 The Diathesis–Stress Model

In this model, diatheses, or predisposing factors, together with stresses, or triggers in the environment, determine one's risk of disorder.

and violence in the home is associated with increased risk of child and adolescent antisocial behaviour (Loeber & Farrington, 2000; Reese et al., 2000).

Given the relationship of these social factors to rates of emotional and behavioural disturbances, how might they work together with the biological and psychological factors associated with such outcomes? The **diathesis–stress model** of psychological disorders proposes that biological, psychological, and social factors can create a vulnerability that might increase one's likelihood of developing a particular disorder. For example, a genetic predisposition for Schizophrenia might be inherited from one's parents. However, other vulnerabilities, including psychological (e.g., attentional difficulties) and social factors (e.g., parental conflict), will further increase one's likelihood of developing the symptoms of Schizophrenia. Despite these vulnerabilities, however, it's possible that a youth will never develop symptoms—until he is exposed to a significant stress, which can take the form of a biological (e.g., exposure to cocaine), social (e.g., death of a parent), or psychological (e.g., loss of self-esteem) trigger. A greater number of diatheses together with a greater number of stresses further increases one's risk of developing a disorder. See Figure 1.4 for an overview of the diathesis–stress model.

A CYC LENS ON THE PSYCHOLOGICAL PARADIGMS: A HOLISTIC CONCEPTUAL MODEL

As we've seen, while some psychological paradigms don't fit well with a CYC approach, many others do. Overall, each of the psychological models used to explain mental health has something important to offer CYC students and practitioners. Here we briefly review each to assess their goodness of fit from a CYC perspective.

Biological Paradigm The biological paradigm, sometimes referred to as the *medical, biological,* or *disease model,* looks to biological causes to explain disorders, or exceptionalities. These include genetic predispositions, brain and neurotransmitter abnormalities, prenatal and birth factors, and environmental hazards (Kendall & Comer, 2010; Winzer, 2005). For example, geneticists have long recognized a link between DNA and behaviour (Winzer, 2005), and research has shown that child and adult temperaments (defined as *biologically determined behavioural styles*) are inherited. As well, neuroscience has established that the central nervous system and neurochemical activity are involved in all human behaviour. The neurotransmitters serotonin, dopamine, and norepinephrine have important roles to play in regulating behaviour, stress responses, aggression, addictions, and stress management (Mate, 2008; Winzer, 2005).

Neuroscience-based approaches to understanding troublesome behaviours explore ways to restore healthy brain functioning in youth struggling with trauma and other mental health issues. Although traditional biophysical treatments focus almost exclusively on administering psychotropic medications in order to stabilize crises and manage troublesome behaviours, insights into how the brain works have helped us learn much about the effects of trauma and the benefits of positive human connection (Brendtro et al., 2005). Neuroscience research is demonstrating that lasting change requires new programming of the brain with new connecting experiences. Such reprogramming requires corrective interpersonal attachments, the establishment of trusting relationships, healthy communication, and the opportunity to learn new strategies of emotional control and coping skills (Perry, 2014).

Psychodynamic Paradigm According to Charles Sharpe (2001), the psychodynamic model is based on the theory that emotional and behavioural disorders are symptoms of internal, unobservable, unconscious conflicts between the components of one's personality. Such unresolved conflicts were experienced in the early stages of childhood and have become reactivated in problem situations in adulthood. Freud's theories represent the primary examples of a psychodynamic theory; other psychodynamic theorists include Carl Jung, Alfred Adler, and Harry Stack Sullivan. Early methods focused on resolving inner conflict by uncovering these early childhood traumas (Brendtro et al., 2005), although such practitioners as Fritz Redl, August Aichhorn, and Anna Freud saw love as the primary unmet need of troubled children (Sharpe, 2006). Many aspects of the psychodynamic paradigm are important for CYCPs to understand. Freud's hypothesis that early childhood experiences can profoundly influence adult behaviour has endured over time (Kendall & Comer, 2010), and the idea that unconscious processes influence our conscious lives and behavioural actions remains undisputed. Early childhood trauma and attachment difficulties have indeed been found to influence the development of difficult behaviour and to negatively affect relationships in adolescents and young adults. However, Freud's specific ideas about the sources of the conflict have not been supported by research over the years (Kendall & Comer, 2010). There is no compelling evidence, for example, that notions of the id, ego, and superego are relevant or even accurate as explanations for child and adolescent psychological difficulties (Kendall & Comer, 2010). Similarly, the notion that sexual instincts and sexual drive determine development and behaviour hasn't been proven. Nevertheless, Freud's ideas related to defence mechanisms continue to be relevant in understanding human thought and behaviour.

Behavioural Paradigm Behavioural approaches assume that all behaviour is learned. In this model, behaviours that are exceptional and that are associated with behavioural or emotional disorders are understood to be conditioned responses or habits that can be modified by the same principles of learning that govern all behaviour.

Behaviour theory holds that all human actions are the result of what we've learned or have been conditioned to do (McKenzie, 2008). Further, the behavioural paradigm emphasizes the observed behaviour of the child in the context of the environmental factors reinforcing the response (Kendall & Comer, 2010). By modifying influences in the environment, we can help change the undesirable behaviour patterns. To assist in behaviour change, then, CYCPs need to provide young people with corrective learning or different "conditioning" experiences.

Behavioural approaches have changed substantially over the years. While older practices focused almost entirely on eliminating deviant behaviours, current practices involve teaching pro-social behaviours through such techniques as aggression replacement training and social skills training. Moreover, there has been a shift from coercive and punishment-based methods to building positive behavioural supports (Brendtro et al., 2005). In other words, behaviourally based models now revolve around strength-based goals, making them a good fit for CYC practice.

As we discussed earlier, the behavioural model encompasses three types of learning: classical conditioning, operant conditioning, and observational learning (Kendall & Comer, 2010). CYCPs should have at least a cursory understanding of each, paying close attention to observational learning and social learning theory and their relationship to cognitive-behavioural interventions. CYCPs continually use learning theory in their practice, perhaps without naming it as such. Whenever you've administered a time-out or given a consequence to a child for misbehaving, you've applied concepts from the behavioural model and from learning theory.

Behavioural methods have always been used both formally and informally in out-of-home care and other CYC settings. These methods involve using external rewards as a way to reinforce desired changes in behaviour. In social learning theory, a child is conditioned to behave by having certain behaviours rewarded and others punished. Behaviour is also learned by observing the behaviour of significant others. Therefore, any so-called dysfunctional behaviour could be learned behaviour. Domestic violence is a classic example of the application of social learning theory to explain behaviour. Research has shown that boys who witness their fathers perpetrating violence against women often grow up to be perpetrators of violence against women themselves, and girls who witness violence against their mothers may become later victims of violence (Ehrensaft et al., 2003).

Attachment Theory. In any discussion of using a behavioural model in CYC practice, it's important to consider the relationship of attachment theory to learning theory. Sprinson and Berrick (2010) emphasize that the behavioural processes of modelling and reward are involved in the development of the child's attachment to his caregiver and thus in the construction of a working model of attachment (Sprinson & Berrick, 2010). Further, the repeated exchanges, or relational interactions, between child and care provider can be viewed through a behaviourist's lens, whereby both are learning how to regulate each other in the process of mutual reinforcement as the relationship develops (Sprinson & Berrick, 2010). As we know from attachment theory, the repeated reinforcement of these exchanges results in the development of or change in the child's **internal working model;** that is, the child's view of himself and of the world (Sprinson & Berrick, 2010). Once we understand the child's negative internal working model, we can respond to his efforts at **re-enactment.** For example, if the child yelled and swore at his caregivers in the past and they responded by yelling and swearing back or perhaps by hitting him, he may yell and swear at the adult in an attempt to duplicate these past responses from caregivers. He's trying to pull his current caregivers into that cycle, thus "re-enacting" the past cycle. Therefore, as the CYC team is observing this behaviour in order to understand its antecedents, contexts, and consequences, they can respond with interventions designed to challenge or interrupt the factors that have reinforced such negative behaviour (Sprinson & Berrick, 2010). It's easy to see, then, how attachment theory fits with a CYC perspective in the behavioural model.

Another model of attachment, Pat Crittenden's (2005) **dynamic-maturational model (DMM),** outlines the various attachment strategies that individuals use to cope with stress, many of which include psychopathological responses. This model highlights the idea that "there is more to attachment than promoting security. Troubled people make meaning from their past experience and use it to protect themselves and their children as best they can, given their circumstances" (Crittendon, 2005).

Five central ideas underlie the DMM: (1) all patterns of attachment are self-protective strategies; (2) self-protective strategies are learned in interaction with attachment figures, most often one's parents; (3) psychological, emotional, and behavioural "symptoms" are functional aspects of a dyadic strategy (e.g., acting out, inhibition) or consequent to it (e.g., anxiety behaviours); (4) these strategies will change when they no longer fit the context; that is, symptoms of anxiety will disappear when one is no longer anxious; and (5) therefore, the focus of treatment should be the fit of strategy to context to yield maximum safety and comfort (Crittenden, 2005).

Viewing the development of emotional and behavioural disorders through an attachment theory lens represents a major paradigm shift for most of us, and fits well with a CYC perspective: it not only avoids negative labelling and stigma, but also highlights the relational aspect of exceptional behaviours. If we acknowledge the development of psychopathology as an adaptive self-protective or coping strategy and can identify the type of attachment strategy an individual may be using, we can then respond appropriately in our interventions.

Cognitive Paradigm The cognitive paradigm is based on the idea that an individual's cognitive functioning, or thinking patterns, contributes to his or her emotional or behavioural difficulties (Kendall & Comer, 2010). The fundamental premise of the cognitive model is that if individuals can change the way they think, they can change their emotional and behavioural responses to events—an idea that is consistent with CYC practice.

Cognitive theories suggest that individuals are influenced in their actions by their conscious and unconscious beliefs about the world and themselves in the world. As we saw earlier, individuals develop *schemas* (similar to attachment theory's internal working model) that consist of their fundamental assumptions, beliefs, and values. The cognitive model focuses on dysfunctional cognitive (thinking) processes that are either cognitive distortions (maladaptive thinking patterns) or deficiencies (the absence of thinking altogether) (Kendall & Comer, 2010). One cognitive distortion is jumping to conclusions; for example, assuming that a friend hasn't returned your calls because she's angry with you (rather than ill or really busy) before gathering evidence to support your conclusion. Feelings of sadness and behavioural withdrawal may result from such an assumption.

Sociocultural Paradigm   As described earlier, the sociocultural paradigm examines how the influence of social and cultural factors may explain the development of abnormal or exceptional behaviours in young people. This sociocultural paradigm fits very well with a CYC perspective, in that such influences as mainstream cultural norms, dominant societal standards, and our ideas about sex, gender, ethnicity, and race all play a role in our understanding of what constitutes abnormal or exceptional behaviours in children and youth.

Most importantly, CYCPs will recognize the role of poverty, race, and ethnicity in becoming marginalized in society and, for many, in the consequent mental health issues. In addition to socioeconomic disadvantage, the mental health problems of Aboriginal youth in Canada, particularly rates of substance use, depression, and suicide, "may at least partly reflect alienation and disenfranchisement from the land and a way of life that resulted from colonization by European cultures" (Nevid, Rathus, & Greene, 2010, p. 62). Elders in Aboriginal culture often explain the development of mental health problems among young people, especially suicide and substance use, in relation to the collapse of their traditional culture brought about by colonization, and research has corroborated this (Nevid, Rathus, & Greene, 2010). One Anishinabe Elder explains depression in the following way:

> Before the White Man came into our world we had our own way of worshipping the Creator. We had our own church and rituals. When hunting was good, people would gather together to give gratitude. This gave us close contact with the Creator. There were many different rituals depending on the tribe. People would dance in the hills and play drums to give recognition to the Great Spirit. It was like talking to the Creator and living daily with its spirit. Now people have lost this. They can't use these methods and have lost conscious contact with this high power. The more distant we are from the Creator the more complex things are because we have no sense of direction. We don't recognize where life is from. (Timpson, Roundhead, McKay, Matewapit, Kakegamic, and Cohen, 1988, p 5–8)

Thus, the sociocultural model highlights the failure of other conceptual models to consider cultural variations in what are considered to be acceptable and unacceptable behaviour patterns. It is acknowledged in this paradigm that poverty, racism, and discrimination can cause psychological struggles, and that consideration of such contextual variables is essential to understanding all behaviour. Therefore, the sociocultural model fits well with a CYC holistic model of understanding exceptional behaviours.

After reviewing these conceptual models, you might conclude not only that you have you used one or more of them—whether formally (when you use level systems, star charts, and consequences) or informally (when you challenge a youngster's irrational or faulty thinking)—but that you've used them simultaneously. The fact is that these paradigms do overlap in the real world of CYC practice. Each of these models may guide your approaches and each may be helpful individually, depending on the needs of the children, youth, and families you're working with. The diathesis–stress model, for example, fits very well with a CYC perspective, as it emphasizes that disorders stem from both precipitating and predisposing causes. A *precipitating cause* is an immediate trigger that instigates a person's action or behaviour. A *predisposing cause* is an underlying factor that interacts with the immediate factors to result in a disorder. According to this model, both causes play a key role in the development of a psychological disorder. In suicide, for example, a precipitating cause may be a breakup with a partner, and a predisposing cause might be longstanding clinical depression.

Holistic/Ecological Model   The attempt to explain all mental disorders with just one theory leads to reductionism; that is, an attempt to explain complex phenomena using only one idea or perspective. We've seen that most mental health issues in young people develop as a result of several coalescing factors, which is why it's important to consider several theoretical perspectives when attempting to explain a particular mental health issue. An explanation of mental disorders that uses a combination of theoretical perspectives is known as a **multiple causality** approach.

In this approach, we consider all aspects of the possible causes of young people's exceptional behaviours or mental health issues. Many clinicians and writers agree that, from the perspective of contemporary neuroscience and developmental psychology, the traditional psychiatric diagnostic system of the DSM, based as it is on a nineteenth-century medical model of disease, is out of date. Contemporary CYCPs (and many psychologists) instead embrace the holistic paradigm. Keep in mind, though, that within this paradigm there may always be something to be gained from applying aspects of a more traditional psychodynamic and/or a sociocultural perspective (Sharpe, 2001).

CYCPs' use of the holistic model in assessing behaviour means that they consider the context of the young person's family and his or her social environment. The **holistic model** acknowledges that the cause of exceptional or inappropriate behaviours may be related to a variety of factors contributing to a youth's vulnerability, including illness, trauma, maltreatment, attachment issues, difficult relationships with peers, learning difficulties, and many other factors (Winzer, 2005).

This way of understanding exceptionalities is also known as the **ecological model**. The ecological model examines the overall pattern of relationships between a young person and all the variables in his or her environment: teachers, parents, caregivers, peers, and so on. Thus, it is a *relational* model. The ecological model suggests that problems in behaviour are not just the inappropriate actions of the child, but rather that undesirable behaviours are developed and maintained by difficulties in her interactions, reflecting a lack of "goodness of fit" between the child and the surrounding ecological system (Winzer, 2005).

Urie Bronfenbrenner, the primary author of the ecological or "systems" model, proposed two principles in working with vulnerable youth. First, *always involve adults directly in the life space of children and youth*. Second, *involve a child or youth in finding his or her own solutions to problems*. In these ways young people can avoid becoming disengaged from the community without ever having had the opportunity to make contributions to others (Brendtro, 2010). Bronfenbrenner's two principles became the basis of all ecological and relational models used in CYC work with troubled and troubling children and youth (Brendtro, 2010).

Bronfenbrenner adamantly opposed diagnosing mental health issues in young people as "pathology" or "disease," and instead focused on their immediate "circles of influence": their family, peers, and school. So, as Brendtro summarizes, when CYCPs assess a child's ecology in order to design positive interventions, the following two questions are most important:

1. What are the interactions (or "transactions") between the child, family, peers, and school?

2. Does this "circle of influence" create stress or offer support for the child?

WHERE DO YOU STAND?

Consider the psychological and CYC perspectives we've discussed. Do you believe that any one of these perspectives can offer better explanations for exceptional behaviour than the others? If so, you're not alone. Some psychologists, and some CYCPs, will also agree more readily with the assumptions of any one particular perspective. Generally, however, most practitioners acknowledge that each of these paradigms must be considered in order to achieve the most comprehensive understanding of abnormal behaviour. This eclectic or **integrative approach** (known in CYC practice as the *ecological model*) recognizes the importance of all paradigms in describing, explaining, predicting, and managing abnormal behaviour. Accordingly, each of us would be wise to consider explanations from a variety of perspectives. After considering abnormal/exceptional behaviour from both a psychological and a CYC perspective, try the *Take Action!* exercise and apply your knowledge of both approaches to Darren's case. Where do you stand when it comes to the explanations for emotional and behavioural difficulties?

According to the ecological model, then, when the circles of influence are in balance, young people are in harmony with themselves and others. However, if their ecology is disrupted or in tension, they will experience conflict, difficulties, and maladjustment. The aim of CYC interventions in the ecological model, therefore, is to build a supportive ecology around the child (Brendtro, 2010).

Take Action! Exercise: *Darren's Case*

Darren is a 17-year-old boy who was charged with sexually interfering with a female under the age of 13 one year ago. The police placed him in the Manitoba Youth Centre, where he was on remand awaiting assessment and trial. The forensic psychiatrist who assessed him accessed Darren's school files and learned that he'd been diagnosed with Obsessive-Compulsive Disorder (OCD) and Attention-Deficit/Hyperactivity Disorder (ADHD), and had received medication (Ritalin) for the latter. His file notes also showed a Statement of Special Educational Needs, previous high-level support in school, and treatment from a speech and language therapist. The psychiatrist found no evidence of ADHD or OCD during the assessment. However, Darren did show evidence of specific learning difficulties, such as slow and laboured speech, difficulty in structuring sentences, and speaking in a fragmented fashion. He was open, honest, and matter-of-fact, and was observed to lack the ability to be strategic in his responses. The psychiatrist found that Darren appeared to lack insight into his behaviour and had no real awareness of right and wrong. Darren's stepmother reported no concerns about his behaviour around children. When the psychiatrist contacted Darren's school, they described him as a boy who lacked social skills and stayed near teachers at lunchtime in order to avoid being alone or bullied. Darren was sentenced to one year open custody and referred to mental health services.

What do you think? Which aspects of the psychological paradigms might inform your understanding of what's happening with Darren? What information do you need to form a hypothesis? Are there aspects of both the CYC models and the psychology models that together would help inform your understanding of Darren's behaviour?

HELPING CHILDREN AND ADOLESCENTS WITH EMOTIONAL AND BEHAVIOURAL DISTURBANCES

Troy's Case: *Revisited*

Troy became so incapacitated by his ongoing separation anxiety and his increasing panic attacks that his parents took him for an assessment at the child and adolescent psychiatric hospital. The psychiatrist recommended group-based cognitive behavioural therapy (CBT) and anti-anxiety psychotropic medication. Troy's parents were reluctant to put him on the medication but agreed to try CBT. Troy was referred to an outpatient program where youth participated in daily CBT therapy groups. Troy progressed very well in group and was able to learn to manage his anxiety symptoms. He returned to school and his panic attacks subsided. When he did experience a panic attack, Troy was able to successfully use the relaxation techniques he'd learned from the CYCP who ran the therapy groups at the outpatient program.

Psychological Approaches to Treatment

Various methods associated with the major psychological perspectives are used in an attempt to decrease symptoms of any particular disorder, with the general goal being to restore healthy functioning. As you read about the different strategies of treatment for each of the paradigms, notice the relationship between their ideas about what causes disordered behaviour (as discussed earlier in the chapter) and their recommendations for how to treat these disturbances.

Biological Paradigm   A biological approach to treatment for emotional and behavioural disorders primarily depends on the use of medications that alter the activity of neurotransmitters in the central nervous system. For example, anti-anxiety medications can be effective in decreasing the symptoms of anxiety and inducing feelings of relaxation and calm by increasing the sensitivity of neurons in the brain to GABA, an inhibitory neurotransmitter. Box 1.5 summarizes the general drug classes that will be discussed throughout the text, including the general mechanisms by which they exert their effects and the disorders they're typically used to treat.

Although CYCPs aren't responsible for prescribing medications for youth, understanding how they work and being able to identify their side effects and drug-interaction effects are an important component of mental health literacy. This is discussed at length in the CYC approach later in this chapter.

Psychodynamic Paradigm   In their review of the literature, Blagys and Hilsenroth (2000) identified seven features that distinguish psychodynamic therapy from other intervention approaches. First, the psychodynamic approach encourages the individual to explore and discuss his emotions, particularly those associated with distress. Second, attempts by the individual to avoid feelings of distress/anxiety are also examined. For example, if one fears public speaking, skipping classes or failing tests might be considered as attempts to avoid situations that trigger distress. Third, part of this process involves identifying recurrent patterns of behaviour. Fourth, psychodynamic therapy takes a developmental approach. This is associated with in-depth exploration of past experiences and how

Medications Used in the Treatment of Youth Disorders

Drug Class	Examples of Mechanism of Action	Disorders Commonly Treated	Common Names
Anti-anxiety drugs (tranquilizers)	Increase GABA sensitivity (an inhibitory neurotransmitter)	Anxiety, panic, and mood disorders	Valium, Xanax
Mood stabilizers	Alter sodium and potassium pump; increase GABA	Bipolar Disorder	Depakene, lithium
Antidepressants	Increase serotonin activity	Depression and anxiety disorders	Paxil, Zoloft
Psychostimulants	Increase dopamine activity	ADHD	Ritalin, Dexadrine
Antipsychotics	Decrease dopamine activity	Schizophrenia	Haldol, Zyprexa

prior events are associated with current behaviour patterns and emotional difficulties. In doing so, the aim is to help the individual live his life in the present rather than in the past.

Fifth, psychodynamic therapy emphasizes the importance of interpersonal relationships. The sixth feature includes an examination of the relationship between the individual who's seeking assistance and the therapist. For example, if the individual fears his parents' rejection and disapproval, it's assumed that these concerns will be reflected in his interactions with the therapist (e.g., feeling fearful of sharing feelings of anger with the therapist because his father disapproved of the expression of anger). Seventh, psychodynamic therapists are willing to explore the dreams, fantasies, and daydreams of the individual more readily than those who adopt other approaches to intervention. The assumption is that this material is a rich source of information about what the individual values, what he seeks to avoid, and what is interfering with adaptive functioning.

The goal of psychodynamic therapy is not simply to reduce symptoms of disturbed functioning but to develop personal capacities and resources so that one achieves more satisfying relationships, gains a sense of competence, and face stressors with greater flexibility.

Behavioural Paradigm   From a behavioural paradigm, if basic learning processes (i.e., classical conditioning, operant conditioning) are responsible for establishing dysfunctional and impairing emotional and behavioural patterns, approaches to treatment should use such processes to decrease symptoms and increase adaptive behaviours.

One important learning process used to decrease symptoms associated with various disorders is that of **exposure**. Specifically, being exposed repeatedly to a particular object, situation, or memory that triggers negative emotions (e.g., a dog) followed by the absence of negative outcomes (e.g., no dog bite) will result in the eventual decrease in fear triggered by that stimulus. From a behavioural standpoint, this extinction of or decrease in a particular emotional and/or physiological response results under the following conditions: (1) you are *exposed* to the stimulus you fear, (2) you feel the fear or distress associated with the stimulus, but (3) you have nothing bad happen after the exposure. Exposure treatment is used extensively for anxiety and trauma- and stressor-related disorders.

Operant conditioning processes are also extensively used in the treatment of various psychological disorders. For example, providing reinforcements (e.g., verbal praise) following desirable behaviour (e.g., working hard on a school assignment) is an effective way to increase the likelihood of those behaviours occurring in the future. Although punishments might also be presented following undesirable behaviour, they're generally less effective in changing behaviour and are also ethically questionable. The focus, then, is on how to use reinforcements to increase adaptive behaviour.

Cognitive Paradigm   From a cognitive approach, thoughts and beliefs are considered to be important factors in influencing emotional states and related behaviour. Therefore, if you seek to change behaviour, altering thoughts is the optimal approach to treatment. The goals of cognitive therapy include increasing awareness of personal cognitive biases and how these negative thoughts contribute to negative emotional states. Keeping a *thought record*, in which one records the thoughts associated with specific daily experiences and notes how these thoughts result in particular emotions, is a common strategy used to increase this awareness. Together with a counsellor or therapist, the youth is encouraged to consider his or her automatic thoughts in various situations, evaluate the extent to which these are rational, and consider alternative thoughts in relation to situations that might be associated with negative emotions. By consistently challenging these dysfunctional cognitive beliefs, alternative interpretations become more likely to be used in the future, with negative emotions and dysfunctional behaviour decreasing as a result.

Because these cognitive approaches usually include behavioural exercises, they're often referred to as **cognitive behavioural therapy (CBT)**. An abundance of research documents the effectiveness of cognitive behavioural therapy with a variety of disorders. As discussed later in this chapter, CBT fits well with a CYC perspective and is likely to be used by CYCPs in their practice. CBT interventions include strategies and techniques focused on enhancing problem solving, assertiveness training, cognitive restructuring, family communication skills training, relaxation, exposure, and increasing pleasant activities (Weersing, 2004). The primary focus of all these techniques is examining the relationship between thoughts, feelings, and behaviours and teaching effective coping responses to stress and negative emotions (Garber & Weersing, 2010).

Sociocultural Paradigm   Sociocultural approaches to treatment emphasize altering the social and cultural factors involved in emotional and behavioural disturbances. From this perspective, including family in the treatment of affected young people is considered essential to the success of any intervention. **Family engagement** refers to the involvement of family members at various levels of intervention and treatment decisions and includes the process by which family members come to understand that their child/adolescent is in need of mental health care (Trunzo, 2006).

> Engagement has been defined as a process that begins with a child being identified as experiencing mental health difficulties and ending with a child receiving mental health care. More specifically, engagement in care is described as beginning with the recognition of a child mental health problem by parents, teachers, or other adults within a child's context. (McKay & Bannon, 2004, p. 906)

Engagement might initially include parents seeking services or accompanying the youth to a scheduled appointment; later it can include being involved in the assessment of the child as well as in any treatment interventions agreed upon by mental health professionals together with family input. Such participation not only ensures that the family's values and beliefs are considered, but also increases the likelihood that broader cultural factors will be considered when developing any approach to treatment.

> By involving family and youth at all levels a system of care assures itself that the culture of the system will be impacted by the perspectives and the cultures of the families and youth in the community. (Penn & Savage, 2004, as cited in Chovil, 2009, p. 14)

For each disorder discussed in the remaining chapters of this text, we will explore strategies that seek to involve parents and other caregivers in meaningful ways so that they may best support the youth undergoing treatment.

CYC Approaches for Youth Struggling with Emotional and Behavioural Disturbances

> Child and youth care is about caring and acting—about being there, thinking on your feet, interacting, and growing with children. It is rich, intense, difficult work that requires passion and commitment. (Krueger, 2000)

As Brendtro, Brokenleg, and Van Bockern (2005) point out, many of the major psychological models used to understand the mental health issues and other problems of troubled youth operate from a deficit perspective. These authors note the popularity of five major approaches to working with troubled children based on Googling the word *children* with each of the following terms: *behavioural, psychodynamic, neuroscience, ecological,* and *sociological*. The resulting numbers of hits were as follows: behavioural (problems are seen as behavioural disorders), 270 000 hits; psychodynamic (problems are seen as emotional disturbance), 131 000; neuroscience (problems are seen as brain disorders), 80 000; ecological (problems are seen as dis-ease in the ecology), 43 200; and sociological (problems are seen as social maladjustment, 9420 (Brendtro et al., 2005).

This web search shows that there is much available online that tries to explain childhood social, emotional, and behavioural problems, but that all five models are negative and pessimistic, with the first three focusing on deficits in the child and the last two on deficits in the environment (Brendtro et al., 2005). Conversely, the authors found that a Google search for *resilience and children* produced 700 000 hits—more than the entire negative, or pathology-based, labels combined.

As Brendtro et al. (2005) have suggested, we are currently engaged in a resilience revolution in how we see the worlds of troubled or at-risk young people—a paradigm shift from disordered to exceptional, from fixing flaws to finding strengths. Brendtro et al. (2005) examine each of the key theories about troubled children and youth and point out ways in which each now appear to be moving from a focus on deficits toward a focus on strengths.

Strength-Based Relational CYC Practice

> We have a choice about how we wish to view the young people whom we assist. We can either view them as manifestations of pathology and deficit or we can view them as representing a degree of competence and skill. We cannot do both. Further, if we

choose to view them in terms of pathology, then the focus on problems that this perspective requires makes it much more difficult for us to recognize their strengths and resources. . . . [I]f we choose to view them as competent and resourceful, then our focus on strengths is more likely to obscure their deficits from our view. (Durrant, 1993, p. 12)

According to McWhirter et al. (2007), a youth being "at risk" denotes a set of presumed cause–effect dynamics that place an individual youth in danger of future negative outcomes. But in the **risk–resiliency model**, the term *resilience* refers to those at-risk youth who have good outcomes despite experiencing chronic stress and adversity (McWhirter et al., 2007).

Of course, resiliency is not a new idea in the area of emotional and behavioural disorders. Eleanor Guetzloe (1994) has outlined some themes of resiliency that have emerged from relevant research since the mid-1990s. Family environments that are considered to be unstable, hostile, or negative are characterized by external forces that can lead to mental illness or other serious problems in youth. These families can be described as dysfunctional; they may, for example, have substance abuse issues and/or they may be neglectful or physically abusive of children. Or, as in the case of homeless youth, children may have no families at all. And yet Guetzloe notes that in some of these children at risk there is a surprising absence of mental illness; they seem to possess an inner strength that enables them to sustain healthy development and to maintain focus and hope. Indeed, children and youth experiencing a variety of extreme and challenging circumstances have not only survived, but thrived (Guetzloe, 1994).

Guetzloe (1994) further points out that many resilient children seem to have an entire cluster or pattern of "protective factors" instead of just one or two. The development of resilience seems to depend on the multiple "transactions" between the individual characteristics of a child/youth and the protective factors in the environment. Resilience depends on at least "four interacting trajectories in human development: biological, social, and environmental factors, and finally, a chance event." Interestingly, these "same interacting and transecting trajectories can also contribute to the development of violent behavior, suicidal tendencies, and other serious problems" (Guetzloe, 1994, p. 4).

Guetzloe stresses that "certain components of resilience can be taught and reinforced, modeled and learned." Whereas "learned helplessness" develops in the face of experiences where individuals learn that absolutely nothing they do will make a difference, this can be altered by showing these youth that their own actions *will* in fact make a difference. "Resilient children somehow know that their actions will work; less-resilient children can learn this through achieving success in school and in other environments" (Guetzloe, 1994, p. 5).

Guetzloe summarizes the resiliency protective factors noted in the research. They are as follows:

An "easy" temperament: Temperament refers to inborn tendencies that influence activity level, feeding patterns, adaptability, intensity of reaction, and responsiveness to new situations. A child born with an easy temperament adapts more easily to new experiences than one born with a difficult disposition and is more likely to receive support from others (which, as Guetzloe notes, is another protective factor associated with resilience).

The presence of an adult mentor: As we pointed out earlier in this chapter, one of the most important protective factors is a trusting relationship with an adult. Youth-serving programs, schools, and communities can provide these caring adults. Note that it's very helpful to provide youth with mentors who have ethnic backgrounds and experiences similar to their own.

Informal sources of support: Resilient youth tend to seek help from peers, older friends, and other informal sources rather than mental health professionals.

Activities and creativity: "All children, particularly those at risk, should be provided the opportunity to participate in art, crafts, music, drama, dance, and other activities aimed at fostering and enhancing creativity. . . . With a clear understanding that the phenomenon of resilience is complex and that specific interventions must be carefully selected with individual needs in mind, we can work toward a comprehensive system of positive interventions" (Guetzloe, 1994, p. 6).

Michael Unger, a leading researcher, author, and speaker about resiliency in children and youth, points out that "it is important that resilience be preserved as a concept that describes positive growth during adversity" (Ungar, 2008, p. 2). He also notes that risk and resiliency are "two sides of the same coin" (Ungar, 2008, p. 2), where **risk factors** refer to any force that threatens one's normal development.

Unger distinguishes between strengths and resilience. **Strengths** encompass a roster of internal and external assets for the entire population. Simply put, the more assets a young person has, the more likely she is to succeed in culturally and socially acceptable ways over her lifespan. *Resilience* describes "the presence of these strengths when a population is exposed to multiple risks" (Ungar, 2008, p. 3).

> Resilience can be understood as follows: first; the capacity of individuals to navigate the resources that sustain wellbeing; second, the capacity of individuals' environments to provide resources; and third, the capacity of individuals, their families and communities to negotiate culturally meaningful ways for resources to be shared. (Ungar, 2008, p. 4)

Assessment

The following is a general introduction to strength-based assessment in CYC practice; later chapters describe relevant assessment techniques for each identified mental health concern. The DSM-5 can be a very useful overall guide to the signs and behaviours that children and youth experiencing mental health issues will demonstrate and that you'll need to understand, observe, and document.

In conducting their assessments, CYCPs need to know how to identify all the signs and symptoms of the mental health concerns described in this text. CYCPs should be familiar with the mental status examination (MSE) format, reviewed in Chapter 9. The MSE provides a guideline for practitioners' observations about how a young person looks, feels, and behaves at the time of observation (Morrison, 2007) in terms of appearance, mood and affect, insight, judgment, and so on. *Assessment* can be defined as the gathering and synthesizing of information about, and with, a youth and his or her family in order to assist in planning effective interventions. Assessment is central to good child and youth care practice, and it is key to engaging in a focused and helpful way with youth in order to mutually plan successful interventions. Assessments need to be strength-based in child and youth care. According to Rudolph and Epstein, a strength-based assessment approach is based on four important assumptions:

> Every child, regardless of his or her personal and family situation, has strengths that are unique to the individual; Children are influenced and motivated by the way significant people in their lives respond to them; Rather than viewing a child who does not demonstrate a strength as deficient, it is assumed the child has not had the opportunities that are essential to learning, developing, and mastering the skill; When treatment and service planning are based on strengths rather than deficits and pathologies, children and families are more likely to become involved in the therapeutic process and to use their strengths and resources. (Rudolph & Epstein, 2000, pp. 207–208)

Assessments also need to be trauma-informed in child and youth care. Depending on their education level and training, the sector within which they work, and their role in the organization, some CYCPs may be able to conduct clinical assessments. Generally speaking, however, in most jurisdictions, a thorough clinical mental health assessment ought to be conducted by a licensed clinical practitioner, who may or may not be a CYCP. The CYCP may need to refer the child, youth, or family for this type of more formal clinical assessment. Nonetheless, it's important for the CYCP to remember that although trained therapists will make very important contributions to child and youth assessment and intervention, "it would be well to debunk the myth and mystique surrounding psychotherapy" (Brendtro, Brokenleg, & Van Bockern, 2002, p. 82). Indeed, "sometimes an adult who is actively involved in the life experiences with a youth can engage in more genuine and helpful communications than can a therapist tethered to an office desk" (Brendtro et al., 2002, p. 82).

Assessment in child and youth care is complex. It involves assessing any exposure to traumatic events as well as any potentially severe impact of trauma exposure across the domains of development ("Assessment of complex trauma," n.d.).

Here are some key steps for conducting a comprehensive, trauma-informed mental health assessment: Assess for a wide range of potentially traumatic events in the child/youth's history. Ensure that you determine when they occurred so that they can be linked to developmental stages. Assess for a wide range of symptoms, risk behaviours, functional impairments, and developmental difficulties. Gather information using a variety of techniques (clinical interviews, behavioural observations) and from a variety of perspectives (youth, caregivers, teachers, other providers, etc.). Always be sure to engage the child and family about what makes sense, what's working, and the most useful next steps for intervention ("Assessment of complex trauma," n.d.). As we discussed earlier, the CYCP's belief system will invariably influence the way youth behaviour is viewed and how the data are interpreted. Depending on their training and frames of reference, any two professionals may interpret the same data completely differently. Even though we try to maintain objectivity, we know that our beliefs and values can significantly affect our picture of the child or youth. Such influences may result in inaccurate assessments, which will in turn affect how services are provided. A CYCP who looks for problems, weaknesses, or deficits will find them; therefore, searching for strengths, solutions, resources, and skills is always preferred (Rudolph & Epstein, 2000).

A strength-based assessment approach provides several advantages for CYC practitioners and the young people they assist. First, focusing on strengths allows practitioners to involve young people and their families in service planning in a positive way by highlighting what is going well. Second, strength-based assessment provides a method for documenting a young person's strengths and competencies and offers a way to establish positive expectations for the youth and family. Third, through strength-based assessment, family members will be empowered to take mutual responsibility for decisions that will affect their child's life (Rudolph & Epstein, 2000). Children and youth don't want to be interrogated by adults; they want to feel that someone is listening to their story. All youth have the right to be fully involved in an assessment process that not only looks at their problems but also focuses on their strengths.

Artz and her colleagues stress that CYCPs need to know when a young person's life circumstances call for a focus on assessing *need* and when they call for a focus on assessing *risk* (Artz et al., 2004). Nowhere is this distinction more critical than in the area of child and adolescent mental health. And yet, as Artz et al. (2004) point out, in CYC research and practice, risk and need are frequently collapsed. A needs assessment that is collapsed into a risk assessment tends to be deficit-focused; that is, concerned only with problematic conditions and behaviours rather than with strengths and potential. In CYC practice, strengths-based assessment is preferable to the other pathology-based models that focus on young people's vulnerability. Further, having experts assess risk doesn't necessarily help CYC professionals determine who needs services and what kinds of services are required. Nor does it help in predicting what will happen in a youth's future without such services or support. Artz et al. (2004) thus emphasize that to facilitate appropriate service provision, accurate needs assessment is a must.

However, shifting the focus exclusively to needs assessment brings another challenge: some risks, especially the risk of harm to self and others, must take precedence over any other call for service and intervention. In planning effective intervention, then, both need and risk must be understood contextually.

Although CYCPs don't traditionally use rating scales or other "paper-and-pencil" tests in their assessments, it's important to familiarize yourself with the assessment scales in each area of CYC practice. Such familiarity will give you (1) an awareness of what clinicians and psychologists use in their own assessments and (2) guidelines for both your observations and your formal and informal interview questions. Each chapter in this text therefore includes relevant and accessible rating scales.

The Youth Bill of Rights (see Box 1.6) was developed by Laura Burney Nissen (1994) specifically for young people in the juvenile justice system. These principles provide benchmarks for respect in assessment as the foundation of planning for positive outcomes. We encourage CYCPs to embrace these principles in their assessment practices.

Indicators to Recognize   Parents, teachers, friends, CYCPs, and caregivers are often the first to recognize that a child or adolescent may be having concerning and/or significant difficulties with their emotions or behaviours. The Canadian Psychiatric Association provides general indicators that a formal mental health assessment may be useful or required; these are summarized in Table 1.6. In this text we highlight the specific indicators to recognize for the mental health issue presented in each chapter.

Intervention

In a relational CYC model the actual child–professional caregiver relationships may be the key to successful interventions with a child who has experienced severe early relationship disruptions. It is clear that a security enhancing practitioner or surrogate

I have the right to . . .

- be viewed as a person capable of changing, growing, and becoming positively connected to my community no matter what types of behaviour I have exhibited

- participate in the selection of services that build on my strengths

- contribute things I am good at and other strengths in all assessment and diagnostic processes

- have my resistance viewed as a message that the wrong approach is being used with me

- learn from my mistakes and to have support to learn that mistakes don't mean failure

- view past maladaptive or antisocial behaviours as a lack of skills that I can acquire to change my life for the better

- experience success and to have support connecting previous successes to future goals

- have my culture valued and to have services that honour and respect my cultural beliefs

- have my gender issues recognized as a source of strength in my identity

- be assured that all written and oral, and formal and informal, communications about me include my strengths as well as my needs

- surpass any treatment goals that have been set too low for me, or to have treatment goals that are different from those generally applied to all youth

- be served by professionals who view youth positively and understand that motivating me is related to successfully accessing my strengths

- have my family involved in my care and treatment in a way that acknowledges and supports our strengths as well as our needs

- stay connected to my family no matter what types of challenges we face

- be viewed and treated as more than a statistic, stereotype, risk score, diagnosis, label, or pathology

- a future free of institutional or systems involvement and to services that most centrally and positively focus on my successful transition from institutions

- service providers who coordinate their efforts and who share a united philosophy that the key to my success is through my strengths

- exercise my developmental tasks as an adolescent—to try out new identities, to learn to be accountable, and to say I'm sorry for the harm I've caused others—all of which is made even more difficult if I'm labelled as a "bad kid"

- be viewed and treated as a redeemable resource, potential leader, and success of the future.

Source: Adapted from Heckenlaible-Gotto, 2006.

parent who can look beyond a child's disruptive behaviours and emotional volatility to a child's strengths and developmental needs may promote the development of a secure attachment orientation in a child. (Curry et al., 2011, p. 6)

Research into the effectiveness of various psychotherapies and counselling techniques has concluded that, no matter which conceptual models or theories practitioners follow, the effectiveness of the chosen intervention depends most significantly on the quality of the relationship between client and therapist (Sharpe, 2006). Indeed, depending on the needs of individual children, in actual practice many approaches may be helpful (Sharpe, 2006). Thus, for youth who are facing adversity and a multitude of risk factors in their lives, the single most important opportunity for change is a positive and consistent relationship with a caring significant adult in their lives, whether that person is a grandparent, a

Table 1.6 Behavioural Indicators Checklist: General Indicators of Mental Health Issues

✓ Marked drop in school performance or increase in absenteeism

  Increased or excessive use of alcohol and/or drugs

  Marked changes in sleeping and/or eating habits

  Many physical complaints (headaches, stomachaches)

  Aggressive or non-aggressive consistent violations of rights of others: opposition to authority, truancy, thefts, vandalism, etc.

  Withdrawal from friends, family, and regular activities

  Depression shown by sustained, prolonged negative mood and attitude, often accompanied by poor appetite, difficulty sleeping, or thoughts of death

  Frequent outbursts of anger and rage

  Low energy level, poor concentration, complaints of boredom

  Loss of enjoyment in what used to be favourite activities

  Unusual neglect of personal appearance

  Intense fear of becoming obese with no relationship to actual body weight

  Uncharacteristic thrill seeking or sexual acting out

  Marked personality change or bizarre behaviour

  Comments about "feeling rotten inside," wanting to "end things," and soon no longer being a problem for others

  Hearing voices and/or talking to self

Source: "Canadian Psychiatric Association," 2012.

teacher, an aunt, or a CYCP. As Urie Bronfenbrenner noted, "Every child needs at least one adult who is irrationally crazy about him or her" (Brendtro, 2006, p. 165).

Carol Stuart (2009a) refers to planned CYC interventions as those that develop when we design activities and interactions to best meet young people's identified needs and to support their individual goals and objectives. Thom Garfat (1998) defines intervention as "an intentional caring action, taken into one of the daily life systems of which the youth is a part, which facilitates a change in that system such that a context is created for the youth to have a different experiencing of herself and/or the meaning that she gives to her experiencing" (p. 168). Based on a qualitative analysis of the subjective experiences of both CYC practitioners and the youth they worked with, Garfat (1998) identified key characteristics of successful interventions. He recommends a framework for CYC assessment and intervention based on four key stages: *noticing, reflecting, preparation*, and *intervention* (Garfat, 2003).

Behavioural and Cognitive-Behavioural Techniques for CYCPs   The fundamental assumption of the cognitive paradigm when applied to the exceptionalities of children and youth is that through intervention and training, young people's thinking processes can be changed. The way we work with them depends on whether they exhibit a pattern of deficits or a distorted pattern. If there's a deficit, CYCPs will teach them how to use cognitive skills and strategies, with the underlying assumption that young people either haven't been taught particular cognitive skills or have learned them but use them incorrectly. If there is a distortion, CYCPs will attempt to alter their perceptions, beliefs, and thinking patterns. This usually means helping youth shift from negative thinking patterns to positive self-talk patterns. Specific options for accomplishing this are explored in each chapter.

The cognitive-behavioural model combines elements of the behavioural and the cognitive conceptual paradigms. Cognitive behavioural therapy (CBT) emphasizes the learning process based on the influence of environmental factors while also focusing on the information or thinking process involved in the development of disorders. Much research supports the efficacy of the CBT model. Indeed, in the area of mental health for children and youth it's considered the gold standard of evidence-based interventions, and as such is used frequently in CYC practice. The following chapters outline its use for each mental health disorder of children and youth.

The Role of Medication

> Yes. Every single kid—it's very rare that we'll get a young person that is not on medication, and I've seen young people so over-medicated that they can't even hold a conversation. They fall asleep halfway through the day. (Lambe & McLellan, 2009)

The use of psychotropic medications as a first-line treatment for children and youth diagnosed with psychological disorders is a significant issue, and of particular importance for those in the CYC field. Given that psychotropic drugs are inexact, unpredictable instruments at best, using these medications for children and youth is likely ill advised. And yet critics argue that physicians are increasingly prescribing these medications to children in order to treat what are merely the normal pains of daily living. In Canada, over 200 000 prescriptions for antidepressants were given to children and youth in 2003, representing a 75 percent increase in five years (Fewster, 2004).

Furthermore, many authors point out that once the DSM has established a child psychological disorder, the number of young people diagnosed as having that disorder inevitably expands. Children and youth once considered odd, difficult, melancholy, or unconventional have now joined the ranks of the mentally ill. ADHD is viewed by many as one such disorder: "Hyperactivity in children, for example, has become a hotly contested diagnosis. Aided no doubt by the availability of drugs like Ritalin and Adderall, the disease has crept outward from its core population of children who cannot concentrate, to children whose behaviours may be troublesome, but hardly abnormal" (Karp & Sisson, 2010, p. 122).

And as Fewster has argued for many years, once a psychiatric diagnosis has been established, pharmaceutical companies promote and market their medications for exclusive use in treatment. Indeed, the relationship between the pharmaceutical industry and psychiatry has been called into question by many authors and clinicians (Fewster, 2002), and there is no disputing the fact that marketing psychotropic medications for use with children is now a multimillion-dollar industry. In the United States, sales of antipsychotic drugs were estimated at $2.8 billion in 2003, and by 2011 that number had risen to $18.2 billion ("Are too many kids," 2013). Recent data from the Centers for Disease Control and Prevention in the United States show that the ADHD diagnosis had been given to 15 percent of all American high-school age children, and that the number of children on medication for the disorder had soared to 3.5 million in 2003 from 600 000 in 1990. The rise of ADHD diagnoses and prescriptions for stimulants over the years has coincided with a hugely successful two-decade campaign by pharmaceutical companies to publicize ADHD and promote their meds to doctors, educators, and parents (Shwarz, 2013).

The long-term implications of psychotropic medications on children's physical, emotional, and social development is unknown. Exposure to antidepressants and other medications may affect those areas of the brain having to do with stress, emotion, and the regulation of emotions (Foltz, 2008a). As Foltz points out, there is an urgent need for more research on how these medications may affect a child or youth across childhood and adolescence. For example, in contrast to an average eight-year-old boy, the average teen boy experiences a dramatic increase in testosterone, yet if these two youth were each diagnosed with Bipolar Disorder, they would likely receive the same or similar medications—and it is not known how these medications may react with this or any other developmental event (Foltz, 2010a).

As well, the effectiveness and overall safety of antidepressants with children and youth are, at best, highly questionable. In a U.S. FDA review of short-term, placebo-controlled antidepressant trials, only 3 of 15 studies demonstrated any superiority over the placebo. The increase in self-injurious behaviour and suicide ideation after taking antidepressants, and the increased likelihood of agitated, irritable, and impulsive behaviours (potentiating mania), have been well documented. In 2003, the FDA, Health Canada, and the MHRA all warned against the use of SSRIs in children and adolescents. Since 2004, a "black box warning" about potential suicidality in this age group was added to all antidepressant monographs ("Depression in children," n.d.).

> In children, SSRIs and other new anti-depressants produce a higher rate of behavioural and emotional adverse effects (such as: agitation, disinhibition, irritability and occasionally thoughts of self-harm). The largest drug-placebo difference in the number of cases of suicidal ideation and behaviour is greatest for the under-24 age group. For all ages, the risk is highest during the first few months of drug therapy, therefore, monitor patients closely during this time. ("Anxiety and depression," 2010)

According to the Canadian National Youth in Care Network (NYICN) (Lambe & McLellan, 2009), the practice of using mood-altering and behaviour-modifying psychotropic medications as an intervention for young people who've been diagnosed with a mental health issue in the justice and child welfare systems is a serious issue. The NYICN conducted a study in which 41 young people aged 18 to 28, in and from care, were asked about the types of "chemical management strategies" that had been used with them. Seventy percent of the participants had been prescribed psychotropic medications while living in the system. On average, participants began taking medication at 13 years of age. Of the 70 percent who had been prescribed medications while in the system, 30 percent were still using psychotropic medications at the time of the interview. In addition, many children and youth did not have a say about whether they wanted to take the drugs or not.

Approximately 90 percent of caregiver or "intervener" respondents identified benefits of using medication to treat the symptoms of mental illness with the children and youth they worked with. They thought that the medications had minimized the disruption associated with such conditions as depression, anxiety, and panic attacks, and that those who had been prescribed medication for conditions such as ADHD had developed increased levels of concentration. Interveners shared their observations of how youth were able to participate with their peers and had successful and rewarding school experiences. The child/youth participants also acknowledged many benefits of using psychotropic drugs in the treatment of psychiatric disorders; for example, when medication had alleviated disruptive or distressing symptoms they had experienced, they were in support of this method. They did, however, specify that when medication was required, it was most effective when used in combination with forms of counselling and psychotherapy. It's important to note, then, that such medications do benefit some children and youth. Nonetheless, feedback about the consequences that arose from the overuse and misuse of psychotropics overshadowed all other commentary (Lambe & McLellan, 2009).

> There are some advantages when they're used. Some of the advantages are: to help with sleep patterns, to help with concentration in schools, to help as a mood stabilizer, to help with depression, to help control anxiety and panic attacks, etc. (Intervener, Ontario)

> In my opinion, the advantages of using psychotropic medications are they help control some problems that occur. If it's being prescribed by a doctor and under a doctor's supervision, it should be okay. (Intervener, Atlantic)

> Depending on the child and the severity of the behaviour, with some it would help with concentration with school work and day to day living so they are able to have a positive and successful future. (Intervener, Prairies)

According to the NYICN's *Drugs in Our System* report (Lambe & McLellan, 2009), youth feedback had indicated five main areas of serious concern: (1) psychotropics were pre-scribed immediately upon or shortly after their entry into the child and family services sys-tem; (2) informed consent from the young person was not required or requested; (3) workers had relied on medications as a quicker, easier, and cheaper alternative to "fix" emotional and behavioural struggles; (4) chemical management strategies were used as a means of control-ling their behaviour, enforcing compliance, and restraining aggression; (5) the healing needs of participants had not been appropriately addressed through the use of psychotropics, and had resulted in dependency. The top five psychotropic medications prescribed to youth who'd been medicated while in systems care were Ritalin (34 percent), Paxil (17 percent), Dexe-drine (15 percent), Effexor (15 percent), and Prozac (15 percent). For the 41 young people who said they'd been medicated while in the out-of-home care system, the top five psychiat-ric diagnoses reported were Attention Deficit Disorder (ADD) and Attention-Deficit/ Hyperactivity Disorder (ADHD) (41 percent), depression (39 percent), anxiety (15 percent), Bipolar Disorder (7 percent), and Obsessive-Compulsive Disorder (7 percent).

> I don't like the idea of being force-fed meds at all. I think that it's kind of perverted. It is. It's a violation, like strapping me down and sticking me with a needle, I consider that raping me. Yes it is. You're putting a chemical in my body. (17-year-old male)

> I think they're used as a control measure. I think it's a way of dealing with issues, by not having to deal with issues. (22-year-old staff)

CYCPs need to decide for themselves where they stand on the issue of using psychotro-pic medications with children and youth. Gerry Fewster (2004) offers the following approaches to the question of whether to administer psychotropic medications in CYC work: Ask yourself whether you'd take the meds yourself, and whether you'd give them to your own children. Carefully articulate your stance on this issue, write it down, and revisit it occasion-ally. Be prepared to conduct research in order to offer alternative, drug-free interventions and to challenge those who argue that psychotropic medications are the only or the most effective treatment for children with difficulties. Ensure that you know all the potential side effects, and observe for and document these. Finally, ensure that youths are well informed about the side effects as well as about their right to refuse to take the medication (Fewster, 2004).

In the following chapters we describe the most commonly prescribed psychotropic medications used to treat each disorder. CYCPs ought to examine this issue very carefully and determine their own position on it.

Psychoeducation and Individual Counselling   As discussed earlier, psychodynamic theories have had a significant influence on all therapeutic approaches, including individual and group counselling. Indeed, the classic CYC texts on therapeutic milieu and the need for external controls, predictability, and structure to calm the chaotic internal world of the "disturbed child" (Trieschman et al., 1969; Redl, 1966; Redl & Wineman, 1952) are based on the psychodynamic conceptual model. This model influenced the development of the theory of group care of children as well as Fritz Redl's classic CYC concept of the "life space interview" or "life space crisis intervention" (LSCI), which uses informal, day-to-day situations as the space for therapeutic engagement with troubled youth. Group work with children has also been influenced by Bruno Bettelheim's ideas about the therapeutic potential of this milieu.

The psychodynamic model stresses the importance of understanding the emotional and psychological development of children and young people, and can be used to explain what happens when development is disrupted in childhood (Sharpe, 2006). Therefore, it's critical that CYC professionals working with vulnerable young people understand the psychodynamic paradigm.

Many of Freud's theories are central to the writings of Fritz Redl, Redl and Wineman, Bruno Bettelheim, and other CYC pioneers (Garfat, 1987). As Thom Garfat has observed, "Trying to understand child and youth care without reading Redl and Wineman is like trying to understand algebra without learning addition, it's that basic" (Garfat, 1987). Psychoeducation and strength-based individual counselling approaches are without a doubt among the most effective and well-used approaches in the CYC intervention tool kit.

Family Support Interventions   CYCPs use a family-focused approach in their work. Families need to be included in every aspect of the therapeutic or healing relationship. And when family members are unable or unwilling to be involved in the young person's case planning and healing process, the CYCP will seek suitable alternative people in the youth's support circle, or "ecology," such as grandparents, aunts, teachers, and adult mentors. Being family focused and family driven is a core principle of CYC practice. It means that CYCPs will ensure that they afford families every opportunity to take an active decision-making role in the care of their own children. It also means that the family and the youth have a voice in defining what successful outcomes are. Having respect for a family's unique set of needs, strengths, opinions, and beliefs is the foundation of the family-driven value ("Working definition of family-driven care," 2008).

> Child and youth care practitioners who engage with families are not family therapists in the normal or traditional sense of that term. Nor are they social workers, psychologists or some other human services professional, although many of the tasks, philosophies and skills across the various professions are quite similar. . . . We do not follow the models of other professions, although we learn from and in many cases contribute to them. We believe that in order to be an effective practitioner with families, the child and youth care worker must know and be fully grounded in our own profession and the way in which we consider family in our field. (Garfat & Charles, 2010, p. 6)

In the chapters that follow we introduce a wide variety of ways for CYCPs to engage with families. Although CYCPs are not trained family therapists, they do borrow family-intervention ideas from other professions, and so we'll also discuss the family-therapy types of intervention that fit well with particular mental health concerns.

In providing support to families who are struggling with a child with a mental health issue, CYCPs might, for example, help young people within the family context in developing social skills, life skills, problem-solving skills, coping skills, relaxation skills, anger-management skills, and so on. They might also assist the family in learning or developing parenting skills or child-management skills.

According to Lahn Jones (2007), the reality is that many youth and families don't want CYCPs to be involved in their lives. However, this reaction is minimized when CYCPs use a strength-based approach to their work with families. The CYC approach to family work means "being with [families] while they are doing what they do. It means the utilization of daily life events as they are occurring for therapeutic purposes" (Garfat, 2003, p. 43). CYCPs acknowledge families as being their own experts, recognizing that parents usually do want what is best for their children. Jones points out that youth behaviour is contextually anchored within the family, including any mental health difficulties that have been identified. When CYCPs are with the family, they can identify strengths and point out the exceptions to the identified problematic patterns while offering support, guidance, and alternative methods of coping (Jones, 2007, pp. 1–3).

Family group conferencing (FGC) is one highly successful method that CYCPs can use to actively engage families in a youth's healing process. Although it was developed as a way to engage families primarily in the child protection and youth justice contexts, it can be adapted for any therapeutic context. FGC's main objective is to give the entire family a voice and ownership in case-planning and decision-making processes. FGC is a culturally sensitive, strength-based approach to working with all families, but in particular, it helps empower marginalized families by bringing together family members to develop a plan of care for their child that addresses the concerns identified by a mental health professional (Desmeules, 2007).

The concept of FGC originated in New Zealand, and was based on concerns about the overrepresentation of Maori children in that country's child welfare and juvenile justice systems. As such, FGC fits well in the Canadian context, where Aboriginal children are similarly overrepresented in our child welfare system.

> Family conferencing embraces the principle of inclusion and shared leadership through consensus decision-making. It offers a model of service delivery that promotes family empowerment and self-reliance. The family system, once mobilized, is more powerful than professional services. It is the participation process that makes the plan created by the family come alive as a personal reality. (Desmeules, 2007, p. 6)

Box 1.7 lists some common CYC techniques for intervention with youth.

Prevention: Advocacy, Community, and School-Based Strategies   Given that most school-aged children and youth spend most of each day within the school setting, schools are a very important venue for mental health service information and, potentially, program delivery (Mental Health Commission of Canada, 2013). The Mental Health Commission's report *School-Based Mental Health in Canada* highlights the

Box 1.7

Techniques for CYC Intervention

Be familiar with the signs and symptoms of each DSM-5 disorder.

Use multiple data sources in assessment.

Use a strength-based assessment model: observe and document behaviours, noting triggers along with their severity/intensity, frequency, and duration.

Look for and use already existing, informal sources of support.

Identify resources, and harness what is going right in the ecology of the family.

Be relational.

Be family focused in your work; include young people's significant others in your assessments and interventions.

Use family-support techniques, including family group conferencing.

Help young people make well-informed decisions about their treatment wherever possible, especially regarding the use of psychotropic medications.

Encourage and teach social skill building.

Think outside the box; be open to alternatives to traditional Western treatment by exploring holistic, alternative, and traditional Indigenous healing practices.

importance of schools in promoting universal mental health, in working toward stigma reduction, and in assisting in the early recognition of mental health problems (Mental Health Commission of Canada, 2012). The report recognizes the link between mental health and the academic performance of children and youth and recommends increasing "comprehensive school health and post-secondary mental health initiatives that promote mental health for all students and include targeted prevention for those at risk" (Mental Health Commission of Canada, 2012).

According to the Mental Health Commission, there are several unique advantages to offering mental health programming within the school setting. For example, class-wide programs may reach at-risk youth who would not otherwise access children's mental health services; and during class-wide social-emotional learning instruction, high-risk students may benefit from observing their emotionally skilled peers model good coping behaviour and attitudes (Mental Health Commission of Canada, 2012). While school-based programming facilitates the identification of mental health difficulties when they first emerge, it also has the potential to maximize positive mental health development for all children and youth, not only for those who are on a negative trajectory (Rowling & Weist, 2004). Finally, the implementation of mental health promotion and prevention programming in schools is associated with improved emotional and behaviour functioning for all youth (Mental Health Commission of Canada, 2013).

Community-based intervention strategies encompass all the accessible mental health services offered in the community, including self-help groups. Every community ought to have crisis and mental health services for children, youth, and families available. An important responsibility of CYCPs is to be aware of all the relevant community-based services and to identify any gap in service availability and accessibility. If such gaps exist, CYCPs will work to promote awareness and to develop and implement the required resources. Promoting awareness of mental health concerns, working toward reducing discrimination and stigma, and improving accessibility to mental health information, resources, and services together represent an important role for CYCPs in the community.

Alternative Healing Complementary and integrative medicine, also called *alternative medicine*, includes a wide array of mental health care practices not usually considered part of mainstream medicine. Naturopathy, natural psychology, and homeopathy, for example, are fields of practice used to treat many psychological difficulties. Such alternative healing approaches to mental health issues are premised on the belief that individuals can overcome mental health disorders with all-natural methods, without drugs, by using self-help strategies and making lifestyle changes. Nonconventional healing practices are most often used in conjunction with conventional/traditional medicine practices (AACAP, 2012). Since many families today opt for natural healing approaches in the treatment of mental health issues, CYCPs should be aware of the various options for holistic treatment in each area of mental health concern for children and youth. Families and older youth may be supported by CYCPs in investigating any of these approaches.

Alternative therapies include art therapies, music therapy, poetry and journalling, coaching and mentoring, neurofeedback, and biofeedback. A wide range of therapies are used with children and youth, including mindfulness-based stress reduction (MBSR), yoga, meditation, laughter therapy, music, art, play, diet, sleep, nutrition, exercise, spirituality, chiropractic care, body/energy therapies, relaxation techniques, massage, herbal therapies, folk remedies, acupuncture, self-help groups, and homeopathy (AACAP, 2012).

Biofeedback, reflexology, Reiki, shiatsu, and gemstone therapy are all used for energy work. Homeopathic medicine is a system based on the belief that "like cures like," meaning that small, highly diluted quantities of medicinal substances are given to cure symptoms when the same substances, given at higher or more concentrated doses, would actually cause those symptoms.

Reviews of the literature suggest that alternative approaches are most often used for autism and ADHD in children, with nearly 50 percent of children with autism and 20 percent of children with ADHD being treated in this way (AACAP, 2012).

Relational CYC Practice CYC practice is, and always has been, relational, with all the pioneers in the field having enacted the relational model in their work. Relational CYC practice evolved, as the name suggests, from our historical focus on relationship in the days of poorhouses and orphanages, and even long before that (Garfat, in Bellefeuille & Ricks, 2008). After all, relationship has always been essential to any interpersonal healing.

> The focus on relationships and the relational is not new. . . . Yet it seems that many look at a relational approach as if it was something invented by contemporary practitioners, eager to engage in intimate ways with young people and their families. . . . Relations and relationship have been a part of Child and Youth Care practice for as long as there has been written material and surely long before that as well. (Garfat, 2003, p. 1)

The term *relational-based interventions* (RBIs) (Hackney & MacMillan, 2008) is used to describe the CYC relational approach. In this approach, the focus of all CYC treatment interventions is to help young people see themselves as valuable, connected, and safe: "RBIs emphasize that how we respond to others, and how they respond to us, defines how we view ourselves as a people" (Hackney & MacMillan, 2008, p. 58). Hence, relational-based intervention has an attachment focus. Further, RBIs constitute treatment in and of themselves.

This means that the first and most important task of caregivers is to develop this valuing and respectful relationship that increases the safety and trust the young person has with us and gives them a new message about themselves. Most of the young people in our treatment programs do not see the safety or value in a relationship with us until they have been taught by our behaviour that there is. (Hackney & MacMillan, 2008, p. 59)

RBIs include any interventions that (1) demonstrate to young people that they are of value; (2) demonstrate and teach appropriate socio-emotional responses; and (3) provide young people with safety, structure, and security.

In addition to drawing upon principles of attachment, these three interrelated aims reflect the goal of resilience in young people by strengthening intrapersonal factors, such as feelings of self-worth, as well as building interpersonal skills and drawing upon available supports from the young person's environment, which . . . uses an ecological conceptual model base. (Hackney & MacMillan, 2008, p. 61)

Box 1.8 summarizes useful communication strategies that might facilitate your application of these treatment principles.

Box 1.8

CYC Communication Strategies

Be respectful and strength-based in your language and your approach.

Always use person-first language.

Use an anti-oppressive practice focus: be culturally respectful and strive toward cultural competence.

Encourage young people to share their voice by engaging them fully in the assessment and intervention process.

Use the Youth Bill of Rights as a guideline.

Use praise to reinforce strengths.

Communicate caring, love, and respect, and demonstrate empathy.

Teach identification of feelings.

Reflect feelings and challenge all cognitive distortions.

Base expectations on developmental stage, not chronological age.

Use standard CYC communication strategies: give choices, keep promises, admit mistakes, and apologize.

WHERE DO YOU STAND?

The CYC approach to understanding and intervening in the mental health concerns of young people can use aspects of all the major psychological paradigms. These paradigms can inform the CYC perspective, which highlights understanding young people's ecology and relationships and identifying their resiliencies and strengths. In some cases, diagnostic labels used in the DSM-5 are antithetical to the CYC approach, as with the "disruptive" behaviour disorders where context is either not adequately addressed or largely ignored. The strengths and resources of young people, or what is "going right" in their ecology, are not addressed in the DSM-5 diagnostic approach. As we'll see in later chapters, however, with other mental health issues of children and youth, such as autism, psychosis, and Schizophrenia, the DSM-5 and the medical model are important in informing our understanding.

Notwithstanding the critics of the DSM-5 in the CYC field, we believe that CYC professionals need to understand the DSM-5's use of diagnostic labels regardless of the system within which they may be working. However, a strength-based, resiliency-focused, relational CYC approach to helping young people struggling with behaviours related to these diagnoses is still how we do what we do. It is the appropriate approach of a CYC professional regardless of the diagnostic label that has been applied or the ideological context of your work.

To evaluate your understanding of Chapter 1 concepts, try the *Viewpoint Challenge* exercise that revisits the cases of Troy and Darren one last time.

Troy's and Darren's Cases: *Viewpoint Challenge Exercise*

Reread the cases of Troy and Darren discussed in this chapter. How would the psychological and the CYC perspectives differ in their approach to better understanding Troy's and Darren's behaviour, respectively? Can you identify any similarities between the two perspectives? How do the approaches to intervention differ? What might be the major differences? What information would you need when you conduct your CYC assessment with Troy and with Darren? Which intervention approach might you try with each? Why?

CHAPTER SUMMARY

- According to the psychological perspective, the basic elements of abnormal behaviour include deviance, personal distress, impairment or maladaptiveness, and risk to self and others.

- *The Diagnostic and Statistical Manual of Mental Disorders*, Fifth Edition, or DSM-5, is a publication of the American Psychiatric Association that provides detailed descriptions of all major psychological disorders currently recognized.

- The CYC perspective on young people's emotional and behavioural disorders differs from the psychological perspective, sometimes a little and sometimes a lot. Your learning needs as a CYC student/practitioner are greatly dependent upon the context of your CYC experience and practice.

- Historical views of abnormality included supernatural and natural explanations. The primary modern psychological paradigms used to explain and treat abnormal behaviour include the biological, psychodynamic, behavioural, cognitive, and sociocultural paradigms.

- Major challenges might arise during your learning experience. Important considerations for CYC practice that are particularly relevant in working with young people experiencing mental health concerns include cultural respect, awareness of your explanatory paradigm, mental health literacy, person-first language, evidence-based practice, and knowledge of child and adolescent development.

- A review of the major psychological perspectives through a CYC lens demonstrates a variation in the degree to which each might be considered to have a good fit with a CYC orientation.

- The predominant CYC conceptual model used to explain exceptionalities is the ecological model, which emphasizes the role of contextual and relational factors in explaining troublesome behaviours. Of particular relevance from a CYC perspective is the role of resiliency, strengths, and the relational nature of CYC practice.

Critical Thinking Questions

1. Based on the psychological indicators of abnormality, do you think a clear distinction can be drawn between "normal" and "abnormal"? Explain.

2. What do you think about the use of the DSM-5's diagnostic labels in CYC practice? How did you decide where you stand on this issue?

3. Why do you think CYC professionals prefer to use the term *exceptionality* or *pain-based behaviours* rather than *abnormal* or *mentally ill* to describe the emotional and behavioural disorders of children and youth?

4. Explain why it's important to use person-first language and to be culturally respectful in your CYC practice.

5. Is the sociocultural perspective a good fit for CYC practice? Why or why not?

6. Do you agree that a CYC perspective is ecological? Why or why not?

7. What do you think about the use of psychotropic medications with children and youth?

8. How do you think poverty, race, and ethnicity influence the development of exceptionalities or abnormalities?

9. Do you agree with the use of the term *relational* in describing the CYC approach? Why or why not?

Key Terms

abnormality, 3

abnormal psychology, 8

assessment, 11

attachment, 30

behavioural paradigm (behaviourism), 31

biological paradigm, 26

biopsychosocial perspective, 25

cerebral cortex, 28

classical conditioning, 32

cognitive behavioural therapy, 44

cognitive distortions, 33

communication, 14

comorbidity, 22

culturally competent, 18

cultural safety, 18

defence mechanisms, 30

diagnosis, 12

Diagnostic and Statistical Manual of Mental Disorders, Fifth Edition (DSM-5), 9

diathesis–stress model, 35

dynamic-maturational model (DMM), 38

eclectic or integrative approach, 41

ecological model, 40

etiology, 23

Supplemental Readings

Bellefeuille, G., & Ricks, F. (Eds). (2008). *Standing on the precipice: Inquiry into the creative potential of child and youth care practice.* Edmonton: MacEwan Press.

Brendtro, L. L., Brokenleg, M., & Van Bockern, S. (2002). *Reclaiming youth at risk: Our hope for the future.* (2nd edition). Bloomington, IN: National Education Service.

Fewster, G. (2002). The DSM-IV you but not for me. *Journal of Child and Youth Care, 15*(4), 113–129.

Fewster, G. (2003). If you meet the pill fairy on the road, kill it. [Editorial]. *Relational Child and Youth Care Practice, 17*(1), 3–10.

Foltz, R. (2008). Medicating relational trauma in youth. *Reclaiming Children and Youth, 17*(3), 3–8.

Foltz, R. (2010). Searching for strengths: Rethinking disorders. *Reclaiming Children and Youth, 18*(4), 26–28. Retrieved from http://reclaimingjournal.com

Lambe, Y., & McLellan, R. (2009). Drugs in our system: An exploratory study on the chemical management of Canadian systems youth. Retrieved from the National Youth in Care Network, http://www.youthincare.ca

Lavin, P., & Park, C. (1999). *Despair turned into rage.* Washington: Child Welfare League of America.

Seligman, M. E. P., & Czikszentmihalyi, M. (2000). Positive psychology: An introduction. *American Psychologist, 55*(1), 5–14.

Stuart, C. (2009). *Foundations of child and youth care practice.* Toronto: Kendall-Hunt.

Treischman, A., Whittaker, J., & Brendtro, L. (1969). *The other 23 hours.* New York: Aldine.

Online Resources

Discussion of misleading terms, www.huffingtonpost.com/allen-frances/can-we-replace-misleading-terms-likemental-illness-patient-schizophrenia_b_7000762.html

Mental Health Commission of Canada's Youth Anti-Stigma Initiative, www.youtube.com/watch?v=lvknTTAV6Kk

Developmental milestones, 13–18, www.education.com/topic/teenage-developmental-milestones

Forty Developmental Assets, http://pathways.wcdsb.ca/ccc/pdf/40-Developmental-Assets.pdf

Manitoba Mental Health Act, www.gov.mb.ca/healthyliving/mh/act.html

International Child and Youth Care Network, www.cyc-net.org

Child Trauma Academy, www.childtrauma.org

International Association for the Study of Attachment, www.iasa-dmm.org

Canadian Association of Naturopathic Doctors, www.cand.ca

Mood Disorders Association of Ontario, www.mooddisorders.on.ca

Dr. Bruce Perry and the neurosequential model, www.childtrauma.org

To hear Dr. Perry speaking, search his name at www.youtube.com.

Information on the DMM model, www.patcrittenden.com

To hear Dr. Crittenden speaking, search her name at www.youtube.com.

Chapter 2
Trauma- and Stressor-Related Disorders

A wide range of potential consequences are associated with exposure to traumatic events in childhood and adolescence.

Case Example: *Jennifer*

Ten-year-old Jennifer has been living with her Kookum (grandmother) for about six months in a downtown housing unit in a western Canadian city. Her grandmother reports that Jennifer often has violent temper tantrums at home, during which she screams and throws things. Jen's Kookum says she has no idea what's causing these outbursts; they seem to be happening at random times. Jen's teachers report that she gets into verbal and physical fights regularly with the other children at school. Before coming into the care of her Kookum, Jen lived with her birth mother in a northern Manitoba First Nations community.

One night, Jen's mom and stepfather got into a violent argument. Jen's mother was stabbed and she died of her injuries. Jen, who was hiding under the bed during the fight, witnessed her mother's death. Her siblings weren't home at the time. Subsequently, Jen and her two older siblings were placed in the care of their maternal grandmother in the city, away from her friends, her community, and her extended family. Jen's Kookum loves her very much, but says that when Jen isn't angry she's usually quiet and moody, and that it's difficult to connect with her.

Learning Objectives

1. Distinguish between stress and trauma.

2. Distinguish between the three trauma- and stressor-related disorders and the three dissociative disorders summarized in the text, and describe their primary symptoms.

3. Summarize the concepts of complex trauma, developmental trauma, and relational trauma.

4. Compare and contrast primary psychological explanations (biological, behavioural, cognitive, psychodynamic, and sociocultural) for trauma- and stressor-related disorders.

5. Summarize the NMT model and describe how the brain is affected by trauma.

6. Describe the psychological treatment approaches used in treating trauma- and stressor-related disorders.

7. Describe the impact of trauma in seven domains of functioning.

8. Describe behaviours associated with a trauma response in youth, including the symptoms of complex-trauma.

9. Explain trauma-informed care and identify CYC strategies to help young people with memories of trauma and those engaged in self-harm behaviour.

Chapter Overview

Before examining the various psychological disorders relevant to children and adolescents in subsequent chapters, here we specifically consider the role of traumatic events in the lives of youth. Most of the children and adolescents encountered by CYCPs will have been exposed to some form of significant stressful or traumatic event(s). Understanding the impact of such events on young people's biological, cognitive, and socio-emotional functioning is necessary for effective CYC practice and will facilitate a greater understanding of all psychological disruptions in youth.

What is stress? How does it differ from trauma? What kinds of traumatic events are young people likely to experience, and what are the consequences of these experiences? From a psychological perspective, this chapter will summarize the major features of those disorders outlined in the DSM-5 as resulting directly from exposure to extreme events. We'll look at psychological explanations and approaches to intervention for trauma, emphasizing those diagnoses that CYCPs are most likely to encounter in the field. From a CYC perspective, we'll review the concept of complex trauma and the symptoms of PTSD with a focus on trauma-informed care, CYC practice assessment, and CYC intervention modalities. Our look at the relationship of attachment to trauma will build on the discussion of this topic introduced in Chapter 1. You're encouraged to explore the important topics of trauma and attachment elsewhere, as the discussion presented here is intended as an introduction only in the context of CYC practice and mental health literacy.

WHAT IS TRAUMA?

Exposure to **stressors**, events that challenge the individual, is a part of daily life for everyone. The behavioural, emotional, cognitive, and physical responses that result from exposure to these events are referred to as **stress** and are also a part of everyday experience. Although stress is generally viewed as something to avoid, our reactions to various challenges can also have positive effects, including motivating adaptive behaviours that increase our likelihood of survival. For example, the rush of adrenalin and increased attention experienced by a child who encounters a barking dog on the street serves to provide the necessary energy and resources to effectively manage the threat (e.g., to run away). By comparison, **traumatic events** refer to sudden or unexpected events (or ongoing repeated events) that are extreme in nature and threaten or cause harm to the emotional (e.g., sense of self) and physical well-being (i.e., safety and survival) of the individual or another person (Moroz, 2005). The lasting undesirable social, emotional, physical, and cognitive effects that result from exposure to such events are referred to as **trauma** and have been directly related to various psychological, socio-emotional, and cognitive symptoms that impair functioning and make up some of the major psychological disorders identified in the DSM-5.

Before turning to a discussion of trauma- and stressor-related disorders, examine your own experiences of stress and negative events by trying the *Think About It!* exercise.

WHAT ARE TRAUMA-RELATED DISORDERS? THE PSYCHOLOGICAL PERSPECTIVE

We saw in Chapter 1 that, in the diathesis–stress model, stress may contribute to the development and onset of any psychological disorder. However, exposure to traumatic events may or may not result in adverse reactions depending on a variety of individual

---

Think About It! Exercise: *Experiences of Stress and Trauma*

Everyone experiences stressful events, but not everyone responds in the same way to these challenges. Answer the following questions to better understand your own responses to stressful events.

1. Identify three stressful events you have experienced in the past six months.

2. In relation to any of these events, did you . . .
   Have problems sleeping? Have difficulties concentrating? Feel as if you had to be on guard or ready to act? Experience physical symptoms? If so, what were they? What other reactions did you have to these events?

3. Have you ever experienced a traumatic event? If so, what was it?

4. In relation to this event, did you . . .

Feel anxious and on guard? Feel irritable or have episodes of anger?

Avoid thoughts, feelings, or conversations about the event?

Notice that certain things reminded you of the event, and that you would avoid them as a result?

Have thoughts and feelings about the event that you could not control?

These are just some of the common experiences that follow exposure to stressful and traumatic events. Notice that while these reactions may not be unusual, the more extreme/severe they are, the more likely they are to interfere with daily life. Accordingly, in order to meet the criteria for any Trauma- or Stressor-Related Disorder, these experiences must interfere with daily functioning.

factors, including inborn predispositions, the developmental stage of the individual, available supports, resiliencies, and coping resources. Since reactions to traumatic events can thus differ widely from one person to another, the DSM-5 acknowledges that trauma- and stressor-related disorders can include some combination of symptoms in each of the following areas:

- *fear or anxiety* (e.g., feeling fearful and/or worried)
- *anhedonia* (the inability to experience pleasure) and *dysphoria* (feeling unwell or unhappy)
- *anger and aggression* (can be expressed as irritability)
- *dissociative symptoms* (ranging from mild to severe detachment from physical and emotional experience)

You might notice that many of these symptoms are associated with other diagnoses. For example, if a youth is demonstrating irritability and aggressive behaviour, it may be interpreted to be the result of a *disruptive behaviour disorder* (discussed in Chapter 5). Similarly, anhedonia and dysphoria might be assumed to reflect a *mood disorder* (discussed in Chapter 7). Accordingly, CYCPs and other practitioners should always consider the possibility that behaviours and/or emotions that create distress for youth and/or impair their functioning may be the result of exposure to stressful and/or traumatic events. We now turn to a discussion of specific diagnoses that relate directly to stress and trauma reactions.

DSM-5 Categories

The DSM-5 considers psychological disturbances associated with exposure to stressful and traumatic events in the general category of Trauma- and Stressor-Related Disorders. Following this chapter in the DSM-5 is one that summarizes criteria for Dissociative Disorders (APA, 2013). Given that dissociative symptoms can be associated with exposure to traumatic events, we'll consider this group of diagnoses in this chapter as well.

Trauma- and Stressor-Related Disorders The DSM-5 acknowledges the variable nature of responses to stressful and traumatic events—responses that can range from angry and aggressive symptoms to dissociation, anxiety, and depression. Accordingly, **trauma- and stressor-related disorders** are clearly associated with exposure to a stressful or traumatic event but vary significantly in their expression, whether through internalizing symptoms such as withdrawn behaviour or externalizing symptoms of aggression. The DSM identifies seven disorders in this category, including *Reactive Attachment Disorder*, *Disinhibited Social Engagement Disorder*, *Posttraumatic Stress Disorder*, *Acute Stress Disorder*, and *Adjustment Disorders*.

Events that might result in trauma are as varied as the possible responses. Among the most researched events are disasters (natural and person-made), war, accidents, serious illness, acts of violence, and various forms of maltreatment, including neglect and physical and sexual abuse. Recent research, however, has also found a relationship between everyday events (e.g., viewing violent or frightening scenes on television) and PTSD in children (Kousha & Tehrani, 2013). So it's important to acknowledge that the experience of trauma is a *subjective* one and that caution must be applied in order to avoid assuming that (1) everyone exposed to a stressful or traumatic event will experience a

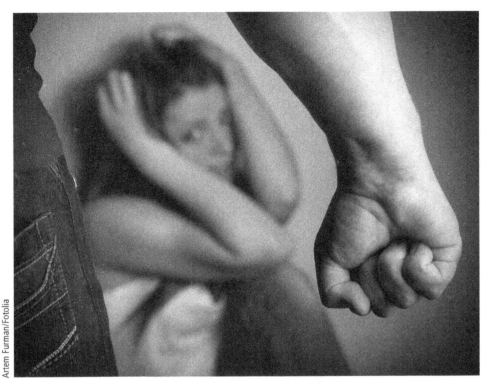

Various forms of maltreatment, including neglect and abuse, are among the most notable events associated with trauma in youth.

stressor- or trauma-related disturbance and (2) everyone displaying traumatic symptoms has experienced an extreme event that is generally viewed as intense or unusual.

Dissociative Disorders   For most people most of the time, our conscious experiences are integrated with our memory, sense of identity, emotions, perceptions of external and internal stimuli, and behaviour. But in the case of **dissociative disorders**, the integration of these aspects of psychological functioning is disrupted. For example, feelings of being detached or separated from one's body, referred to as **depersonalization**, are outside of expected conscious experience and considered a dissociative experience or symptom. **Derealization**, another dissociative symptom, refers to recurrent experiences in which individuals feel a sense of unreality in relation to their environment (as if the world is distant, dreamlike, or distorted). See Table 2.1 for a summary of dissociative symptoms that can be observed in the context of many disorders.

Table 2.1 Dissociative Symptoms
Sense of numbing, detachment, or absence of emotional responsiveness
Reduction in awareness of surroundings (e.g., "being in a daze")
Derealization (a sense that reality has been altered or lost; a sense of unreality, foggy)
Depersonalization (feelings of detachment from oneself, being outside one's body)
Dissociative amnesia (inability to recall an important aspect of the trauma)
Source: Adapted from American Psychiatric Association, 2013.

As noted in the DSM-5, the onset of a dissociative disorder is often (although not always) associated with exposure to a traumatic event. The DSM identifies five disorders in this category, including *Dissociative Identity Disorder*, *Dissociative Amnesia*, and *Depersonalization/Derealization Disorder*.

Trauma- and Stressor-Related Disorders: Diagnoses and Criteria

Although we'll consider the role of stressful and traumatic events in each of the psychological disturbances discussed in this text, we begin with a discussion of those trauma- and stressor-related disorders that have been the focus of considerable scientific study and that CYCPs are most likely to encounter in their work. Specifically, we'll examine the diagnoses of *Posttraumatic Stress Disorder*, *Acute Stress Disorder*, and *Adjustment Disorders*.

Posttraumatic Stress Disorder   **Posttraumatic Stress Disorder (PTSD)** is characterized by symptoms ranging from feelings of sadness and anxiety to demonstrations of irritability and anger, and follows exposure to an *extreme stressor* that involves either actual or threatened injury or death to the individual or someone else. Possible events that may trigger the symptoms of PTSD include being personally threatened by death or injury (e.g., being held at gunpoint), witnessing the death or injury of someone else, or learning of the death or harm of another (e.g., sexual assault, violent crime, natural disaster, severe automobile accident). The greater the intensity and duration of the stressor and the more physically close one is to it, the greater the risk of developing the disorder. The central symptoms of PTSD are as follows: (1) *intrusion symptoms* (e.g., recurrent dreams or memories); (2) persistent *avoidance* of objects, thoughts, people, or situations that trigger memories of the stressor; (3) *negative changes in cognitions and mood* associated with the event (e.g., inability to recall important aspects of the event, exaggerated negative beliefs about oneself, feelings of fear, horror, anger); and (4) persistent increased sympathetic nervous system *arousal and reactivity* (e.g., difficulty concentrating or sleeping, hypervigilance, and irritable, angry, or aggressive outbursts).

It has been recommended that complex PTSD be included in future versions of the DSM. **Complex PTSD** is characterized by exposure to multiple extreme stressors, interpersonal victimization, and/or enduring trauma resulting in the central symptoms of PTSD as well as additional impairing symptoms. This is consistent with research findings that youth experiencing multiple traumatic events demonstrate more significant impairments in relationships, school, and physical health (Copeland et al., 2007). Complex PTSD, or *complex trauma*, is discussed later in this chapter.

The onset of PTSD symptoms typically occurs within three months of exposure to the extreme stressor; however, the DSM acknowledges that symptoms may not appear for months or years. Accordingly, **PTSD with Delayed Expression** is the term used to refer to cases in which symptoms aren't observed until after at least six months following the trauma. The DSM-5 also lists a subtype of PTSD that includes dissociative symptoms (i.e., depersonalization, derealization). Specifically, the diagnosis *PTSD with Dissociative Symptoms* is applied in cases where the criteria for PTSD are met and dissociative symptoms (not better explained by substance use or other medical conditions) are present.

Note that a PTSD diagnosis requires that symptoms cause significant distress or impairment in one or more areas of functioning and be observed for *more than one month*.

This *duration* of symptoms is of particular importance to the diagnosis of PTSD. If symptoms have been observed for less than a month, this diagnosis is inappropriate; instead, a diagnosis of *Acute Stress Disorder* would be applied.

Acute Stress Disorder   The DSM distinguishes between PTSD and **Acute Stress Disorder (ASD)**, which is characterized by symptoms similar to those of PTSD. Specifically, following exposure to an extreme stressor, one experiences intrusion symptoms, negative mood, dissociative symptoms, avoidance symptoms, and arousal symptoms. Despite the similarity in symptoms, ASD is distinct from PTSD with respect to time: ASD symptoms must have occurred for *less than one month* (but a minimum of three days). Following an extreme stressor, an individual may be first diagnosed with ASD and then, after a one-month period, meet the criteria for PTSD. Although the expression of ASD symptoms is varied, the DSM notes that expression of symptoms typically includes anxiety reactions, re-experiencing the event, and emotional and physiological reactivity to reminders of the event.

Adjustment Disorders   Note that in both PTSD and ASD, symptoms begin following exposure to an *extreme stressor*. What about situations in which individuals are exposed to a relatively minor or less severe stressor but still exhibit symptoms that create significant distress and impair functioning? In such instances, a diagnosis of Adjustment Disorder may be appropriate. **Adjustment Disorder (AD)** is characterized by emotional and behavioural symptoms that occur within three months but for no longer than six months following exposure to a specific stressor or stressors. The symptoms are considered significant in that they (1) create marked distress that exceeds the expected reaction to such a stressor and/or (2) create significant impairment in functioning (e.g., social, occupational, or academic). Indicators associated with these criteria include decreased work or school performance, suicidal thoughts or attempts, substance use, and bodily complaints. Possible events that may result in the onset of AD include single stressors (e.g., loss of a job) or multiple stressors (e.g., parental divorce and failing grades), either of which can be short or long in duration.

The DSM distinguishes between various subtypes of adjustment disorders in relation to predominant symptoms. For example, **AD with Depressed Mood** is associated with symptoms commonly associated with a Depressive Episode (e.g., depressed mood, tearfulness, feelings of hopelessness), while **AD with Anxiety** is characterized by symptoms of worry and nervousness. A third subtype, **AD with Disturbance of Conduct**, is associated with violating the rights of others, social norms, and rules and laws. Additional subtypes are based on various combinations of these three subtypes.

Dissociative Disorders: Diagnoses and Criteria

Of the seven diagnoses included in the DSM-5 chapter on Dissociative Disorders, we consider the three you're likely to encounter in your studies and work as CYCPs. Although dissociative disorders are also associated with exposure to traumatic events, they're distinct from trauma- and stressor-related disorders in that dissociative symptoms take centre stage rather than being just part of the picture (as in PTSD and ASD). Although the prevalence of these disorders is significantly lower than that for trauma- and stressor-related disorders, familiarity with the features of these diagnoses can be useful in your work with those exposed to traumatic events.

Dissociative Identity Disorder   Formerly referred to as *Multiple Personality Disorder*, **Dissociative Identity Disorder (DID)** is associated with (1) repeated experiences of amnesia (loss of memory for specific events, time) and (2) the presence of two or more different personality states. You can see how these symptoms represent the lack of integration of various aspects of psychological functioning we mentioned earlier. Memory, sense of identity, and behaviour (aspects of oneself that usually fit together and are continuous) are fragmented and separated from one another. For example, those with an outgoing sense of identity will socialize with people in the halls and easily recall these experiences. Their sense of identity, behaviour, and memories are integrated or related to one another. But if they experience disintegration in the context of DID, these same people might have an outgoing sense of identity but at times, avoid people in the halls, and have no memory of these experiences: their sense of identity, behaviour, and memories don't go together, representing a lack of integration of these aspects of psychological functioning.

The loss of memory or *dissociative amnesia* that occurs in the context of DID can be quite puzzling and frightening to the individual, and it's not difficult to understand why. Imagine being unable to recall important life events (e.g., the death of a parent) or forgetting how to drive or use your cell phone—and yet these are ways in which memory loss is experienced in this disorder. Some individuals also experience *dissociative fugues* in which they find themselves at the beach or in another city without an awareness or memory of how they got there. Understandably, such experiences can be extremely distressing. Although the prevalence of DID is low compared with other disorders, it's important for CYCPs to be aware of these symptoms, especially given that physical and sexual abuse is associated with an increased risk for this disorder.

Dissociative Amnesia   Most people are familiar with the term *amnesia*—it relates to a loss of memory. In the case of **Dissociative Amnesia**, the individual loses the ability to recall important personal information that is typically remembered easily. We expect ourselves and others to recall specific events during high school, or how to ride a bike, or who our friends are. Although there may be neurological explanations for such memory loss, it's worth noting the relationship of Dissociative Amnesia and exposure to negative experiences, including physical and/or sexual abuse in childhood.

The DSM-5 distinguishes between various types of amnesia, including *Localized Amnesia* (loss of memory for a certain period of time), *Selective Amnesia* (loss of some memories from a specific period of time), *Generalized Amnesia* (a complete loss of memory of one's life history), *Systematized Amnesia* (loss of memory for specific categories of information, such as for a particular person), and *Continuous Amnesia* (loss of memory for each new event as it happens). Thus, memory loss might look very different from one person to the next. The DSM-5 also includes a subtype, *Dissociative Amnesia with Dissociative Fugue*, which is associated with travel or wandering in the context of a loss of memory for personal identity and history.

Depersonalization/Derealization Disorder   Depersonalization and derealization are two types of dissociative symptoms. When these symptoms are the predominant cause of disrupted functioning and distress, the diagnosis of **Depersonalization/Derealization Disorder** is applied. Although experiences of unreality and detachment with respect to one's body and sensations (depersonalization) as well as experiences of unreality and attachment in relation to one's environment (derealization) can occur in the context of PTSD and other trauma- and stressor-related disorders, repeated episodes of these symptoms that occur in the absence of other symptoms (e.g., mood disruption, avoidance symptoms) are representative of Depersonalization/Derealization Disorder. Similar to the other diagnoses in this chapter, symptoms associated with this disorder are more likely to occur when a youth has experienced an interpersonal trauma in childhood. Stressors that are most related to this diagnosis include emotional abuse and neglect (APA, 2013).

As noted in the DSM-5, the average age of onset of this disorder is 16 years, although symptoms might be observed in childhood (APA, 2013). Accordingly, knowing the symptoms of this disorder may be particularly relevant to CYCPs.

Before turning to a discussion of the CYC approach to trauma, try the *Test Your Understanding* exercise to review your understanding of the core symptoms of trauma- and stressor-related disorders and dissociative disorders by reading each case and identifying the most appropriate diagnosis for each.

A CYC APPROACH TO TRAUMA: UNDERSTANDING TRAUMA- AND STRESSOR-RELATED DISORDERS

In the past, the symptoms of trauma and PTSD-related behaviours seen in children and youth were misunderstood. The prevailing clinical thought was that young people would recover without too much difficulty from the psychological, emotional, and physical effects of exposure to trauma. However, over the past decade it's been established that such major stressors as war, natural disasters, and maltreatment affect young people in ways that are similar to those experienced by adult survivors. These effects are likely to be quite severe and long-lasting, and, in extreme cases, life threatening. Notwithstanding the young person's resiliency, the consequences of trauma exposure will have a significant effect on a child's development and overall functioning, whether in the short term or in the longer term. PTSD is just one of the potential outcomes of trauma exposure in children and youth; many other DSM-5 diagnoses are commonly experienced by trauma survivors.

"A trauma is a wound" (Schiraldi, 2000, p. 4); that is, trauma reactions can be considered as behavioural manifestations that result from the infliction of deep and lasting emotional wounds. This is referred to as *pain-based behaviour*.

The idea of PTSD as a bona fide mental health diagnosis was recognized in the late 1970s and early 1980s after American soldiers returned home from Vietnam with combat-related invasive memories, nightmares, loss of concentration, feelings of guilt and irritability, addictions, and depression. Consequently, the American Psychological Association (APA) formally recognized PTSD as an anxiety disorder in the DSM.

Brain research shows that children and youth who experience trauma display increases in stress hormones comparable to those seen in combat veterans. More than 35 percent of children exposed to a single traumatic event will develop serious mental health problems ("About attachment," n.d.). As well, maltreatment disrupts attachment processes and affects the development of important relational capacities; nearly 35 percent of children and youth who are reported for maltreatment demonstrate significant deficits in social and emotional skills ("About attachment," n.d.).

Adverse childhood experiences and childhood trauma can lead to many difficulties in adulthood, including depression, suicide, addictions, sexual acting out, family violence, smoking, obesity, physical inactivity, and sexually transmitted diseases. And, as indicated in the Adverse Childhood Experiences (ACE) study (one of the largest investigations ever conducted to assess associations between childhood maltreatment and later-life health and well-being), the more adverse childhood experiences reported, the more likely a person is to develop significant physical ailments as well, including heart disease, cancer, and stroke (Fellitti et al., 1998).

In contrast to the single-incident trauma experienced in the physical environment, clinicians now recognize that the intensity of the stress associated with repeated relational trauma over time in the interpersonal environment is cumulative. Thus, developmental, relational, or complex trauma is understood to be attachment trauma.

> Relational trauma thus can be understood as the quintessential expression of complex trauma which has been defined as repeated interpersonal trauma occurring during crucial developmental periods. (Schore, 2013, p. 3)

The terms *complex trauma*, *developmental trauma*, and *relational trauma* all refer to the exposure to multiple or prolonged traumatic events and the impact of this exposure on the young person's development. Typically, **complex trauma** exposure involves child maltreatment (including psychological maltreatment, neglect, physical and sexual abuse, and exposure to family violence) that is *chronic* and occurs within the primary care-giving system in childhood and adolescence.

In describing the cluster of symptoms seen in children and youth who've been maltreated, van der Kolk (2005) proposed using the term *complex trauma* rather than *PTSD*, given that multiple exposures to interpersonal trauma, such as abandonment, betrayal, physical or sexual assaults, and domestic violence, have consistent and predictable consequences that affect most, if not all, areas of young people's functioning. Further, children exposed to trauma experience multiple potential negative outcomes, including attachment difficulties, mood dysregulation, dissociation, self-concept challenges, and behavioural, cognition, and biological changes, all of which can have a negative impact on learning and academic achievement.

Complex trauma results from chronic maltreatment, neglect, physical and sexual abuse, and exposure to family violence.

Vkara/Fotolia

The behavioural symptoms related to PTSD are not new. Throughout history, it has been recognized that war has a severe psychological impact on soldiers and individuals.

> Three thousand years ago, an Egyptian combat veteran named Hori wrote about the feelings he experienced before going into battle: "You determine to go forward. . . . Shuddering seizes you, the hair on your head stands on end, your soul lies in your hand." History tells us that among the Egyptians, Romans, and Greeks, men broke and ran in combat circumstances—in other words, the soldiers of antiquity were no less afraid of dying. (Bentley, 2005, p. 1)

In a U.S. research study of 1420 children, 68 percent had experienced at least one *traumatic event* (defined as an intense event or ongoing repeated events) that threatened or caused harm to their emotional and physical well-being, and 37 percent had been exposed to more than one (Scheeringa, Zeanah, & Cohen, 2011). For children and adolescents, the data clearly show that posttraumatic symptoms are *common and to be expected* following exposure to trauma. For example, months after 1992's Hurricane Andrew, while some children showed improvement with their PTSD symptoms, 70 percent were still within the moderate-to-severe category of experiencing symptoms. In addition, a group of 35 traumatized children aged 1–6 showed no significant decrease in PTSD symptoms two years after exposure. Thus, researchers and clinicians are increasingly recognizing that for many children and adolescents, PTSD symptoms do not lessen or disappear as spontaneously as was previously thought (Scheeringa, Zeanah, & Cohen, 2011).

Children and youth in the justice and child welfare systems have usually experienced maltreatment, including physical abuse, sexual abuse, and psychological trauma, often in the extreme. They have also commonly experienced many disrupted attachments. As defined earlier, *trauma* occurs when young people experience an intense or an ongoing repeated event that threatens or causes harm to their emotional and physical well-being. The Children's Mental Health Initiative (2012) reported that 84 percent of children who are identified to child protection services have experienced childhood trauma. Youth with high rates of abusive and neglectful experiences have correspondingly high rates of dissociation, depression, posttraumatic stress, anger, and/or anxiety symptoms.

In predicting and understanding one's response to trauma, it's critical to examine the individual's risk and resiliency factors, including individual personality characteristics, family stressors and supports, community environment, and access to treatment. Involvement in the child welfare system in Canada is itself both risky and protective. Out-of-home care, for example, can bring young people out of abusive circumstances, and yet often doesn't do a good job in helping young adults with trauma-related mental health and substance abuse issues (Fallon & Shlonsky, 2011). In fact, most youth perceive that they're better off staying with their families than coming into care (Manitoba Youth in Care Network, 2013, personal communication).

It may be surprising to learn that PTSD isn't the most common psychiatric diagnosis in children with histories of chronic trauma. Research has shown that for these children the most common DSM diagnoses, in order of frequency, are Separation Anxiety Disorder, Oppositional Defiant Disorder, and phobic disorders, followed by PTSD, and finally ADHD (van der Kolk, 2005). Numerous studies have found that affected young people will frequently have problems with aggression, attention and impulse control, and dissociative difficulties, but they also have great difficulty establishing relationships with caregivers, peers, and intimate partners. According to van der Kolk (2005), a history of trauma related to childhood physical and sexual abuse is associated with a host of other psychiatric diagnoses in adolescence and adulthood, including substance misuse, Borderline Personality Disorder and Antisocial Personality Disorder, and eating, affective, somatoform, cardiovascular, metabolic, immunological, and sexual disorders (van der Kolk, 2005). Dissociation and *somatization* (physical symptoms with no apparent physical cause) can also be common manifestations of unresolved trauma. Any physical problems that don't have a medical cause, including eating disorders, substance abuse, and self-harm, are all possible consequences related to trauma (Smith, 2011).

When faced with these trauma-associated symptoms or behaviours, clinicians are now more appropriately asking: "Is it a disorder, or is it a trauma?" We know that many of the behaviours associated with some of the most commonly diagnosed problems in children and youth, such as ADHD, Bipolar Disorder, and depression, are quite likely to be behaviours associated with trauma reactions.

One of the authors of this text is aware of just such a case. A young person living in a secure residential treatment program had been diagnosed with numerous mental health issues, including Fetal Alcohol Spectrum Disorder (FASD), and was being heavily medicated with a psychotropic cocktail, as is so often prescribed for youth in care. She was later assessed as primarily struggling with the effects of complex trauma. Evidently, the behaviours of concern were all related to the aftermath of trauma, not to any other DSM disorder. Fortunately, the medications were consequently re-examined and terminated in light of the assessment results.

The signs and symptoms of PTSD and trauma reactions in children can include all or some of the following: anxieties, worries, nervousness, and thoughts of death; psychosomatic complaints such as sore tummy, headache, and other aches/pains; inattentiveness, distractibility, difficulty concentrating, daydreaming, dissociation, and tantrum behaviours; difficult to soothe, excessive crying, anger, rage, aggression, violence, and threatening others; self-injurious behaviours, including cutting; difficulty processing, learning, and retaining information and difficulty retrieving information already learned; compulsive behaviours, including eating disturbances; and sleep disturbances, including nightmares, sleepwalking, and night terrors. Children who have experienced trauma also will often struggle with school phobia, separation anxiety, Obsessive-Compulsive Disorder, and panic attacks; there will often be frequent re-enactment of the trauma accompanied by obsessive thoughts and fears regarding a reoccurrence. Alternatively, children and youth can appear to be fearless, can be difficult to engage, and can appear to be perfectionists, with a tendency toward being rigid and inflexible; some may experience enuresis and/or encopresis.

The causes of enuresis and/or encopresis can be medical or psychiatric. CYCPs would need to refer to a medical practitioner to first rule out any medical causes prior to referral for assessment of underlying psychological issues. *Encopresis* involves having bowel movements or smearing feces in inappropriate places after the age when bowel control is expected. *Enuresis*, usually called bed-wetting, involves urinating into bedding, clothing, or other inappropriate places. These behaviours may be voluntary or involuntary ("Elimination disorders," 2015). The psychiatric causes of Encopresis are largely unknown. Children who exhibit this pattern of soiling behaviour often have clinical behaviour issues diagnosed as Conduct Disorder or Oppositional Defiant Disorder. Enuresis also has both medical and psychiatric causes. Like Encopresis, it can be associated with psychiatric conditions such as CD and ODD. Both of these elimination difficulties can be a red flag for sexual abuse ("Elimination disorders," 2015).

Older youth are likely to self-medicate with various substances. Children and youth who've been traumatized may bully others, or they may be victimized by bullying. They can be excessively clingy, easily startled and jumpy, irritable and agitated, and withdrawn; they can appear sad or listless, and have decreased activity; there may be extreme sensitivity to light and sound; and there may be sexual acting out. Many of these pain-based behaviours are also indicative of attachment difficulties that have resulted from relational trauma. Unfortunately, if we don't know the history of the child (which happens all too often in the child welfare or justice systems), we may not know the specific cause of the behaviours or even whether they've been exposed to trauma, and we'll likely not know extent or details of the trauma.

After exposure to a traumatic event, two different patterns of responses may emerge: some children and youth may appear hyperactive and highly irritable (an *over-aroused pattern*) while other children seem withdrawn or dissociated (an *under-aroused pattern*). The key to understanding the pain-based behaviour of children who've been exposed to trauma is to recognize that their nervous system is unregulated and may be completely out of balance. The under-aroused pattern only *looks* as if the trauma survivor is calm and less aroused than in the over-aroused pattern; however, internally, the nervous system is just as revved up. Over-arousal often looks as if children have completely lost control of themselves, while under-arousal looks as if children have just given up (Melrose, 2006). Some children and youth may demonstrate one or the other response pattern most of the time, but others may display both at different times throughout the same day. Some children alternate between staring blankly for several minutes at a time and suddenly becoming enraged or aggressive (Boyd-Webb, 2006).

Examples of traumatic events in the lives of young people include incidents where they witness or are involved in a death, a threatened death, or the serious injury of themselves or someone else. Traumatic events to which children and youth who develop PTSD symptoms may have been exposed include physical and sexual abuse, sexual assaults, and physical attacks (gang-related or not), sexual exploitation, serious motor vehicle accidents, homelessness, witnessing a drive-by shooting, witnessing the suicide of a friend or a family member, and natural disasters.

The potential impact of both environmental and interpersonal traumatic episodes can be assessed by examining the nature of the victims' involvement in the incident, their relationship with the perpetrator, and whether they were a direct victim, a participant, or an observer (Boyd-Webb, 2006). It's important that all traumatic events young people may have experienced are assessed and understood by CYCPs in context: the trauma may be interpersonal or non-interpersonal, depending on such interacting factors as the presence or absence of others, the roles played by those involved in the incident, and the nature of the relationships.

The known risk and resiliency factors should be examined. First to consider are the aspects of the trauma itself. Whether or not the child perceives a life threat is critical. The loss of possessions and disruption of everyday normalcy contribute to the development of post-trauma symptoms, and the duration of the events is also important. Girls report more PTSD symptoms than boys, and disadvantaged or minority youth show more symptoms than other children. As well, the child's prior psychological functioning is a factor, particularly any pre-existing anxiety, depression, stress, and ruminative coping styles (Steele, Elkin, & Roberts, 2008). Aspects of the recovery environment will also affect children's reactions, including the presence or absence of social support, the caregivers' psychosocial functioning, and whether other disruptive major life events follow the trauma event. Finally, the child's internal psychological resources, including intelligence and established coping skills, will play a role.

Younger children don't experience the same reliving of the traumatic experience as adults or even older youth. Young children may initially experience and talk about bad dreams about the traumatic event; these frequently appear as generalized nightmares about monsters or threatening situations where they or another person is in danger. Because it's difficult for children to express such emotions and fears verbally, it's critical that caregivers or other adult observers recognize whether they're experiencing distressing dreams. CYCPs should pay close attention to a decreased interest in activity or an expression of an altered sense of the future (e.g., the child may now believe that he or she will die). Other signs of childhood PTSD may occur in the form of repetitive play, where children recreate the incident over and over again. They may seek reassurance from their caregiver while engaged in this type of re-enactment (Melrose, 2009).

Rare cases of PTSD in children and youth may involve *auditory hallucinations* and *paranoid ideation*. Individuals who experience auditory hallucinations may experience *tinnitus*, a constant ringing in one's ears, or they may hear a voice or set of voices that are not physically present. Youth who are experiencing *paranoid ideation* are highly guarded and constantly suspicious of being harmed and harassed by those around them (Melrose, 2009).

Before turning to a discuss of development, prevalence, and comorbidity, consider the details of the opening case in relation to the criteria of PTSD, ASD, and adjustment disorders in *Jennifer's Case: Revisited*.

Jennifer's Case: *Revisited*

Reread the opening case of Jennifer. Given the details in the case and the symptoms that outlined in the previous section, which diagnosis/diagnoses do you think a psychologist would most likely apply in the case of Jennifer? Identify specific details in the case and specific symptoms for your chosen disorder(s) to support your answer. How might you apply a CYC perspective to understanding Jennifer's case? Do you think Jennifer's behaviour is pain-based or trauma-related? How might the CYC and psychology perspectives differ? If you were working with Jennifer, what other information would you like to have about her?

HOW MANY YOUNG PEOPLE STRUGGLE WITH TRAUMA-RELATED DISORDERS?

Exposure to traumatic events is common across the lifespan, including in childhood. Survey research suggests that 13–43 percent of girls and boys have been exposed to at least one traumatic event (Cohen, 1998). One longitudinal study following 1500 American children over an eight-year period found that more than 65 percent had been exposed to at least one traumatic event (Copeland et al., 2007). Trocmé (2010) conducted a Canadian national survey and found that 1.4 percent of children experienced considerable maltreatment. Some of the most frequent traumatic events experienced by children and youth include traumatic loss of a loved one, being witness to domestic violence, living with a caregiver with impaired ability, and abuse, maltreatment, and neglect. In addition, a significant number of children and youth are exposed to multiple traumatic events. For example, in one community representative sample of 1420 American children, 37 percent reported being exposed to more than one traumatic event (Copeland et al., 2007). This is particularly concerning given that research findings consistently report that those exposed to multiple traumatic events are more likely to meet the criteria of PTSD and are more likely to experience a variety of disruptions (e.g., anxiety, depression, and aggressive behaviour). It's worth noting that rates of trauma exposure and associated development of PTSD have been found to be quite comparable in Canada and the U.S. (Van Ameringen et al., 2008).

Prevalence rates vary in relation to a number of variables. For instance, the *nature of the event* significantly impacts the rate of ASD, with the highest rates (20–50 percent) being reported for interpersonal traumatic events (e.g., sexual assault, witnessing mass shooting), moderate rates for motor vehicle accidents (13–21 percent), and lower rates for industrial accidents (6–12 percent). In the case of PTSD, diagnosis is significantly more likely in relation to major accidents, kidnapping, natural disasters, physical assault, or sexual abuse (Davis & Siegel, 2000) and in cases where the event is life-threatening (e.g., Fletcher, 2003). Prevalence also varies in relation to *group characteristics*. For example, children in the child welfare system exhibit particularly high prevalence rates of maltreatment (Dubner & Motta, 1999; McCloskey & Walker, 2000) and accordingly high levels of PTSD symptoms (Copeland et al., 2007; Kolko et al., 2010). Research in Canada has found high rates of exposure to violence in some Aboriginal communities (Health Canada, 2003b). Although published literature examining the relationship between PTSD and exposure to violence is limited, one American study found that of 234 Native American women, 75 percent reported experiencing early abuse or maltreatment, and that severe maltreatment was a significant predictor of PTSD (Duran et al., 2004).

Although stressor- and trauma-related disturbances that emerge in childhood and adolescence may be temporary for some youth, research has found long-term effects for others. Longitudinal studies suggest that PTSD symptoms may remain and disrupt functioning for years (e.g., Scheeringa et al., 2005).

TRAUMA-RELATED DISORDERS AND DEVELOPMENT

Trauma- and stressor-related disorders can arise at any point in development. In fact, in the case of PTSD, the disorder is equally likely in childhood and adolescence. However, it's not surprising that traumatic responses (including reactions and reporting of symptoms)

Table 2.2 Common Trauma Reactions in Childhood and Adolescence

Age	Common Trauma Reactions
1–6 years	Aggression; re-experiencing trauma through play; absence of fearful reactions during exposure or during re-experiencing, negative alteration in mood; restricted play or exploratory behaviour
6–12 years	Difficulties expressing emotions (anger, sadness); reliving the traumatic event; frightening dreams; verbalization of traumatic memories
13–18 years	Feelings of fear, seclusion, guilt; avoidance of developmental opportunities (e.g., driving); view of self as cowardly; beliefs that they are different and undesirable (e.g., "Now I'll never fit in"); loss of aspirations for the future; substance use

are partly dependent on the developmental age and stage of the individual (Nader & Einarsson, 2010). For example, young children exposed to trauma are significantly more likely to demonstrate aggression and developmental regression (e.g., loss of language) and to restrict exploratory behaviour. School-aged children are likely to decrease their participation in new activities, and adolescents are likely to avoid developmental opportunities (e.g., dating, driving) that the majority embrace (APA, 2013). See Table 2.2 for a comparison of common trauma reactions in childhood and adolescence.

Accordingly, the DSM acknowledges that reactions to stressful and traumatic events vary depending on age. For example, in children older than six, repetitive play or re-enactment of the event and frightening dreams without recognizable content are common (APA, 2013). The DSM's criteria for PTSD symptoms in children younger than six acknowledge the developmental abilities of this age group, noting, for example, that intrusive memories may not appear distressing, and that, given the child's language and cognitive capabilities, it may not be possible to determine whether dream content is related to the traumatic event. Similar to the criteria for those older than six, the DSM includes a subtype that is associated with dissociative symptoms (including depersonalization or derealization) and another that is associated with delayed expression.

In addition to making a clear distinction between child and adult symptoms of PTSD, the DSM-5 identifies two specific disorders associated with **social neglect**, meaning the lack of sufficient caregiving during childhood (APA, 2013). Both **Reactive Attachment Disorder** and **Disinhibited Social Engagement Disorder** refer to impairing childhood reactions to inadequate care and are age-specific, applied to those between the ages of nine months and five years. These early manifestations of stress- and/or trauma-related experiences are summarized in Table 2.3 It is worth noting that although these two categories might collectively be referred to as *attachment disorders* by some, the DSM does not include such a category and as such the term **attachment disorder** remains a general term that refers to disruptions in functioning associated with a failure to establish healthy attachment relationships as a result of insufficient care in childhood.

Not all traumatic reactions will meet the diagnostic criteria for a stress or- or trauma-related disorder. However, symptoms may still be disruptive and can include angry outbursts, self-injurious behaviour, sexualized behaviour, repetitive play, and nightmares (Cohen, Berliner, & Mannarino, 2010). In addition, an important aspect of exposure to traumatic events is their potential to disrupt not only current health and functioning, but also the child's developmental progression in various domains of development (e.g.,

Table 2.3 Other Trauma- and Stressor-Related Disorders in Childhood or Adolescence

Disorder	Diagnostic Features
Disinhibited Social Engagement Disorder	Following exposure to inadequate childcare (e.g. the child's physical, social, emotional, or safety needs are not met, instability in home environments), the child does not go to caregiver for comfort, demonstrates few social and positive emotional responses to others, and may demonstrate unexpected fear or other negative emotions in the presence of nonthreatening carers.
Reactive Attachment Disorder	Following exposure to inadequate childcare (e.g. the child's physical, social, emotional, or safety needs are not met, instability of home environments), the child expresses unexpected and culturally inappropriate levels of comfort, informality, and relaxation with strangers.

cognitive, emotional, physical, social). For example, recent research suggests that brain development is significantly impaired as a result of exposure to various traumatic events (Cohen, Berliner, & Mannarino, 2010). The impact of exposure to trauma on development will be discussed at length in the remainder of this chapter.

COMORBIDITY

Consistent with the observation that reactions to traumatic and stressful events are varied, it's not surprising that a number of comorbid disorders have been associated with trauma- and stressor-related disorders. "Individuals with PTSD are 80% more likely than those without PTSD to have symptoms that meet diagnostic criteria for at least one other mental disorder (e.g., depressive, bipolar, anxiety, or substance use disorders)" (APA, 2013, p. 280). The comorbid disorders vary according to age group and sex, with "oppositional defiant disorder and separation anxiety disorder predominating" in young children and with "comorbid substance use disorder and conduct disorder more common among males than females" (APA, 2013, p. 280). Kilpatrick et al. (2003) found that of those diagnosed with PTSD aged 12–17, approximately 75 percent also met the criteria for a diagnosis of a mood disorder and/or substance abuse. More recently, Kousha and Tehrani (2013) found that the most frequently observed comorbid conditions associated with PTSD included ADHD, depression, and anxiety disorders. Other investigations have found that children and youth exposed to multiple traumatic events not only demonstrated increased levels of depression and anxiety, but were also more likely to present with aggressive behaviours and rule violations.

Consistent with the developmentally based expression of trauma-related symptoms, it has been proposed that those experiencing repeated exposure to traumatic events over the course of their lifetime will exhibit particular disruptions that vary according to life stage. Specifically, "it is assumed that the same fundamental deficiencies (like impaired regulation of emotion, low self-efficacy, tendency toward dissociation) have variable consequences at different developmental stages of the patient, thus resulting in typical age-related psychopathological symptoms" (Schmid, Petermann, & Fegert, 2013, p. 2). Different comorbid conditions will be observed depending on the age of the affected individual. For example, in toddlers, exposure to trauma might be expressed as an attachment disorder, whereas school-aged children might be more likely to express symptoms associated with ADHD. Figure 2.1 illustrates comorbid conditions in relation to developmental stage.

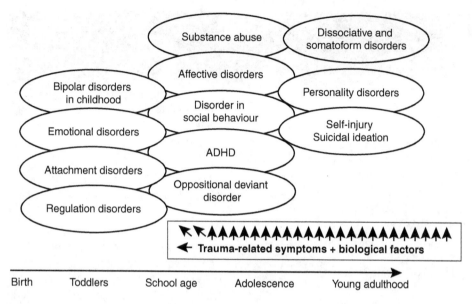

Figure 2.1 Trauma-Related Comorbid Disorders Across Development

The expression of trauma-related symptoms is express variably over the course of development.

Source: From "Developmental Trauma Disorder: Pros and Cons of Including Formal Criteria in the Psychiatric Diagnostic Systems" by Marc Schmid, Franz Petermann, and Joerg M Fegert in BMC PSYCHIATRY, 13(03); 2013. Copyright © 2013 by BioMed Central. Used by permission of BioMed Central.

In addition to specific comorbid diagnoses, traumatic events are associated with more general disturbances observed in various areas of functioning. For example, general cognitive disturbances include limitations in planning and behavioural self-regulation (De Bellis, 2001; van der Kolk, 2005) and deficits in the ability to sustain attention. Sensory and bodily perception can also be impaired (Schmidt, Petermann, & Fegert, 2013). In addition to bodily complaints, common physical disturbances include sleep abnormalities (Noll et al., 2006). Social and emotional impairments are also frequently observed, and include impulsive and high-risk behaviour (Shafii et al., 2009), preoccupation with sexuality (Elkovitch et al., 2009), non-suicidal self-injury (Yates, Carlson, & Egeland, 2008), and suicidal behaviour (Bruffaerts et al., 2010). The expression of any one of these impairments can look quite different depending on the age and developmental context in which they're experienced.

Before turning to a discussion of the explanations and treatment of trauma- and stressor-related disturbances, read the statements in Box 2.1 and examine your own feelings about these behaviour patterns. How might your position on these issues relate to your reactions toward someone struggling with the consequences of exposure to traumatic events?

EXPLAINING REACTIONS TO TRAUMA: PSYCHOLOGICAL PARADIGMS

It's understandable that witnessing or experiencing traumatic events might result in lasting feelings of distress and other reactions that can disrupt daily functioning. But why doesn't everyone demonstrate these reactions? Why are some people more likely than

Common Myths About Trauma- and Stressor-Related Disorders

MYTH: *PTSD only affects war veterans. Children and youth don't get PTSD.*

FACT: Although PTSD does affect war veterans, it also affects children and youth. As many as 70 percent of people in North America will experience at least one traumatic event in their lifetime. Of those people, up to 20 percent will go on to develop PTSD. An estimated 1 out of 10 women will develop PTSD at some time in their lives. "Victims of trauma related to physical and sexual assault face the greatest risk of developing PTSD. Women are about twice as likely to develop PTSD as men, perhaps because women are more likely to experience trauma that involves these types of interpersonal violence, including rape and severe beatings. Victims of domestic violence and childhood abuse also are at tremendous risk for PTSD" ("Myths about Posttraumatic Stress Disorder," 2001, p. 1).

MYTH: *It's all in their heads. If it were real, everyone exposed to a traumatic event would have PTSD.*

FACT: The reality is that PTSD is a very real condition caused by traumatic events that change how the brain functions, affecting how individuals react to the world. It is a highly individual response based on many factors.

MYTH: *People should be able to get over it and move on with their lives after a traumatic event. Those who can't cope are weak.*

FACT: Most people who experience an extremely traumatic event go through an adjustment period following the experience. Stress caused by trauma can affect all aspects of a person's life, including spiritual, mental, emotional, and physical well-being. Research has shown that prolonged trauma disrupts and alters brain chemistry. For some people, a traumatic event changes their views about themselves and the world around them. This may lead to the development of PTSD.

Source: Adapted from "Myths about Posttraumatic Stress Disorder," 2001; "Dispelling the myths about Post-Traumatic Stress Disorder (PTSD)," n.d.

others to develop reactions that are associated with the diagnosis of trauma- and stressor-related disorders and dissociative disorders? From a psychological perspective, each major paradigm (outlined in Chapter 1) offers a unique perspective and different explanation for these disorders. We now turn to a discussion of the biological, psychodynamic, behavioural, cognitive, and sociocultural paradigms and their explanations for differing reactions following exposure to traumatic events.

Biological Paradigm   From a biological approach, the impact of stressors and traumatic events on the functioning of various systems (e.g., immune, nervous) has been examined extensively. It's important to note, however, that most of these investigations have been conducted with adults or with children exposed to abuse. With these considerations in mind, let's consider the role of genetic, neurobiological, and biochemical factors in relation to trauma- and stressor-related disturbances.

Heredity and Genetics. Given the obvious role of environmental stressors/events in the development of trauma- and stressor-related disorders, it might seem surprising that genetics appears to play a role in the onset of these disorders. However, the importance of genetic influences in relation to PTSD has been acknowledged for some time (Slater & Slater, 1944). Research demonstrates that identical twins have a significantly higher concordance rate for PTSD than fraternal twins (Stein et al., 2002; True et al., 1993). Given that identical twins share essentially 100% of the same genetic material but fraternal twins share only 50%, greater concordance rate or similarity in PTSD diagnosis in identical twins suggests that genetics plays some role in this disorder. Similarly, it has been argued that genetic factors may predispose or protect the individual with respect to developing PTSD symptoms following exposure to traumatic events (APA, 2013). It should be noted, however, that identification of the specific genes associated with such risks are as yet unknown.

Brain Structures. Much of the research investigating the relationship between exposure to stressors and traumatic events has examined the lasting impact that such experiences have on the brain, particularly on the developing brain, and how these impacts influence psychological functioning, emotional regulation, and behaviour. For example, exposure to repeated trauma (i.e., maltreatment) has been associated with smaller head size and brain volume in children (Mulvihill, 2005; see Figure 2.2). The consequences of smaller brain volume can include deficits in cognitive abilities, in emotional regulation, and in social functioning (De Bellis, 2005; Glaser, 2000). Other research shows that repeated exposure to traumatic events results in *sensitization* of the nervous system (Perry et al., 1995; Ziegler, 2002), resulting in an increased likelihood that even minor events and/or stressors will be responded to as if they were a significant threat (Glaser, 2000).

What brain structures are affected by traumatic events? Studies seem to suggest that of particular relevance are the hippocampus (responsible for memory), the amygdala (related to emotion), the cerebral cortex (responsible for high-level cognitive processing), and the corpus callosum (which allows for communication between the right and left hemispheres of the brain). Specifically, exposure to traumatic events (particularly at a young age) is associated with both changes in structure and impaired functioning of these structures (refer to Appendix 2 to see their location in the brain). Given these structures' functions, it's easy to see how changes in them relate to the presentation of specific symptoms. For example, loss of memory for various aspects of events and time periods appears to be associated with the hippocampus; similarly, hypervigilance, irritability, and aggression

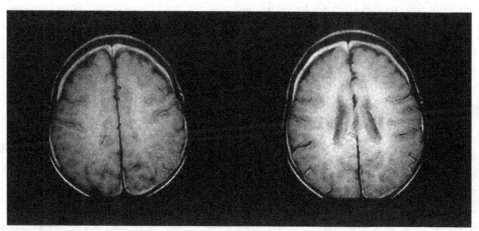

Living Art Enterprises, LLC/Science Source

Figure 2.2 Trauma and the Brain

Early maltreatment has a significant impact on the size of the brain and hence the functions for which it is responsible.

have been associated with altered functioning (Diseth, 2005) and size (i.e., smaller in those with a history of abuse) of the amygdala (Heide & Solomon, 2006). Alterations in the functioning of the cerebral cortex associated with experiences of neglect have been related to impulsivity, deficits in self-monitoring, altered cognitive functioning that relates to poor academic performance (De Bellis, 2005; Stein & Kendall, 2004), and deficits in interpreting the emotions of others, which impairs social functioning (Bremner, 2005). Finally, the corpus callosum has been found to be smaller in those with a history of trauma (Jackowski et al., 2008; Watts-English et al., 2006), which has been associated with deficits in emotional regulation (Heide & Solomon, 2006) and in language and memory processes (Weber & Reynolds, 2004).

It's worth noting that *extreme neglect* (failure to provide for the basic physical and emotional/social needs of the child) is most strongly associated with long-term effects on the brain and its development (Perry et al., 2002; Ziegler, 2002). According to Ziegler (2002), when the child's brain is in survival mode, the expected and necessary exploration of the environment that provides the foundation for learning that is necessary to development does not occur.

Neurotransmitters. From a biological approach, another explanation for the symptoms of trauma- and stressor-related disorders is unusual levels of activity of certain neurotransmitters in the brain. As discussed in Chapter 1, neurotransmitters are chemicals in the nervous system that are responsible for communication between neurons. For example, serotonin is a neurotransmitter that is associated with feelings of well-being and emotional stability. Exposure to early emotional abuse or significant deprivation has been associated with long-term effects on release and use of serotonin (Healy, 2004).

Hormones, another group of body chemicals, also play a role in the response to stressful and/or traumatic events. In particular, exposure to events that result in fear or stress is associated with the release of *corticotropin-releasing hormone* (CRH), which then stimulates the release of *cortisol*. While this stress hormone helps the individual respond to immediate threats and challenges by increasing the activation of the body's resources (i.e., release of glucose, endorphins, adrenalin), high levels of this hormone have been found to damage or destroy neurons in various brain areas (Putnam, 2006).

Psychodynamic Paradigm   When a challenging or threatening event is encountered, we respond physically, emotionally, and psychologically. Following exposure to such an event, we use various strategies to cope or manage our thoughts and emotional reactions with respect to memories of that event. Some coping strategies are *conscious* (e.g., an adolescent is aware of his decision to listen to his favourite song to take his mind off a recent accident he was in) while others are *unconscious* or outside of one's awareness. From a psychodynamic perspective, symptoms of trauma- and stressor-related disorders can be explained in relation to these unconscious processes. These unconscious coping strategies, or **defence mechanisms** (described in Chapter 1), include *repression*, where one excludes memories that could cause the recurrence of stress if they were allowed to enter awareness. For example, an adolescent who suffered abuse by a family member might repress that memory and have no recollection of the event. Recall that impaired or lost memories are symptoms of both trauma-related disorders and dissociative disorders. Accordingly, from a psychodynamic perspective, the individual copes with the traumatic event by repressing the memory (pushing it out of conscious awareness).

Although repression can be effective in avoiding thoughts or memories of the event, Freud noted that these memories are not eliminated. As such, they can still impact behaviour. For example, a youth who's been physically abused by a family member might *repress* the memory for the event, but below her level of awareness, she unconsciously harbours anger and resentment toward the perpetrator of the abuse. Rather than showing that anger directly toward the person she's angry with (which would be distressing and may be dangerous), the defence of *displacement* might be used in which the emotion (anger) is transferred or displaced to another person or situation that causes less distress. Accordingly, she might yell and/or physically attack a younger sibling (a safer object to display these emotions to and act toward in this way).

Dissociation can also be considered a defence used to cope with traumatic experiences (Brenner, 2001), and includes emotional numbing, substance use, forgetting, social withdrawal, and freezing. Short-term use of this defence is adaptive and makes sense. However, long-term use of this strategy takes one away from expected conscious experience and reality and is associated with lasting negative outcomes (Engelhard et al., 2003; Krenichyn, Saegert, & Evans, 2001).

Behavioural Paradigm   From a behavioural paradigm, reactions that follow exposure to stressful and/or traumatic events are explained in relation to classical and operant conditioning models. When one is exposed to a specific event (e.g., witnessing death of a loved one) that creates negative emotional, cognitive, and biological responses (e.g., fear, release of stress hormones, increased heart rate), other cues that are present in the environment (e.g., smell of gasoline, sight of summer flowers) get associated (often without the individual's awareness) with the event. Later, these same cues serve to trigger the negative emotional, cognitive, and biological responses that occurred during exposure to the traumatic event. Such behavioural explanations are supported by the observation that the severity of the event and severity of response to that event is associated with the degree of traumatic reactions (Carr, 2004; Keane, Zimering, & Caddell, 1985).

While classical conditioning explains the *development* of posttraumatic reactions, operant conditioning helps explain why traumatic symptoms persist long after exposure to the stressful or traumatic event. Recall that one of the primary symptoms associated with PTSD and other trauma-related disorders is avoidance of cues that remind the person of the event. For example, if a young person witnessed his brother being shot and killed in a video store, sights, smells, and sounds associated with that event (e.g., the smell of popcorn, the sight of the video store) might trigger negative memories, emotions, and thoughts long after the event has passed. In order to prevent these negative reactions from being experienced, he might avoid cues associated with such reactions (e.g., avoid popcorn, video stores). This avoidance of specific cues is reinforced (i.e., more likely to occur in the future) because it's followed by the removal of something painful or unpleasant to the individual. While avoiding stimuli that trigger negative reactions makes sense and is a form of coping with trauma, the end result is that the fear will never be extinguished, allowing these cues to remain triggers for negative emotional reactions. The behavioural explanation for the development and maintenance of negative emotional reactions following stressful and/or traumatic events is discussed at length in the context of anxiety disorders in Chapter 6.

Cognitive Paradigm   From a cognitive perspective, reactions to traumatic events are considered in relation to thoughts and beliefs that follow exposure to stressful and/or traumatic

Table 2.4 Examples of Cognitive Distortions Following Traumatic Events
"What happened is my fault."
"I can't survive these feelings."
"I must always be prepared to protect myself."
"Life is pointless."
"I'm helpless."
"I'm a bad person."
"I'll die if I think about what happened to me."

events. For example, numerous studies show that PTSD is associated with significant alterations in beliefs about the safety of the world, about the future, and about one's ability to control and/or master challenges in daily life (Fletcher, 2003; Roth et al., 1997; Wolfe & McGee, 1991). In the case of violence or abuse, it's not uncommon to observe decreased belief in the ability to trust others. Other research demonstrates that exposure to traumatic events results in alterations in cognitive functioning, including deficits in memory and an increased tendency to focus attention on traumatic information (Moradi et al., 1999).

One cognitive model of PTSD (Foa & Riggs, 1994; Foa, Rothbaum, & Molnar, 1995) emphasizes the **fear structure** that develops following exposure to a traumatic event. Part of this fear structure includes the meanings one develops in relation to stimuli associated with the event and with one's reactions to the event. When a traumatic event violates a commonly held assumption or schema (e.g., "The world is a safe place" or "Events are controllable"), individuals try to make sense of the experience, perhaps by changing their assumptions and schemas and developing new ones (e.g., "The world is unpredictable and dangerous"). These new assumptions and schemas represent cognitive distortions that can interfere with emotional, psychological, and social functioning. Refer to Table 2.4 for examples of distorted thoughts and assumptions associated with exposure to negative events.

Sociocultural Paradigm   As we've seen, not all youth exposed to traumatic events develop disruptions in functioning following the event. Risk factors that increase the likelihood of such responses can be considered in relation to both cultural and family factors.

Culture and Trauma.   Culture plays a role in trauma- and stressor-related disorders in a most basic way—it determines the types of traumatic events that are encountered. For example, members of cultures that use a horse and buggy for transportation will be exposed to very different forms of travel-related trauma than members of cultures that use airplanes and motor vehicles.

Cultures also differ with respect to the resources and supports that are available to its members. *Resilience* refers to the ability to thrive when faced with harsh conditions (Masten & Powell, 2003). While individual factors can contribute to this resilience, available resources (e.g., education, economic security, cultural traditions) can of course also contribute, serving to buffer the effects of traumatic events (Lerner & Benson, 2003; Ungar, 2001). Therefore, members of society with access to fewer resources, including those with ethnic minority status, lower education, and lower income, are at greater risk for developing PTSD (Brewin et al., 2000). The importance of access to resources was demonstrated in a study by Hobfoll, Tracy, and Galea (2006) that found that those who experienced significant economic/material loss following the terrorist attacks in the United States on September 11, 2001, were more likely to experience PTSD symptoms.

Culture also plays a role in how individuals interpret and respond to traumatic events. For example, consider the case of death and bereavement:

> The Condolence Ceremony of the Haudenosaunee (Iroquois) is a perfect example of a cultural process wherein part of the group (the non-mourners) act as caretakers to those who are mourning—wiping their eyes so they can see more clearly; cleaning their ears so they may again be able to hear the truth; and clearing their throat so they may once again breathe, speak, and eat in a healthy manner. (Mitchell & Maracle, 2005, p. 19)

Other social factors, including prejudice and discrimination, also play a role in trauma and onset of traumatic disturbances. For example, one Canadian study found that Aboriginal participants who had experienced racial discrimination in the past year were significantly more likely to experience and report PTSD symptoms (Currie et al., 2012).

Family Influences. Generally, it has been found that individuals with greater degrees of social support are at lower risk for psychological distress following exposure to traumatic events (Brewin et al., 2000; Norris et al., 2005). Given that the family environment is one of the social units responsible for providing such support, it's not surprising that family factors can impact the risk for developing trauma symptoms. According to McFarlane (1988), the quality of the bond between youth and parent is the most significant determinant of trauma outcomes following exposure to severe stressors. Consistent with this idea, numerous studies have demonstrated that support from the family and the emotional reaction of the parent(s) to the trauma have a significant impact on the trauma symptoms of the child. Specifically, in the case of natural disaster (La Greca et al., 1996), war (Garbarino & Kostelny, 1996), and community violence (Breslau et al., 1991), PTSD symptoms were lower in those youth who received greater familial support. Also, youth with parents who responded with less distress to the trauma (suggesting greater ability to cope with the traumatic event themselves) were less likely to develop PTSD symptoms. This is consistent with Lyons's (1987) suggestion that the ability of caregivers to cope with trauma is the best predictor of positive outcomes for youth following exposure to traumatic events.

Trauma that is experienced in the home is particularly likely to have a lasting effect on the child. This makes sense, given our earlier discussion of cues that remind the individual of the trauma; there are more cues and a lasting relationship with the source of the trauma (Mulvihill, 2005). Accordingly, exposure to family violence (Jack et al., 2006) as well as *neglect* (the most common form of child maltreatment in Canada, which can include failure of a caregiver to provide for the basic physical and psychological needs of the child) (Perry, Colwell, & Schick, 2002) and abuse have each been found to be associated with PTSD and other trauma-related disturbances.

A CYC LENS ON THE PSYCHOLOGICAL PARADIGMS: A HOLISTIC CONCEPTUAL MODEL

The emotional and behavioural consequences of complex trauma are a critical topic for CYCPs. As we've seen, there is a highly significant relationship between adverse childhood experiences (especially maltreatment and trauma) and emergent adult difficulties, including depression, suicide, substance misuse, family violence, obesity, physical inactivity, and sexually transmitted diseases (van der Kolk, 2005).

Certain characteristics of the traumatic event or the nature of the stressor—namely, its controllability, predictability, ambiguity, and chronicity—are important factors in determining the young person's stress response. Specifically, it has been shown that whether the stressor is *controllable* influences the extent of the neurochemical changes associated with it, which may be basic in understanding the psychological ramifications of the trauma experience. Thus, unpredictable events are typically viewed as being more troublesome and have greater negative consequences than predictable events. Ambiguity and uncertainty are always very stressful (Bombay, Matheson, & Anisman, 2009).

Once traumatized, children's stress responses, or their baseline levels of arousal and anxiety, often become elevated or "stuck on high," even when it may seem as if they're underaroused. This is the result of several neural and biochemical systems responding to the experience(s) of extreme stress or terror. Individuals who've been traumatized develop abnormalities in the release of brain chemicals that regulate arousal and attention (van der Kolk, 2005). In untraumatized children (and adults), stress activates all the principal anti-stress hormones that enable active coping behaviours. Traumatized children, however, have relatively low levels of these anti-stress hormones, which causes an inability to regulate or manage responses to stress (van der Kolk, 2005). This is why traumatized children are easily overwhelmed by the demands of their environment, especially in school. Their elevated baseline levels of arousal and anxiety leave them in a persistent and biologically based state of low-level fear; they remain *hypervigilant*, with all senses in a state of heightened sensitivity (Perry et al., 1995). Their more sensitive systems become highly aroused by what we may consider minor stressors, such as everyday routine tasks like attending school and making friends.

Arousal has the potential to stimulate learning and memory; when functioning within the *optimal zone of arousal*, we're able to process, integrate, and remember information (Perry et al., 1995). But when we're stressed, we have great difficulty learning and performing, including or especially in school. Police trainees and CYCPs alike know that when they're required to document their observations related to critical-incident events, stress affects their ability to be accurate in recall. Health professionals suggest that patients

CYCPs help young people understand the impact of their early trauma and how they've done the best they can.

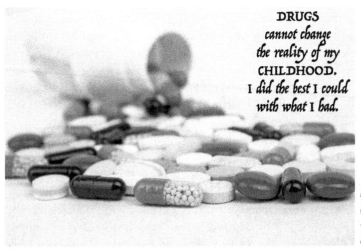

DRUGS *cannot change the reality of my* **CHILDHOOD.** I *did the best* I *could with what* I *had.*

Creativa/Fotolia

bring a friend or family member with them to the doctor's office, especially when facing diagnoses of potentially life-threatening conditions like cancer, since when individuals are in a highly aroused state, they're less likely to remember what the doctor said.

The child or youth who has experienced trauma will also have difficulty processing verbal information. Many studies assessing trauma's impact on the brain have found increased activity in the right hemisphere, which is involved in nonverbal processing, and decreased activity in the left hemisphere, which is responsible for language processing (van der Kolk, 2005).

High levels of arousal will cause children and youth to feel more anxious, and in this state they'll pay closer attention to nonverbal than to verbal cues (Perry et al., 1995). They may become fixated on those nonverbal cues that the brain interprets will aid in their survival, even when no real threat exists in the present moment. It's important to keep in mind that young people who've been trauma-exposed live in a state of fear almost all the time. Their brain's first and only concern when feeling threatened is survival; all other demands of the environment will be ignored. It makes sense, then, that these children will have great difficulty concentrating (Melrose, 2009), including following directions, recalling (and even making sense of) what is heard, and problem solving (Perry et al., 1995). And when they can't concentrate, it's nearly impossible to consolidate memories (that is, move them from sensory memory into short-term memory, and from short-term memory into long-term memory).

Intergenerational trauma or *historical trauma* refers to the collective emotional and psychological injury over the lifespan and across generations that has resulted from a history of genocide (Yellow Horse Brave Heart, 2005). For example, the impact of historic and collective traumatic events on survivors and their offspring has been documented among the descendants of Holocaust survivors. Children of residential school survivors display poorer overall well-being (e.g., elevated depression) than the children of Aboriginal people who did not attend residential schools. Residential schools, along with what's known as the Sixties Scoop (wherein from the 1960s to 1990s, large numbers of children were taken from reserves and placed in non-Aboriginal homes by child welfare workers or adopted by distant non-Aboriginal families), have had devastating effects on Aboriginal communities in Canada. These consequences have gone far beyond the First Nations individuals who were institutionalized, and have affected children, families, entire communities, and indeed all First Nations peoples (Bombay, Matheson, & Anisman, 2009). The impact of such historical trauma can be considered equivalent to that of PTSD on an individual, except that the effects of trauma apply to the entire culture.

Despite the high rates of trauma documented in First Nations communities in Canada, no studies to date have compared the prevalence rates of PTSD in First Nations individuals with those in the general Canadian population. However, in a sample of First Nations residential school survivors who had experienced abuse, 64 percent were diagnosed with PTSD (Bombay, Matheson, & Anisman, 2009).

WHERE DO YOU STAND?

Consider the psychological and CYC perspectives on reactions to traumatic events. Where do you stand with respect to these viewpoints? You'll likely notice that, although they differ, there are some commonalities. To examine these more closely, read the case of Alyssa in the *Take Action!* exercise.

Sixteen-year-old Alyssa, an Aboriginal girl, is currently homeless in a small western city. Adopted at age 3 by a deeply religious non-Aboriginal family in a Manitoba town, she ran away from home at 15. She disclosed to the youth outreach workers at the safe house where she stops by occasionally to talk that for about six years she'd been physically and sexually abused by her adoptive parents. It started when she was 10, when her adoptive parents began drinking. The abuse included being forced to watch them during sex, being forcibly confined, and being consistently physically assaulted as a disciplinary measure. Alyssa hadn't disclosed the abuse to anyone before.

When Alyssa arrived in the city, she was quickly befriended by a 20-year-old man who is now her "boyfriend." They live on the streets. He supplies her with food, drugs, and alcohol, and in return, Alyssa poses for pictures that her boyfriend advertises online. The youth outreach workers know she's being sexually exploited, and are working with police to bring her to a secure unit. When Alyssa was assessed by the therapist at the shelter, she disclosed that she has nightmares and dissociates during the episodes of exploitation. She explained that she learned how to do

this when her parents forced her to have sex with them. She told the youth workers that sometimes she's so numb that she cuts herself so that she can feel something. "Cutting helps me to know I'm still alive," she said. Alyssa has recently become uncooperative with her CYC workers, and is starting to disengage. She's now on the "high-risk victim" list, and everyone is very concerned about her safety.

1. What explanations for Alyssa's high-risk behaviour might be offered from the psychological perspectives discussed previously?

2. What explanations would you use from the CYC perspective?

3. How do you think the trauma of the past sexual abuse factors into her current sexual exploitation?

4. What specific interventions might you recommend from a psychological approach?

5. What benefits are there for Alyssa in receiving a diagnosis of complex trauma or PTSD?

6. As a CYC youth outreach worker in this case, what approach might you take with Alyssa?

HELPING CHILDREN AND ADOLESCENTS WITH TRAUMA-RELATED DISTURBANCES

Psychological Approaches to Treatment

Aside from trying to minimize the exposure of youth to such events, what can be done to best help youth avoid the negative consequences of trauma? From a psychological perspective, interventions for those experiencing disrupted emotion and behaviour following a traumatic experience have been proposed from each of the major paradigms. The best interventions for these behaviour patterns are likely to emerge from consideration of biological, psychological, and social factors; there is no single best approach to helping those

Jennifer's Case: *Revisited*

Jen refuses to talk to anyone about what happened to her mother. However, her grandmother has told the CYCP and the family case worker that she acts out the incident when playing with dolls or drawing pictures. Jen wakes up from night terrors

and has frequent thoughts about "monsters" chasing her and killing her. After a recent assessment at a mental health outpatient clinic, Jen was diagnosed with PTSD. She is now involved in ongoing play therapy with her case worker.

suffering from traumatic symptoms. With this inclusive approach in mind, let's consider some of the most common psychological approaches to intervention for trauma- and stressor-related disorders.

Biological Paradigm   Biological treatments for PTSD have been primarily based on adult samples. Thus, there is limited research that specifically informs the biological treatment of youth with trauma-related disturbances. Investigations have, however, found that the effectiveness of such medications differed between youth and adults. For example, while SSRIs (medications that increase the activity of serotonin by preventing the reuptake of this neurotransmitter in the central nervous system) have been found to be very effective in reducing symptoms of PTSD in adults (Pervanidou, 2008), a recent review of the literature found no support for the use of SSRIs as the first line of treatment for PTSD in children and adolescents (Strawn et al., 2010).

Despite this limited research, the use of medications to treat some of the symptoms associated with trauma-related disorders in youth (e.g., disruptive behaviour, depression, dysregulated attachment) does occur. Commonly prescribed medications include not only SSRIs but also tricyclic antidepressants, adrenergic blocking agents, anxiolytics, antipsychotics, and anticonvulsants (Cohen, Mannarino, & Rogal, 2001; Stoddard, Usher, & Abrams, 2006). Refer to Table 2.5 for an overview of these medications and their potential impact on trauma-related symptoms. Although the effectiveness of these medications has been demonstrated in research (see Huemer, Erhart, & Steiner, 2010, for a review), it's worth noting that the number of studies is small, as are the sample sizes typically used in these investigations.

Thus, while it's important to be aware that medications might offer some relief to youth suffering from trauma-related symptoms, medication is not (and should not be) the first line of intervention for children and adolescents. CYCPs are most likely to see these medications being used in combination with non-biological treatment approaches. Despite this practice, however, there is a lack of evidence on which to draw any firm conclusions regarding the efficacy of these medications in reducing trauma-related symptoms in youth (Wethington et al., 2008).

Table 2.5 Common Medications for Trauma-Related Symptoms

Drug	Outcomes for Children/Adolescents
SSRIs (e.g., citalopram)	Reduces core PTSD symptoms (re-experiencing, avoidance, and hyper-arousal)
Other antidepressants (e.g., trazodone, nefazodone)	Reduces core PTSD symptoms
Adrenergic blocking agents (e.g., clonidine, guanfacine, prazosin)	Reduces hyper-arousal, intrusive symptoms, and impulsivity
Antipsychotics (e.g., quetiapine, risperidone)	Reduces intrusive thoughts and other symptoms of ASD (including dissociation and aggression)
Mood stabilizers (e.g., carbamazepine)	Reduces PTSD symptoms

Psychodynamic Paradigm   From a psychodynamic approach, treatments for trauma and related symptoms focus on identifying and altering dysfunctional defence mechanisms (McWilliams, 1994). Helping individuals become aware of the function of their defences and how these relate to coping with the traumatic event gives them insight into how unconscious memories and thoughts around the trauma affect their current behaviour. Important elements of psychodynamic interventions include bringing unconscious fears and conflicts into awareness and analyzing the defences used to keep them below the level of awareness. In one model of psychodynamic treatment for PTSD (Horowitz, 1997; Krupnick, 2002), therapy consists of developing the relationship between therapist and client, and allowing the client to tell his or her story, work through and examine the loss associated with the trauma, and learn about its impact.

Although psychodynamic treatments for PTSD and other trauma-related disorders haven't been widely studied (Schottenbauer et al., 2008), a growing number of investigations support the idea that they can be effective in enhancing social functioning and reducing psychological symptoms (see Leichsenring, Rabung, & Leibing, 2004, for a review). The American Psychological Association (2004) recognized that psychodynamic practice might be of particular relevance in addressing developmental, interpersonal, and intrapersonal issues associated with exposure to traumatic events.

Behavioural Paradigm   Recall that, from a behavioural approach, trauma-related symptoms are associated with fears of those things that serve as reminders of the event (e.g., memories, pictures, sounds, smells, and dreams) established through classical conditioning. Avoiding these reminders helps prevent the youth from experiencing fear; however, it can also interfere with daily functioning, create significant distress, and prevent the fear from diminishing. One way to help reduce this fear and other negative emotions associated with its reminders, then, is to have the individual confront these reminders.

Exposure therapy involves presenting feared (and usually avoided) reminders to young people in a safe environment after they've been taught relaxation skills. For example, if a youth has been traumatized by abuse in his home, providing a photo of this environment in a safe place will still serve to produce fear and anxiety; upon experiencing these emotions, he would then use his relaxation techniques. After repeated exposure to these reminders, he learns that he can manage the anxiety and fear when it occurs (rather than avoiding it). Through the process of *extinction* (discussed in Chapter 1), the reminders of the trauma become less likely to evoke fear responses, and avoidance is no longer required. (For a more detailed discussion of such exposure approaches to intervention, see Chapter 6, as these techniques are most often used in the treatment of anxiety disorders.)

In a recent meta-analytic study, Powers et al. (2010) concluded that exposure therapy for PTSD is effective in decreasing traumatic symptoms (as compared with control groups that received no treatment). Even thoughts and memories of traumatic events can become conditioned stimuli that trigger significant emotional and behavioural reactions. Therefore, situations in which one is exposed to feared thoughts can also be effective in reducing trauma-related symptoms. This type of exposure typically occurs in the context of *cognitive therapy*. In fact, behavioural approaches are often combined with cognitive elements of treatment.

Cognitive Paradigm   From a cognitive standpoint, one reason exposure therapy is effective is that individuals learn how dangerous a stimulus (object or situation) actually is and are thus able to correct their faulty beliefs (Foa & Kozak, 1986). Such identifying of distorted cognitions and changing of beliefs are key elements in decreasing the symptoms of trauma-related disorders.

Cognitive restructuring aims to help young people identify distorted assumptions and schemas associated with the traumatic event, consider their validity, and hence replace these with more balanced/accurate beliefs. For example, if a young person believes that "other people can't be trusted," therapeutic sessions would involve asking him to list the persons who are trustworthy in his life and describe the ways in which they can be trusted. A behavioural component might also be employed by having him conduct experiments that involve trusting other people in small ways. Together, these activities serve to expose him to what he fears (i.e., other people being untrustworthy) as well as challenge his distorted assumptions and schemas and develop more accurate views of self and the world. You might recognize this as the *cognitive-behavioural* approach to therapy discussed in Chapter 1. In a recent review of 8 studies with a total of 708 young people, Kowalik et al. (2011) reported that cognitive behavioural therapy was effective in the treatment of youth PTSD.

Sociocultural Paradigm   From a sociocultural perspective, trauma- and stressor-related disturbances can be managed by considering various social elements in the youth's environment.

Culture and Trauma. It is generally acknowledged that essentially every aspect of trauma- and stressor-related disturbances is influenced by cultural factors (Marsella, 2010; Wilson, 2008; Wilson & Tang, 2007). Any approach to treatment, therefore, must consider the particular patterns, rituals, and treatment approaches that are a part of the affected individual's culture.

> Depending on the culture, these mechanisms may include what Western medico-psychological experts would classify as nontraditional or alternative modalities of treatment or assistance. Included within this group of "healers" are shamans; medicine "men and women" of non-Western practices; herbal therapies; physical and somatic (bodily) treatments of many varieties; aboriginal dances and incantations, recitations. (Marsella, 2010, p. 22)

The importance of recognizing cultural variables in interventions for trauma-related disturbances is illustrated in a South American study that explored traumatic reactions in Peru and Columbia (Elsass, 2001). Citizens in both countries had been exposed to extreme violence and demonstrated posttraumatic symptoms. However, the optimal psychosocial intervention depended on the cultural orientation of the group. Peruvian villagers demonstrated a greater degree of collectivism and community spirit and were open to psychological interventions focused on strengthening the community as a whole. Villagers in Columbia, however, had a more individualist orientation and were more open to psychological interventions focused on personal emotional reactions to these extreme events. This is a powerful illustration of the importance of matching the intervention with important cultural variables.

Family Influences. Findings show that family support is a primary protective factor for youth who've experienced a significant stressful or traumatic event (Kliewer et al., 2004; Ozer et al., 2003). A powerful demonstration of the impact family support can have comes from the finding that even in the instance of intra-familial abuse, children's symptoms decrease when the non-offending parent provides support to the child (Boney-McCoy & Finkelhor, 1995; Margolin, 1998).

Based on these findings, Berkowitz et al. (2011) developed the Child and Family Traumatic Stress Intervention (CFTSI), a four-session, caregiver–child intervention for children aged 7–17 designed to prevent the development of long-term PTSD symptoms. This intervention seeks to enhance social support and coping skills in the family by (1) increasing communication between the affected child and caregivers and (2) providing specific behavioural coping skills to both caregivers and child. An evaluation of the intervention suggests that the CFTSI was effective in reducing PTSD symptoms and holds promise as a family-based intervention to prevent long-term traumatic reactions in youth (Berkowitz et al., 2011).

CYC Approaches for Youth Struggling with Trauma-Related Disturbances

The best intervention approach for behaviours related to trauma affecting children and youth is *relational practice* (Perry, 2009). As Perry points out, because human beings have evolved in relationships—in small tribal groups competing with other small groups—the key to survival was (and still is in traditional tribal cultures) building and maintaining strong relationships with one another. Consequently, *relational health* emerges as vital to proper human brain development and to a successful, happy life. One of the most destructive aspects to healthy lifespan development is a poverty of relationships. Further, Perry argues that the poverty of consistent relationships is a major reason why the child welfare system in Canada continues to have significant problems. Poverty of attachment relationships creates stress for individuals, which in turn creates a craving for the reward that usually comes from positive attachment relationships during development. As a result, individuals will find substitutes that satisfy the craving, such as substance misuse and other unhealthy behaviours.

Dr. Gabor Maté (2008) similarly holds that healing is based on developing an environment of healthy relationships, known as a *reclaiming environment* or a *therapeutic milieu*—wherein the child feels safe and not overwhelmed with unpredictable events creating harmful stress. Traumatized youth need an environment that is both safe (to allow the brain to heal and reorganize from the unhealthy earlier life experiences) and has enough novelty for the brain to learn and develop. Perry reminds that we can all create an internal vision of a better place, a better way, and a better life; this capacity is called hope. As he has said, our job is to give children hope that not all adults are abusive, unpredictable, or violent. Role models, mentors, and heroes, including CYCPs, can provide new formative experiences for children and youth (Perry, 2004, p. 10).

The most important aspects of the "transforming therapeutic interaction" (Perry, 2004) are safety, predictability, and nurturance, the basics of trauma-informed care. Perry also points out that the most therapeutic interactions often come from those who have no training (or interest) in psychological or psychiatric labels, theories, or treatments and the adult expectations of the child that go with these. Using respect, humour, and flexibility when interacting with young people allows them to feel cared for and valued for who they are with no strings attached (Perry, 2004)—in other words, the very essence of CYC.

Therapeutic intervention must create new patterns in the brain that reflect young people's new experiences, and the best way to do this is to expose them to repeated experiences that break old associations. The new patterns must be consistent, predictable, patterned, and frequent. All adults in a young person's life must work together during therapeutic interventions in order for these patterns to be consistent across all facets of his or her life.

Perry (2004) also notes that effective interventions begin by helping young people understand what they feel and why they behave a certain way in given situations. Traumatized children frequently act impulsively, and don't understand why they behave as they do. They tend to blame their behaviours (as will the adults around them) on themselves— that they're stupid, bad, sick, or damaged in some way. These distorted cognitions need to be addressed and changed. A second important element is educating the adults in young people's world about the ways in which maltreated and traumatized children think, feel, and behave. This is imperative in order to understand their behaviours through a neuro-developmental lens.

Perry (2004) describes the DSM as an attempt to categorize complex behaviours largely through checklists of symptoms. As we stress throughout this text, using the DSM as the primary assessment tool in your CYC work means basing your understanding of young people's troublesome behaviours on the categorization of presenting symptoms instead of on the causes. In turn, this means that diagnoses and use of psychotropic drug interventions are more a trial-and-error process based on observations of *symptoms* rather than on isolating and treating the root cause of the problematic behaviour—which, according to Perry, lies in the brain.

What's key, then, in Perry's neurosequential model of therapeutics (NMT) is a total change in focus. Instead of looking at symptoms and a DSM checklist as a guide, the helper looks beyond symptoms to the brain as the root cause of the troublesome behaviours. Interventions are thus focused on healing the brain, which will take care of the problematical behaviours. Children and youth are understood to be unable to behave more appropriately, not unwilling (Woodbury, 2008).

Strength-Based Relational CYC Practice The most important treatment principles for a strength-based relational response to assisting children and youth affected by trauma include the following (Smith, 2011):

- Ensure you have all the historical information about the trauma.
- Assess for substance misuse and self-harming behaviours.
- Regard the behavioural symptoms as adaptations or coping mechanisms.
- Consider all cultural aspects of the behaviours and coping strategies.
- Assess developmental stage at the time of trauma and presently.
- Consider strengths, vulnerabilities, resources, and supports.
- Focus on relationship.
- Establish safety.
- Help develop the capacity for self-regulation.

In addition, it's important that CYCPs understand the basic principles of NMT for use in relational practice. Therapeutic interventions that are informed by principles of neuro-development are more likely to be effective if they accurately target the appropriate areas of brain dysfunction resulting from maltreatment and complex trauma. As well, since NMT represents a major departure from the assumptions and techniques of mainstream psychological or psychiatric assessment and therapy (the DSM), it fits well with a CYC approach.

NMT is both brain-based and developmentally informed. According to Perry (2004), it is neither a specific therapeutic technique nor a specific intervention, but rather a way for helpers to understand the impact of young people's trauma history on their current functioning. The goal of NMT is to guide assessment, identify primary troublesome areas and key strengths, and then develop supporting interventions to best meet the needs of the young person (Perry, 2004).

NMT is based on the premise that the brain is organized in a hierarchal fashion (refer to Figure 2.3). The brain develops through the life experience of the child in a sequential way, and because different areas of the brain are developing at different times, vulnerability to trauma varies with age. Promotion of healthy development of the brain requires exposure the "right" stimulation at the time the brain is ready to develop in that particular area. The human brain is also organized from the most simple (e.g., the brainstem contains the fewest cells) to the most complex (e.g., the frontal cortex contains the most cells and synapses). The various functions of the brain, from the most simple (e.g., regulation of body temperature) to the most complex (e.g., abstract thought), are mediated in different areas; these areas change in the mature brain in a "use-dependent" fashion. That is, the more a certain neural system is activated, the more it will develop, creating an internal representation of the experience corresponding to this neural activation (Perry, 2004).

The brain responds to trauma with changes in cognition, in affect, in behaviour, in neurophysiology, and in physiology. One of the key functions of nervous tissue in the brain is to store information. All areas of the brain store information related to the functions they mediate:

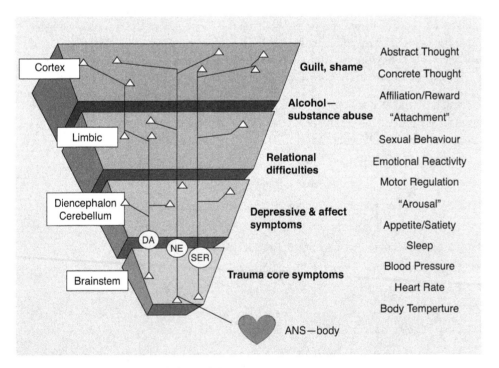

Figure 2.3 Neurosequential Model

Bruce Perry's neurosequential model emphasizes the need for interventions that repair damage to increasingly higher areas of the brain.

Source: "The Neurosequential Model (NMT)" from *Integrating Principles of Neurodevelopment into Clinical Practice* by Bruce D. Perry, MD PhD. Copyright by Child Trauma Academy. Used by permission.

for example, the cortex stores cognitive information (names, faces, facts); the limbic system can store emotional information (fear, pleasure, sadness); and the brainstem stores the anxiety or arousal states associated with a traumatic event. The symptoms of PTSD and complex trauma are stored throughout the brain in these various systems and areas. Re-exposure to cues associated with the trauma (e.g., sights, sounds, and smells) can elicit these stored memories and result in the signs and symptoms of complex trauma and PTSD.

Assessment

The assessment of complex trauma involves assessing children's exposure to multiple traumatic events and its wide-ranging impact across their domains of development. Such assessment is difficult for many reasons, but an important factor is that many children, especially very young children, have limited verbal abilities to describe their feelings. As well, children in the care system with multiple caregivers are at particular risk for having trauma histories, yet these histories may be nearly impossible to confirm. It is vital, then, to have the required clinical skills to accurately identify traumatized children and youth.

The National Traumatic Stress Network ("Assessment of complex trauma," n.d.) recommends the following steps for conducting a comprehensive assessment of complex trauma:

- Always explore for a wide range of traumatic events and determine when they occurred, if possible, so that they can be linked to the child's developmental stages.

- Observe and assess for a wide range of symptoms, risk behaviours, functional impairments, and developmental difficulties.

- Gather assessment information using a variety of techniques, including interviews, standardized measures, and behavioural observations; also gather information from a variety of individuals: the child, caregivers, teachers, other care providers, and so on.

A trauma assessment needs to be conducted by a clinically trained therapist or practitioner who understands child development and complex trauma. Ideally, the assessment should involve a multidisciplinary team. In residential treatment settings, a multidisciplinary team would include the CYCP staff ("Assessment of complex trauma," n.d.).

Perry (2004) argues that therapeutic interventions informed by principles of neurodevelopment are far more likely to effectively target the brain dysfunction that results from children's maltreatment. Assessment through NMT is conducted using the clinical online assessment tool, which is accessible to professionals who have entered the training certification programs available at the Child Trauma Academy. Practitioners do need to be trained in using the NMT assessment model. Alberta's Hull Services is one example of a CYC agency that's using NMT in its work with vulnerable children, youth, and families.

The NMT assessment incorporates reviews of the key insults, stressors, and challenges that have occurred and the relational history of the young person during development. The aim of the first review is to determine and score the timing, nature, and severity of the developmental challenges that young people have experienced in order to estimate their developmental capacity. The second review provides insight into the attachments and related resiliency/vulnerability factors that have impacted their functional development (Perry & Hambrick, 2008, pp. 39–40).

Although training is required, CYCPs still can use the theory underlying NMT in their work. The impact of trauma on the developing child is global, meaning that it affects every aspect of the child's development and functioning. According to Cook et al. (2007), seven domains of impairment are observed in children exposed to complex trauma: attachment, biology, affect regulation, dissociation, behavioural control, cognitive processes, and self-concept. In the following summary of the consequences of trauma on each domain of development, CYCPs will recognize the symptoms observed in the young people for whom they provide care.

Attachment. According to Cook et al. (2007), in complex trauma, the energy normally dedicated to the child's growth and development is devoted to survival. If the caregiver is dangerous or absent, the infant or child is in a constant state of stress. If the caregiver is the source of the danger, the child will feel helpless and abandoned. Recall our Chapter 1 discussion of the *internal working model*: as the child develops, in order to cope she tries to exert some control over her environment, often by disconnecting from social relationships or by acting aggressively toward others. Over the long term, the child is at high risk for ongoing physical and social difficulties due to the increased susceptibility to stress, the inability to regulate emotions, and the inappropriate help-seeking (Cook et al., 2007).

Biology. Infants, toddlers, and preschool-aged children have a higher risk of failing to develop the brain capacities necessary for regulating emotions in response to stress. Trauma interferes with the integration of the left- and right-hemisphere brain functioning, meaning that a child can't access rational thought in the face of overwhelming emotion. Traumatic stressors or deficits in self-regulatory abilities will impede the successful development of these areas and can lead to difficulties in emotional regulation, cognition, and even identity formation (Cook et al., 2007).

Affect Regulation. The regulation of affect begins with an accurate identification of internal emotional experiences (e.g., "I'm happy" or "I'm afraid"). According to Cook et al. (2007), when children are provided with inconsistent models of affect and behaviour (e.g., a smiling expression from caregiver coupled with angry and rejecting behaviour) or with inconsistent responses to affective display (e.g., the child's crying is met inconsistently: sometimes with anger, sometimes with rejection, sometimes with love and nurturance), there is no coherent framework provided to allow them to accurately interpret their experiences. Given their limited ability to self-regulate and self-soothe, traumatized children and youth may display dissociation, chronic numbing of emotional experience, dysphoria, avoidance of emotional situations (including positive experiences), and maladaptive coping strategies (including use of substances; Cook et al., 2007).

Dissociation. Dissociation—whereby the failure to absorb or integrate information and experiences leads to thoughts and emotions becoming disconnected from reality—is one of the key consequences of complex trauma in children and youth. Dissociation begins as an effective coping mechanism, but over time it can become a dysfunctional strategy, affecting behavioural management, affect regulation, and self-concept (Cook et al., 2007).

Behavioural Regulation. According to Cook et al. (2007), complex childhood trauma is associated with both under-controlled and over-controlled behaviour patterns. Maltreated children may demonstrate very controlled behaviour patterns, including compulsive compliance with adult requests, resistance to changes in routine, inflexible bathroom rituals, and rigid control of food intake. Childhood victimization has also been shown to be associated with the development of aggressive behaviour and ODD.

Cognitive Processing. Research shows that, when compared with nonabused children, maltreated children already have impaired cognitive functioning as infants. Neglected infants and toddlers demonstrate delays in expressive and receptive language development and deficits in overall IQ. As well, research has shown that by early childhood, maltreated children demonstrate less flexibility and creativity in problem-solving tasks than their same-age peers (Cook et al., 2007).

Self-Concept. A healthy internal working model, or positive sense of self, is developed through repeated positive interaction attachment cycles with a responsive, sensitive caretaker. Many positive early life experiences allow a child to develop a model of self as generally worthy and competent, also known as a *positive internal working model*. However, repetitive experiences of maltreatment by significant others lead to a sense of self as ineffective, helpless, deficient, and unlovable: a *negative internal working model*. "Children who perceive themselves as powerless or incompetent and who expect others to reject and despise them are more likely to blame themselves for negative experiences and have problems eliciting and responding to social support" (Cook et al., 2007, p. 3).

I
am a PERSON
not a CASE

Trauma is an individual experience; each person will respond to it in a unique way.

Rating Scales. A variety of standardized measures may be used to assess complex trauma. Rating scales used by psychologists include the Achenbach Child Behavior Checklist (CBCL), the Trauma History Checklist and Interview (THC) (Habib & Labna, 2006), the Family Assessment of Needs and Strengths: Trauma Exposure and Adaptation (FANS-TEA) by Lyons et al. (2009), and the Coping Responses Inventory–Youth (CRI-Y) (Moos, 1993). For a more detailed list, go to www.nctsn.org/content/standardized-measures-assess-complex-trauma.

Indicators to Recognize   Child and adolescent trauma survivors who've been diagnosed with PTSD or have experienced complex trauma struggle with the constant fear that the traumatic event is still happening and may feel terrified that it's going to happen again. When young people relive the traumatic event to such a degree that they're unable to maintain contact with their present reality, it's known either as dissociation (described earlier) or as a flashback. Young people may also feel intense shame and guilt about the event, believing that they're somehow responsible for what happened, or they may feel guilty about what they had to do in order to survive. With the associated chronic hypervigilance and over-arousal, children may feel perpetually exhausted; night terrors will lead to difficulty concentrating in the day. Most children will purposefully avoid sleep to avoid such night terrors.

Due to emotional numbing, youth may lose the sense of being connected to others, withdraw from friends and caregivers, and/or lash out. Youth will usually self-medicate by misusing substances, and they may also engage in self-injurious behaviours; both of these can be defined as coping mechanisms, however dysfunctional, to avoid and numb the feelings and memories of the trauma ("Dissociation FAQ's," 2014).

Self-injurious behaviours, deliberate self-harm, or **Nonsuicidal Self-Injury (NSSI)** include such behaviours as cutting, burning, punching oneself, and inserting objects into the skin. These are defined as intentional, self-inflicted, low-lethality, and socially unacceptable bodily harm that an individual uses to reduce emotional and psychological distress (Walsh, 2006). The internalized negative working model (inner representation of a defective, unlovable self) of the world as a dangerous place that results from maltreatment is known to be a risk factor of self-harming behaviour in children and youth (Smith, 2011). The most important point about self-injury that CYCPs need to consider is that the motivation (needs) behind the behaviour or the intent (purpose) of the behaviour is vastly different from those related to suicidal behaviour. "Self-injury is not about ending life but reducing psychological distress. . . . Self-injury is often a strangely effective coping behaviour, albeit a self-destructive one" (Walsh, 2006, p. 3). NSSI is now included in the DSM under "conditions for further study," as is Suicidal Behaviour Disorder.

The dynamics and the societal context of self-injuring behaviour among children and youth have dramatically changed over the last two decades. In the 1970s and 1980s it was assumed that youth who self-injured were disturbed individuals; and indeed these youth had had seriously adverse childhood experiences and maltreatment, particularly sexual abuse, physical abuse, family violence, and/or exposure to the suicide or mental illness of a caregiver (Walsh, 2006). This pattern has changed considerably over the last two decades in Canada and the U.S. Since the late 1990s, self-injuring behaviours have drastically increased both in the general youth population and outside of mainly therapeutic, clinical, or managed-care residential settings. It appears that these "new" self-injurers have experienced far less trauma than their counterparts in previous decades. There are many theories as to why this behaviour has increased so dramatically, including increased stress at school due to increased competitiveness at all levels, and reliance on mood-altering prescription medications to "fix" whatever may be causing difficulty. It's also been proposed that healthy self-soothing behaviours aren't being modelled or taught; popular movies and TV shows portray self-injurers; numerous prominent media stars have reported self-injurious behaviour; a plethora of websites promote self-injury; self-injury works very well in the short term to relieve tension; and, much like eating disorders, self-injury provides youth with a strong sense of control (Walsh, 2006).

CYCPs should be familiar with the communication strategies and intervention approaches used specifically to respond to NSSI behaviours. What follows is an overview of the basic principles; we encourage CYCPs to pursue additional information on this topic.

First, ensure that you don't use language associated with suicide (i.e., don't describe the behaviour as a suicide attempt or a suicide gesture). Second, use young people's language to describe the behaviour (i.e., "cutting") if that is appropriate and as long as there is no minimizing of the behaviour. Third, don't respond with dramatic or intense concern, as this type of response may inadvertently reinforce the behaviour; instead, respond with a low-key, dispassionate demeanour and respectful curiosity. Keep in mind that conveying *nonjudgmental compassion* is central to an effective CYC response to a youth engaged in NSSI behaviours (Walsh, 2006).

Age and Stage. As we've discussed, the responses of children and youth to trauma vary with age and developmental stage. Table 2.6 lists possible reactions to, and symptoms of, trauma by age. Since these symptoms can also be associated with other stressors, traumas, and developmental disturbances, they should be considered in the context of the child and family's total functioning.

Table 2.6 Behavioural Indicators Checklist: Complex Trauma

✓ Birth to 5 Years	✓ 6 to 11 Years	✓ 12 to 18 Years
Sleep and/or toileting and/or eating disruptions	Nightmares, sleep disruptions	Antisocial behaviour
Withdrawal/lack of responsiveness	Aggression and difficulty with peer relationships in school	School failure
Intense/pronounced separation anxiety	Difficulty with concentration and task completion in school	Impulsive, risky, and/or reckless behaviour, e.g.,
Inconsolable crying	Withdrawal and/or emotional numbing	School truancy
Developmental regression, loss of acquired skills	School avoidance and/or truancy	Substance abuse
Intense anxiety, worries, and/or new fears	Somatic complaints	Running away
Increased aggression and/or impulsive behavior	Re-enactment in stories and play	Involvement in violent or abusive dating relationships
Nightmares		Depression
Startle responses to loud noise		Anxiety
		Withdrawal
		Accident proneness
		Vengefulness
		Shame and guilt
		Intense memories
		Difficulties in interpersonal relationships

Source: From Ages and Developmental Stages: Symptoms of Exposure. Copyright © by the National Child Traumatic Stress Network. Used by permission of the National Child Traumatic Stress Network.

Intervention

In order to effectively restore children who have been traumatized or maltreated to a healthier developmental state, therapeutic interventions must take into account the key principles of neurodevelopment (Perry, 2004) so that such interventions will be more likely to address the parts of the brain that have been impacted by maltreatment. This means that CYCPs will focus their interventions on repairing damage that has occurred to the lower parts of the brain (the regulatory functions) before attempting repair to the more complex parts of the brain.

These brain-altering interventions need to reflect the patterned activities or experiences that are required for development in a sequential order. The experiences should be repetitive in order to mediate the functions/dysfunctions being targeted by the intervention (Perry, 2009, p. 251). Without appreciating how the brain is organized during development, therapeutic interventions are likely to be ineffective (Perry, 2006, p. 30).

Six core strengths need to be developed by children in order for them to be "more resourceful, more successful in social situations and more resilient" (Perry, 2005, p. 4): attachment, self-regulation, affiliation, awareness, tolerance, and respect for self and others. These six strengths need to develop sequentially and to build upon each other. In addition, it's important to remember that trauma is both *subjective* and *relative*; that is, it is an individual experience. If an event has not been experienced by the young person as traumatic, then there was no trauma.

There are three main elements in **trauma-informed care**, defined as the approaches CYCPs and other caregivers should use in supporting young people who have experienced trauma: to provide safety overall; to build safe, supportive, caring relational connections;

and to teach self-regulation and how to manage emotions (Bath, 2008). These three elements fit well within a cognitive behavioural therapy (CBT) approach but are also designed to be specific to the consequences of complex trauma. According to Ziegler (2002), our interventions ought to focus on challenging cognitions, dealing with emotions, and teaching effective coping skills, as follows:

1. *Cognitions:* Help by reframing thoughts about the trauma so that they're accurate and reality based; work on building a new, healthy worldview.

2. *Emotions:* Help by deconditioning the affective responses to the trauma; work with teaching youth to be in touch with their body; use relaxation exercises and mindfulness-based stress reduction (MBSR).

3. *Behaviours:* Help the child or youth learn new responses to stress and teach specific coping strategies. Again, use MBSR.

The core principle of CYC practice is understanding children's pain-based behaviour in the context of the needs underlying the behaviour. This is a skill that CYCPs develop through experience, reflective practice, and good clinical supervision.

> It is essential that care workers understand the meaning behind the children's troubling behaviours in order to respond effectively. Pain based behaviour takes many forms. Most commonly it appears as impulsive outbursts, aggressive acts, inability to tolerate uncertainty or ambiguity, withdrawing, or running away, clinginess and self injury. (Holden, 2009, p. 69)

As explained earlier, children and youth will demonstrate both internalizing (symptoms directed inward including anxiety, depression) and externalizing (symptoms directed outward, such as aggression, defiance) responses to trauma. Dr. Bruce Perry identifies this response variation as the **hyper-arousal and dissociative continuum** (Perry et al., 1995). Young people who dissociate as their primary learned response to threats look detached, exhibit avoidant behaviours, and may become immobilized in perceived threatening situations. Those with hyper-arousal as their primary response to threats usually respond with anxiety, then fear, and finally terror. These young people will perceive threats in any situation, and they often appear aggressive, defiant, oppositional, and inflexible (Holden, 2009). Other young people will exhibit both patterns in any given situation.

Behavioural and Cognitive-Behavioural Techniques for CYCPs Strong evidence supports the use of individual and group cognitive behavioural therapy (CBT) as an intervention for children and adolescents who've been exposed to trauma. CBT for trauma and PTSD symptoms proceeds by helping young people first identify the associated troublesome behaviours and understand that these are related to the trauma, then become more aware of their associated thoughts and feelings, and finally challenge, reframe, and discard any distorted thoughts. CYCPs need to teach young people that it's common to change one's beliefs after going through trauma; indeed, most post-trauma individuals have problems understanding how to live in the world. Beliefs about safety, trust, control, self-esteem, other people, and relationships have all been altered and need to be re-established.

There are a few standardized CBT treatment programs for children who've experienced trauma. For example, trauma-focused cognitive behavioural therapy (TF-CBT) is an evidence-based approach designed to treat the related emotional and behavioural difficulties in children and adolescents. The TF-CBT model was first developed to address the psychological trauma associated with child sexual abuse but has since been adapted for use with children who have a wide array of traumatic experiences, including family violence, traumatic loss, and the multiple psychological traumas experienced in the child welfare system. TF-CBT combines cognitive-behavioural and family theory, and is based on the fact that children (and others) have difficulty processing the strong, complex emotions that result from exposure to single or multiple traumatic events. By providing both child and caregiver with the support, skills, and techniques to process traumatic events and their psychological consequences, TF-CBT claims to minimize the resulting emotional disorders. The acronym PRACTICE reflects the components of the TF-CBT treatment model: Parenting skills and Psychoeducation, Relaxation skills, Affect expression and regulation skills, Cognitive coping skills and processing, Trauma narrative, In vivo exposure (when needed), Conjoint parent–child sessions, and Enhancing safety and future development (Child Welfare Information Gateway, 2012).

Exposure therapy is an intervention used to overcome the fears associated with the triggers and reminders of the traumatic event. These triggers are usually in the environment; for example, certain pictures, smells, or sounds may bring about thoughts and feelings connected with the traumatic event. The goal of exposure therapy is to help reduce the level of fear and anxiety connected with the triggers. This may be achieved by actively exposing the child or youth to a reminder of the traumatic event or through the use of imagination. The child learns that anxiety and fear will lessen on its own, eventually reducing the extent to which these reminders are viewed as threatening and fearful. Exposure therapy is usually paired with teaching the child relaxation skills. For example, the KIDNET program helps children draw a new "lifeline." This program was developed to _____ed refugee children who have experi-_____who live in exile. Traumatized refugee _____d have high rates of PTSD symptoms _____ in this chapter, psychotropic medication isn't, and shouldn't be, the first line of intervention for children and adolescents struggling with symptoms of complex trauma and PTSD. However, if you're assisting a child or youth who's been prescribed any of the medications listed to manage symptoms, including SSRIs, mood stabilizers, or antipsychotics, we recommend that you follow the guidelines outlined in Chapter 1 for safely administering such medications to young people.

Psychoeducation and Individual Counselling   The purpose of psychoeducation is to teach children and youth about PTSD, how it might affect them, and what kind of activities or treatment might help. Through psychoeducation, young people and their families learn that others have similar problems and that there are treatments that work. Psychoeducation for trauma includes problem-solving skills, stress management, MBSR, and relaxation skills; it might also include safety planning and education about appropriate physical boundaries.

Children and adolescents with PTSD are often overwhelmed by their emotions and have difficulty recognizing and coping with them. Individual counselling that includes emotional processing helps children learn about feelings, talk about how they feel, express emotions appropriately, and cope with uncomfortable emotions.

Eye-movement desensitization and reprocessing (EMDR) is used by many therapists. It involves clients making eye movements or being instructed to follow hand taps, for instance, while they recount traumatic events. It's not clear why EMDR works, and for that reason it's controversial; however, it is supported by research (Schnurr, 2007). EMDR therapy uses right/left eye movements that repeatedly activate the opposite sides of the brain, theoretically releasing the emotional experiences that are "trapped" in the memories of the nervous system. According to its proponents, this process allows the neurophysiological system, which is the basis of the mind–body connection, to free itself of blockages and reconnect itself. As troubling images and feelings related to trauma are processed by the brain using the eye-movement patterns of EMDR, resolution of the issues are achieved (Boulware, 2006).

CYCPs can use myriad activities and/or play-based therapeutic interventions to support children and youth in trauma resolution: music therapy, art therapy, drama therapy, theraplay, and so on. Indeed, an expansive repertoire of therapeutic activities is one of the key items in the CYCP tool kit.

Family Support Interventions   It is a fundamental tenet of CYC practice to involve family in all interventions, and especially in the treatment of traumatized children, whenever possible. If the parent was the perpetrator (e.g., in domestic violence, sexual abuse, or physical assault) and the child is still living with, or in contact with, that parent, it is likely that the parent will not yet have accepted responsibility for the offences. Non-offending parents may experience significant conflicts between the victim and the perpetrator. They also may feel distress and helplessness in not having been able to prevent the victimization in the first place. In addition, parents who witness their children's exposure to trauma are likely to experience significant posttraumatic stress themselves ("Trauma-focused interventions," 2004).

Not surprisingly, there is growing evidence from studies of children exposed to different types of trauma that less overt parental distress and more familial support mitigate the negative impact of trauma on children. For example, several studies have directly examined the impact of including a parent component in trauma-focused CBT sessions. These studies have demonstrated that interventions that help parents deal with and resolve their own distress about the child's trauma, thus optimizing their ability to be supportive of the child, are highly likely to improve outcomes for all ("Trauma-focused interventions," 2004).

Approaches to conducting interventions with families include the following: family sessions used in conjunction with individual or group treatment for the child; teaching families to use their previously effective coping skills to build a framework for present and future resilience; and helping families understand that *everyone* is impacted by the event, even if this isn't initially apparent. Not only do family members have very different psychological needs and different courses of recovery, but family members can actually serve as traumatic reminders to each other of the event. One goal of therapy, then, is to help family members anticipate, identify, and manage the loss and trauma ("Trauma-focused interventions," 2004).

Refer to Box 2.2 for a summary of CYC intervention techniques.

Prevention: Advocacy, Community, and School-Based Strategies   Resilience serves as a protective barrier for children and youth and prevents PTSD from developing. Thus, teaching children coping and problem-solving skills, stress-management skills, and relaxation techniques will be preventative by promoting resiliency in the face of trauma.

Box 2.2

Techniques for CYC Intervention

Use an NMT framework to guide assessment and intervention.

Gently challenge and reframe cognitive distortions; work on building a healthy worldview.

If appropriate and if possible, assist in changing the affective responses.

Teach young people to be in touch with their body; use relaxation exercises, feelings charts, MBSR.

Teach new responses to stress and specific coping strategies, including MBSR.

Believe and validate the child/youth's experience.

Practise good self-care; monitor your ability to tolerate the youth's affect; manage your own emotional responses.

Know your own triggers.

Be aware of the symptoms of vicarious trauma.

Ensure that the child always feels safe, nurtured, and cared for.

Surround the young person with a healing community; do not allow him or her to isolate.

Be open to use non-traditional healing approaches, such as healing circles, sweat lodge, yoga, and MBSR.

Praise, praise, praise. In order to develop a sense of competency, value, worth, pride, satisfaction, and strength, children need positive recognition; this is especially true for the child who has experienced trauma.

Teach young people CBT strategies. Help them to accurately identify bodily sensations as signals or triggers of potential response symptoms.

Use a strength-based approach to help youth retell their story and identify the resources, assets, and strengths that contributed to their survival.

School-based programs for trauma-related events are usually designed to be used to assist groups of children who have experienced disaster-related trauma or a serious crisis, including a peer's suicide. Treatment groups engage children in play, in art, and in talk, all of which are designed to identify and express feelings around losses.

One such intervention, known as critical incident stress debriefing (CISD), is used with children who've been exposed to abnormally stressful and potentially traumatizing events. CISD allows these children to express their feelings, normalize their responses to the disaster, and learn about common responses to the disaster or crisis (Steele, Elkin, & Roberts, 2008).

Another program, Psychological First Aid (PFA), is an evidence-based, culturally informed, and developmentally appropriate school-based intervention (Steele, Elkin, & Roberts, 2008) designed to minimize stress reactions post-impact. PFA comprises a set of standardized helping actions that are undertaken to reduce initial post-trauma distress and to support short- and long-term adaptive functioning and coping post-crisis. PFA aims to instill a sense of safety, provide calming, promote self- and community efficacy, and build connectedness and hope in crisis situations (Steele, Elkin, & Roberts, 2008).

Alternative Healing   As we've already emphasized, CYCPs must recognize the role of cultural factors when considering their therapeutic response to children and youth exhibiting behaviours related to complex trauma issues. Young people's exposure to trauma, and their responses to it, will likely be affected by where they live, by their worldview and life experience, and by their heritage and traditions. War and genocide are life experiences that newcomers to Canada will bring with them. Moreover, core areas and inner cities in Canada are often characterized by poverty, gang involvement, high levels of violence, and the experience of systemic racism. Young people, families, teachers, and the media will define key trauma-related constructs in different ways depending on their cultural and ethnic backgrounds (Cook et al., 2007).

> [I]n order to learn about cultural aspects of coping, [let] survivors and their families teach us their traditions. We can also do research or ask colleagues what they know. The more we learn, the more we can help survivors incorporate culture into their coping. (Goelitz, 2013, pp. 58–59)

Traditional Aboriginal healing, for example, includes such practices as sharing circles, sweat lodge, sun dance, full moon ceremony, pipe ceremony, and storytelling. Smudging and drumming are central features in all ceremonies. Perry (2012) suggests that drumming is an effective healing method for early trauma survivors because the repetitive sound of the drum over time replaces the traumatic memory embedded at the cellular level in the limbic system with the sound of the mother's heartbeat.

Relational CYC Practice   When assisting young complex-trauma survivors, CYCPs must maintain a high level of self-awareness—in part to avoid reacting to the young person's attempt to engage the CYCP in a re-enactment of the abusive relationship with the previous abusive caregiver. CYCPs and other caregivers who have themselves had impaired, difficult, or abusive relationships with attachment figures are especially vulnerable to these types of issues when relating to children with complex-trauma needs. In particular, the victimized child's simultaneous need for and fear of closeness and intimacy can trigger a caregiver's own memories of emotional pain with issues of loss, rejection, or abuse (Cook et al., 2007).

Although exposure to complex trauma can have a potentially devastating impact on young people and their development, many young people will continue to function quite well in some domains while exhibiting difficulties in others, and some will fully survive and thrive notwithstanding the traumatic events.

> Several factors have been shown to be linked to children's resilience in the face of stress: positive attachment and connections to emotionally supportive and competent adults within the family or community, development of cognitive and self-regulation abilities, and positive beliefs about oneself and motivation to act effectively in one's environment. Additional individual factors associated with resilience include an easygoing disposition, positive temperament, and sociable demeanor; internal locus of control and external attributions for blame; effective coping strategies; a high degree of mastery and autonomy; special talents; creativity; and spirituality. (Cook et al., 2007, p. 5)

While maintaining a focus on strengths and resiliency, CYCPs need to incorporate the following core components of complex-trauma intervention into their work with children, as suggested by the National Child Traumatic Stress Network (Melrose, 2009):

Safety: Establish a home, school, and community environment in which the child feels safe, nurtured, and cared for.

Self-regulation: Help the child learn to modulate her arousal and restore balance following the deregulation of affect, behaviour, physiology, cognition, interpersonal relatedness, and self-attribution.

Self-reflective information processing: Help the child construct self-narratives, reflect on past and present experience, and develop skills in problem solving, planning, and decision making.

Traumatic experiences integration: Help the child resolve traumatic triggers and memories by using such therapeutic strategies as meaning making, traumatic memory containment or processing, mourning of the traumatic loss, symptom management, and development of coping skills. Cultivate present-oriented thinking and behaviour.

Relational engagement: Teach the child to form appropriate attachments. Apply this knowledge to current interpersonal relationships, with emphasis on the development of such skills as assertiveness, cooperation, perspective-taking, boundary- and limit-setting, reciprocity, and social skills (Cook et al., 2007).

CYCPs working with children and youth who've been exposed to trauma should also keep in mind the following (Melrose, 2009):

- Recognize that your internal emotional state and your energy, negative or positive, will affect and be reflected in the child's internal emotional state.

- Recognize that your own unresolved trauma is highly likely to be triggered by the child's experience and may engender in you an anxious internal state, which will certainly interfere with the child's ability to express and to heal. As practitioners, it's your responsibility to access therapeutic support so that you can respond appropriately.

- In response to trauma, young people lose their grounding—their sense of connectedness to themselves, to nature, and to others. Help young people re-establish a sense of being grounded by having them sit in a chair with their feet firmly planted on the floor. Encourage them to fill their tummy with air as they take a deep breath in through the nose. Use MBSR techniques, including the mind–body scan.

- Maintain a moderately quiet, safe place in the home or treatment centre where all children can go for rest and relaxation.

- The high arousal levels of traumatized children require structure, routine, and firm yet flexible limits and boundaries. The more children can predict exactly what will happen, the safer they will feel.

- It's not advisable or necessary to encourage children to talk about a traumatizing event(s); in fact, it can be harmful. However, if they do want to talk about it, it's important to use a solution-focused or a strength-based approach. Remind them throughout their story of what their resources were—who or what was helpful to them or what their strengths were that contributed to their survival; praise them for their resourcefulness.

Refer to Box 2.3 for a summary of useful communication strategies that might be used in your CYC practice with traumatized children and youth.

For millennia, healing rituals from Indigenous cultures around the world have provided extremely effective and intensely relational experiences of healing from trauma. Retelling the story, holding one another, using massage, meditating, dancing, singing, drumming, celebrating, eating, sharing, and being in community are all very important. The most remarkable quality of these traditional healing practices is that together "they create a total neurobiological experience influencing cortical, limbic, diencephalic, and brainstem systems (not unlike the pervasive neurobiological impact of trauma)" (Perry, 2008 as cited in Malchiodi, 2008, p. xi). Traditional Indigenous healing rituals are repetitive, rhythmic, relational, and rewarding.

CYC Communication Strategies

Practise good self-awareness: always respond, don't react.

Identify and build on young people's strengths and resources.

Encourage recreational, physical activities to help manage hyper-arousal.

Instruct in relaxation strategies to help develop skills in managing hyper-arousal (e.g., yoga, exercise, mindfulness-based stress reduction).

Provide predictable routines and create a safe therapeutic environment.

Use respectful and inclusive language.

Encourage decision making and choice making to enhance a sense of generosity, mastery, independence, and empowerment (the "Circle of Courage" model).

Always avoid the use of labels (e.g., "Jake is a traumatized child").

Manage behaviour and set limits.

Recognize that emotions and feelings underlie behaviour, and identify the underlying needs (e.g., aggressive outbursts may be related to feelings of insecurity).

Keep in mind the CYC mantra: *"All behaviour serves a purpose and all behaviour meets a need."*

Believe and validate the child/youth's experience.

Tolerate the young person's affect.

Manage your own emotional response to the young person.

Source: Based on Massachusetts Advocates for Children, 2005.

WHERE DO YOU STAND?

Consider the approaches to treatment and intervention summarized above. Where do you stand? Most psychologists and CYCPs would agree that the best interventions involve an approach that is sensitive to the needs and strengths of the individual. As you can see, however, there are varying approaches to intervention for those exposed to trauma. Before leaving our discussion of trauma, assess your understanding of CYC explanations and interventions in contrast to the psychological perspective by revisiting the cases of Jennifer and Alyssa in the *Viewpoint Challenge* exercise.

Jennifer's and Alyssa's Cases: *Viewpoint Challenge Exercise*

Reread the excerpts of Jennifer's and Alyssa's stories that were presented earlier in this chapter. If Jennifer and Alyssa were being treated by a psychologist for their disorders, what explanations and interventions would likely be offered for their behaviour? How does this compare with likely explanations and interventions offered from a CYC perspective? List and explain how to use three approaches from each perspective. Choose one to use with Jennifer and another to use with Alyssa. Defend your choices.

CHAPTER SUMMARY

- The lasting undesirable social, emotional, physical, and cognitive effects that result from exposure to stressful or extreme events are referred to as *trauma*.

- The DSM-5 considers psychological disturbances associated with exposure to stressful and traumatic events in the general categories of Trauma- and Stressor-Related Disorders and Dissociative Disorders.

- A CYC perspective views complex trauma as the behavioural manifestation of the infliction of deep and lasting emotional wounds.

- From a psychological perspective, explanations for trauma-related symptoms include alterations in brain function and structure, the use of defence mechanisms, classically conditioned fear associations that result in avoidance of stress-related stimuli, and a cognitive fear structure.

- From a CYC perspective, the intensity of the stress associated with relational trauma in the interpersonal environment repeatedly over time is cumulative. Thus, developmental, relational, or complex trauma is understood to be attachment trauma.

- From a psychological perspective, the most common treatment approaches for trauma-related disorders include exposure therapy and cognitive restructuring.

- CYC therapeutic intervention must create new patterns that reflect new experiences in the brain. The best way to create new patterns in the brain is to expose the child to repeated experiences that break old associations using the NMT approach.

- CYC interventions for children and youth who have been trauma-exposed highlight the tenets of trauma-informed care. A CYC intervention approach for behaviours related to trauma affecting children and youth is relational practice.

Critical Thinking Questions

1. How does ongoing stress contribute to the development of a trauma response in a child or youth?

2. What factors do you think contribute to the development of dissociative behaviours in a child or youth?

3. Why do you think some children and youth exposed to trauma develop the symptoms of PTSD and others do not?

4. Which of the psychological paradigms used to explain trauma and stressor-related disorders do you think best fits with the CYC conceptual model? Why?

5. Why do the lower parts of the brain develop before the top part? What implications does this have for our work?

6. Which of the psychological treatment approaches could fit with a CYC-focused intervention approach? Why?

7. Why do CYCPs need to practise good self-awareness when working with children and youth with complex trauma needs?

8. Why do you think self-harming behaviours like cutting have become so prevalent among adolescent girls?

9. Why do you think it's so important to remain unemotional when responding to a youth who has self-harmed?

Key Terms

Supplemental Readings

Hopper, E. K., & Hidalgo, J. (2006). Posttraumatic Stress Disorder in individuals working in the sex industry. *Encyclopedia of prostitution and sex work*. New York: Greenwood Press.

Perry, B., & Szalavitz, M. (2007). *The boy who was raised as a dog and other stories from a child psychiatrist's notebook: What traumatized children can teach us about loss, love, and healing*. New York: Basic Books.

Spinazzola, J., Rhodes, A., Emerson, D., Earle, E., & Monroe, K. (2011). Application of yoga in residential treatment of traumatized youth. *Journal of the American Psychiatric Nurses Association*, *17*(6), 431–444.

Stolback, B. (2007). Developmental trauma disorder: A new diagnosis for children affected by complex trauma. *International Society for the Study of Trauma and Dissociation News*, *25*(6), 4–6.

van der Kolk, B. A. (2005). Developmental trauma disorder. *Psychiatric Annals*, *35*(5), 401–408.

Online Resources

Treating complex trauma video, www.youtube.com/watch?v=a497RNcxTQg&feature=related

Complex trauma syndrom video, www.youtube.com/watch?v=Xoc0VXZjXrk&feature=related

Trauma Center, www.traumacenter.org/products/publications.php

Symptoms of trauma exposure, www.nctsnet.org/content/ages-and-developmental-stages-symptoms-exposure

National Child Traumatic Stress Network, www.nctsnet.org/nctsn_assets/pdfs/edu_materials/trauma_focused_interventions_youth_jjsys.pdf (This is a report entitled *Trauma-Focused Interventions for Youth in the Juvenile Justice System*.)

National Child Traumatic Stress Network, www.nctsnet.org/resources/topics/treatments-that-work/promising-practices (The fact sheets linked from this page describe some of the clinical treatment and trauma-informed service approaches implemented by National Child Traumatic Stress Network centres, with the common goal of reducing the impact of exposure to traumatic events on children and adolescents.)

PTSD self-assessment checklist, www.ptsdassociation.com/ptsd-self-assessment.php

Trauma-informed care and services, http://trauma-informed.ca/wp-content/uploads/2013/10/Trauma-informed_Toolkit.pdf

Neurodevelopmental disorders are associated with behaviours that are observed early in development and create significant impairments in the ability to achieve expected developmental milestones.

Case Example: *Jason*

Jason is a creative, highly intelligent 16-year-old who's recently been diagnosed at the Manitoba Adolescent Treatment Centre (MATC) with a Generalized Anxiety Disorder. At the age of 7 he was also diagnosed with Asperger's syndrome. When the CYCP met with Jason, he told her that he had no friends at school, and that he was feeling nervous and anxious almost all the time. He said that he still really liked the academic "parts" of school, particularly his math and science courses. Jason's mother verifies that Jason is becoming increasingly anxious in all social situations. Jason also told the CYCP that he prefers to be alone. He knows he's different from other kids, and although that makes him feel upset, he has no interest in making friends. Jason's anxiety is now also causing him extreme distress in exam situations and when doing home-work. Because he's entirely focused on getting good grades, he's tending to obsess and perseverate about assignments as well. When he's not studying, he usually spends his leisure time playing video games. There has been a referral back to MATC for a psychiatric assessment, since the level of anxiety Jason is experiencing is signifi-cantly disrupting his daily functioning.

Learning Objectives

1. Define *developmental psychopathology* and distinguish between the seven general categories of neurodevelopmental disorders.

2. Summarize the primary features of Autism Spectrum Disorder (ASD).

3. Summarize the psychological explanations for neurodevelopmental disorders, with an emphasis on ASD.

4. Define *theory of mind* and explain how it relates to ASD.

5. Explain whether inclusiveness is always the preferred approach for every young person with an ASD.

6. Describe the psychological approaches used in treating neurodevelopmental disorders.

7. Summarize interventions that CYCPs could use with children diagnosed with ASD.

Chapter Overview

In this chapter we explore the diagnoses that are among those first identified in the course of one's development. Although young children are still developing various skills and abilities, certain expectations or norms exist in relation to when a young person should begin to use language to communicate, read, and problem solve. Why do some children fail to develop certain skills and abilities? From a psychological perspective, this chapter will identify those neurodevelopmental disorders presented in the DSM-5 and summarize their major symptoms and characteristics. Psychological explanations and approaches to intervention for those diagnoses that CYCPs are most likely to encounter in their work are presented.

In the CYC sections of this chapter, we introduce the main principles of strength-based practice with children and youth affected by one of the neurodevelopmental disorders: Autism Spectrum Disorder (ASD). We present a variety of theoretical causes of the ASDs; discuss the notion of "ableism" and the principles of inclusion; and suggest ways everyone can work to reduce labelling and stigma. As well, we examine the key features of ASDs and present interventions for the Autism Spectrum Disorder umbrella that fit well with a CYC approach.

Why do we focus primarily on ASD? Although CYCPs won't likely work exclusively with young people diagnosed with an ASD or another neurodevelopmental disorder (except ADHD), it's important to have a solid foundational knowledge of the difficulties these children may experience. In any given youth population, CYCPs will likely be engaged with some children who are affected by neurodevelopmental difficulties, and so you'll need to be aware of the sensory integration problems that affect many children and youth with special needs. However, given CYCPs' limited involvement this area of practice, most of the DSM-5 categories of the neurodevelopmental disorders of children and youth are briefly introduced in the psychology section only. If this is an area of interest for you, we encourage you to explore it more fully. (ADHD, which is also categorized as a neurodevelopmental disorder in the DSM-5, is the subject of Chapter 4 and so is not discussed in this chapter.)

WHAT IS A DEVELOPMENTAL DISORDER?

From a psychological perspective, human development is associated with specific age-related changes in the physical, social-emotional, and cognitive domains. Early developmental changes lay the foundation for future developmental change. For example, learning to differentiate between basic sounds in language lays the foundation for later ability to combine these sounds into specific words with particular meanings. Accordingly, problems that arise early in development (e.g., the inability to distinguish between such basic sounds as s and z) are likely to have lasting impacts on later development (e.g., the inability to read or understand language). **Developmental psychopathology** is the study of how disorders emerge in the course of one's development and how they change or persist over time (Scott, 2012). The primary focus in this area of psychology is to identify the specific processes that underlie a particular behaviour pattern that creates distress or impairs functioning. For example, knowing that deficits in the ability to sustain attention and in inhibiting behaviour underlie the symptoms of ADHD allows these limitations to be addressed and altered so as to maximize functioning and future developmental changes. Thus, it's important to keep in mind that although these disorders tend to occur early in one's development, it doesn't mean that early identification and interventions are not important.

Before moving on to a discussion of the psychological approach of developmental disorders, examine your own ideas and assumptions about one particular developmental disorder, Autism Spectrum Disorder (one form of which was previously referred to as Asperger's), in the *Think About It!* exercise.

Think About It! Exercise: *Experiences of Autism Spectrum Disorder*

How I long for rest.
Every moment seems a battle,
As I try to keep up with the buzz of the world that surrounds me.

Scary and out of my control, life happens around and within me.
When I'm overwhelmed, I act out.
I behave in ways that are frightening even to me.

To others it seems I'm not trying.
Yet I work endlessly to understand and to reveal my unseen gifts.
Am I what they say? Useless? Strange?

Alone in this never-ending struggle I grow weary.
I long to be understood but sometimes,
I think it might just be better to let go of it all.

Oh my, how I long for a rest.

What are your thoughts after reading this poem describing the experience of living with Autism Spectrum Disorder? Can you better imagine what fears and concerns someone with this diagnosis might have? Do you think that a person who wrote this might be vulnerable to depression? When she writes "sometimes I think it might just be better to let go of it all" what does this suggest about her, or about anyone with ASD? Might you be concerned about suicide ideation? Do you know anyone who struggles with an ASD? Does this poem change your thoughts in any way?

WHAT IS A NEURODEVELOPMENTAL DISORDER? THE PSYCHOLOGICAL PERSPECTIVE

Although all psychological disorders are influenced to some degree by neurological factors, the DSM-5 distinguishes those disorders that are primarily neurological in nature in the general category of **neurodevelopmental disorders** (APA, 2013). Because they're largely neurologically based, disorders in this grouping are observed early on in the child's development. However, the challenges associated with these disorders continue through the life course. General impairments in this category include the following:

- deficits in general mental abilities (e.g., problem solving, planning, abstract thought)
- deficits in specific areas of learning (e.g., mathematics, spelling)
- deficits in communication (e.g., difficulty producing or understanding speech)
- deficits in social communication and interaction
- deficits in motor skills (e.g., motor or vocal tics)

Similar to all disorders identified in the DSM-5, the developmental deficits associated with these disorders interfere with young people's personal, academic, and social functioning, creating impairments in a number of different areas.

DSM-5 Categories

Neurodevelopmental disorders are considered together in a single chapter in the DSM-5. Let's briefly review this general category before considering the specific symptoms of those diagnoses you're most likely to encounter in your CYC practice.

Neurodevelopmental Disorders   The DSM-5 identifies 20 distinct diagnoses in the category of neurodevelopmental disorders, organized into 7 general categories. Although each category consists of disorders that appear early on in development and are associated with academic, social, and other impairments in functioning, they are distinguished on the basis of the nature of the impairment. Since one of these general categories, Attention-Deficit/Hyperactivity Disorder, is discussed at length in Chapter 4, we omit it from our discussion in this chapter. Refer to Box 3.1 for an overview of the general categories and the specific diagnoses in each grouping.

Neurodevelopmental Disorders: Diagnoses and Criteria

As noted earlier, the DSM-5 groups the neurodevelopmental disorders into seven general categories. In the discussion that follows, we summarize the criteria for the five disorders most likely to be encountered by CYCPs in their practice.

Intellectual Disabilities   Intellectual Disability (ID) or **Intellectual Developmental Disorder** is associated with both intellectual and adaptive functioning that is below the average or expected norms for the developmental age. These deficits must be observed before the age of 18 in order for this diagnosis to be applied. The DSM-5 identifies three domains in which deficits are observed: (1) conceptual (e.g., problem solving, abstract

Box 3.1

DSM-5 Neurodevelopmental Disorders

General Category	Specific Diagnosis
Intellectual Disabilities	Intellectual Disability (Intellectual Developmental Disorder)
	Global Developmental Delay
	Unspecified Intellectual Disability (Intellectual Developmental Disorder)
Communication Disorders	Language Disorder
	Speech Sound Disorder
	Childhood-Onset Fluency Disorder (Stuttering)
	Social (Pragmatic) Communication Disorder
	Unspecified Communication Disorder
Autism Spectrum Disorder	Autism Spectrum Disorder
Attention-Deficit/Hyperactivity Disorder	Attention-Deficit/Hyperactivity Disorder
	Other Specified Attention-Deficit/Hyperactivity Disorder
	Unspecified Attention-Deficit/Hyperactivity Disorder
Specific Learning Disorder	Specific Learning Disorder
Motor Disorders	Developmental Coordination Disorder
	Stereotypic Movement Disorder
	Tic Disorders
	Other Specified Tic Disorder
	Unspecified Tic Disorder
Other Neurodevelopmental Disorders	Other Specified Neurodevelopmental Disorder
	Unspecified Neurodevelopmental Disorder

thinking), (2) social (e.g., developing relationships with others), and (3) practical (e.g., fulfilling daily responsibilities; APA, 2013).

When young people are diagnosed with an ID, the level of severity is specified according to the level of their *adaptive functioning*. Four categories of severity are identified across each of the three domains mentioned above. Specifically, severity can be identified as mild, moderate, severe, or profound. As you might imagine, then, there is great variability with respect to specific abilities for those diagnosed with this disorder, ranging from mild deficits that go unnoticed in everyday activities to profound impairments in which the individual may be unable to care for himself. It's interesting to note that although low intelligence quotient scores are mentioned as a factor associated with this diagnosis (i.e., below 70–75 on tests where the average is 100), the primary emphasis is on level of adaptive functioning, not on scores of intelligence.

Communication Disorders   **Communication disorders** are associated with deficits in speech, language, and communication. *Language Disorder*, for example, is associated with the limited use of speech that is below what the individual can understand. *Social (Pragmatic) Communication Disorder* is associated with difficulties in the social aspects of communication and includes difficulties following the rules for social communication (e.g., taking turns in conversation, knowing that a pause in speech can be an invitation to speak further). *Childhood-Onset Fluency Disorder* (stuttering) is also included in this general category of neurodevelopmental disorders.

Autism Spectrum Disorder   **Autism Spectrum Disorder (ASD)** is associated with early deficits in social communication and interaction that continue in the individual's development. Impairments are observed in two general areas: (1) social communication and interaction and (2) restricted, repetitive interests or behaviours. These symptoms must result in significant impairment in daily functioning and be observed early in development. The DSM-5 requires that the *level of severity* of impairment be noted in each of the two general areas noted above, with severity being defined in relation to requiring (1) support, (2) substantial support, or (3) very substantial support (APA, 2013). Note that this specification of severity replaces the earlier DSM diagnostic categories of *Asperger's Disorder* (associated with relatively low levels of impairment) and *Pervasive Developmental Disorder* (associated with significant impairments), which are no longer included in DSM categorical system.

One of the most noted consequences of these deficits is the failure to establish social relationships (Wong & Kasari, 2012), which is an important developmental milestone at various ages and an indicator of mental health. Accordingly, the DSM-5 requires three additional criteria be met in order for the diagnosis of ASD to be applied: (1) deficits in social-emotional reciprocity (e.g., failure to respond to social interactions);

ASD is associated with deficits in joint attention. This child points to the dog to share her interest with another person, something that is less likely to occur for those diagnosed with ASD.

(2) impaired nonverbal communication (e.g., abnormalities in eye contact or body language); and (3) impaired ability to develop and maintain relationships (e.g., absence of interest in peers; APA, 2013). An impairment often noted in the context of ASD includes a deficit in **joint attention**, the ability to share an interest in an object with another person by pointing or looking at what another person is pointing at. A second characteristic of ASD includes repetitive and restricted patterns of behaviour or interests. For example, a child diagnosed with an ASD may spend hours arranging blocks into a single straight line.

Specific Learning Disorders

Specific learning disorders are associated with below average performance in specific areas of learning, including, reading, writing/expression, and mathematics. As you might imagine, deficits in these areas are typically observed early on in the school years, especially given the increased expectations for performance in these areas in early educational environments. Early diagnosis of a learning disorder is important because it predicts school drop-out rates (Wagner, 1990) as well as unemployment (Shapiro & Lentz, 1991). Specific learning disorders are generally assessed using intelligence tests (which assess overall intelligence) and achievement tests (which assess abilities in specific areas such as math, writing, and reading). Specific learning disorders are diagnosed when a significant difference exists between one's overall intelligence (which is average or above average) and scores on a particular achievement test (e.g., lower than average score on a mathematics test).

Motor Disorders

Motor disorders are associated with impairments in the development and performance of coordinated motor skills. These impairments result in clumsy, uncoordinated movements that can interfere with daily life. For example, *tic disorders* are associated with vocal or motor tics—sudden, recurrent, and rapid vocalizations or movements. One specific type of tic disorder, *Tourette's Disorder*, is associated with both motor and vocal tics that are first observed before age 18 and are present for more than one year. By comparison, persistent (chronic) motor or vocal tic disorder is associated with either motor or vocal tics but not both.

Before turning to a discussion of neurodevelopmental disorders from a CYC perspective, test your understanding of the diagnostic categories we've discussed by trying the *Test Your Understanding* exercise. Can you identify the disorder that most closely matches the description of each case?

Test Your Understanding: *Case Examples of Neurodevelopmental Disorders*

Although an IQ test reveals that seven-year-old Blaine scores slightly above his peers in general intelligence, he has continued difficulty in writing and spelling; for example, rather than writing *was*, he writes *saw*. Teachers find it difficult to read his writing on his assignments and tests.

Three-year-old Crystal is unresponsive to her mother's attempts to draw her attention to various objects, including her brother playing in the yard. While her peers are now using language to communicate, Crystal remains silent and is unresponsive to attempts to interact with others.

Six-year-old Gordon has recently started to blink his eyes repeatedly, more so than needed. Now his parents have noticed that Gordon has also begun clearing his throat over and over again and shaking his head back and forth, particularly when he's anxious or stressed.

A CYC APPROACH TO INTELLECTUAL DISABILITY: UNDERSTANDING NEURODEVELOPMENTAL DISORDERS

An important aspect of CYCPs' mental health literacy is a working knowledge of diagnoses within the neurodevelopmental disorders umbrella. As Kiaras Gharabaghi (2010) points out, over the past decade, CYC practice has expanded into many areas that haven't traditionally been within our professional domain, an expansion that includes work with children diagnosed with ASD—the focus of this chapter's CYC sections.

However, unlike disability, community, and developmental services workers, CYCPs aren't specifically trained in this area. As Gharabaghi notes, although CYCPs generally take great pride in the expansion of the CYC field, we need to recognize that additional training, education, and experience are required in order to work successfully with children affected by such neurodevelopmental disorders (Gharabaghi, 2010). CYCPs need an overall understanding of ASD, the ability to recognize ASD impairments, and the ability to use effective interventions in helping these children and their families. After all, CYCPs working in all systems, and particularly in the mental health and school systems, will undoubtedly engage with young people with behaviours related to an ASD diagnosis.

Famous people throughout history have purportedly had autism; these include Wolfgang Amadeus Mozart, Albert Einstein, Abraham Lincoln, Benjamin Franklin, Ludwig van Beethoven, and Michelangelo, just to name a few. And yet these figures may not necessarily fit within the ASD spectrum. For example, there is controversy about whether Einstein was autistic: Temple Grandin believes he was, but many others feel that he wasn't, even though he may have been eccentric and socially different. CYCPs need to be cautious in their observations and ensure that they don't jump to conclusions about young people who may appear different from the norm or who may act in "nerdy" or bizarre ways.

The term *autism* comes from the Greek word *autos*, meaning "self"; it refers to extreme social withdrawal, signifying an isolated self. Victor, the eighteenth-century "Wild boy of Aveyron," was thought to be a child with autism. In the 1960s, the DSM associated autism in children with child psychosis and Schizophrenia (Kendall & Comer, 2010). By the time of the DSM-IV-T-R (APA, 2000), Asperger's and Pervasive Developmental Disorder–Not Otherwise Specified (PDD-NOS) were identified as developmental disorders rather than as Child-Onset Schizophrenia. The term *PDD-NOS diagnosis* was given to children in the autism spectrum who didn't fit into the other DSM autism categories in the DSM IV-T-R (Kutscher, 2005). The DSM-5 has now categorized all the former titles under PDD into the ASD umbrella (APA, 2012).

The DSM-5's consolidation of autism, Asperger's, Childhood Disintegrative Disorder, and PDD-NOS into one diagnostic category called "Autism Spectrum Disorder" has been controversial. Much of the resistance has come from autistic children's parents and caregivers, who see autism as a much more serious issue than Asperger's. For example, children with Asperger's may lack social skills, but children with autism are quite often unable to talk or interact with others at all. Those who support the change in the DSM-5 point out that many school programs don't adequately accommodate children and youth with Asperger's, and so categorizing it with autism will help address that situation; in addition, the change will help ensure insurance coverage for treatment. According to the

DSM-5 task force revision website, the change was made because (1) the previous diagnoses weren't sufficiently precise and (2) since autism is defined by a common set of behaviours, it should be characterized by a single name according to the severity of symptoms along a continuum (APA, 2014). Nonetheless, in this text we explain the development of both autism and Asperger's diagnoses, given that many people are familiar with both terms and in the belief that it's important to be aware of the history of the autism spectrum disorders.

Autism and Asperger's were first identified by Hans Asperger and Leo Kanner, respectively, in the 1940s (Mandal, 2014). In the United States, Dr. Kanner published a paper, *Autistic Disturbances of Affective Contact*, in which he described the behaviour of 11 children. At the same time, Dr. Asperger was studying children in Germany who had similar characteristics to those whom Kanner was observing, except without the same severe language delays. As Kanner's paper was written in German, it was unknown in English-speaking countries until Uta Frith translated it in 1991. Meanwhile, in 1981, British psychiatrist Lorna Wing proposed that the condition be called **Asperger's syndrome**. Kanner was the first physician to specialize in child psychiatry, and his paper on autism, together with Asperger's work, has become the foundation of our understanding of ASD today (Mandal, 2014). We noted earlier that Asperger's differs significantly from other ASDs in its preservation of linguistic and cognitive development; consequently, it's often referred to as a "mild" form of autism. More specifically, these two conditions are distinguished by the severity of the symptoms and the absence of language delay. Children who were previously diagnosed with Asperger's have good language and cognitive skills, although they typically use language in "different from the norm" ways. Their speech patterns may be unusual, lack inflection, or have a rhythmic nature; their speech can also be too formal and too loud or high pitched. Children with Asperger's often don't understand irony and humour and can't follow the give-and-take of a conversation. They usually want interaction with others but don't know how to interact. Children with more severe autism, by contrast, appear to be completely uninterested in others; they're often uncommunicative, and have limited or no eye contact. They often can't engage in imaginative or creative play, and may engage in ritualistic behaviours, including arm flapping and rocking (Kutscher, 2005). All children with an ASD have difficulty reading others' facial expressions, but children with higher-functioning ASD frequently also have motor skill delays, may appear clumsy or awkward, like to collect categories of things, and are proficient in knowing various categories of information. Their interests in a particular subject may border on the obsessive, and although they may have good rote memory skills, they usually have difficulty with abstract concepts. They may be referred to as "eccentric," "strange," or even "obnoxious" (Kutscher, 2005).

Autism is often referred to as a "puzzle" because there are so many missing pieces in our understanding of this neurodevelopmental disorder.

While some individuals with autism experience "mental retardation," now known as *intellectual disability*, by definition a person with Asperger's does not exhibit a "clinically significant" cognitive delay and may in fact have average to above average intelligence ("Asperger syndrome," 2015). CYCPs are likely to work with young people with what was formerly referred to as Asperger's syndrome. The distinct behaviours usually seen in these individuals are as follows: awkward motor coordination, flat tone of voice, failure to read social signals, awkwardness in social small talk, excellent recall of trivial detail, extremely limited sense of humour, narrow range of interests, and an obsessive impulse to argue and split hairs. There can also be inappropriate social habits, ritualized behaviours, and creativity (Jordan, 2006). Before turning to a discussion of prevalence, development, and comorbidity, consider the details of the opening case in relation to the psychological and CYC views of anxiety disturbances in *Jason's Case: Revisited*.

HOW MANY YOUNG PEOPLE STRUGGLE WITH NEURODEVELOPMENTAL DISORDERS?

All evidence indicates that that autism has changed from being a relatively rare disorder to one that's becoming very common (Paris, 2013). The prevalence of autism has been steadily increasing for the last 40 years; some sources indicate that ASD has increased by 600 percent in the last 20 years. In Canada, as in most other countries in the Western world, ASDs are more prevalent now than ever before, currently reaching "epidemic levels" with 1 in 200 children being diagnosed, compared with 1 in 10 000 just 10 years ago. An estimated 190 000 Canadian children now have an ASD ("Autism: Making sense of a confusing world," 2009). The preliminary results of an epidemiological study conducted at the Children's Hospital in Montreal in 2003–04 found an even higher prevalence rate of 1 in 147. This rate is consistent with other recent studies in the United States and United Kingdom, where rates of approximately 1 per 167 have been reported. A recent Government of Canada study indicates that the reasons for this increase are difficult to pinpoint. There may have been an actual rise in the condition among young children, or it may be explained by other factors, including a broadening of the definition of autism, increased public awareness, improved symptom recognition and diagnosis, and improved survey methodology (Norris, Pare, & Starky, 2006). The increase may also be due to greater exposure to environmental toxins affecting genetic mutations. However, it's important for CYCPs to consider that, as with other so-called disorders discussed in this text, the increased prevalence might very well be attributed to increased diagnosis, not so much from better recognition by health care practitioners but rather from "the pathologizing of subclinical symptoms" (Paris, 2013, p. 142).

> Asperger's syndrome has become a diagnostic fad that is being applied to all kinds of "nerdy" people. Needless to say, we have no biological markers to confirm the diagnosis. Of course, the DSM V has not hesitated to expand the boundaries of the autistic spectrum. (Paris, 2013, pp. 142–143)

According to another study (Arehart-Treichel, 2014), the prevalence of autism, Attention-Deficit/Hyperactivity Disorder, Obsessive-Compulsive Disorder, and Tourette's Disorder in Denmark, Finland, Sweden, and Western Australia increased between 100 and 700 percent between 2000 and 2011. The report indicates that environmental factors, such as rising average age of parents, may contribute to the trend, but that increase in awareness is likely to be the largest factor. Better and more accurate identification of children on the spectrum and earlier diagnosis account for much of the increase, which some refer to as an epidemic of diagnosis (Arehart-Treichel, 2014).

In Canada, estimates of learning disability suggest that it's one of the most common disabilities in children up to 14 years of age (Statistics Canada, 2001). Specific learning disorders vary in their occurrence, with Mathematics Disorder observed in 6 percent of the population (Gross-Tsur, Manor, & Shalev, 1996) and Reading Disorder (the most common) occurring in approximately 5–15 percent (Popper et al., 2003). Estimates of those with intellectual disability in Canada suggest that 2 percent of the general population is affected (including all levels of severity; Cooper & Smiley, 2012).

NEURODEVELOPMENTAL DISORDERS AND DEVELOPMENT

Although adolescence is a difficult transition for all youth, it's obviously challenging for those with an ASD. For some with ASD, adolescence can be a time of major gains; for others it can cause deterioration in their overall behaviour and skills. Prevalence rates of deterioration in behaviours and skills at puberty have been reported to be as high as one-third to one-half of children with "low level" autism. Some adolescents with autism may engage in violent and self-injurious behaviours (Perisse et al., 2010).

One important point for CYCPs to consider is that this deterioration in behaviour may be related to the youth's increasing awareness that he or she is different from peers. Many youth with an ASD can be unaware of their overall deficits and have a tendency to experience the cause of their difficulties as external to themselves (blaming others); they can also be generally lacking in insight about their overall functioning. In addition, it's common for children with an ASD to approach adolescence with a history of peer rejection and bullying. Such bullying, along with a history of school difficulties like Jason's, will invariably contribute to an overall low self-esteem and self-doubt. Children and adolescents with ASD can be aware of their deficits and are at high risk of developing depression and an increased risk of suicide ideation as a result, as we see in the poem in the *Think About It!* exercise at the beginning of the chapter.

COMORBIDITY

Many children and adolescents with ASD have other mental health difficulties. And given these young people's inability to communicate feelings of upset, anxiety, or distress, it can be difficult to identify depression or anxiety symptoms, particularly for those CYCPs, teachers, and/or direct caregivers who have little knowledge or understanding of ASD. Moreover, given their impairment in nonverbal expression, children and youth with ASD may not appear to be depressed. The possible consequences of an undiagnosed clinical depression can be serious: these young people could experience total withdrawal, increased obsessional behaviour, and even suicide ideation. As it can be for all youth, suicide is often seen as the only answer to ending the young person's overwhelming emotional pain and distress ("Depression, suicide risk and autism," 2015).

ASD can co-occur with Schizophrenia. In two large studies that have examined the co-occurrence of childhood-onset Schizophrenia (COS) with autism, it was found that COS is preceded by and comorbid with ASD in 30–50 percent of cases. Epidemiologic and family studies find a strong association between the two disorders. Evidence seems to suggest that risk genes and/or rare small chromosomal variants are shared by Schizophrenia and autism (Rapoport et al., 2009).

> Age of onset is the key in differentiating childhood schizophrenia from autism. Children with schizophrenia have a period of relatively normal adjustment followed by the onset of the severe symptoms of schizophrenia, whereas autism is evident very early in life. Specifically, autism is usually apparent by age three whereas childhood onset schizophrenia typically appears in the seventh year of life. (Kendall & Comer, 2010, pp. 167–168)

As well, ASD is also often comorbid with ADHD; the anxiety disorders, including OCD; and sensory integration problems. There may also be cognitive delays, neurological disorders, and learning disorders; medical issues include sleep difficulties, gastrointestinal problems, and other genetic disorders.

Generally speaking, children and youth with ADHD typically have the capacity to empathize with others but can rarely can inhibit their behaviour long enough to show empathy. Children on the autistic spectrum, by contrast, seem to lack empathy, and although they may also appear to have a short attention span, it's more likely related to their difficulty interpreting situations (Kutscher, 2005). It's important, then, for CYCPs to observe for and differentiate between the two areas of difficulty in functioning for ADHD and ASD.

It has been suggested that a significant brain-based connection exists not only between autism and ADHD, OCD, and sensory integration, but also between autism and Oppositional Defiant Disorder (ODD) and Bipolar Disorder (Kennedy, Banks, & Grandin, 2002). Recall that information is carried across synapses by the neurotransmitters—including serotonin, dopamine, norepinephrine, and acetylcholine—and that each neurotransmitter plays a critical role in brain functioning. Recent research into gene mutations has shown that some genes fail to regulate the neurotransmitters well enough to allow the brain to maintain attention, eliminate distractions, and control impulses. Many of these gene mutations have been discovered to be cross-linked in several neurological or "brain-based" disorders, like ADHD, autism, and Bipolar Disorder. Our growing knowledge of autism may suggest that all the so-called disruptive behaviours, including ADHD, ODD, and Conduct Disorder, may

Box 3.2

Common Myths About Autism Spectrum Disorder (ASD)

MYTH: *Everyone diagnosed with ASD has below average intelligence.*

FACT: ASD is characterized by a wide range of intellectual abilities, including exceptional abilities that exceed the performance of the general population (e.g., outstanding abilities in mathematics, music).

MYTH: *People diagnosed with ASD do not experience emotion and are unable to recognize the emotions of others.*

FACT: Youth diagnosed with ASD do experience emotions, although they tend to communicate them in ways that differ from most others. Although a youth diagnosed with ASD might be less able to detect emotions based on nonverbal signals (e.g., body language, facial expressions), direct communication of emotions to the diagnosed youth can be associated with feelings of empathy.

MYTH: *Poor parenting causes Autism Spectrum Disorder.*

FACT: Although early theories of autism suggested that unemotional mothers were responsible for the development of this disorder, research does not support this explanation. Parents do, however, require support so that they might better provide structure and consistency for their child.

Source: Adapted from "11 myths about autism," 2015; "Addressing myths about autism," 2014.

"actually be layers of higher functioning and very high functioning autism" (Jordan, 2006, p. 187). In fact, a significant proportion of children with severe behavioural and intellectual impairments are believed to carry mutations in key neurodevelopmental genes (Jordan, 2006). Refer to Box 3.2 to review some common myths about ASD.

EXPLAINING NEURODEVELOPMENTAL DISORDERS: PSYCHOLOGICAL PARADIGMS

Since neurodevelopmental disorders are associated with early deficits in cognitive and social functioning, it's not surprising that the biological approach has been most influential in explaining these disorders. However, as for all psychological disorders, a complex interaction of biological and environmental factors are assumed to be associated with the onset of these disturbances. The best evidence for these disturbances is consistent with the biological paradigm, and so we present evidence associated with this approach in detail. The psychodynamic, cognitive, behavioural, and sociocultural factors are discussed together in the Psychological and Social Factors section below.

Biological Paradigm   According to the biological paradigm, neurodevelopmental disorders are largely determined by genetics and damage to brain structures. But not all individuals exhibit such markers, and so identifying specific causes is challenging.

Heredity and Genetics. A variety of genetic conditions has been associated with intellectual disabilities. The most common of these includes Down syndrome, in which the individual has an extra 21st chromosome (i.e., three instead of the expected two). The role of genetics has also been implicated in reading disorders (Popper et al., 2003), with specific genes consistently linked to these disturbances (Cope et al., 2012; Zou et al., 2012). Genetic predisposition also appears to play a role in ASD (Ozonoff et al., 2011; Volkmar,

Klin, & Schultz, 2005), although it's unclear which genes are responsible, and the exact way in which they influence the onset of ASD is complex (Addington & Rapoport, 2012).

Brain Structures. In the case of intellectual disabilities, a great number of factors that damage the developing brain have been found to cause deficits. These include prenatal factors (e.g., alcohol during pregnancy resulting in Fetal Alcohol Spectrum Disorder (FASD), a condition characterized by a range of learning disabilities; Douzgou et al., 2012), oxygen deprivation at birth, and head injuries during early development (Kaski, 2012). *Subtle brain damage* has been associated with learning disabilities, including difficulties processing specific basic sounds (phonemes) that make up a particular language. However, such damage hasn't been observed in all individuals with a learning disability, which might explain the significant variation in types of learning difficulties (Popper et al., 2003).

In the case of ASD, abnormalities have been observed in the amygdala, the structure associated with the processing of such basic emotions as fear and anger. One theory proposes that in those with ASD the amygdala becomes enlarged early in development, which is associated with heightened fear and anxiety that may result in social withdrawal. An increased and persistent stress response stimulates the release of *cortisol*, a stress hormone that damages the amygdala resulting in fewer neurons in this structure as the individual develops (Lombardo, Chakrabarti, & Baron-Cohen, 2009). The high rate of comorbidity between ASD and intellectual disability further supports the role of brain damage in the onset of these disorders.

Neurotransmitters. The neurotransmitter oxytocin has been investigated in relation to deficits in social interaction and communication. Oxytocin has been demonstrated to play a role in enhancing positive feelings when we connect emotionally with other people as well as in developing a sense of trust in others. Wermter et al. (2010) found a relationship between ASD and the genes that influence how this neurotransmitter exerts influence in the brain.

Psychological and Social Factors   Although psychological and social variables aren't considered the most significant factors in determining neurodevelopmental disorders, they can play a role in influencing the *outcome* of any one of these disorders for a particular youth. For example, outcomes for specific learning disorders have been found to be associated with various social factors, including socioeconomic status, child management practices, and school supports (Gregg, 2009). Other research suggests that early intervention for those with ASD is associated with better later language development (Wong & Kasari, 2012) and long-lasting improvements in intellectual and educational functioning (McEachin, Smith, & Lovaas, 1993). In general, then, psychological and social factors are viewed not as causes of these disorders, which are essentially genetically and/or neurobiologically determined, but rather as affecting one's development and level of functioning.

A CYC LENS ON THE PSYCHOLOGICAL PARADIGMS: A HOLISTIC CONCEPTUAL MODEL

In the 1940s, researchers and clinicians believed that autism was caused by poor parenting and the lack of attachment skills of the mother. The idea was that these "refrigerator mothers," as they were called, didn't really want their children and thus did not bond with them. This theory has long since been dismissed, but the stigma associated with it has persisted. CYCPs must recognize, then, that autism is a biological, brain-based disorder that is in no way caused by family dysfunction or inadequate parenting.

In a holistic conceptual model, we examine the interplay between all possible theories of cause (or *etiology*) in all systems. Although it's still not known what causes the brain differences in people with ASD, researchers believe that both genetics and environment play a significant role (Centers for Disease Control and Prevention, 2015a). Autism tends to run in families. Among identical twins, if one twin has autism, the other is up to 90 percent likely to be affected as well. In addition, parents who have one child with ASD have a 2–10 percent chance of having a second child who is also affected. It's been suggested that ASD might result from a disruption in early fetal brain development caused by defects or mutations in genes that control brain growth and regulate how brain cells communicate with each other, but that this may result from the influence of environmental factors (like toxins) on gene function (National Institute of Neurological Disorders and Stroke, 2014).

Another U.S. study found that "if it were possible to eliminate the many different reasons children are born too early, too small, and/or delivered by Cesarean, the number of children with ASD would be reduced by 12–13%" (Schieve et al., 2014, p. 1). And in a University of Missouri study, Dr. Judith Miles (2011) discovered that the children with autism seen in her clinic fell into two discrete groups: two-thirds physically resembled their families and one-third did not. The first group, which she referred to as having "essential autism," tended to have fewer language and social disabilities and higher intelligence test scores, and were more likely to have siblings or other relatives with autism. The second group, referred to as having "complex autism," had "dysmorphic features," including smaller head size, oddly spaced teeth, and unusually placed ears. These children were more likely to have epilepsy and to exhibit the more severe behaviours associated with autism, such as mutism and self-injury. These findings appear to differentiate between genetic and environmental causes of ASD, with the latter including in-utero exposure to such toxins as drugs, alcohol, or infections or disease (Miles, 2011). There is some evidence suggesting that ASD's etiology involves fever infections in the pregnant mother or young child. Most infections result in fever that is routinely controlled with aspirin or acetaminophen. The blocking of fever inhibits processes that have evolved over millions of years and that protect against microbial attack. Immune mechanisms in the central nervous system are part of this protective process. It has been thus theorized that fever suppression using aspirin or NSAIDs could cause autism (Torres, 2003).

With the dramatic rise in ASD prevalence over recent years, many other environmental toxins, including mercury, lead, pesticides, automobile exhaust, and flame retardants, have been suggested as causes of autism. Certain geographic areas and parental occupational statuses have also been associated with higher ASD rates. Such links have similarly been suggested in dramatic increases in other childhood diseases, including asthma and child cancers. There has also been a widespread fear that vaccines—particularly the measles-mumps-rubella (MMR) vaccine, with its mercury-containing thimerosal—cause autism, although no scientific evidence supports this theory. That the introduction of the MMR vaccine was not followed by a surge in ASD diagnoses is just one of the epidemiological findings that have disproved the vaccine theory. According to Canada's National Advisory Committee on Immunization, Health Canada affirms that there is no legitimate safety reason for parents to avoid thimerosal-containing vaccines. Nonetheless, few vaccines available in Canada now contain this chemical (Norris, 2006). Recent research has examined the role of nutrition, digestive problems, and sensitivities to certain foods as factors that may contribute to autistic behaviour in children. Results indicate that children with autism may be unable to digest two kinds of protein: gluten, found in grains like wheat, barley, and oats; and casein, found in dairy products. Further aggravating the problem is the fact that these same foods tend to be craved by children with ASD. Eliminating or restricting the presence of these proteins in the diet of children with ASD has been found to improve their behaviour (Norris, 2006). In addition, scientists have noted that some children with ASD have excessive amounts of the yeast *Candida albicans* in their intestinal tract. As the yeast grows, it releases toxins into the bloodstream and it is theorized that these toxins may contribute to autistic behaviours. These observations are consistent with the other digestive abnormalities seen in children with autism and may be related to poor intestinal absorption of some nutrients.

Theories of biological causes are supported by the association of both physical and neurological disorders with autism. It is also suggested that some children's developing brains are more "fragile" than others and hence more vulnerable to exposure to environmental toxins (Peeples, 2012).

Bruce Perry and Maia Szalavitz propose an *intense world theory* to explain autism. Researchers are beginning to discover that although "difficulties with empathy are clearly involved, not all aspects of empathy are equally impaired and some may actually be enhanced" (Szalavitz & Perry, 2010, p. 73). A device (similar to a lie detector) that measures changes in skin temperature may communicate these children's emotional discomfort and signal an impending tantrum. The success of this device is evidence of the increasing understanding of autism as a combination of emotion, stress, and sensory dysfunction in brain development, and may explain that the social deficits seen in a child with ASD could be secondary to heightened fear and sensory issues.

> This would mean that something similar to the cause of social problems in neglected children is responsible for those problems in autistic children: extreme patterns of stress response system activation and a lack of appropriate stimulation at the right time. Being constantly bombarded with too much information in itself is stressful; autistic children might act like traumatized children, because for them normal experiences can be so overwhelming as to be traumatic. (Szalavitz & Perry, 2010, p. 87)

The **intense world theory** suggests that the brains of children with an ASD may fail to receive the social input required for the development of social skills not because the brain's social areas are damaged but because of sensory (and consequently emotional) overload. An approach known as *sensory integration intervention*, for example, would therefore aim to mitigate the source of this sensory distress. The authors conclude that if this theory is borne out, stories of children with ASD "have extra relevance to everyone . . . [S]o do the stories of neglect. The social brain needs social experience to function; like a muscle, it won't grow if you don't use it" (Szalavitz & Perry, 2010, p. 95).

In summary, whereas we know that ASD is a developmental disability caused by differences in the brain, we still don't know exactly what causes these differences for all children who develop an ASD. There appear to be multiple causes of ASD, although most of them are not yet known.

Autistic Spectrum Disorders. By about age four, children begin to understand that other people have thoughts and feelings just as they do. The **theory of mind (TOM)** refers to our capacity to recognize these in other people by creating a picture of our own thoughts and feelings; we can then predict some of their behaviours and anticipate a response. Since what goes on in other people's minds isn't visible to us, such predictions remain a "theory" we create for ourselves. TOM is also sometimes referred to as the ability to "mind read," not to be confused with the cognitive distortion of mind reading (Attwood, 1999).

Youth with ASD seem to have great difficulty conceptualizing and appreciating the feelings and thoughts of others (Attwood, 1999). And because they're unable to link others' observed behaviour with their inner feelings, these children can neither understand nor predict others' behaviour. This means that they're *unable (not unwilling)* to have empathy for others. The absence of TOM is thus the root of most difficulties people with ASD experience in their communication and social interaction.

The ability to interpret nonverbal cues and correctly identify others' emotions obviously helps children communicate effectively. If children can't sense their listeners' level of interest or interpret their body language, they won't know, for example, that their long monologues are boring to others. Similarly, the rude remarks individuals with high-functioning autism or Asperger's are known to make result from the inability to anticipate how their comments might offend or hurt other people. This absence of theory of mind is known as *mind blindness* (Attwood, 1999). Among the methods clinicians and researchers use to establish the presence of theory of mind in children is the "Sally Anne" test developed by Professor Uta Fruth (Baron-Cohen, Leslie, & Frith, 1985) which requires one to take the perspective of another child in order to correctly solve a problem.

> While the Sally Anne test might be assessing mind blindness, we are curious as to why mind blindness has become such an essential part of describing autism. Over the course of our lives, we have encountered many people without autism who live their lives without empathy for other people and their communities. Though the Sally Anne test sounds pretty simple and straightforward, autism is more complex. (Laursen & Yazdgerdi, 2012, p. 46)

Some suggest that children with Asperger's may be able to intellectualize or imagine what a person is thinking or feeling but can't emotionally recognize what to do in response. This inability to see the relevance of applying knowledge to a particular situation or problem is known as the lack of a **central drive for coherence** (Attwood, 1999). For example, after children with Asperger's take the favourite toy of another child and are asked how they think the other child felt, they can give the correct answer—but apparently the thought wasn't in their mind at the moment they took the toy (Attwood, 1999). Obviously it can be very difficult to make sense of situations or interact socially when you "can't see the forest for the trees," which is sometimes referred to as *living in a fragmented world*. Although children and youth with ASD or Asperger's may also perform poorly on tasks that demand the processing of details into a meaningful whole, their performance on tasks that demand processing of details can also be exceptional (Attwood, 1999). It is theorized that people with ASD have difficulties with the brain's executive functioning, as do those with ADHD, FASD, ODD, and schizophrenia. **Executive functioning** of the brain refers to those higher order thought processes that are necessary to guide our behaviour; these processes include planning, working memory, mental flexibility, response

WHERE DO YOU STAND?

As you can see, the psychological and CYC perspectives are similar in their approaches to neurodevelopmental disorders. *Intense world theory*, *theory of mind*, and *executive functioning* theories are consistent with both the CYC and psychological paradigms. After considering the explanations for ASD from these perspectives, try the *Take Action!* exercise and apply your knowledge of these explanations for neurodevelopmental deficits to Sarah's case. Where do you stand when it comes to the explanations for neurodevelopmental disorders? How do you think genetics and environment might interact to cause ASD? Would this be the case for Sarah?

initiation, response inhibition, and impulse control. Neuropsychological studies originally showed that executive functioning took place in the prefrontal cortex; however, more recent neuroimaging studies have shown that executive functioning is associated with many different regions of the frontal lobes (Robinson et al., 2009).

Difficulties with executive function can be manifested in many different ways. Some children pay attention to minor details and fail to see how these details fit into a bigger picture while others have difficulty with abstract and complex thinking, maintaining attention, or organizing their thoughts and actions. Executive functioning difficulties can also be associated with poor impulse control and the failure to consider the consequences of their actions. In the words of Temple Grandin, "I cannot hold one piece of information in my mind while I manipulate the next step in the sequence" (Grandin, 2010).

Take Action! Exercise: *Sarah's Case*

Eighteen-year-old Sarah was reported to the Crisis Stabilization authorities after she was seen wandering the streets late at night. Sarah was talking to herself and appeared very distraught. The crisis team escorted Sarah to a homeless shelter, where, upon intake, her parents were contacted and arrived soon after. In the intake interview, her parents indicated that Sarah had been having a great deal of difficulty with her anger over the last two months, and had been running away from home frequently. They reported that since early childhood Sarah had had very few friends, poor school achievement, and extreme defiance toward teachers. Sarah had recently refused to attend school entirely. Her parents indicated that Sarah was now often violent at home, hitting and spitting at her mother. Since childhood, Sarah has been fascinated with china dolls and now had an extensive collection that she played with daily. Her parents reported that Sarah can remember the telephone numbers of everyone she's ever known. She can also memorize car licence plates immediately. Sarah told the shelter's intake worker that for the past two months she's been hearing "mean," commanding voices telling her to hit people (these are known as *auditory hallucinations*). She was referred to a psychiatrist, and a diagnosis of ASD with psychosis was made. The brief-treatment team will work with Sarah and her parents with a plan for outpatient family support and daily group programming at the child and adolescent psychiatric community-based centre.

Describe how Sarah's symptoms/diagnosis might be explained and treated from each of the following paradigms: biological, behavioural, cognitive, sociocultural, and holistic. For each paradigm, what additional information about Sarah's situation and history would you need to know more about?

HELPING CHILDREN AND ADOLESCENTS WITH NEURODEVELOPMENTAL DISORDERS

Jason's Case: *Revisited*

The CYCP who's working with Jason in the classroom reports that, as a coping mechanism, he'll often leave the room (or any other anxiety-provoking situation); he also tries to use the positive self-talk she's taught him. However, these techniques are no longer helping him. Jason now stutters when he's anxious; he's been tapping his fingers on the desk constantly; and now he's also blurting out inappropriate and offensive statements to his peers and teacher. When questioned after the fact, Jason says that he doesn't know why he says certain things. He says he's becoming increasingly frustrated by his constant anxiety, and hopes that the CYCP can help him learn ways to manage it. Jason wants to graduate and go to university to study physics. He's motivated to learn ways to manage his anxiety; if he's not able to overcome it, he says, he's afraid that he'll be unable to reach his education and life goals.

Psychological Approaches to Treatment

From a psychological approach, specific interventions are aimed at maximizing functioning despite early onset deficits in cognitive and social functioning. Here we consider some of the most studied and most typically utilized approaches to intervention.

Biological Paradigm   Medical treatments do not help address the core symptoms that create impairment in neurodevelopmental disorders. Although some medications (e.g., antidepressants, antipsychotics) may help reduce specific symptoms of agitation and anxiety (Volkmar et al., 2009), they are not a cure by any means; Bryson, Rogers, and Fombonne (2003) argue that they should not be used to replace other forms of intervention and support. Medications for neurodevelopmental disorders are most often applied in cases of ADHD. As we discuss in Chapter 4, stimulant medications like Ritalin can be helpful in improving attention and decreasing impulsivity.

Psychological and Social Interventions   Various educational strategies are used in the treatment of specific learning disorders. Emphasis is placed on direct, intensive instruction in the area of specific deficit (e.g., reading, writing, mathematics). In the case of ASD, behavioural approaches that emphasize the use of reinforcements in the development of specific skills have shown some success and are based on the assumption that those diagnosed with ASD can learn skills despite their cognitive and social impairments (Ferster, 1961; Lovaas, 1977). Social communication skills such as making requests and playing with others have been found to be increased through the use of specific reinforcements (e.g., being able to play with a toy that the child is interested in; Goldstein, 2002). The development of joint attention skills has also been found to benefit from behavioural interventions targeting social interaction early in development (Lawton & Kasari, 2012). Family interventions include parental education and supports for assistance in managing stressors associated with caring for a child diagnosed with ASD. Similar approaches targeting the development of specific skills are also utilized in the case of intellectual disability, and include communication training as well as specific skill development (e.g., Sigafoos, Arthur-Kelly, & Butterfield, 2006). Specific behavioural approaches are discussed at length below.

CYC Approaches for Youth Struggling with ASD

Given the varying degrees of symptom severity on the ASD continuum, the overall needs of children and youth with an ASD, although sometimes similar, can also be very different. As we stress throughout this text, since the DSM-5 diagnosis cannot identify children's strengths, capabilities, or needs, we must ensure that our interventions are individualized and tailored to each child's unique characteristics. An overall understanding of the neurological disorders and a good knowledge of the ASDs will assist CYCPs when planning individualized CYC intervention strategies and treatment approaches.

Strength-Based Relational CYC Practice A core foundational CYC value is to respect and advocate for the dignity and rights of all children, youth, and families regardless of race, gender, class, sexuality, ability, and so on. This includes children and youth with mental and physical developmental disabilities. The term *ableism* refers to the predominant belief in our society that physically and mentally able individuals are normal and that developmentally disabled persons are somehow abnormal; it also refers to the resulting discrimination or prejudice against those with any disability, including an ASD. In the ableist worldview, people who have disabilities must either strive to become the norm or keep their distance from able-bodied people. A disability is considered an inherently bad thing that must be overcome—an error or a failing rather than a consequence of human diversity akin to race, gender, or sexual orientation. Another type of ableism is the perception of mental illness or developmental disability as a tragedy, whereby developmentally disabled individuals are viewed with pity (Hehir, 2007). "An ableist perspective asserts that it is preferable for a child to read print rather than Braille, walk rather than use a wheelchair, spell independently rather than use a spell-checker, read written text rather than listen to a book on tape, and hang out with nondisabled kids rather than with other disabled kids" (Hehir, 2007, p. 8).

CYCPs should also be aware of the term **neurotypical**, which is used in the literature to refer to those who do not have an ASD. To combat ableism in your CYC practice, first recognize and discourage the use of all disrespectful language; don't use it yourself, and challenge others around you if they use such words as *retarded*, *lame*, *idiot*, *cripple*, *insane*, and *crazy*. Second, embrace the principle of inclusiveness for all children and youth with physical and mental disabilities. Finally, be willing to advocate for young people with disabilities and have the courage to challenge those who are disrespectful toward them (Hehir, 2007).

Inclusiveness in education is a fundamental human right of children and youth with an ASD; however, it may not be the best option for every child, every time. It may not prioritize the needs of the individual child or be able to provide the specialized education required, especially for those children with the most severe language and behaviour disorders. Not all teachers, educational assistants, or CYCPs will have the specific training or experience required for work with autistic children and youth. Moreover, children with autism are sometimes bullied in mainstream classrooms, and their needs may not be met amid the overall demands of the classroom upon the teacher (Harchik, 2014).

One of the most concerning negative consequences of inclusiveness is that children with ASDs may be targeted by other children in the mainstream classroom. Children and youth diagnosed with autism need to feel a sense of belonging, just as all young people do. These youth have the same joys and struggles as their "neurotypical" peers, even though they may lack the social skills to navigate their environment in the same way. Accordingly, support, caring relationships, and guidance from others are necessary. In a more specialized setting, children with an ASD are more likely to be safer from bullying and to receive from adults the special attention they need. These needs were well expressed by Norman, who, diagnosed with autism at an early age, said that for his entire life he'd searched for a sense of belonging, for friends his own age, for a club or any type of community in which he could just be himself and feel safe and at home. Norman found that these needs were met best in a program where all the young people had ASD (Laursen & Yazdgerdi, 2012).

Assessment

A number of rating scales are available to assist parents, professionals, and caregivers in identifying children who may have an ASD. (Keep in mind, however, that a thorough developmental assessment needs to be conducted by a medical practitioner or other clinician to confirm a diagnosis.) Online development assessment tools may be administered by teachers, CYCPs, and community service providers, and some can be used by parents and caregivers as well. These tools include the following (Autism Canada Foundation, 2011):

> Ages and Stages Questionnaires (ASQ)
> Communication and Symbolic Behavior Scales (CSBS)
> Parents' Evaluation of Development Status (PEDS)
> Modified Checklist for Autism in Toddlers (M-CHAT)
> Screening Tool for Autism in Toddlers and Young Children (STAT)

Indicators to Recognize   All ASDs are characterized by social-interaction difficulties, communication challenges, and a tendency to engage in repetitive behaviours. However, as we've seen, symptoms and their severity vary widely across these three core areas. Symptoms may represent relatively mild challenges for those at the high-functioning end of the spectrum, and for others they may be more severe, as when repetitive behaviours and lack of spoken language interfere with everyday life. Thus, it is critical to observe symptoms and assess their impact on the child's day-to-day functioning and development. Figure 3.1 illustrates the differences in symptom occurrence associated with ASD and those forms of ASD previously known as Asperger's. (Recall that PDD-NOS stands for Pervasive Developmental Disorder–Not Otherwise Specified.)

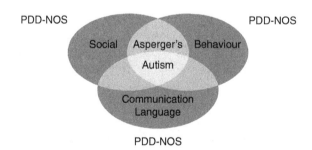

Figure 3.1 Symptom Overlap in Autism Spectrum Disorder

Despite their common symptoms, there are significant differences in symptom occurrence associated with ASD (autism) and those forms of ASD previously referred to as Asperger's.

Source: Capaldi, n.d.

During CYCPs' observation and assessment processes, it's also critical to keep in mind that children with an ASD commonly internalize their thoughts and feelings by retreating into fantasy. They may develop a complex imaginary world with imaginary friends. Whereas this type of escape can be an adaptive strength in childhood, when it occurs in adolescence or early adulthood it may lead to a pattern of escape and social withdrawal that can become a serious concern (Attwood, 1999).

Alternatively, young people with ASD can externalize their thoughts and feelings, blaming and denying any responsibility for problems with others. This can often lead to anger, arrogance, retaliation, and even attacking others with physical violence (Kutscher, 2005). They may also be victim of retaliation from others who were attacked.

Another, more constructive way for young people with ASD to externalize their thoughts and feelings is to imitate the ways of their socially successful peers. To reinforce this behaviour, CYCPs can recognize and praise these efforts.

> The child learns to act in social situations by becoming another child. Some children with Asperger's can be remarkably astute in their observation abilities, copying gestures, tone of voice, and mannerisms. This can be a constructive way of achieving social inclusion if the child mimics an appropriate role model. Unfortunately, some adolescents with Asperger's syndrome may imitate socially popular but notoriously bad guys at school. (Kutscher, 2005, p. 107)

CYCPs must consider and assess any environmental factors that may trigger challenging behaviours. Parents, teachers, CYCPs, or other caregivers may inadvertently reinforce ongoing difficult or maladaptive behaviours. In some instances, a mismatch between the classroom educational or behavioural expectations and the cognitive ability of the child to respond appropriately may be entirely responsible for the child's disruptive behaviours. Functional analysis of behaviour (ABA) completed by a behaviour specialist or CYCP in the setting in which the problems occur will identify factors in the environment that exacerbate or maintain the problematic behaviour.

CYCPs must also be aware of signs that may indicate the child is affected by Tourette's or sensory difficulties. **Tourette's Disorder** signs are divided into three categories. *Motor signs* are characterized by repetitive involuntary movements or tics, including eye blinking, facial twitches, and arm and leg jerking. *Vocal signs* include repeated throat clearing, grunting, barking, or shrieking. **Palilalia** is the repetition of one's own words, and **echolalia** is the repetition of another's words. (CYCP: "Jason, can you point to your shoe?" Jason: "Can you point to your shoe?" CYCP: "Jason, use your finger and point like this to your shoe." Jason: "Point like this to your shoe") (Kendall & Comer, 2010). *Behavioural signs* include obsessive and/or compulsive behaviours such as continuous checking, closing and opening a door, and making and unmaking the bed. Sometimes a youth might develop a compulsion to commit an inappropriate sexual gesture or to shout obscenities in public (Attwood, 1999). In **catatonia**, a youth demonstrates an absence of speech (mutism), absence of movement (akinesia), and maintenance of imposed postures (catalepsy). A diagnosis of catatonia is given when these behaviours seriously interfere with daily functioning. Other abnormalities of behaviour that can be seen in catatonia are a reversal of day and night; tremors, eye rolling, dystonia, an odd stiff posture, freezing in postures, etc.; excitement and agitation; and repetitive, ritualistic behaviour (Wing & Shah, 2000).

Sensory Difficulties. **Sensory processing**, also called **sensory integration (SI)**, refers to the way the nervous system receives messages from the senses and turns them into appropriate motor and behavioural responses. Whether you're reading a book or eating a salad, successful completion of the activity requires that your brain process and integrate the sensations. **Sensory Processing Disorder (SPD)**, also known as **sensory integration dysfunction**, occurs when sensory signals don't get organized properly into the appropriate responses. (Controversially, the DSM-5 doesn't list SPD; one of the arguments against its inclusion was that it more properly belongs with ADHD or ASD.) SPD is like a traffic jam in which certain parts of the brain don't receive the information they need to correctly interpret sensory information. If sensory difficulties aren't recognized or treated effectively, motor clumsiness, behavioural problems, anxiety, depression, school failure, and other impacts may result ("About SPD," 2015).

SPD can affect children and youth in only one of their senses (e.g., the sense of touch) or in multiple senses. Children with autism can be oversensitive (*hypersensitive*) or undersensitive (*hyposensitive*) in any or all of the senses. About 40 percent of children with ASD are extremely sensitive to sound and touch and yet often have very low levels of pain. For some, the mere anticipation of a sensory experience can lead to extreme anxiety or a panic attack. One youth with SPD may over-respond to many physical sensations, finding clothing, physical contact, light, sound, food, or any other sensory input to be extremely unpleasant or even unbearable. Another youth might under-respond and show little or no reaction to stimulation, including pain or extreme hot and cold, which can, of course, be dangerous. In some children the sensory processing of messages from the muscles and joints is affected; their posture and motor skills could be affected in turn. Other children and youth may have a need for overstimulation and an appetite for sensation that's in perpetual overdrive. These children are frequently misdiagnosed with, and consequently inappropriately medicated for, ADHD ("About SPD," 2015).

Here is a brief review of the most commonly seen forms of sensory integration dysfunctions.

> **Sensitivity to sound:** For children with SPD, there are three main types of sounds that can cause extreme discomfort: sudden, unexpected noises (dog barking, phone ringing); high-pitched, continuous noises (lawnmower, electric mixer); and complex or multiple sounds (shopping centres or school hallways). Children with extreme sensitivity to sound will also be distracted or disturbed by low modulating background noise, such as an air conditioner or the hum of a fan. These children's experience of these sounds is analogous to the way most of us would react to the sound of fingernails scraping down a blackboard (Attwood, 1999). Listening to music several times a day can significantly reduce a child's problematic responses to sound (Attwood, 1999).

> **Sensitivity to touch:** For most children with ASD the common forms of touch used in social greetings or gestures of affection are perceived as overwhelming. There can be an extreme sensitivity to a single touch or to the touching of certain parts of the body. Temple Grandin describes her acute tactile sensitivity: "As a baby, I resisted being touched and when I became a little older I can remember stiffening, flinching and pulling away from relatives when they hugged me" (Grandin, 1984, p. 155). Some children hate handling certain textures, such as fingerpaints or playdough, and many

types of clothing items can cause distress. Grandin (1984) found that deep pressure, squeezing, rubbing, and staying in small spaces helped her with her tactile sensitivity.

Sensitivity to taste and texture of food: Some young children with ASD or Asperger's seem extremely fussy in their choice of food. This is not a behavioural problem in which the child is being deliberately defiant, but rather a physiological reaction and a real consequence of SPD.

Visual sensitivity: This can include a sensitivity to colours and to illumination as well as distortion of visual perception. Some children with ASD report being "blinded by brightness."

Sensitivity to smell: Some people with Asperger's find that specific strong smells can be overpowering. Cologne, perfume, and household cleaning items can be perceived as extremely offensive and should be avoided.

Lack of sensitivity to pain: Children with ASD may not show a response to the levels of pain that others would consider unbearable. The consequences can be dangerous, as they may not learn to avoid some actions. If a child with ASD shows minimal response to pain, caregivers must be extremely vigilant for any signs of of an infection, burn, or illness (Attwood, 1999).

Synaesthesia: In this rare condition, an individual receives a sensation in one sensory system but experiences it in another modality. *Synaesthesia* comes from the Greek words *syn* (together) and *aesthesis* (perception). People with synaesthesia might experience colours or tastes when they read words or hear sounds; others may experience any combination of tastes, smells, shapes, colours, or touches. People are generally born with synaesthesia, and it runs in families. This condition isn't specific to those with ASD (Attwood, 1999), but it's important to recognize that it could be present.

See Table 3.1 for a checklist of behaviours that characterize ASD.

Intervention

Given the risk that significant developmental delays will compound over time, early intervention is critical for children with ASD. Such interventions are designed to minimize developmental delays and maximize the children's chances of reaching "normal" milestones.

For CYCPs in the classroom setting, features common to most good intervention programs for children include the following: (1) selecting or developing curriculum that emphasizes selective attention, imitation, language, play, and social skills; (2) caring and highly supportive teaching environments; (3) predictability and routine; (4) a functional approach to problem behaviours; (5) a long-term educational plan to prepare for transitioning classroom placements; and (6) parental involvement in educational planning and treatment (Kutscher, 2005). Most of these can be applied to other settings as general principles to guide interventions.

Behavioural and Cognitive-Behavioural Techniques for CYCPs Cognitive behavioural therapy is not recommended for children with ASD, since the application of learned skills to the real world following this therapy has been problematic. However, many other types of behavioural interventions can be successfully used with

Table 3.1 Behavioural Indicators Checklist: Autism Spectrum Disorders

✓ Speech patterns may be unusual, lack inflection, or have a rhythmic nature.

Speech can be formal and too loud or high pitched.

Often do not understand irony and humour.

Desire interaction, but don't know how to engage.

Are uninterested in others: uncommunicative, limited eye contact, no language.

Have difficulty with imaginative or creative play.

May engage in ritualistic behaviours, including arm flapping and/or rocking.

Have difficulty reading others' facial expressions.

Frequently have motor skill delays; may appear clumsy or awkward.

Frequently like to collect categories of things.

May be proficient in knowing various categories of information.

Are obsessive; have good rote-memory skills.

Have difficulty with abstract concepts.

Usually have a flat tone of voice.

Have a narrow range of interests.

Often have an obsessive impulse to argue and split hairs.

Have "refreshing" honesty.

Have tantrums.

Often have sensory difficulties.

Can have obsessive and/or compulsive behaviours.

Can demonstrate inappropriate sexual gestures or shout obscenities in public.

Can show catatonia: absence of speech (mutism), absence of movement (akinesia), imposed postures (catalepsy).

children with ASD; most are "prescribed," and therefore CYCPs can readily employ them in a classroom or home setting.

The most successful, empirically supported approaches to treating children with ASD are based on behavioural theory (Steele, Elkin, & Roberts, 2008); among the most effective of these is **applied behaviour analysis (ABA)**. ABA, formerly known as "behaviour modification," is the process of observing children's behaviour so as to develop an intervention plan. It's most frequently used as a behaviour management tool, but can be also used to teach social, motor, and verbal behaviours and to manage challenging and/or self-harm behaviours (Steele, Elkin, & Roberts, 2008).

While ABA is most often used in a classroom environment, CYCPs can use informal behaviour analysis in many settings to help in assessment and in understanding a child's behaviour. ABA is particularly helpful in teaching desired behaviours. Because children with ASD don't naturally pick up these behaviours on their own, ABA combines behavioural observation with positive reinforcement or prompting at each step of a desired new behaviour. The aim is to use the least intrusive prompts possible while still leading to the desired response. Prompts can include verbal cues, visual cues, and demonstration.

ABA involves intensive training of ABA therapists, extensive time for the child spent in ABA therapy (20–40 hours per week), and weekly supervision by experienced clinical supervisors known as "certified behaviour analysts" (Steele, Elkins, & Roberts, 2008). CYCPs, although uncertified in ABA, can use its principles in a variety of ways; for example, recording direct observations, conducting a functional analysis of the relationship between the triggers or cues in the environment and the undesirable behaviour, and helping to teach and encourage the desired response from the child.

In teaching new behaviours, the first step in ABA is to analyze the behaviour using the **ABC model**. A refers to *antecedent*: the directive or request for the child to perform an action. B refers to *behaviour*: the child's successful performance of the task, or noncompliance, or non-response. C refers to the *consequence*: the therapist's reaction, ranging from strong positive reinforcement (a reward, such as a special treat; verbal praise) to strong (depending on the riskiness of the behaviour) negative response, "No!"

The Role of Medication   Psychotropic medications are almost always used to manage the difficult, disruptive, or troublesome behaviours that accompany an ASD. These include aggression, self-injurious behaviour, repetitive behaviors (e.g., perseveration, obsessions, compulsions, and stereotypic movements), sleep disturbance, mood lability, irritability, anxiety, hyperactivity, inattention, and destructive behaviours.

> However, there are no medications that directly treat the social and language impairments seen in individuals with ASD. The medications used most frequently for children and adults with ASD include antipsychotics (e.g., risperidone), selective serotonin reuptake inhibitors (SSRIs) to treat mood and repetitive behaviors, and stimulants and other medications used to treat attention deficits and hyperactivity. *The evidence base is good for using atypical antipsychotics (e.g., risperidone and aripiprazole) to treat challenging and repetitive behaviors, but there are also significant side effects associated with the use of these drugs* [italics ours]. (Lindgren & Doobay, 2011, p. 15)

Surveys indicate that approximately 45 percent of children and adolescents and up to 75 percent of adults diagnosed with ASDs will be treated with psychotropic medication. When medications are used for behaviour management with children with ASD, all potential benefits and adverse effects should be explained, informed consent should be obtained, baseline data regarding behaviours and somatic complaints should be collected, and potential strategies for dealing with treatment failure should be planned (Myers & Johnson, 2007). The suggestions by Gerry Fewster cited in Chapter 1 (pp. 54–55) will also assist you in this area.

Psychoeducation and Individual Counselling   Psychoeducation in the form of social skills intervention, whether individually or in a small groups, is very successful with children and youth with ASD. This method builds social interaction skills; for example, how to initiate and maintain a conversation. Most social skill group meetings include instruction, role-playing or practice, and feedback. In this way learners with ASD acquire and practise skills that will promote positive social interactions with peers.

One strength-based intervention technique, called the power-card strategy, focuses on a child's special interest so as to motivate improvement in behaviour and social skills.

Most children with ASD have a keen special interest. The power-card strategy is especially beneficial, then, as it takes into account the unique characteristics of children and youth with autism. The strategy begins with a brief scenario or character sketch describing how the hero solves a problem; then the power card recounts how the child can use the same strategy to solve a similar problem. For example, whether at home or at school, whenever nine-year-old Nancy loses a game, she has a tantrum; the following card addresses the behaviour.

> The Power-Puff Girls like to play games. Sometimes they win the game. When they win games the Power-Puff Girls feel happy. They might smile, give each other a high five or say "yea!" But sometimes they lose the game. When they lose games the Power-Puff Girls might not feel happy. They might take a deep breath, say "good job" to their friend or say, "maybe next time." The Power-Puff Girls want everyone to have fun playing games. They want you to remember these three things when playing games the Power-Puff way:
>
> 1. Games should be fun for everyone.
> 2. If you win a game you can smile, give a high five, or say, "yea!"
> 3. If you lose a game you can take a deep breath, say "good job" to your friend or "maybe next time." (Gagnon, 2001)

Sensory integration therapy (SIT) involves the use of pressure, weight, and movement techniques to alter children's sensory experiences. For example, specific sensory activities (e.g., swinging, bouncing, brushing) help children regulate their sensory responses. SIT is usually conducted by trained occupational therapists, but CYCPs, parents, and caregivers can employ many of its facets. For many children with autism, the reported outcomes of these play-type therapies and activities include better ability to focus, improved overall behaviour, and lowered anxiety (Cheng & Boggett-Carsjens, 2005). The wearing of weighted clothing and blankets is still frequently used in SIT, although this practice is controversial (Cheng & Boggett-Carsjens, 2005).

Cheng and Boggett-Carsjens (2005) suggest a variety of specific SIT interventions, as summarized here.

To reduce excess sensory input:

Visual: Try to use dimmed lighting; allow the child to use sunglasses; have the child sit at the front of the class; allow the child to avoid eye contact when answering a question that requires concentration.

Touch: Always avoid unexpected touch; avoid giving a child light touch, but instead give a soothing firm touch and pressure (e.g., massage); in school, when the child is lining up with peers, allow the child to be at the front or end of the line to avoid jostling with other children.

Auditory: Aim to reduce sound stimulation; for example, covering one's ears, using earplugs; listen to soothing music. In general, quiet, soft sounds are calming.

Oral: Seek out certain textures and tastes to calm the child. Sucking on candies or through a straw can be calming.

Movement: Avoid movement, or use soothing movement. In general, slow, continuous movement (e.g., rocking in a rocking chair) is calming.

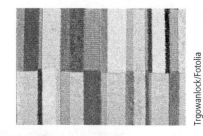
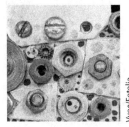

Providing access to objects that enhance visual, touch, and other forms of stimulation is often used when working with those diagnosed with ASD.

Relaxation techniques (such as muscle relaxation and deep breathing) help the nervous system stay calm. When calmer, a person is better able to handle stress (such as sensory stimuli; Cheng & Boggett-Carsjens, 2005).

To increase sensory stimulation:

Visual: Give many sources of visual stimulation: use high-contrast/brightly coloured handouts, use lots of hand gestures and movement when speaking, and use different visual media to keep things visually interesting.

Touch: Allow the use of hand "fidgets" (e.g., a stress ball) in class to increase stimulation; use tactile activities such as playdough or clay; use textured washcloths to help children wake up in the morning.

Sound: Allow background music to study, or background white noise/music to sleep.

Movement: Give frequent breaks so that the child can move around and stretch; use inflatable-ball chairs that permit movement; allow the child to stand at his or her desk to complete work.

Olfactory: Use incense or aromatherapy candles.

Oral: Allow chewing gum, hard candies, spicy foods, ice chips, water.

Modulating activities are sensory interventions that help the nervous system regain a sense of harmony/balance. These activities include, for example, massage and stretching, and can be used with all children regardless of whether they are under- or over-aroused (Cheng & Boggett-Carsjens, 2005).

SIT is not an evidence-based treatment approach; however, it is widely used and supported by anecdotal evidence, and the number of books (e.g., *The Out-of-Sync Child*), websites, and workshops devoted to SIT suggest that many have found its techniques helpful.

Family Support Interventions   Families of children with ASD are known to experience emotional and psychological difficulties. For example, research shows that over half of mothers report significant psychological distress; this has been associated with low levels of family support and with bringing up a child with higher levels of challenging behaviours. Mothers were more likely to report lower levels of support if they were a single parent, were living in poor housing, or were the mother of a boy with ASD. It is vital, then, that CYCPs appreciate the stresses involved for these families, and that they incorporate a CYC family-focused approach in their intervention plan.

Families and CYC staff in mental health centres both report that when children with ASD enter puberty, they often become increasingly difficult to manage, usually due to an escalating pattern of violence. Such violence can take the form of physical aggression toward others and explosive, unpredictable outbursts. Consider just one treatment centre in Toronto: half of the children diagnosed with an ASD had threatened another person with a knife; two had stabbed another person; and four of the five children with Asperger's had made verbal threats to kill a family member. Moreover, 9 of the 10 children admitted had histories of harming themselves (e.g., head banging, slapping themselves, hair pulling), and two children with Asperger's had made suicidal threats.

Ensuring the emotional health of family members is a critical aspect of an overall treatment plan. We can support families by educating them about ASD, helping them obtain access to resources, providing emotional support, and assisting them in advocating for their children's needs. In some cases, referring parents to more professional counselling or other appropriate mental health services may be required.

We recognize, of course, that families have the best understanding of their child's needs, and will provide their own unique suggestions for the treatment plan. In addition, including parents in interventions will help them feel a greater competence as parents—and that in itself will decrease stress and increase the overall well-being of the family (Marshall & Mirenda, 2002). Refer to Box 3.3 for intervention techniques to use in your work with youth diagnosed with ASD.

Box 3.3

Techniques for CYC Intervention

Emphasize school curriculum to focus on selective attention, imitation, language, play, and social skills.

Provide caring and highly supportive teaching and living environments.

Ensure structure, predictability, and routine.

Use a functional behavioural approach to assess and intervene with problem behaviours.

Ensure that the long-term educational plan focuses on transition in placements.

Use family support, and ensure parental involvement in interventions.

Use strengths and any intrinsic interests in play-interaction interventions.

Teach social skills.

Use sensory integration techniques when needed.

Focus on relationship-based techniques; for example, consider using the DIR Floortime approach (see below).

Prevention: Advocacy, Community, and School-Based Strategies An important area for CYC advocacy is combating the stigma, bullying, and labelling that children with ASD may experience. One promising school-based intervention is the DIR (developmental, individual difference, relationship-based) Floortime model. **DIR Floortime** is a treatment approach that first assesses children's intrinsic level of interest and then, through a play interaction, incorporates it into an interest shared between the child and teacher (Hess, 2013). This approach fits well with CYC practice, as it's based on relational work (being in a relationship "right here, right now") and on development (meeting children where they're at).

The Floortime model has two foundational constructs: first, practitioners follow the children's lead and join them in their world; second, they pull them into a "shared world" to help the children master sequential social and emotional developmental levels. A developmental assessment is part of the DIR approach; CYCPs, caregivers, and parents can assess the developmental level of children using their own knowledge and/or the tools available at the website ("DIR and the DIR Floortime approach," 2015).

The DIR approach focuses on teaching children to problem solve so that they may develop interactions with people in their environment while allowing the brain to integrate its sensory-regulatory, communication, and motor functions. Empirically, neuroscience is increasingly supporting the developmental focus of CYC interventions, regardless of the area of difficulty with several studies demonstrating the effectiveness of DIR/Floortime approach (e.g., Greenspan & Wieder, 2005; Pajareya, 2011).

Another school-based intervention is **relationship development intervention (RDI)**. Developed by Dr. Steve Gutstein, RDI is based on a theory of "dynamic intelligence," defined as the ability to think flexibly—to see the grey areas, not just the black and white. RDI has a strong focus on developing interpersonal relationships. Gutstein stresses that "neurotypical" children (i.e., children who don't have autism) develop dynamic intelligence through guided play and involvement with their caregivers, something that children with autism are unable to do. Instead of relying on "static intelligence" (that is, the ability to know information or memorize facts), neurotypical children rely on this dynamic intelligence to flexibly respond to novel situations. The purpose of RDI is to help children with autism build dynamic intelligence and respond appropriately to such situations (Morris, 2008). According to Gutstein, autistic children have six main areas of deficits: (1) the ability to use an emotional feedback system to learn from the subjective experiences of others; (2) the ability to observe and continually regulate one's behaviour in order to participate in relationships involving collaboration and exchange of emotions; (3) the ability to share perceptions and feelings by using language and nonverbal communication to express curiosity and invite others to interact; (4) the ability to adapt, change strategies, and alter plans based on changing circumstances (flexible thinking); (5) the ability to obtain meaning from the larger context and to solve problems that have no right-and-wrong solutions (relational information processing); and (6) the ability to reflect on past experiences and anticipate potential future scenarios in a productive manner (foresight and hindsight). The goal of RDI, then, is to remediate these common deficits using individualized means for each child (Greenspan & Wieder, 2005).

Note that there is some controversy about using non-evidence-based interventions with children with autism. Alternative healing approaches are considered to be among such interventions.

Alternative Healing   Many parents use alternative therapies to assist in the treatment of autism. Natural alternatives include vitamin therapies (increasing the amount of folic acid, vitamin A, vitamin B6, and vitamin C), a gluten-free diet, and a casein (milk products) free diet. Other alternative healing approaches include energy therapy, such as Reiki and healing touch; neurofeedback; movement therapy; music therapy; acupuncture; and animal therapy. None of these are evidence-based.

The Horse Boy is a highly recommended documentary film about Rowen, a young boy with autism who had regular tantrums and was not yet toilet trained. After his father sees how calm he is around animals, particularly horses, the family goes to Mongolia to ride horses and seek the help of shamans; his father's instinct tells him that the trip will have a healing effect on the boy. They travel far north to the region where Indigenous people herd reindeer—and where the most powerful shaman in Mongolia is reputed to live. After his experience with the shaman, all of Rowan's worst behavioural issues, including the tantrums, completely stop; he becomes toilet trained; and he begins interacting with other children. This is a wonderful film about a boy with autism and his family's struggle (www. horseboymovie.com/OurStory.php).

Holding Therapy.   Although we emphatically disagree with holding therapy and it has received no empirical support, we include it here so that CYCPs will be aware of its use with children with autism and attachment disorders. Holding therapy is associated with significant dangers, including physical and psychological harm to the child.

Holding therapy (or so-called "caring physical restraint") is based on two theories: that autism results from a disturbance in the relationship between baby and mother, and that this attachment can be created or repaired by forcing the child to experience adult control through physical closeness. Holding has been theorized to restore and strengthen the bond between child and caregiver; the child is thought to develop closeness with the caregiver after the child realizes that his or her anger cannot break the parent–child bond. A factor in the development of holding therapy as an acceptable intervention is assumed to have been Temple Grandin's suggestion in one of her books that as a child she'd been greatly comforted by physical pressure, and so had constructed what she called a "squeeze machine" that would give her the experience of pressure without human touch, which she much disliked. Some proponents of holding therapy for autistic children suggested that their treatment was parallel to Grandin's squeeze machine; they are, in fact, very different.

Holding therapy consists of forced holding by a therapist or parent until the child stops resisting or until a fixed time period has elapsed. The carer doesn't usually release her hold until the child surrenders and looks into the carer's eyes. The carer then returns the child's gaze and exchanges affection. The therapy has been used to treat a wide range of children with an attachment disorder, including children with autism, Oppositional Defiant Disorder, Conduct Disorder, Attention-Deficit/Hyperactivity Disorder, learning disabilities, and depression ("Holding therapy and autism," 2014). Again, we are opposed to its use.

Relational CYC Practice   Any relational approach based on good CYC practice will be effective in engaging children and youth with ASD, provided you have the required training and experience. There are many prescribed approaches that

CYCPs could explore further for inclusion in their repertoire. One of these is *gentle teaching*, which has been used for years with young people with special needs. One of the authors of this text encountered this approach some time ago when it was introduced into a secure residential facility for youth as an alternative to using physical restraint.

Gentle teaching is a way of being with children in a safe, loving manner that focuses on building relationships and interpersonal interactions. Its goal is to create a trusting bond between caregiver and child—not necessarily with the aim of stopping problem behaviours (except, of course, those related to safety of self and others), but rather to focus on the caregiver's ability to be gentle in the face of aggression or disregard from the child ("Gentle teaching," 2014). The main principles on which this approach is based are unconditional love, valuing, acceptance, interdependence, companionship, and community. Its intervention guidelines (which correspond with CYC practice principles) are as follows:

1. Speak to children in a quiet and calming way (no loud voices or shouting).
2. Give directions precisely, with few words (remove extraneous language that complicates the processing task).
3. Respond gently in all interactions with youth (speaking respectfully, using touch if appropriate).
4. Limit your frustration responses and angry outbursts (i.e., respond, don't react).
5. Reinforce positive behaviours through hugs, pats on the back, smiles, and verbal praise.
6. Don't react impulsively (behave consistently within the theoretical framework).
7. Don't reinforce inappropriate behaviour.

Refer to Box 3.4 for specific communication strategies that can be used in your work with those diagnosed with ASD.

Box 3.4

CYC Communication Strategies

Recognize and challenge the use of disrespectful language by anyone.

Embrace the principle of inclusiveness wherever appropriate.

Be willing to advocate for children and young people with disabilities.

Think outside the box for interventions and be open to alternative therapies: consider nutrition, Reiki and healing touch, neurofeedback, play and movement therapy, yoga, mindfulness-based stress reduction (MBSR), music therapy, and animal therapy.

Listen carefully to young people when they tell you what they need.

Be acutely aware of any heightened arousal.

Assess for sensory difficulties and reduce or increase sensory integration.

Teach MBSR self-soothing and relaxation techniques.

Teach social skills, coping, skills, and feelings identification.

Be careful with use of touch; follow the child's lead.

Use such approaches as DIR Floortime and gentle teaching.

Where Do You Stand?

While no one intervention is right for all children with ASD or other neurological disorders, there is much we can do to help them realize their potential. As with all CYC interventions, we focus on establishing trust in relationships, identifying and building on strengths, and teaching skills designed to help young people with ASD to cope. We can use functional behaviour analysis to help children learn to manage difficult behaviours; work to eliminate self-harming or dangerous behaviours; teach social interaction and communication skills; and assist with identified sensory integration problems.

Grandin (2014) notes that while a treatment method or an educational method that will work for one child may not work for another, the most important thing is not to delay: the one common denominator for all young children is that early intervention does work and seems to improve the prognosis (Grandin, 2014). Where do you stand with respect to CYC interventions with ASD? Are there any in particular that would fit best with your CYC practice? To help you answer this question, revisit the cases of Jason and Sarah in the *Viewpoint Challenge* exercise.

Jason's and Sarah's Cases: *Viewpoint Challenge Exercise*

Reread the cases of Jason and Sarah. Which intervention approach might you try with each? Why? Do you agree that in the case of neurodevelopmental disorders, the psychological paradigm and CYC approaches to intervention are more similar than they are for other disorders discussed in this text?

CHAPTER SUMMARY

- *Developmental psychopathology* refers to the study of how disorders emerge in the course of one's development and how they change or persist over time.

- *Neurodevelopmental disorders* are observed early on in the child's development. Impairments in this category include deficits in general mental abilities; in specific areas of learning, communication, and social interaction; and in motor skills.

- From both the psychological and CYC perspectives, neurodevelopmental disorders are considered to be largely determined by biological factors interacting with environmental factors, although the young person's psychological and social variables can play a role in influencing the *outcome* of any one of these disorders.

- The basic CYC principles for working with children and youth diagnosed with an ASD include the ideas of ableism and inclusion. Educational and behavioural strategies are utilized as well as parent support and education.

- Psychological interventions target specific areas of impairment and also include the use of educational and behavioural strategies as well as parent support and education.

- Interventions most likely to be used by CYCPs in the case of ASD include SIT, Floortime, RDI, gentle teaching, observation, the ABC model, functional or applied behaviour analysis, and social skills training.

Critical Thinking Questions

1. Why do you think ASDs are now more prevalent in Western society than ever before?

2. Does it make sense to you that the DSM-5 includes ADHD together with ASD and other neurodevelopmental disorders? What do they have in common? How are they distinct?

3. What do you think causes autism? Why do you think there is such a strong parent movement advocating against vaccines in the belief that they cause autism? Search the web for readings on this topic and report back to your learning group.

4. Why do you think some children and adolescents with ASD can be very aware of their own deficits and yet unable to have empathy for others?

5. Do you think inclusiveness is always the preferred approach for every child and youth with an ASD, or is a specialized approach sometimes preferred? Why or why not?

6. Do you think ADHD and ODD might actually be forms of high-functioning autism? Explain your position.

7. How would you establish a caring relationship with a child or youth with autism when social relationships can be so threatening or unwanted?

Key Terms

ABC model, 137

applied behaviour analysis (ABA), 136

Asperger's syndrome, 120

Autism Spectrum Disorder (ASD), 117

catatonia, 133

central drive for coherence, 128

communication disorders, 116

developmental psychopathology, 114

DIR Floortime, 141

echolalia, 133

executive functioning, 128

gentle teaching, 143

Intellectual Disability (ID) or Intellectual Developmental Disorder, 115

intense world theory, 127

joint attention, 118

motor disorders, 118

neurodevelopmental disorders, 115

neurotypical, 131

palilalia, 133

relationship development intervention (RDI), 141

sensory integration therapy (SIT), 138

sensory processing, or sensory integration (SI), 134

Sensory Processing Disorder (SPD), or sensory integration dysfunction, 134

specific learning disorders, 118

synaesthesia, 135

theory of mind (TOM), 128

Tourette's Disorder, 133

Supplemental Readings

Attwood, T. (1999). *Asperger's syndrome: A guide for parents and professionals*. London: Jessica Kingsley.

Frith, U. (2008). *Autism: A very short introduction*. Oxford: Oxford University Press.

Gutstein, S. E., & Sheely, R. (2002). *Relationship development intervention with children, adolescents and adults*. London: Jessica Kingsley.

Kutscher, M. L. (2005). *In the syndrome mix: Asperger's, Tourette's, Bipolar and more*. London: Jessica Kingsley.

Laursen, E., & Yazdgerdi, Z. (2012). Autism and belonging. *Reclaiming Children and Youth, 21*(2), 44–47.

Offit, P. (2008). *Autism's false prophets: Bad science, risky medicine, and the search for a cure*. New York: Columbia University Press.

Online Resources

Occupational Therapy Innovations, www.ot-innovations.com (Focuses on sensory modulation, cognition, and mental health.)

Sensory Processing Disorder Foundation, http://spdfoundation.net/about-sensory-processing-disorder.html

SPD and the DSM-5, http://occupational-therapy.advanceweb.com/article/getting-spd-into-the-dsm-v.aspx

Alert Program, www.alertprogram.com (This program teaches self-regulation, and is based on M. S. Williams and S. Shellenberger's 1996 book *How Does Your Engine Run? A Leader's Guide to the Alert Program for Self-Regulation*.)

Uta Frith's selected publications, https://sites.google.com/site/utafrith/recent-publications

Temple Grandin's TED talk, www.ted.com/talks/temple_grandin_the_world_needs_all_kinds_of_minds.html

Autism fact sheet, www.cyc-net.org/reference/refs-autism-fact%20sheet.html

Recent research on autism causes, www.cdc.gov/ncbddd/autism/articles.html

Autism and relational developmental intervention, www.autismspeaks.org/what-autism/treatment/relationship-development-intervention-rdi

Autism/Asperger's information, www.childswork.com/Autism-Asperger-s-Syndrome

Asperger Foundation, www.aspergerfoundation.org.uk/infosheets/sensoryissues.pdf (Detailed information about sensory issues and autism.)

"Expansion to what end?," www.cyc-net.org/cyc-online/cyconline-sep2010-gharabaghi.html (Kiaras Gharabaghi's delightful story in which he challenges our pride in the CYC profession's expansion into other areas, including work with children with autism.)

Autism quiz, www.medicinenet.com/autism_spectrum_disorder_quiz/quiz.htm

"Hope for Autism and Asperger's Syndrome: My Story" video, www.youtube.com/watch?v=OV_CcmLlaw4 (A 17-year-old describes her experience as a child with autism.)

Synaesthesia video, www.vimeo.com/36252713 (This video follows a main character and his experiences with synaesthesia.)

Externalizing behaviour associated with ADHD often attracts the attention of others and can result in impaired functioning in social relationships, academics, and other important aspects of development.

Case Example: *Karyn*

Karyn is a bright, active 13-year-old living in a small town in Saskatchewan. And although her teachers have noted that she's very intelligent, she has always struggled in school. Karyn is also an excellent writer, but has had difficulty reading since elementary school. She was known as a tomboy as a little girl, and still prefers outdoor activities and competitive sports to dance or music lessons. Karyn is entering high school next year, and is struggling academically: she's having increasing difficulty with inattentiveness in the classroom, organization of her homework materials, and time management. Consequently, her assignments are coming in late, if at all, and she's begun skipping school with a small group of girlfriends.

Karyn's parents report that her room is completely disorganized; she's becoming increasingly withdrawn, quiet, and tearful, spending a lot of time alone in her room on the internet; she hasn't been eating, and when she does eat, it's junk food alone in her room; and she's not participating in any of her organized extracurricular sports activities. Her parents are very worried about her; they're concerned that she's using alcohol and marijuana. They've requested a mental health assessment. Karyn is very resistant to this idea: she says she's fine, and refuses to talk to a "shrink."

Learning Objectives

1. Summarize the diagnostic criteria for each of the three presentations of ADHD identified in the DSM-5.

2. Summarize a CYC perspective for understanding attention deficits.

3. Compare and contrast primary psychological explanations for ADHD.

4. From a CYC perspective, summarize predominant explanations for the causes of ADHD.

5. Identify and describe psychological treatment approaches used in treating ADHD.

6. List and describe the most common comorbid conditions and secondary manifestations that can serve as indicators for ADHD.

7. Describe a variety of strength-based, CYC-relevant support strategies and interventions for ADHD behaviours.

Chapter Overview

The child and adolescent behaviours referred to as "externalizing" are frequently discussed as cause for concern; they're experienced as disruptive by parents, teachers, peers, and society at large. These disruptive behaviours have long been the focus of researchers, practitioners, and popular media. *Externalizing* behaviour problems include attention deficits and hyperactivity, which are associated with a diagnosis of Attention-Deficit/ Hyperactivity Disorder (ADHD) in the DSM-5. As discussed in Chapter 3, ADHD is a neurodevelopmental disorder. Given the extensive theory and research related to ADHD, we've devoted an entire chapter to this diagnosis. What are the primary symptoms of ADHD, and which of these is Karyn expressing in the opening case? Why do some children and youth exhibit extreme behaviours in these areas while others do not? What can parents, teachers, CYCPs, and other professionals do to support those diagnosed with this disorder?

From a psychological perspective, this chapter will summarize the major characteristics of ADHD and examine explanations for, and approaches to, intervention for related symptoms. The CYC perspective will focus on alternative ways to view attention deficits or disorders. As Mitchell (2003) points out, "What, if any, alternative theoretical approaches are there to the deficit-focused, future-oriented constructions of childhood? Are there culturally valid ways of defining children's behaviours outside or beyond constructions of 'pathology' such as Attention Deficit Disorder? Of course there are—this is the nature of theoretical and conceptual development in all fields" (p. 285). We'll discuss the controversies surrounding the ADHD diagnosis: whether it's overused; whether ADHD-associated behaviours represent a new phenomenon of neurological disorder or are more closely related to normal childhood behaviours; and whether an ADHD diagnosis ever really fully benefits the child. In addition, we'll review the appropriateness of medicating children and youth with attention difficulties and explore the high rates of co-occurrence of ADHD with a variety of other disorders, including Conduct Disorder, Oppositional Defiant Disorder, anxiety, depression, and substance misuse.

Finally, we'll present a variety of interventions for CYCPs to consider in their work with children, youth, and families who are struggling with attention difficulties.

WHAT ARE ATTENTION DEFICITS?

Attention deficits, or *inattention*, generally relate to difficulties in maintaining or directing attention. **Inattention** associated with ADHD typically involves difficulties in *sustained attention*, which requires persisting with a particular task despite fatigue, boredom, disinterest, or competing interests (e.g., studying for a test despite your desire to sleep). ADHD is also characterized by deficits in *selective attention*, which requires ignoring irrelevant stimuli in order to focus on a particular task (e.g., ignoring the television your roommate is watching and continuing to study for a test). Accordingly, those diagnosed with ADHD are more easily distracted by irrelevant but prominent or interesting objects or events in the environment. It's interesting to note that those diagnosed with ADHD don't demonstrate deficits in *attentional capacity*, which refers to the amount of information they can remember.

From a psychological standpoint, inattention seldom occurs alone. In particular, problems of attention often co-occur with *hyperactivity* and *impulsivity*. **Hyperactivity** refers to excessively energetic, high-energy activity that is inappropriate and not directed toward any particular goal (e.g., fidgeting, running aimlessly, climbing). Most often, this high-energy but directionless activity is accompanied by **impulsivity**, or the inability to consider the consequences of actions prior to acting. *Cognitive impulsivity* is associated with disorganized or hasty thought (e.g., not handing in homework even though it's complete) while *behavioural impulsivity* relates to difficulties inhibiting behaviour (e.g., shouting an answer out in class, touching a stove to see if it's hot). Most often, hyperactivity and impulsivity occur together and are considered to reflect a fundamental deficit in regulating motor behaviour, resulting in difficulties stopping or adjusting actions to suit the situation. Not surprisingly, these difficulties are most likely to be observed in situations where one is expected to sit still, be quiet, and regulate behaviour (e.g., classrooms, movie theatres).

Before turning to a discussion of other ADHD symptoms, examine your own experiences of inattention and hyperactivity by trying the *Think About It!* exercise.

Difficulties in ignoring irrelevant stimuli and remaining focused on a task despite fatigue, boredom, or disinterest are some of the ways in which concentration is impaired in ADHD.

WHAT IS ATTENTION-DEFICIT/HYPERACTIVITY DISORDER? THE PSYCHOLOGICAL PERSPECTIVE

Attention-deficit disorders are characterized by inattention, high levels of hyperactivity, and/or difficulties regulating impulsivity. Specifically, the DSM-5 identifies abnormalities in at least one of the following three general areas:

- *inattention* (e.g., not paying attention to instructions being given by teacher or parent)
- *hyperactivity* (e.g., fidgeting and jumping up and down in seat)
- *impulsivity* (e.g., blurting out an answer before the teacher has finished asking a question)

Thus, to be diagnosed with **Attention-Deficit/Hyperactivity Disorder (ADHD)**, one must exhibit signs in one or more of these general areas. Such symptoms must result in impairments in daily functioning in more than one context (e.g., at home *and* at school), with at least some of these symptoms being observed prior to age 12.

In addition to these primary or core symptoms of ADHD, some researchers and theorists identify **secondary manifestations** of ADHD, concerns associated with and often resulting from primary ADHD symptoms. For example, feelings of incompetence and low self-esteem might result from the inability to focus attention. As expressed by Debra, an adult living with ADHD, "I feel so dumb . . . I can never keep up with discussions. People talk about politics and current affairs and I have no head for these things. I try hard to remember facts and names and dates from the newspaper, but it doesn't stick. I tune out" (Maté, 1999, p. 242). Secondary manifestations of ADHD include academic and learning problems, motor coordination difficulties, distorted self-perceptions, low self-esteem, and deficits in cognitive processing.

DSM-5 Categories

The DSM-5 includes ADHD in the general category of neurodevelopmental disorders, those disorders that first appear "in the developmental period" (APA, 2013, p. 31). We saw in Chapter 3 that these typically appear prior to school age and are associated with significant developmental deficits that interfere with various aspects of functioning. ADHD is included in the DSM-5's chapter on disorders because it, too, appears early in development, has lasting implications for individual functioning, and is generally considered to be a **neurobiological condition** (or illness of the nervous system).

Neurodevelopmental Disorders   The DSM-5 includes ADHD as one of its seven general categories of neurodevelopmental disorders (as described in Chapter 3). Although the specific behaviours associated with these diagnoses may be observed into adulthood, they begin early in development.

Attention-Deficit/Hyperactivity Disorder: Diagnoses and Criteria

Three specific diagnoses are associated with the general ADHD category. Given how likely CYCPs are to work with young people diagnosed with an attention-deficit disorder, let's review their specific diagnostic criteria.

Attention-Deficit/Hyperactivity Disorder   The characteristic symptoms of ADHD include inattention, hyperactivity, and impulsivity. As we've seen, the inattention associated with ADHD typically involves difficulties in sustained attention, or the ability to stay focused despite other motivations. Symptoms of hyperactivity and impulsivity may or may not be present.

To be diagnosed with ADHD, a child must exhibit signs of inattention and/or hyperactivity-impulsivity that interfere with daily functioning in more than one context (e.g., at home *and* at school), with at least some of these symptoms being observed prior to age 12. How does ADHD differ from "normal," expected behaviour? While all children demonstrate some or all of these "symptoms" on occasion, the diagnosis requires that the pattern of behaviour be severe, persistent, impairing, and developmentally inappropriate given the child's chronological age. The diagnostic criteria for ADHD are presented in Box 4.1.

Box 4.1

DSM-5 Criteria for ADHD

A. A persistent pattern of inattention and/or hyperactivity-impulsivity that interferes with functioning or development, as characterized by (1) and/or (2):

   (1) Inattention: Six (or more) of the following symptoms have persisted for at least 6 months to a degree that is inconsistent with developmental level and that negatively impacts directly on social and academic/occupational activities:
   Note: The symptoms are not solely a manifestation of oppositional behaviour, defiance, hostility, or failure to understand tasks or instructions. For older adolescents and adults (age 17 and older), at least five symptoms are required.

   a. Often fails to give close attention to details or makes careless mistakes in schoolwork, at work, or during other activities (e.g., overlooks or misses details, work is inaccurate).

   b. Often has difficulty sustaining attention in tasks or play activities (e.g., has difficulty remaining focused during lectures, conversations, or lengthy reading).

c. Often does not seem to listen when spoken to directly (e.g., mind seems elsewhere, even in the absence of any obvious distraction).

d. Often does not follow through on instructions and fails to finish schoolwork, chores, or duties in the workplace (e.g., starts tasks but quickly loses focus and is easily sidetracked).

e. Often has difficulty organizing tasks and activities (e.g., difficulty managing sequential tasks; difficulty keeping materials and belongings in order; messy, disorganized work; has poor time management; fails to meet deadlines).

f. Often avoids, dislikes, or is reluctant to engage in tasks that require sustained mental effort (e.g., schoolwork or homework; for older adolescents and adults, preparing reports, completing forms, reviewing length papers).

g. Often loses things necessary for tasks or activities (e.g., school materials, pencils, books, tools, wallets, keys, paperwork, eyeglasses, mobile telephones).

h. Is often easily distracted by extraneous stimuli (for older adolescents and adults, may include unrelated thoughts).

i. Is often forgetful in daily activities (e.g., doing chores, running errands; for older adolescents and adults, returning calls, paying bills, keeping appointments).

(2) Hyperactivity and impulsivity: Six (or more) of the following symptoms have persisted for at least 6 months to a degree that is inconsistent with developmental level and that negatively impacts directly on social and academic/occupational activities:
Note: The symptoms are not solely a manifestation of oppositional behaviour, defiance, hostility, or failure to understand tasks or instructions. For older adolescents and adults (age 17 and older), at least five symptoms are required.

a. Often fidgets with or taps hands or feet or squirms in seat.

b. Often leaves seat in situations when remaining seated is expected (e.g., leaves his or her place in the classroom, in the office or other workplace, or in other situations that require remaining in one place).

c. Often runs about or climbs excessively in situations where it is inappropriate. (Note: In adolescents or adults, may be limited feeling restless.)

d. Often unable to play or engage in leisure activities quietly.

e. Is often "on the go", acting as if "driven by a motor" (e.g., is unable to be or uncomfortable being still for extended time, as in restaurants, meetings; may be experienced by others as being restless or difficult to keep up with).

f. Often talks excessively.

g. Often blurts out an answer before a question has been completed (e.g., completes people's sentences; cannot wait for turn in conversation).

h. Often has difficulty waiting his or her turn (e.g., while waiting in line).

i. Often interrupts or intrudes on others (e.g., butts into conversations, games, or activities; may start using other people's things without asking or receiving permission; for adolescents and adults, may intrude into or take over what others are doing).

B. Several inattentive or hyperactive-impulsive symptoms were present prior to age 12 years.

C. Several inattentive or hyperactive-impulsive symptoms are present in two or more settings (e.g., at home, school, or work; with friends or relatives; in other activities).

D. There is clear evidence that the symptoms interfere with, or reduce the quality of, social, academic, or occupational functioning.

It's important to note that the DSM-5 requires that practitioners distinguish between three presentations of ADHD: a *Predominantly Inattentive Presentation*, a *Predominantly Hyperactive/Impulsive Presentation*, and a *Combined Presentation*. The *Predominantly Inattentive Presentation* is applied when six or more symptoms of inattention but fewer than six symptoms of hyperactivity-impulsivity are observed for the past six months. The *Predominantly Hyperactive-Impulsive Presentation* is characterized by six or more symptoms of hyperactivity-impulsivity but fewer than six symptoms of inattention for the past six months. Most children and adolescents diagnosed with ADHD fall into the third category, *Combined Presentation*, in which six or more symptoms of both inattention and hyperactivity-impulsivity are observed for the past six months. Notice that for each presentation type, the symptoms must be observed for a period of at least six months. Because it's the most common, the *Combined Presentation* is most often considered in research studies investigating causes and treatment. But from a practical standpoint, it's important to recognize that not everyone with a diagnosis of ADHD will exhibit the same behaviours or experience the same difficulties.

In addition to these formal diagnostic categories, the DSM-5 includes two other attention-deficit disorders. *Other Specified Attention-Deficit/Hyperactivity Disorder* is diagnosed when ADHD symptoms are present but don't meet the formal criteria for the disorder; for example, a youth may have fewer and less severe or persistent symptoms of inattention. Along with this diagnosis, the mental health practitioner provides an explanation as to why the ADHD diagnosis doesn't apply. *Unspecified Attention-Deficit/Hyperactivity Disorder* is diagnosed when attention deficits are present and cause significant impairment but the youth doesn't meet all criteria for a specific disorder and no explanation is given as to why or what criteria aren't met.

Before turning to a discussion of the CYC approach to ADHD, try the *Test Your Understanding* exercise to review your understanding of the core symptoms. Can you identify the diagnosis that most closely matches the description for each case?

A CYC APPROACH TO ATTENTION DEFICITS: UNDERSTANDING ADHD

In the previous edition of the DSM (the DSM-IV-TR), ADHD was included not as a neurodevelopmental disorder, as it is now, but rather as one of the "disruptive disorders"— a category that included Conduct Disorder and Oppositional Defiant Disorder. You might ask yourself, "Why was such a change made?" According to the APA, the change better reflects how ADHD is now conceptualized as involving brain development issues. As well, the DSM-IV-TR chapter that included all diagnoses usually first made in infancy, childhood, or adolescence was eliminated altogether.

The DSM-5's diagnostic criteria for ADHD remain the same, except for these alterations: (1) the criterion items can be now applied across the lifespan; (2) the cross-situational requirement has been strengthened to include "several" symptoms in each setting; (3) the onset criterion has been changed from before age 7 to before age 12; (4) subtypes have been replaced with presentation specifiers that map directly onto the prior subtypes; (5) a comorbid diagnosis with Autism Spectrum Disorder is now allowed; and (6) a symptom threshold has been made for adults in order to reflect the substantial evidence of clinically significant ADHD impairment, with the cutoff of five instead of the six symptoms required for younger persons, both for inattention and hyperactivity and impulsivity ("Highlights of changes," 2013).

ADHD is often referred to as a "mild" to "moderate" dysfunction of the regulatory apparatus of the brain. Specifically, it appears that ADHD interferes with the complex functional systems identified with the prefrontal cortex. This interference affects children's ability to regulate their attention and manage their behavioural and emotional responses. ADHD is known to run in families, and although it tends to persist over the lifespan, individuals can learn to successfully adjust and compensate. Because ADHD affects outer-directed functions (attention, behaviour, and emotional responding), the difficulties young people experience usually involve their adaptation to external events. We need to appreciate, then, that some environments will evoke or aggravate the symptoms and others may not (Gualterie & Johnson, 2005).

Does viewing ADHD as a neurological disorder help CYCPs support children with ADHD? As Gabor Maté points out, shifting responsibility for negative behaviours onto brain circuitry makes these children into victims, helpless in the face of their disability: "People commonly say that this adult or that child 'is ADD' [now known as ADHD]. That, indeed, is labeling, identifying the whole person with an area of weakness or impairment. No one *is* ADD, and no one should be defined or categorized in terms of it or any other particular problem" (Maté, 2000, p. 23).

Is ADHD a mental disorder, or is it really pretty much "normal" childhood behaviour? Descriptions of ADHD symptoms date back as far as ancient Greece, when the physician Galen prescribed opium for colicky and restless infants (Flick, 1998). In 1845, Heinrich Hoffman wrote "The Story of Fidgety Philip"; published in 1904 in one of the most prestigious medical journals of the time, it's believed to be the first account of ADHD in the medical literature.

> "Let me see if Philip can be a little gentleman; Let me see if he is able to sit still for once at the table."
> Thus Papa bade Phil behave; And Mama looked very grave.
> But Fidgety Phil, He won't sit still;
> He wriggles, and giggles,
> And then, I declare,
> Swings backwards and forwards, And tilts up his chair,
> just like any rocking horse—"Philip! I am getting cross!"
> See the naughty, restless child growing still more rude and wild,
> till his chair falls over quite. Philip screams with all his might,
> Catches at the cloth, but then that makes matters worse again.
> Down upon the ground they fall, Glasses, plates, knives, forks and all.

How Mama did fret and frown, when she saw them tumbling down!
And Papa made such a face! Philip is in sad disgrace . . .

We recognize the behaviours of Fidgety Philip in such well-known characters as Dennis the Menace and Calvin in *Calvin and Hobbes*, and we may even know someone like him: the youngster who climbs the furniture, jumps out of windows, climbs to the top of trees, talks back to adults, and seems to be generally out of control despite his caregivers' best efforts.

In his book *Scattered Minds*, Gabor Maté (1999) provides an effective analogy for what it's like to struggle with ADHD:

> Imagine . . . you're standing in the middle of a really crowded room. Everyone around you is talking. Suddenly someone asks you "What did so-and-so just say?" That's what it's like inside the ADD brain and how it is for your child. A parallel analogy suits the situation the parents of ADD children find themselves in: you're stuck in the middle of heavy traffic at an intersection; the engine has stalled and you are trying your best to get moving. Everyone is yelling and honking angrily at you, but no one offers to help. (p. xviii)

Owing to their low tolerance of frustration, children and youth with ADHD often experience extreme mood swings and frequent temper tantrums. They can be known as stubborn, strong willed, and bossy, and often will exhibit a poor overall response to adult direction and to authority figures in general (Samuels & Sikorsky, 1998). Many engage in persistent obsessive thinking, have poor motor coordination skills, and can be inconsistent and unpredictable in their responses to others. They may also engage in serious risk-taking behaviours; when combined with impulsivity, these can often result in injuries, especially in adolescence.

Children struggling with ADHD are very likely to be acutely aware and emotionally sensitive to their considerable impairments and almost always suffer a great deal of emotional pain. Many, if not most, children with ADHD live with low self-esteem, which can persist throughout the lifespan; consequently, they're at high risk of developing clinical depression, whether as children or adults. They invariably have difficulties with academic functioning and social relationships; in fact, many children are so alienated from others that they may have no friends. Besides their own acute awareness of their personal and academic failures, they bear frequent teasing and criticism from their peers and struggle with those seemingly never-ending confrontations with adults.

Children with ADHD have many strengths as well. They're often skilled at math, can be very good readers, have artistic and creative talents, and have good memories. They're also generous, kind to others, good with animals, and helpful overall (Fidler, 2015). Many children with ADHD are good with gross motor skills and excel at computers and computer games. They can be deep thinkers and highly intelligent. Because the intelligence of a child with ADHD is typically at least average or above average, it's important that caregivers, parents, and teachers nurture their intellectual abilities and provide them with activities that will allow them to be creative, to think outside the box to solve problems (Fidler, 2015). It's especially important to find ways to harness their extra energy and to give specific praise and positive reinforcement for everything good they do.

Although ADHD is defined as a psychiatric disorder in the DSM, it's not considered a mental illness in the same way that depression and Schizophrenia are. A variety of biological factors, including brain functioning, account for the variance in explaining the onset of ADHD. Regardless of the etiological pathway, the result is a "core deficit in response inhibition," or in these children's ability to manage their own behaviour

(Kearney, 2003, p. 80). ADHD is best defined as a constellation of traits that cluster in a relatively small number of people. It's typical of a large group of neuropsychiatric conditions that affect many people to a mild or moderate degree and much smaller numbers of people to a very great degree (Gualterie & Johnson, 2005).

ADHD is still often thought of as the psychiatric diagnostic label used for children and youth who are "hyper" and exhibit inappropriate, difficult, or annoying behaviours. ADHD is certainly the most well known of the externalizing behaviour disorders. It's also the one diagnostic label used for children about which so many people have disagreed so intensely: on whether it's a real disorder, on how it should be defined, and on how it should be treated (McClure & Teyber, 2003). As Maté (1999) notes, "attention deficit disorder is usually explained as the result of bad genes by those who 'believe' in it and as the product of bad parenting by those who don't" (p. xvii). Some have suggested that the diagnosis is given solely to children who, like Fidgety Philip, constantly frustrate parents and teachers by their impulsive and distractible behaviour (Brendtro & Shahbazian, 2004). "Ironically, these disorders are defined mainly by the emotions they stir up in adults. Can a youth have a 'disruptive behaviour disorder' without somebody to disrupt? Does a tree falling in the forest make any sound if no one is there to hear it fall? Kids are called disruptive and disturbed when others in their life space feel disrupted and disturbed. Conflicts in interpersonal relationships are at the center of all major emotional disorders of children" (Brendtro & Shahbazian, 2004, p. 71).

As CYCPs, you may already have strong views about whether ADHD should be considered a psychiatric disorder, about whether all children diagnosed have received legitimate diagnoses, and about whether the most common medications used to treat ADHD are appropriate or if they could even be dangerous. However, for CYCPs, the main question is this: Does viewing ADHD as a neurological disorder help us in supporting these children and their families?

Regardless of our stand on these controversies, then, our role as CYCPs is to help support these children and youth in their emotional, self-regulation, relational, and behavioural difficulties related to ADHD. Understanding the implications and the usual related struggles of an ADHD diagnosis for children and their families will help us recognize the most common areas of difficulty these young people are experiencing. With this knowledge—and as we begin to establish a therapeutic relationship with them, identify their strengths, and develop an understanding of the context of their behaviour—we'll be better able to help them manage their behaviour in any setting, including the classroom, where it is often most difficult.

Before turning to a discussion of prevalence, development, and comorbidity, consider the details of the opening case in relation to the psychological and CYC views of attentional disturbances in the *Karyn's Case: Revisited* box.

Karyn's Case: *Revisited*

Consider the case of Karyn presented in the beginning of the chapter. Identify behaviours that would be associated with the diagnostic categories of ADHD. Identify any possible co-occurring disorders based on the description of her behaviours. What additional information might you ask Karyn, her teachers, and her caregivers in order to determine whether an ADHD diagnosis is the best fit?

HOW MANY YOUNG PEOPLE STRUGGLE WITH ATTENTION DEFICITS?

According to most researchers, ADHD is the second most common mental health problem in children, with as many as 5–8 percent to as high as 11 percent of Canadian children reportedly experiencing problems with inattention, hyperactivity, and impulsivity severe enough to warrant a clinical diagnosis of ADHD (Hoza, Kaiser, & Hurt, 2008). This essentially means that at any given time in Canada well over 270 800 children may experience an ADHD diagnosis and display the accompanying defined behavioural difficulties related to ADHD. Is this an overdiagnosis (Polanczyk et al., 2007; Schwartz et al., 2007; Waddell et al., 2005)?

In 2000, 43 percent of Canadian children with ADHD were taking medications; in 2007, this number had risen to 59 percent. According to Marie-Christine Brault (2012), "the increased use of medications by children with ADHD in Canada is a reflection of the global trend." The use of drugs like Ritalin has more than doubled since 1994, when it was 1.3 percent (Brault, 2012). More than two million prescriptions for Ritalin were written specifically for children under 17, a jump of 43 percent since 2005—and at least 75 percent of them were for young males: "a ratio some see as evidence that society is making a malady of boyhood itself" (Abraham, 2010).

One of most significant challenges in determining ADHD's prevalence is identifying those children and youth in its broad middle range. Given that ADHD is defined by the context of a situation and almost always by other people—in families, in classrooms, and in schoolyards—children at either end of the spectrum are relatively easily identified; however, there is a large population in the centre for whom a diagnosis would be far less clear. There is no question that, at minimum, an ADHD diagnosis is a matter of degree, with no clear boundaries; it's better thought of as a continuous variable rather than a categorical one (Charach et al., 2011).

There are consistent sex differences in diagnoses, with boys four to nine times more likely to meet the criteria for an ADHD diagnosis (Barkley, 2006). Age differences are observed as well, with the rates of ADHD higher in children under 12 than in adolescents. Other differences in ADHD prevalence rates may also be the result of diagnostic variations. However, the reported differences in gender, in ethnic background (higher in Aboriginal children), and in socioeconomic groups (higher in lower socioeconomic groups) raise questions about the socio-cultural implications of an ADHD diagnosis. For example, the findings of one Canadian study suggest either that Aboriginal children do have higher ADHD rates or that their unique cultural variations in learning and behavioural patterns have erroneously led to a diagnosis based on typical screening questionnaires. We know that cultural differences, expectations, ethnicity, and child-rearing practices very likely influence prevalence rates (Baydala et al., 2006). Different cultures interpret hyperactivity in children very differently. Some cultures are more tolerant of activity and more child-centred while other cultures are far less so.

Concerns regarding each of the externalizing disorders (ADHD, Conduct Disorder, and Oppositional Defiance Disorder) have been forwarded in the literature. The fact that each has been increasingly diagnosed in younger and younger populations over the years has led some to question the methods by which children and adolescents are assessed and how the diagnostic categories are applied. Typically, symptoms checklists, medical examinations, and interviews with parents, teachers, and others are part of the assessment process and provide information on which the diagnosis is based. Because there is no one single test for these disorders, and given that behaviour can change significantly from one day to the next, it's been argued that the increasing prevalence rates are a reflection of overdiagnosis rather than actual changes in incidence. What do you think about the politics of the ADHD diagnosis? Where do you stand with respect to this issue?

ADHD AND DEVELOPMENT

ADHD is most often diagnosed in school-aged children. In fact, the DSM notes that it's difficult to diagnose the disorder in children younger than four or five, given their developmentally limited abilities in attention and motor inhibition. Nevertheless, very young children later diagnosed with ADHD do tend to have higher levels of excessive activity, with parents reporting difficulties in restraining their child's behaviours.

Diagnosis is more likely in school-aged children as a result of increased expectations for children to sustain attention and inhibit their actions (e.g., sit still at a desk and listen to instruction despite competing interests). Behaviours associated with this diagnosis are most noticeable during the elementary school years and include *inattention*, which affects academic performance, *impulsivity*, resulting in rule violations, and high levels of *motor activity* (e.g., aimless running, climbing). Moving through to late childhood and adulthood, indicators of hyperactivity are more likely to include fidgeting and *subjective* feelings of restlessness rather than excessive motor activity, as well as restlessness and avoidance of activities that limit opportunities for movement.

In general, ADHD has a variable course, with some showing a decrease in symptoms as they move from childhood into adolescence and adulthood and others demonstrating a continuation of symptoms that impair functioning. Those children whose ADHD symptoms don't attenuate as they enter adolescence are at increased risk for poor outcomes, including decreased high-school completion, early substance use, increased driving infractions, early parenthood, increased contact with the law, and the onset of concurrent mental health issues (Wilens et al., 2006).

COMORBIDITY

As we've seen, attention deficits are frequently observed with disruptive behaviours. Several studies have found high rates of comorbidity between ADHD and Oppositional Defiant Disorder (ODD) (e.g., Biederman & Faraone, 2005; Costello et al., 2003), particularly in the case of the combined type of ADHD, although recent research also suggests an association between inattentive-type ADHD and ODD (40 percent; Acosta et al., 2008). Similarly, ADHD is often comorbid with Conduct Disorder (CD) (APA, 2000; Thapar, Harrington, & McGuffin, 2001). The comorbidity between ADHD and disruptive behaviour disorders is particularly concerning, given that outcomes during adolescence are usually much worse when a youth meets the diagnostic criteria for a comorbid disorder, especially ODD or CD. Such comorbidities increase the difficulty of working with adolescents with ADHD; hence, treatments for this subset of the population need to address a wide range of potential impairments (Evans et al., 2006).

Further, it's estimated that 15–75 percent of children and youth diagnosed with ADHD will also be diagnosed with a mood disorder (Fonagy et al., 2002), and up to one-third will be diagnosed with an anxiety disorder ("ADHD and coexisting disorders,"

2009). Interestingly, the type of comorbid problem appears to vary between those with hyperactivity and those without, with the former being more at risk of internalizing symptoms such as anxiety and depression (Werry Centre, 2008).

Studies show that youth living with ADHD experience the onset of Substance Use Disorders (SUD) at younger ages and at higher rates than their same-gender peers. As well, ADHD symptoms usually, though not always, precede the development of an SUD (Wilens, 2006). The exact mechanism influencing the development of an SUD in adolescents with ADHD is unknown. According to one well-known theory, youth use substances to self-medicate. This hypothesis is compelling in that ADHD is chronic and often associated with low self-esteem, demoralization, and an overriding sense of failure—all factors also associated with SUDs in adolescents. Adolescents with ADHD report using substances more frequently to manage their mood and to help them sleep. However, Wilens (2006) suggests that the self-medication theory needs to be tempered against more compelling and systematic data showing that the strongest association between ADHD and SUDs is the family influence, which includes exposure to parental SUDs during vulnerable developmental periods.

Since many other physical health problems can lead to concentration and hyperactivity difficulties, health care practitioners must consider these first. CYCPs must carefully assess the child's social history and then pass on this information, along with their behavioural observations, to the clinician. This will help rule out other health or social problems, such as anxiety, trauma, learning disabilities, and maltreatment. If children are experiencing undetected neglect or abuse, they may present with symptoms (such as inattentiveness) that stem from an anxiety related to other circumstances; if these children are wrongly labelled as having ADHD, the underlying issues remain unaddressed. ADHD, then, should only be diagnosed when all other possible causes for a child's symptoms have been ruled out (Schwartz et al, Fall 2007).

ADHD also co-occurs with other neurodevelopmental disorders (e.g., learning, communication, and tic disorders, described in Chapter 3; CADDRA, 2007; Nutt et al., 2007), major and bipolar depression, substance use disorders, and anxiety disorders. In addition to the primary symptoms of ADHD, secondary manifestations of this disorder include academic and learning problems, motor coordination difficulties (associated with accidents and injuries, poor handwriting), distorted self-perceptions (i.e., exaggerated expressions of

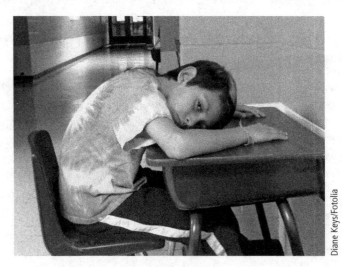

Diane Keys/Fotolia

Academic and learning problems are among the secondary manifestations of ADHD.

Common Myths About ADHD

MYTH: *ADHD is usually related to low intelligence.*

FACT: ADHD affects persons of all levels of intelligence. And although everyone sometimes has symptoms of ADHD, only those with chronic impairments from these symptoms warrant an ADHD diagnosis.

MYTH: *ADHD doesn't really cause much damage to a young person's life.*

FACT: Inadequately recognized ADHD syndrome can severely impair learning, family life, education, work life, and social interactions.

MYTH: *ADHD is really a label for misbehaviour issues. Children with ADHD just refuse to sit still and don't listen to teachers or parents.*

FACT: Many children with ADHD actually have few behaviour problems; chronic inattention causes more severe problems for them later.

Source: Adapted from "10 Myths and Facts about Attention Deficit Disorder (ADD/ADHD)" in Attention Deficit Disorder: The Unfocused Mind In Children and Adults by Thomas E. Brown. Copyright © 2005 by Yale University Press. Used by permission of Yale University Press.

self-worth and competence), and low self-esteem. Deficits in **executive functioning** (brain functions responsible for organizing, integrating, and managing other functions) are associated with difficulties in many areas, including self-regulation, self-awareness, language processes (e.g., communication and self-directed speech), and the inability to delay responses and plan ahead. As a result, risk taking is common, often leading to increased traffic accidents, risky sexual behaviours, and early substance use. Another secondary manifestation includes the conduct problems discussed earlier. Aggressive behaviour is observed in approximately 50 percent of those diagnosed with ADHD, and when it is, the prognosis is poorer (Gelfand & Drew, 2003). As we've seen, the loud, sometimes aggressive, disruptive behaviour associated with ADHD symptoms results in peer rejection and frequent conflict; accordingly, those diagnosed with ADHD often have few friends and are frequently disliked by their peers despite their attempts to interact with others.

Before turning to a discussion of the explanations and treatment of ADHD, read the statements in Box 4.2 and examine your own feelings about these behaviour patterns. How might your position on these issues relate to your behaviours toward someone diagnosed with ADHD?

EXPLAINING ADHD: PSYCHOLOGICAL PARADIGMS

What are some of the most common explanations for ADHD? As with all disorders, the best explanation will vary in relation to one's theoretical framework. From a psychological perspective, predominant explanations of ADHD include those proposed from the biological and sociocultural paradigms. Consistent with previous discussions of explanations for disorders, it's likely that the best explanations for these behaviour patterns emerge from consideration of biological, psychological, and social factors. In other words, there is no single cause for any of these diagnoses, although some explanations have greater empirical support than others.

Biological Paradigm   It has been argued that genetics and neurobiological factors are the most significant determinants of ADHD (Barkley, 2003; Kuntsi & Stevenson, 2000). From a biological paradigm, the role of genetics, brain structures, and biochemical processes have been considered.

Heredity and Genetics. As we mentioned earlier, ADHD runs in families (APA, 2000; Smalley et al., 2000; Thapar et al., 2007), suggesting that genetics predisposes an individual to developing the disorder. More specifically, levels of hyperactivity, impulsivity, and inattention appear to be influenced by genetics. Research suggests that those with greater degrees of genetic relatedness (e.g., identical versus fraternal twins) have a greater similarity in activity levels, impulsivity, inattention, and reading disabilities (Nadder et al., 2001; Thapar & Thapar, 2003; Willcutt, Pennington, & DeFries, 2000). Specific genes associated with these characteristics have yet to be established, although it's been hypothesized that genes regulating dopamine activity may be particularly relevant (Sikström & Söderlund, 2007; Solanto, 2002).

Brain Structures. As early as 1902, the overactivity, inattention, and other characteristics that comprise the current diagnostic criteria for ADHD were noted to occur in the context of brain damage caused by injury and/or *anoxia* (lack of oxygen) during birth. Observations made in the context of viral epidemics and brain injuries in soldiers and children (e.g., Strecker, 1929) also supported the link between hyperactivity, impulsivity, and damage to the brain. Accordingly, neurological abnormalities have been explored in relation to ADHD, and findings reveal abnormalities in the frontal lobes, basal ganglia, and cerebellum in some cases (Casey, 2001; Castellanos, 2001). In particular, abnormalities in the frontal lobes are associated with impaired executive functioning and behaviour inhibition, believed by some to underlie all the symptoms of ADHD (Barkley, 2008). Refer to Appendix 2 to view the location of these brain structures.

Both genetic and non-genetic factors, then, may relate to these neurobiological differences that predispose the individual to developing ADHD. Other non-genetic factors associated with ADHD include low birth weight, prenatal exposure to alcohol and nicotine, birth complications, and exposure to stress shortly before or after birth (Biederman, 2005; Patel et al., 2010).

Although relationships between brain structures, brain function, neurotransmitter activation, and the diagnoses of ADHD have been observed, it can't be assumed that these biological factors *cause* the behaviours they're associated with or that they alone explain the development of this disorder. Rather, it may be that any of a long list of possible factors (e.g., birth trauma, prenatal exposure to toxins, physical trauma in childhood) creates subtle damage to the developing brain, increasing the likelihood that a young person will exhibit one or more of the behaviours that characterize ADHD. The extent to which functioning is affected, however, will also depend on the social and environmental context in which the child or adolescent is developing.

Neurotransmitters. Genetics influence neurochemical systems, and in the case of ADHD, the neurotransmitters dopamine and norepinephrine have been of particular interest. This is consistent with the fact that the effectiveness of biological treatments for ADHD appears to lie in their interfering with the reuptake of dopamine and/or norepinephrine, thereby increasing the activation of these neurotransmitters in various brain areas (particularly the frontal lobes).

Psychodynamic Paradigm Generally, the psychodynamic paradigm explains ADHD in relation to behavioural difficulties in responding to various environments, including family and school (Rafalovich, 2001). From this perspective, ADHD represents difficulties in interaction between the self and the social environment (Salomonsson, 2011). Rather than being viewed as a cause of ADHD symptoms, however, such interactional difficulties are considered as the result of neuropsychological deficits. From a psychoanalytic approach, then, the goal is to "develop an adequate understanding of the neuropsychological deficits in patients' development" (Palumbo, 2011, p. 1) and how these impact psychodynamic processes, including how the individual perceives his behaviour in relationships with family and peers as well as how he understands the connection between symptoms and emotions.

Behavioural Paradigm Gray (1987) proposed that motivation and behaviour are explained by two brain systems (composed of different neural structures and regulated by different neurotransmitter systems): a *behavioural activation system (BAS)* and a *behavioural inhibition system (BIS)*. The **BAS** *stimulates* behaviour (particularly in the context of possible reinforcements) and is associated with seeking rewards and pleasure. The **BIS** *inhibits* behaviour (particularly in the context of possible punishments) and is associated with the experience of fear and avoiding pain. Research has demonstrated that those diagnosed with ADHD have greater sensitivity to rewards, particularly immediate rewards (Luman, Oosterlaan, & Sergeant, 2005). It has therefore been proposed that those with ADHD will learn best when frequent reinforcements are provided; conversely, situations that offer few rewards are likely to be those that elicit the primary symptoms of the disorder. Thus, rather than being a cause of the disorder, behavioural factors may predispose the individual to demonstrate symptoms in some environments more than others.

Also relevant from a behavioural perspective are the negative experiences (i.e., punishments) that are common for youth exhibiting symptoms of hyperactivity, impulsivity, and inattention. These symptoms evoke negative reactions from parents, peers, and teachers that might then be associated with feelings of frustration and failure.

Cognitive Paradigm Multiple cognitive factors can be considered relevant in the occurrence of ADHD symptoms. Deficits in problem solving, cognitive self-regulation, memory, lack of organization, and impaired attentional processes might all be considered as part of cognitive functioning. As we've seen, these deficits can be related to specific neurological abnormalities in structures and processes. Other cognitive theories, however, consider thoughts and schemas that youth might develop as a consequence of negative treatment by others. For example, constant reminders from parents and teachers to "sit still" and "pay attention" can have a negative impact on the youth's self-concept and lead to negative self-schemas (Scanlon, 2006). Such negative views of self can serve to impair various aspects of cognitive, social, and psychological functioning.

Sociocultural Paradigm Although biological factors appear to play an important role in ADHD, it's clear that there is no single *cause* for this disturbance. Instead, it's more realistic to think about the development of ADHD in relation to the diathesis–stress model discussed in Chapter 1. Accordingly, biological factors create a predisposition for developing the disorder but social and cultural factors contribute to the likelihood that the inclination will manifest as well as impact the severity of symptoms and occurrence of comorbid conditions. From the sociocultural paradigm, explanations for externalizing behaviour patterns, including ADHD, have included cultural factors as well as the immediate family environment of the child and/or adolescent.

Culture and Externalizing Disorders. It's been argued that the externalizing disorder of ADHD is significantly more prevalent in industrialized societies, including Canada, the United States, Australia, Japan, and South Africa (APA, 2000). More recent investigations, however, bring this general conclusion into question. The incidence of ADHD appears to be relatively consistent across cultures, supporting the role of genetic and neurobiological factors in the occurrence of the disorder (Canino & Alegria, 2008; Polanczyk et al., 2007). Such findings suggest that biological factors play a greater role in the onset of ADHD than in other externalizing disorders (i.e., Conduct Disorder, Oppositional Defiant Disorder). Cultural factors (e.g., social norms, beliefs, values) do, however, have a significant impact on how others perceive and react to those diagnosed with ADHD.

Family Influences. The immediate social environment has been considered extensively in relation to ADHD. Early psychological trauma (including exposure to stressors associated with various family factors) may affect the developing brain with consequences for later executive functions (Perry, 2009). Although psychosocial factors likely play less of a role than biological factors in ADHD, elements of the immediate social context will still affect the characteristics and severity of the symptoms in this disorder. Studies show that a number of family factors (e.g., poverty, family conflict, marital discord, separation, divorce, and other stressors) are related to ADHD. Parent psychopathology (e.g., depression, anxiety) is also correlated with ADHD (Nigg & Hinshaw, 1998). The nature of the relationship between child and parent has been observed to affect the symptoms displayed by those diagnosed with ADHD, with parents more likely to be impatient, restrictive, and controlling (Woodward, Taylor, & Dowdney, 1998). Of course, this parenting is likely to be impacted by the behaviour of the child as well, suggesting a bidirectional relationship (Johnston & Mash, 2001). Some studies have observed that following medical treatment, not only do ADHD symptoms decrease in the child/adolescent, but the number of negative and controlling communications by parents also decreases (Barkley, 1988; Humphries, Kinsbourne, & Swanson, 1978). It should be noted that although these family factors correlate with ADHD, the nature of the causal relationship between these and the biological factors discussed previously and how they interact to shape the disorder is currently unknown (Wicks-Nelson & Israel, 2006).

A CYC LENS ON THE PSYCHOLOGICAL PARADIGMS: A HOLISTIC CONCEPTUAL MODEL

Although there is no one single hypothesized cause of ADHD (Kendall, & Comer, 2010), it is increasingly accepted that coalescing risk factors influence the onset of the troublesome behaviours associated with this diagnosis. So in order for CYCPs to understand how ADHD may be affecting a particular young person, they must use an ecological, holistic framework to examine all the potential influencing variables. They must also examine the unique strengths and needs of every individual who struggles with ADHD and its associated difficulties.

Specifically, CYCPs must understand the interplay between genetic predisposition and environment in the onset of ADHD. They need to review the research demonstrating that ADHD tends to run in families—that it is *genetic and inheritable*—but that it's not known whether the genetic or environmental factors or their interaction can cause it to occur (McClure & Teyber, 2003). Most researchers and clinicians now agree that "an individual may genetically acquire a predisposition to develop ADHD in response to environmental events" (Kendall & Comer, 2010, p. 83). In addition, the more serious the symptoms of the parent's ADHD, the more likely or more significant will be the contribution of genetics to the development of ADHD in the child (Kendall & Comer, 2010). This is important to consider for assessment purposes.

Environmental influences include maternal smoking and alcohol consumption during pregnancy, perinatal stress, low birth weight, traumatic brain injury, neglect, maltreatment, and early deprivation (Schwartz et al., 2007). Since some behavioural symptoms of ADHD mirror the symptoms of Fetal Alcohol Spectrum Disorder (FASD), this disorder must first be ruled out, especially if there is a risk for parental alcohol use during pregnancy. Other potential causes must be similarly considered and ruled out before concluding that ADHD is the best explanation for the hyperactivity, impulsivity, and/or inattention exhibited by a child or adolescent.

Attachment and early childhood familial relationships have also been implicated in the development of ADHD. As explained earlier, genetically and biochemically, ADHD is characterized by atypical dopamine activity in the brain, although no one knows whether this process is caused by genes or by the environment. Although it's generally presumed to be genetic, the same processes could result from environmental causes or from the interaction of genetic and environmental conditions (Crittenden & Kulbotten, 2007). With regard to the environment, and from an attachment perspective, we know that certain family characteristics are associated with ADHD. These include marital discord, hostile parent–child relationships, and overall conflictual family life (Crittenden & Kulbotten, 2007).

Among the most important early family influences is the quality of child attachment to the caregiver. **Attunement** is the "quintessential component" of attachment (Maté, 2000, p. 74); it refers to the process of sharing emotional space, whereby baby leads and caregiver follows or responds to the infant's emotional state. Attunement is necessary for the normal development of brain pathways and the neurochemical apparatus of both attention and emotional self-regulation (Maté, 2000). As Maté (2000) recounts, parents of the children with ADHD he sees in his practice almost always describe extreme power struggles and strained parent–child and family relationships. For example, 11-year-old Brian has all the classic signs of ADHD: he's disorganized and easily distracted, his moods fluctuate, and he can erupt suddenly into a rage or a sulk. His mother reported that she can't predict what will set him off; that Brian won't listen to her, covering his ears with his hands when she talks to him; and that getting ready for school is impossible, suppertime is a zoo, bedtime is a nightmare, and so on. When his parents came to see Dr. Maté, they reported that Brian had recently become rude and insulting, sometimes shouting obscenities at them (Maté, 2000). As Maté explains, this all-too-familiar story usually results in treatment approaches directed toward the child. However, if interventions were based on attachment theory (Crittenden & Kulbotten, 2007), the functioning of all family members would be considered, which is precisely what Maté indicated to Brian's parents. For Brian, unconditional positive regard and an atmosphere of safety and support helped establish a home in which he felt safe. Three months later, Brian's parents reported a changed atmosphere in the home and fewer outbursts.

"Bad parenting" or maltreatment doesn't cause ADHD; instead, CYCPs need to understand that parenting a child with ADHD-related behaviours can involve significant challenges. Although CYCPs must explore young people's attachment strategies and early childhood experiences, they must avoid the assumption that parents simply need to be taught different parenting strategies and additional skills.

Another critical issue for CYCPs to understand is that a lack of self-regulation is symptomatic of both ADHD and complex trauma disorders. The brain of a child who's experienced trauma is wired to respond to perceived threats in the external environment and is thus constantly preoccupied with external stimuli. These children are known to be hypervigilant; consequently, they may misinterpret threats and are considerably less able than others to be aware of their internal emotional state. The ability to self-regulate is based on this awareness, which is in turn used to manage emotions, to make decisions, and to act accordingly. The brain of maltreated or neglected children, like that of children with ADHD, is often unable to make the connection between their own internal emotional state and their external behaviour. The lack of self-regulation prevents the conscious ability to tune out some stimuli and focus on other stimuli. As Ziegler (2002) recommends, "Always look for the cause behind the symptoms" (p. 57).

WHERE DO YOU STAND?

Consider both the psychological and the CYC perspectives on ADHD. Clearly, even psychologists disagree on the relative contributions of genetics and environment to ADHD. Although there are many concerns about the diagnosis of ADHD from a CYC perspective, understanding the multiple views on this pattern of behaviour can empower CYCPs to develop their own informed view of ADHD and to better understand the views of others (including the diagnosed youth) on its behaviours and challenges. Try the *Take Action!* exercise to evaluate your understanding of some of the predominant paradigms used to understand attentional disturbances.

Take Action! Exercise: *Tyler's Case*

Sixteen-year-old Tyler is in Grade 11 in an alternative school program in eastern Canada. He was referred to this program after being expelled numerous times for belligerence and aggressive behaviour. Tyler struggles academically, but he excels in computer, drama, music, and art. He's managing his acting-out behaviour, and with the help of a CYCP's one-to-one support in the classroom, he's passing his courses. Tyler has never been assessed for a learning difficulty or for any mental health concerns, but, like Karyn, he struggles with managing his time, organizing his assignments, maintaining focus on his work, and making and keeping friends. He lacks appropriate social skills and easily *loses his temper. Tyler complains about not having any friends, but claims it doesn't matter to him. His mother is a single parent raising four children on social assistance. She's been a strong support for Tyler, and is actively engaged with the school and the CYCP. If Tyler has one more extreme acting-out episode, he'll be expelled from the alternative school program.*

Explain how Tyler's symptoms/diagnosis might be explained and treated from each of the following paradigms: biological, behavioural, cognitive, sociocultural, and holistic. For each paradigm, what additional information about Tyler's history would you need to know more about?

HELPING CHILDREN AND ADOLESCENTS WITH ATTENTION DEFICITS

Psychological Approaches to Treatment

From a psychological perspective, what is the best way to help a child or adolescent suffering from symptoms associated with ADHD? Although biologically based disorders tend to be treated using biological interventions, psychological research demonstrates the

Recently, Karyn has been having great difficulty making friends or participating in social situations; she prefers to be home alone in her room. Her mother has described her as "being unhappy" most of the time. Within the past few months, Karyn has been bullied on Facebook by a group of girls, and she's becoming more and more despondent. The girls tell her that she's ugly, doesn't know how to dress, has body odour, is fat, and so on. Her mother told the CYCP that she's worried Karyn may hurt herself. School reports note that Karyn has withdrawn completely and stays away from the girls. Recently her support worker found her in the school washroom sobbing. Karyn told her that she couldn't take it anymore, and that she was going to kill herself. The CYP completed a suicide safety plan and called the local mental health agency's Youth Mobile Crisis Support Services.

effectiveness of treatment approaches that are based in other paradigms. In particular, cognitive and behavioural approaches have been evaluated extensively in relation to their effectiveness in decreasing ADHD symptoms. Let's review the predominant approaches to intervention from the biological, psychodynamic, behavioural, cognitive, and sociocultural paradigms and compare their relative effectiveness in the management of ADHD symptoms.

Biological Paradigm   One common myth is that the brains of those diagnosed with ADHD are overactive and that medication is needed to help them calm down. In fact, it's the *underactivity* of various brain areas that results in ADHD symptoms. The traditional use of **stimulants** or **psychostimulants** (methylphenidate or amphetamines) to treat ADHD is one of the most controversial topics in the area of child psychology. These medications increase the activation of dopamine and norepinephrine in various brain areas, including the frontal lobes, resulting in more sustained attention, enhanced impulse control, and decreased directionless activity, aggression, and disruptive behaviours (Connor, 2002; Murphy, Pelham, & Lang, 1992; Swanson et al., 1995; Van der Oord et al., 2008). Although these effects sound desirable, they're temporary (lasting only a few hours), particularly for the *short-acting agents*. Consequently, the child or adolescent has to take the drug several times per day, which can decrease the likelihood of adherence (i.e., a dose is forgotten). *Long-acting stimulants* offer the advantage of requiring only one dose per day, and so are less likely to be misused for their stimulant effects. However, these long-acting agents are more expensive and may be more likely to negatively impact appetite and sleep later in the day. A non-stimulant alternative, atomoxetine (Strattera), has also demonstrated some effectiveness in reducing the primary symptoms of ADHD. Because it inhibits the reuptake of norepinephrine (rather than dopamine), there is little to no abuse potential, although it takes significantly longer to see behavioural effects (Dickson et al., 2011) and may be less effective than methylphenidate (Michelson et al., 2002). As a result, this medication is best suited to those who don't require immediate reduction in symptoms. See Table 4.1 for an overview of common medications used to treat ADHD.

Despite the evidence from controlled studies demonstrating the effectiveness of stimulant medication in reducing the core symptoms of ADHD (Connor, 2007), not all youth show benefits from treatment (Swanson et al., 1995). For example, those with ADHD who also demonstrate aggression seem to benefit less from such treatments than those with ADHD symptoms alone (Wang et al., 2011). In addition, practitioners,

Table 4.1 Common Medications for ADHD

Drug	Mechanism of Action	Outcomes for Children/Adolescents	Possible Side Effects
Short-Acting and Intermediate-Acting Stimulants (require multiple administrations, although intermediate may last up to eight hours) Dexedrine Dexedrine Spansule Ritalin Ritalin SR	Believed to increase levels of action of various neurotransmitters (dopamine, norephinephrine) through increased release and blocking of reuptake mechanisms	Decrease core symptoms in approximately 75 percent of users; should *not* be used in context of significant substance use/abuse; multiple doses may decrease adherence	Headache, sleep and appetite disturbance; tics, irritability, rebound hyperactivity; blurred vision, cardiac concerns (most clearly for those with pre-existing cardiac problems), growth stunting, possible misuse; psychotic or manic symptoms (particularly in those with bipolar disorder or previous manic episodes); seizures
Long-Acting Stimulants (once-daily dosing) Adderall XR Biphentin Concerta Vyvanse	Same as above	Same as above; advantage is that administration is only once daily	Less likely to be misused for stimulant properties
Non-Stimulant Strattera (atomoxetine)	Inhibit reuptake of norepinephrine	Reduces primary symptoms in approximately 65 percent of individuals after 6–12 weeks of treatment but has slower onset of action (2–4 weeks) and decrease of symptoms is less pronounced than with stimulant treatment	Nausea, dizziness, headaches, sleep and appetite disturbance, nervousness, jitteriness, hypertension

researchers, and parents have all raised concerns about the use of these drugs—particularly their side effects, their overuse and misuse, their long-term developmental consequences, and their role in aggression and suicidal thoughts. Controlled studies investigating these issues often show inconsistent results, and few have evaluated the drugs' long-term effectiveness (Hechtman & Greenfield, 2003). Potential hazards of medical treatment are even less clear in cases where there are comorbid conditions (Jun, 2009). As pointed out by Jun (2009), beyond efficacy, "safety, both short- and long-term, is a very important consideration, particularly in pediatric patients" (p. 2003). Clearly, in each case the benefits and risks must be evaluated extensively and repeatedly during treatment (Flisher et al., 2010).

Without question, controversy continues over the use of biological treatments for ADHD, ODD, and CD. Despite existing concerns, medication is typically the first line of treatment for ADHD, and as we will see in the next section, often part of the most effective interventions available. What is your position on the use of such treatments?

Psychodynamic Paradigm   From a psychodynamic perspective, ADHD symptoms are seen as resulting from difficulties with interacting in the social environment. Therefore, psychodynamic approaches to treatment seek to help these young people learn about their inner world and relationships with others. The therapeutic relationship provides a context in which they might explore and come to better understand their experiences in relationships as well as the meaning they assign to their experiences in the environment. However, Zabaranko (2011) suggests that psychodynamic approaches to treating ADHD have been slowed in their development for two reasons. First is the assumption that if ADHD is neurobiological, those diagnosed with the disorder will be unsuitable for approaches that encourage self-discovery. Second, it's sometimes felt that medications used to treat ADHD symptoms might interfere with the psychoanalytic process.

Despite these concerns, Zabarenko (2011) argues that psychoanalysis can significantly contribute to ADHD interventions by helping young people develop emotionally and by providing therapists with insights into their internal world. Rather than as stand-alone interventions, however, psychodynamic treatment might be viewed best as a complement to other standard treatments (e.g., medication). Consistent with the acknowledgment of neurobiological factors in ADHD, psychodynamic therapists need to consider the neuropsychological strengths and weaknesses of each client (Zabarenko, 2011).

Behavioural Paradigm   Behavioural interventions are frequently used together with biological approaches in treating ADHD. These interventions emphasize operant conditioning principles by teaching caregivers the effective use of consequences (i.e., rewards and punishments). Following desired behaviour, *social reinforcers* (e.g., praise) are given and tokens or points can be exchanged for a variety of rewards (e.g., movies, time on playground). Following undesired behaviour, negative punishment (removing a desired stimulus) is used; for example, if the child doesn't complete his homework, his television privileges might be suspended for the evening.

Although most research has focused on younger children (Smith et al., 2000), behavioural interventions for ADHD have generally been found to be highly effective for both children and adolescents (Evans, Pelham, & Grudberg, 1995; Fabiano et al., 2009). It's worth noting, however, that some research suggests behavioural approaches alone are less effective than when used together with medication (Dopheide, 2005). Some consider *multimodal treatment*—which combines medication with behaviour-based approaches and other psychosocial interventions—as the most effective approach (American Academy of Child and Adolescent Psychiatry, 2007).

Cognitive Paradigm   A cognitive-behavioural approach to treating ADHD generally involves educating the individual about the diagnosis and helping him or her develop coping and problem-solving skills (e.g., time management strategies, cognitive restructuring). Although cognitive-behavioural interventions are considered likely to be effective for those diagnosed with ADHD (Roberts et al., 2003), particularly children, and some research suggests they may be beneficial (Kazdin & Wassell, 2000b; Toplak et al., 2008), they're not currently evidence based. There is little empirical support for their effectiveness, suggesting that observed effects don't last and that the skills aren't likely to be generalized beyond the therapeutic context to real-life settings (Pelham & Fabiano, 2008). Of particular note is their lack of effectiveness with adolescents. More promising is the use of CBT in the treatment of persistent ADHD in adults (Safren et al., 2010).

Sociocultural Paradigm: Approaches to Treatment
From a sociocultural standpoint, the treatment of ADHD involves changing variables in the young person's social environment. Although most of these interventions focus on the family and the classroom, some are directed more specifically toward the child or adolescent. Many programs have been developed in an attempt to decrease the symptoms of externalizing disorders and their negative consequences. While each has its own unique approach, most are multimodal treatments that combine elements of behavioural and/or cognitive-behavioural therapy with medication. Here we consider some of the basic components of such programs and evidence supporting their effectiveness.

In addition to being used alone, behavioural strategies serve as the basis for *parent training* programs, *classroom management* interventions, and *intensive behaviour modification* programs (the latter provided in a summer-camp context in which the child receives individualized instruction from trained staff; e.g., Pelham and colleagues' Summer Treatment program).

Parent Training. Parent training programs generally aim to teach parents of youth with a diagnosis of ADHD, ODD, or CD how to effectively use specific child-management techniques (Anastopoulos & Farley, 2003). Typically, these programs consist of 8–12 sessions and are considered appropriate for those between 4 and 12 years of age (Seligman & Reichenberg, 2012). While the specific goals of such programs may vary, the general objectives tend to be focused around effective use of behavioural strategies to improve parental discipline and monitoring, increase family unity, and improve parent–child communication and problem solving.

A review of the literature found that behavioural management training for parents (PMT) was associated with significant improvements in ADHD symptoms; the review thus recommends that such approaches be considered among the first line of response for the disorder (Pelham & Fabiano, 2008). Despite these encouraging findings, some limitations are worth noting. Additional results suggest that the effects of stimulants are as strong as or stronger than the effects of PMT in treating primary symptoms of ADHD. For example, the *Multimodal Treatment Study of Children with ADHD*, or MTA (the largest long-term treatment investigation ever conducted, studying 560 children aged 7–9 for 14 months) found that the most positive outcomes were observed in children who had received medication (either alone or in combination with cognitive-behavioural strategies), although long-term effects did not hold for everyone (Swanson et al., 2008). Still, compared with those who received medication alone, lower dosages of medication were required when behavioural interventions were included in treatment (Vitiello et al., 2001). It has also been observed that PMT is less effective if one or more parents also have the disorder (Sonuga-Barke, 2002). Other challenges include high drop-out rates for parents (Mulford & Redding, 2008) and the fact that these interventions aren't equally available among all social classes (Jensen, 2000; Schachar & Tannock, 2002). The greatest effects of PMT are observed when training is offered via specialists versus routine care (Sonuga-Barke, 2005), further limiting accessibility to this treatment. And since the greatest effect of behavioural strategies is observed when they're applied across settings (i.e., home and school) rather than in a single context (Smith, Barkley, & Shapiro, 2006), a unified approach across care providers is important, but this is not always possible.

Additional Psychosocial Approaches. A long list of other treatment approaches have been recommended and evaluated in the literature. For example, *family therapy*,

There is no "one size fits all" CYC intervention that can be used to support youth struggling with ADHD.

Naluwan/Shutterstock

which focuses on coping with stressors associated with ADHD, has been used but there is no empirical support for its effectiveness (Roberts et al., 2003).

Generally, psychosocial treatments are more effective with children than with adolescents. For the latter, strategies that emphasize problem solving and parent–adolescent communication may be preferred (Zisser & Eyberg, 2010). However, for those with ADHD alone, data from two of the largest studies of ADHD treatment found that medication was just as effective as medication combined with psychosocial treatment that included parent training, psychotherapy, and skills training (MTA Cooperative Group, 2004). Interestingly, those with ADHD and either a comorbid disorder (Conners et al., 2001) or significant stressors (Arnold et al., 2003) did demonstrate added benefits from parent training and behavioural interventions provided together with medication. Clearly, then, the optimal intervention for any particular child or adolescent is dependent on many factors.

CYC Approaches for Youth Struggling with ADHD

Since there is no one-size-fits-all CYC intervention to support young people and their families struggling with the impairments related to ADHD, CYCPs need to approach their work with children and youth affected by ADHD in the context of their life space, taking into account their existing strengths, resiliencies, and risk factors (both past and present). In other words, we need to observe them in the context of their relational and behavioural difficulties and respond accordingly. Consequently, our discussion of CYC approaches and interventions for the behaviours associated with ADHD is very broad.

Strength-Based Relational CYC Practice   As we've stressed throughout this text, one of the foundations of CYC practice is the understanding that young people's problem behaviours usually "say as much about the context in which these problem behaviours occur as they do about the child" (Long, 2009, p. 1). All behaviour serves a purpose, all behaviour meets a need, and all behaviour is multidimensional: each child is unique, with her own gifts and strengths.

Assessment

Because ADHD is one of those conditions whose symptoms may or may not be present depending on the circumstances—known as *situational variability*—it's particularly important to consider observational data from many sources and contexts. In order for ADHD to be diagnosed, the DSM-5 requires observations of several of the problematic behaviours in two or more settings. The signs of ADHD tend to be more noticeable in structured and task-oriented settings like classrooms, and less observable in unstructured or play settings or at home. Signs are also more likely to be observed when children are in their peer groups than when they're in one-to-one situations. Moreover, as McClure and Teyber (2003) note, some children are more *situationally hyperactive* (hyperactive only in one setting) and others are more *pervasively hyperactive* (hyperactive in many or all settings). Unsurprisingly, situationally hyperactive children have an overall better likelihood of successful symptom management than those whose pervasive hyperactivity makes their behaviour more disruptive and thus more likely to result in lasting difficulties with adults and peers (McClure & Teyber, 2003).

A mental health practitioner, a medical doctor, or a therapist/clinician will complete the assessment process for an ADHD diagnosis. The role of CYCPs in most instances is to assist with observations and documentation. The assessing clinician or health practitioner will obtain multiple sources of information from all the individuals who observe a child across the different settings. One factor affecting the assessment process is the likelihood that children with ADHD will often display co-occurring difficulties in combination with various other mental health concerns.

A thorough assessment for ADHD should address not only the symptoms but also all aspects of the child's behavioural, emotional, and social functioning. The clinical evaluation of ADHD must be fully comprehensive and multidimensional in nature in order to capture all situational variability and the impact on the child's functioning in home, school, and social relationships (McClure & Teyber, 2003).

The literature suggests that, at minimum, a multi-method assessment approach should include caregiver/parent and child interviews; caregiver/parent- and teacher-completed child behaviour rating scales; caregiver/parent self-report measures; clinic-based psychological tests; review of prior school and medical records; intelligence testing, educational achievement testing, and screening for learning disabilities; and a standard pediatric examination or neurodevelopmental screening to rule out any unusual medical conditions that might produce ADHD-like symptoms (Anastopoulos, Klinger, & Temple, 2015).

Indicators to Recognize   There are a variety of ADHD indicators that CYCPs should observe for. Before examining these, however, keep in mind that although young people diagnosed with ADHD may be impulsive and distractible, they can learn from their mistakes; they can come to understand the consequences of their behaviour and to change it. With ongoing assistance, their thought processes will improve over time and can eventually lie within the normal range.

Cognitive deficits are known to be central ones for children with ADHD, who tend to have difficulty with tasks managed by the executive functioning areas of the brain. These areas are responsible for problem solving, planning, abstract thinking, and inhibition. EEG recordings show delayed patterns of brain maturation; other brain imaging studies show that circuitry in the temporal and frontal lobes of the brain are also delayed

(Kauffman, 2001). As well, brain scans show that memory and fine and gross motor coordination are affected. In addition, problems of motivation appear to be involved; children and youth with ADHD often don't do what they know how to do (Kauffman, 2001).

As we saw earlier, the DSM-5 lists three core dimensions of ADHD: inattention, impulsivity, and hyperactivity. CYCPs need to recognize these dimensions in order to effectively help children and youth in a variety of settings; these young people will benefit from your well-informed understanding of their outward struggle and from your compassion toward their inner pain.

Young people with ADHD who exhibit *inattention* may seem as if they're not listening; they may fail to follow direction or to complete tasks (Kendall & Comer, 2010). They often appear to be extremely disorganized—they may shift rapidly from one uncompleted activity to another, lose items, forget things, and seem distracted. Those with *impulsivity* act without thinking. Although many (if not most) children are impulsive, the hallmark characteristics of impulsivity observed in young people with ADHD include blurting out answers in the classroom (even before questions are finished), interrupting others, being unable to wait for their turn, and pushing others out of line. When confronted about such behaviours, they will often become angry. Impulsivity can present a serious safety concern; for example, when children run across the street or otherwise act or react without thinking, and when these children reach adolescence and begin to engage in more serious risk-taking behaviours. *Hyperactivity* encompasses the fidgeting and constant movement that are so characteristic of these young people, particularly younger children. They seem unable to sit still even for a moment, constantly moving, humming, singing, talking, tapping their feet and fingers, and so on.

Sensory Integration Disorder (SID) and Regulation Disorders of Sensory Processing (RDSP).

Children and youth who constantly fidget and move about may also be struggling with a neurological condition known as *sensory integration disorder* (SID) and *regulation disorders of sensory processing* (RDSP). They usually have difficulty with transitions, can be very reactive to noise and touch, tend to be impulsive and even aggressive, and demonstrate more fine and gross motor problems than their peers. They often exhibit poor social skills, which seems to be related to their difficulty in taking perspective. Young people with both RDSP and ADHD exhibit more complex needs than those with ADHD alone, given that dysregulation, temperamental problems, and sensory, motor, and spatial problems can interact and often compound the challenges created by ADHD (Reebye & Stalker, 2007).

Fetal Alcohol Spectrum Disorder (FASD).

As we pointed out earlier, children and youth diagnosed with ADHD can learn to change their behaviour, responding to support and feedback. Children with FASD, by contrast, have irreversible damage to their brains that usually leaves them without the cognitive capacity to remember, to reason, to understand consequences, and/or to learn from past mistakes; consequently, they're incapable of being held accountable for their actions. Behaviourally, the signs of FASD and ADHD can look quite similar, particularly with respect to problems related to very limited attention, physical restlessness, and extreme impulsivity ("Children with Fetal Alcohol Spectrum Disorders," 2009). But whereas children with ADHD experience many social problems because of poor self-regulation, children with FASD experience more severe problems as a direct result of their lack of ability to understand and interpret others' mental states and emotions.

A "profile" of children with FASD would include items such as high distractibility and restlessness, as well as behaviours often described as "out of control" . . . Based on previous work . . . children and adolescents with FASD were more likely than children with ADHD to engage in antisocial behaviors, such as cheating, stealing and acting young, as well as sociopathic behaviours including lying and stealing. Importantly, the findings from our present study, specifically the significant differences in social cognition and emotional processing between children with FASD and ADHD, may underlie the severe conduct problems observed in children prenatally exposed to alcohol. ("Children with Fetal Alcohol Spectrum Disorders," 2009, p. 1)

The differences in the causes of the same difficult behaviours found in children with ADHD and children with FASD have important implications for our interventions with those who display the signs and symptoms of both. This is especially important in the child welfare system, where social workers, foster parents, and CYCPs may not be able to determine whether a child's history includes a prenatal exposure to alcohol. If there are reasons to be concerned about a possible FASD diagnosis, a full assessment must always be conducted.

Clinical Rating Scales. In distinguishing between those with and without ADHD, rating scales that are ADHD-specific are noted to be more accurate than global, nonspecific questionnaires and rating scales that assess a variety of behavioural conditions. According to the National Resource Center on ADHD (2015), referencing the American Academy of Child and Adolescent Psychiatry, the most commonly used scales to assess for ADHD are the following:

Achenbach Child Behavior Checklist
Conners Parent and Teacher Rating Scales
ADD-H: Comprehensive Teacher Rating Scale (ACTeRS)
Barkley Home Situations Questionnaire (HSQ)
Barkley School Situations Questionnaire (SSQ)
Conners Continuous Performance Test II (CPT II)

Refer to Table 4.2 for a summary of behavioural indicators for ADHD in the classroom.

Table 4.2 Behavioural Indicators Checklist: ADHD	
✓ **Signs of Hyperactivity and Impulsivity**	✓ **Signs of Inattention**
Fidgeting with hands or feet	Forgetting to write down assignments
Inability to sit still in assigned seat	Not turning in work on time
Running or climbing in inappropriate situations	Making careless mistakes
Striking out at a peer	
Difficulty taking turns or waiting in line	
Interrupting peers	

Source: From APPROACHES TO BEHAVIOR AND CLASSROOM MANAGEMENT: INTEGRATING DISCIPLINE AND CARE, VOL(01), pp. 227. Copyright © 2009 by Sage Publications. Used by permission of Sage Publications via CCC.

Intervention

Research evidence indicates that children and youth diagnosed with ADHD are best supported by a combination of interventions that include individual support, family support, CBT, and classroom support (Reamer & Siegel, 2008).

As we've seen, medication treatments for ADHD typically consist of psychostimulants, and are usually the most first and most frequently recommended course of treatment. The literature indicates that, aside from medication, CBT is the only consistently evidence-based intervention for ADHD. Specific components of behavioural interventions include direct contingency management and CBT. Direct contingency management consists of teachers or counsellors directly rewarding target skills and employing effective consequences when problems arise. Although multiple interventions are always preferred, the evidence indicates that the greatest likelihood of symptom normalization occurs when medication and at least a CBT intervention are combined (Miller & Hinshaw, 2012).

For youth who also have a Substance Use Disorder (SUD), ADHD and SUD can be addressed simultaneously; however, the SUD needs to be considered prior to establishing a treatment plan for the ADHD (Weins, 2006). If the SUD is ongoing, attention must be paid to its stabilization. Depending on the extent of the SUD's severity and duration, adolescents may require residential addiction treatment. AA and other self-help groups can also offer helpful treatment modalities for youth with SUDs (Weins, 2006).

Behavioural and Cognitive-Behavioural Techniques for CYCPs   Behavioural interventions in both home and classroom settings aim to help children and youth learn to self-regulate and control disruptive behaviours. As we discussed in Chapter 1, the behavioural approach is founded on the principle that behaviour is affected by both its antecedents and its consequences. Rewarding consequences should follow desirable behaviour (theoretically increasing its rate) and undesirable consequences should follow undesirable behaviour (thus decreasing its rate). The *functional behaviour assessment* and the *behavioural intervention plan* (*BIP*) used in most Canadian classrooms are based on this principle, as are contingency contracts, token economies, star charts, level charts, and time-outs. As we've seen, behavioural interventions have been shown by empirical evidence to be successful in increasing adaptive behaviour in children and youth with ADHD (Jensen, 2004). It is important to note, however, that there is considerable controversy in the CYC field regarding these types of behavioural interventions. What do you think about this issue?

CBT is an evidence-based intervention that helps most young people with ADHD change the ways they think and behave. For example, before reacting, impulsive children can learn to stop and think—to take a step back and think about an appropriate response. CBT is also helpful in managing other problems such as low self-esteem, social skills deficits, and relationship difficulties. In one CBT strategy, known as **self-monitoring**, children learn to increase their awareness of their thought processes; for example, by asking themselves during class whether they're paying attention. In another strategy, known as **positive self-talk**, children learn to change their automatic negative cognitions and challenge their cognitive distortions (Sherman, 2015).

The Role of Medication   The most widely used treatment for ADHD is pharmacotherapy using stimulant medication. These stimulants increase norepinephrine and/or dopamine release in the prefrontal cortex of the brain, which reportedly helps enhance attention and focus and decrease accompanying physical activity or fidgeting (Kendall & Comer, 2010). Medication's efficacy as a form of treatment for ADHD is research based and has been well established empirically (Hoza, Kaiser, & Hurt, 2008), and thus is the treatment regimen against which all others are compared. Foltz (2010) notes that, because mental health professionals are using stimulants more than ever before in the treatment of ADHD, they're widely assumed to be the most effective; however, Foltz maintains that research has shown they are not. Indeed, notwithstanding the DSM diagnosis, many clinicians are vehemently opposed to the use of any psychotropic medications for children and youth for any diagnosis, but particularly for ADHD (Baughman, 2006; Fewster, 2004). Refer to Chapter 1 for more on this debate.

As we mentioned earlier, one of the largest efforts to measure the effectiveness of treatments for children with ADHD is the MTA study. This study determined that children in the combined-treatment and medication groups showed significantly greater improvement overall (Foltz, 2010a), and that combined behavioural–psychosocial interventions are the treatment of choice for ADHD-related difficulties, including oppositional and aggressive behaviour, internalizing symptoms, social skills deficits, difficult parent–child relationships, and poor academic functioning (Hoza, Kaiser, & Hurt, 2008). However, a follow-up study conducted 36 months afterward reported that "all of the initial gains provided by the medications disappeared and benefits from behavioural treatments were sustained" (Foltz, 2010a, p. 12). Long-term use of medications, especially without a behavioural intervention, should not be considered evidence-based practice for ADHD, Foltz (2010a) argued, because it doesn't demonstrate a treatment advantage in terms of improved outcomes over behavioural strategies. Consistent with this idea, William Pelham argues that the benefits of medication have been overstated with little evidence to suggest that medication improves behaviour in the long-term ("ADHD medications," 2008). Best-practice evidence indicates that medications alone don't address all the functional impairments associated with ADHD. Nonetheless, CYCPs must understand the role of medications commonly prescribed in its treatment. They must also make their own well-informed decision as to whether they agree with the use of these psychotropic stimulant drugs or instead prefer to rely on psychosocial and behavioural interventions. Only with all the available information about medication, practice experience, and assessment of the young person's individual strengths and needs can CYCPs decide what might work best for a particular child or adolescent in any practice context. CYCPs also need to ensure that young people know they have the right to decide not to use a medication and that the aim of medication is not to manage or control their behaviour but rather to help them focus. Medications should never be the first or only treatment, and both the short- and long-term risks and benefits need to be considered (Maté, 2000, pp. 307–317).

With each young person they work with, CYCPs need to observe for the potential therapeutic benefits of combined medication and psychosocial interventions, particularly in the area of improved self-esteem. Medication will often help manage or positively influence the basic neurological and self-regulation skills required for children and youth to respond well to behavioural support (Kutscher, 2005). For example, a CYC program manager once remarked to one of the authors of this text that, as a result of both prescribed medication and the CYCP's behavioural support measures in the classroom, the boys his staff worked with were able to focus better in school. They thus experienced much more success in this environment, which in turn contributed to an overall feeling of efficacy and improved self-esteem. This, of course, was a highly desirable outcome, and one that apparently led to improved behaviours in the group home and family home environment as well as influencing positive family-reconciliation outcomes after discharge.

Psychoeducation and Individual Counselling   Individual and group psychotherapy and counselling can be very effective in the treatment of ADHD. These approaches can help young people to appreciate their own individual strengths and recognize their limitations, to reduce impulsivity and behavioural outbursts by developing their ability to let go of emotional reactions, and to learn how their ADHD symptoms can be managed in ways that enhance and positively influence their day-to-day functioning (Honos-Webb, 2011).

Social skills training teaches children the behaviours necessary to develop and maintain good social relationships, such as waiting for one's turn, not shouting out, sharing, asking for help, and responding to teasing in appropriate ways. For most children these skills don't have to be taught; they're learned naturally by watching and repeating others' behaviours. But some children, especially those with ADHD, have a difficult time learning these skills. In social skills training, CYCPs teach behaviours that are appropriate for different situations and then help children practise them in a safe, one-on-one environment. These skills include having conversations with others, seeing others' perspectives, listening, taking turns in the conversation, asking questions, practising eye contact, and learning what body language, facial expressions, and tone of voice mean (Martin, 2013).

Family Support Interventions   The literature on evidence-based practice suggests that parent training and classroom behavioural approaches are highly successful as interventions for children with ADHD. Effective approaches include educating parents, caregivers, and teachers about ADHD; educating them about strategies for praising positive behaviours and consistently using consequences for negative behaviours; and helping them structure the classroom and home environment with clear expectations and consistent reinforcing of rules and guidelines for activities (Steele, Elkin, & Roberts, 2008).

The goal of parent and teacher training for ADHD is to help CYCPs, parents, caregivers, and teachers develop tolerance, better coping strategies, and more appropriate positive and consistent responses (rather than reactions) to young people's disruptive behaviours

Social skills training teaches the behaviours necessary to develop and maintain good social relationships, such as waiting for one's turn, asking for help, or responding appropriately to teasing.

William Perugini/Shutterstock

related to ADHD. *Psychosocial training* (or parent support training) for parents and caregivers has been shown to be highly effective in helping parents assist their children with ADHD, similar to the effectiveness of social skills training for children. See Box 4.3 for an overview of CYC techniques for intervention.

Prevention: Advocacy, Community, and School-Based Strategies   Given the broad range of negative impacts upon all whose lives are touched by ADHD, including their families, peers, and schools, there is an obvious need to develop broad, effective, and accessible services for young people with ADHD in the school setting (Evans et al., 2006). To the extent that barriers to traditional mental health services, therapy, and other assistance accounts for a lack of treatment accessibility among children and youth with ADHD, school-based services are very likely to increase treatment accessibility and utilization. School-based services allow greater access to treatment in that, compared with outpatient or treatment clinic-based care; school programs present fewer accessibility barriers, including transportation and financial obstacles to families (Evans et al., 2011).

Box 4.3

Techniques for CYC Intervention

Here are some fundamental general principles for teaching and supporting young people with ADHD:

The adult takes active responsibility for the relationship.

The adult doesn't judge the child.

The adult doesn't overpraise the child.

The adult doesn't react to behaviour with anger, but instead remains calm and responds to the behaviour in a planned way.

The adult takes responsibility for restoring the relationship.

The adult uses a "disability" outlook: the child isn't "unwilling," but rather "unable."

The adult doesn't take difficult behaviours as personal affronts.

The adult adjusts his or her expectations every day, thereby minimizing frustration.

If a strategy is working, the adult keeps doing it; if not, he or she tries something else.

Source: Maté, 2000, pp. 153–158.

Additional approaches include the following:

Teach psychosocial skills to parents and caregivers.

Educate parents (e.g., about symptom recognition and causes) to facilitate an accurate understanding of ADHD and to decrease feelings of responsibility.

Help parents and caregivers identify and observe for problem behaviours (including ignoring trivial noncompliance).

Help parents establish effective contingency systems (i.e., positive and negative consequences for behaviour) in the home.

Teach parents and caregivers how to issue clear requests, monitor compliance, and administer consequences.

Teach parents communication skills, and encourage their daily positive interactions with the child or adolescent.

Help parents learn how to depersonalize negative interactions with their child or adolescent.

Teach parents how to use praise effectively.

Teach parents how to respond, not react, to the behaviours.

Help parents develop personal coping strategies (e.g., decreasing stress through various strategies).

Provide one-to-one academic and behavioural support in the classroom.

One-to-One Support. In their role as a one-to-one support in the classroom for young people with ADHD, CYCPs' goal is to reduce their vulnerability to risk factors by increasing the protective factors in as many different ways as possible: (1) Begin by asking the child or youth how they learn best, since, as always, the best expert on how children learn is the children themselves. (2) Physical space: Allow for a quiet place with reduced noise and distraction, and sit in close proximity when needed; make sure young people are allowed to leave the space when they need to. (3) Routines: All children need structure, and children with ADHD more so. Make lists. Give reminders, repeat instructions, give direction, and set clear, firm limits. Ensure that daily routines are in both written and pictorial form; use reminders, but don't nag. (4) Supportive teaching style: Use a variety of one-to-one teaching methods, according to the child's predominant learning styles, whether visual, auditory, or kinesthetic. (5) Behavioural management: Ensure that the class rules are easy to see; have a rewards plan with clear, positive rewards for desired behaviours and negative consequences for inappropriate behaviours; "catch them being good" instead of using negative confrontation; use contingency contracts and token economies ("Behaviour support strategies," 2006). (6) Teach social skills and behaviours. Help young people practise the required key skills. (7) Home/school: Use a daily message book and actively involve support staff, teachers, and caregivers in the young person's day-to-day activities. Be a known face in the school. (8) Review and record dates for tests and assignments. Make and review ongoing calendars for long- and short-term projects, breaking down large tasks and assignments into smaller parts. (10) When the child is off task, gently redirect him or her back to task. (10) Demonstrate organizational strategies for lockers and belongings. (11) Use the school/home communication book. (12) Actively encourage physical exercise, either team sports, if the child can handle it, or individual. (13) Build connectedness. Help children feel engaged. Engagement with you builds motivation. In the home or in residential treatment settings, set up a structure for a daily morning and night schedule/routine.

Advocacy. CYCPs can develop and implement support groups for children and youth with ADHD. A sense of regular connection to peers who are struggling with the same issues will lead to openness, problem sharing, and problem solving. When young people and their families can share their pain, fears, and struggles in a compassionate, supportive environment, it can be very beneficial to all group members.

Alternative Healing   A wide variety of alternative healing, holistic, and/or naturopath therapies is available for the treatment of ADHD and attention difficulties. Although none is defined as evidence based, many young people and their caregivers use these alternatives successfully. Individuals struggling with attentional difficulties need to explore and adopt their own effective solutions and medication-free techniques.

What about diet? Although there is no empirical evidence suggesting that a diet high in sugar or food dyes causes ADHD, parents of children with ADHD often disagree with this. CYCPs should observe for patterns of behaviour related to food intake and possible sensitivities. For example, although there is no good research evidence that strict exclusion diets are beneficial for children and youth with ADHD, when caregivers notice a deterioration in behaviour following the ingestion of a particular additive or food, it stands to reason that these should be avoided (Fonagy et al., 2002). Research indicates that although dietary supplementation with omega-3 and omega-6 fatty acids has no substantial effect on motor skills in children with coordination difficulties, studies have shown that they may have a positive effect on reading, spelling, and ADHD-related behaviours (Wolpert et al., 2006).

Biofeedback is an option that is reputed to help many children. It aids affected individuals in becoming more aware of their physiological responses and then learning how to manage the functioning of their brain's frontal lobe (the executive functioning centre). One technique, called electroencephalography (EEG) neurofeedback, records electrical activity within the cells of the scalp, providing moment-to-moment feedback to the client and therapist about activity in the brain. Children with ADHD have higher rates of EEG abnormalities than those without ADHD (DeName, 2012), and neurofeedback provides audio and visual interpretations of these brain waves. Children are taught how to control the appropriate levels needed for optimal functioning. According to neurofeedback's proponents, the exercises restore the strength of the frontal region of the brain and build a better connection between the mid-brain and forebrain, allowing focus, attention, impulses, and emotional reactions to become more manageable (DeName, 2012).

As we suggest throughout his text, yoga, meditation, and MBSR practices are increasingly used to help children, youth, and adults successfully manage their ADHD symptoms. A systematic review identified 24 studies of yoga for children and concluded that there was evidence for its benefits in mental health rehabilitation. As well, physical exercise, especially swimming, has been found to be of great benefit for all youth at risk (Kemper, Gardiner, & Birdee, 2013; Root, 2009).

Equine therapy also can work very well for children and youth with ADHD, and can be successful for children with autism as well (Root, 2009). In equine-assisted therapy (EAP), children learn how to be safe around horses, how to groom them, and how to work with them in motion, all guided by a trained equine therapist. In their interaction with horses, youth are gently encouraged to try new patterns of behaviour in an enjoyable and unique environment and following each session, discuss their experiences and insights with counselors. (Kessler, 2015)

Relational CYC Practice   CYCPs can use all the approaches we've discussed to understand and support young people and their families struggling with the behaviours associated with ADHD. Think outside the box. Keep trying alternatives until you find success; identify, praise, and use young people's strengths; and take advantage of every teachable moment. Role-model and teach young people that they always have the choice to define themselves by their strengths rather than by their deficits—that by focusing on their assets and gifts they'll gain the confidence to manage their difficulties. Challenge them to redefine themselves by what they're good at, and help them become creative problem solvers. There are countless reference resources available for CYCPs to research regarding effective intervention and communication strategies for use in their work with children and youth affected by ADHD. Refer to Box 4.4 for a brief summary of specific communication strategies to use in your work.

Box 4.4

CYC Communication Strategies

Here are some specific strategies and techniques for supporting young people with ADHD:

Communicate closely with classroom teachers; be an active and known presence at school.

Observe how the young person's brain might be working, especially when under stress.

Pay careful attention to any behavioural triggers.

Help the child to identify feelings related to stress and anxiety.

Pay close attention to the child with ADHD who withdraws rather than acting out.

Teach skills to manage impulsivity. Keep the child safe.

Use few words to get attention, especially when safety is a concern.

Always remember that some of the observed troublesome behaviour will be quite normal child/youth behaviour; it's critical to learn to distinguish between the two.

Develop a safety plan for potential behavioural difficulties: anticipate the problems and have an agreed-upon plan in place.

Always plan for transitions.

Never argue, don't nag, and don't lecture: "Act, don't yak" (Kutscher, 2005).

State expectations clearly.

Give the child immediate feedback and consistent consequences.

Always use incentives more than discipline. Avoid all punishment.

Use humour where appropriate. Never use sarcasm.

Source: From Abnormal Child and Adolescent Psychology by Jean E. Dumas and Wendy J. Nielsen. Copyright © 2003 by Pearson Education Inc. Used by permission of Pearson Education Inc.

WHERE DO YOU STAND?

Consider the various intervention approaches from a psychological and a CYC approach. Where do you stand? Most psychologists agree that there is no single cause of ADHD, and that the best interventions involve an approach that is sensitive to the needs and strengths of the individual. Without question, there is great debate with respect to the best practice in the treatment of ADHD. Although medication is often the most recommended approach to treatment, concerns about side effects, efficacy, and appropriateness remain. Behavioural and parent-training approaches have also demonstrated efficacy, and yet they are expensive and therefore often not accessible to those with limited resources (Evans, 2010). Complicating matters further is the fact that different treatments are effective for some symptoms but not others (Schachar & Tannock, 2002). Clearly, each case of this externalizing disorder must be considered individually. There is no best treatment for all children with a diagnosis of ADHD; interventions must be adapted to fit the needs of each individual youth.

Before we conclude our discussion of ADHD, consider the cases of Karyn and Tyler in the *Viewpoint Challenge* exercise in order to evaluate your current understanding and position with respect to explanations and interventions for ADHD.

CHAPTER SUMMARY

- From a psychological perspective, *attention deficits* or *inattention* generally refers to difficulties in maintaining or directing attention, and often co-occurs with hyperactivity and impulsivity.

- In the DSM-5, ADHD is considered a neurodevelopmental disorder and has three presentations: Inattentive, Hyperactive-Impulsive, and Combined.

- CYCPs engage with young people who exhibit some of the externalizing behaviour patterns that the DSM labels as ADHD. Although the CYC view of these behaviours is far from the DSM's pathology-focused approach, understanding the differences between the diagnostic categories as well as knowing the risk factors and effective approaches to interventions will enable CYCPs to better support the child or youth as well as their families, teachers, and other professionals.

- From a psychological perspective, genetics and neurobiological factors are the most significant determinants of ADHD and include an overactive BAS and an underactive BIS.

- From a CYC perspective, although ADHD is recognized as a neurobiological condition, attachment and early childhood familial relationships have also been implicated in its development.

- Psychological interventions for ADHD include stimulant medication, changing variables in the social environment, and parent training.

- CYC assessments for ADHD should be multimodal and conducted in many contexts, both relational and ecological.

- Effective intervention strategies include parent training, CBT, problem-solving skills training, social skills training, anger management, and empathy-building programs.

Critical Thinking Questions

1. What do you think of the diagnostic criteria changes for ADHD from the DSM-IV-TR to the DSM-5? Do you think it's a good thing that we need to discern more problematic behaviours across more settings now?

2. Consider the estimates of ADHD prevalence in the Canadian population. What implications might these estimates have for your CYC practice? Do they reflect what you've seen in your practice to date?

3. Do you think there are sociopolitical and cultural explanations for variations in the rates of ADHD prevalence in different cultural groups? Around the world?

4. What are your thoughts about the role of attachment in the development of ADHD?

5. Why do you think ADHD sometimes attenuates in adolescence and at other times leads to lifelong impairment?

6. Why do you think ADHD is so often comorbid with an SUD in adolescence? Why do you think ADHD is comorbid with ODD and CD, and with anxiety? What are suitable interventions?

7. What interventions do you think fit best with a relational approach? Defend your thinking.

Key Terms

attention deficits, 149

Attention-Deficit/Hyperactivity Disorder (ADHD), 150

attunement, 164

behavioural activation system (BAS), 162

behavioural inhibition system (BIS), 162

biofeedback, 179

equine therapy, 179

executive functioning, 160

hyperactivity, 149

impulsivity, 149

inattention, 149

neurobiological condition, 151

positive self-talk, 174

secondary manifestations, 150

self-monitoring, 174

stimulants or psychostimulants, 166

Supplemental Readings

Barkley, R. A. (2000). *Taking charge of ADHD: The complete authoritative guide for parents.* New York: Guilford Press.

Baughman, F. A., & Hovey, C. (2006). *The ADHD fraud: How psychiatry makes patients out of normal children.* Victoria, BC: Trafford. (Examines the controversial diagnosis of ADHD and questions the validity of this and other diagnostic categories of the DSM.)

Blackman, J. A. (1999). Attention-Deficit/Hyperactivity Disorder in preschoolers: Does it exist and should we treat it? *Pediatric Clinics of North America, 46*(5), 1011–1025. (Considers the appropriateness of early diagnosis of ADHD.)

Honos-Webb, L. (2007). *The gift of ADHD activity book: 101 ways to turn your child's problems into strengths.* Oakland, CA: Raincoast Books. (Tips and activities for supporting children diagnosed with ADHD.)

Knapp, S. E. (2005). *Parenting skills homework planner.* Hoboken, NJ: Wiley. (Exercises for working with parents with children exhibiting disruptive behaviours.)

Ziegler, D. (2002). *Traumatic experience and the brain: A handbook for understanding and treating those traumatized as children.* Phoenix, AR: Acacia Publishing.

Online Resources

Dr. Russell Barkley's online resource, www.russellbarkley.org/courses.html

Review of different treatments for inherited vs. acquired ADHD, http://daysofwonderandgrace.wordpress.com/2012/01/18/omalley-on-adhd-in-fasd-part-ii

"Cutting words may scar young brains," http://hms.harvard.edu/news/cutting-words-may-scar-young-brains-2-20-09

Simon Fraser University's Children's Health Policy Centre, www.childhealthpolicy.sfu.ca

Canadian ADHD Resource Alliance (CADDRA), www.caddra.ca

Centre for ADHD Awareness, Canada (CADDAC), www.caddac.ca

Benefits of equine therapy, www.specialneedsdigest.com/2012/10/3-ways-equine-therapy-can-help-adhd.html

Externalizing behaviour problems include disruptive behaviours that are related to rule violations, impulse control, and aggression.

Sascha Burkard/Fotolia

Case Example: *John*

Twelve-year-old John came into the care of Nova Scotia's Child Services after his mother approached the agency to report that he was completely out of her control. He's now been placed in a structured, community-based group home with three other boys aged 13–14. Ever since Grade 1 John has experienced many difficulties in school, but he recently began skipping school every day and getting into trouble with a group of boys. The group, known to police in their small rural town of Pictou, has been caught shoplifting, vandalizing, and writing graffiti. Just before his mother approached the agency, John and four other boys set a garage on fire; it burned to the ground, and fortunately no one was hurt. John's mother, a single parent with four other children under the age of 10, reports that John won't listen to her, talks back, swears at her, and shouts and screams "No" or "I don't care" when she asks him to complete tasks. In an angered state he recently threatened to hit her; so far, he's only pushed her. His mother reports that John is always moving around (she says he's twitchy) and has great difficulty keeping still. He's described by his teachers as extremely fidgety but very bright. John's mother reports that he frequently misbehaves in public places (he runs around, won't comply with requests, yells and swears). She's very concerned about John, and is willing to work with the group home's CYC staff to help him. John's mom hopes he can eventually come home. She sees him every weekend, although he seems distressed when she visits. John's father is a fisherman, and doesn't visit his children.

Learning Objectives

1. Summarize the DSM criteria for ODD, Intermittent Explosive Disorder, CD, Pyromania, and Kleptomania.

2. Summarize the CYC perspective on the disruptive behaviour disorders.

3. Compare and contrast primary psychological explanations (biological, psychodynamic, behavioural, cognitive, and sociocultural) for disruptive behaviour disorders.

4. Outline CYC theoretical explanations for the development of ODD and CD.

5. Describe psychological treatment approaches used in treating disruptive behaviour disorders.

6. Summarize specific indicators of disruptive behaviour disorders, including specific forms of aggression.

7. Describe the various CYC-focused and evidence-based interventions for disruptive behaviours.

Chapter Overview

Child and adolescent behaviour that disrupts the daily lives of parents, teachers, peers, and society at large has long been the focus of researchers, practitioners, and popular media. Such *externalizing* behaviour problems include both attention deficits and disruptive behaviour disorders. While ADHD is included under Neurodevelopmental Disorders in the DSM-5, disruptive disorders are grouped together in a single chapter titled Disruptive, Impulse-Control, and Conduct Disorders. What are the different types of disruptive behaviour disorders identified in the DSM-5, and what are their symptoms? Is there a relationship between these disorders and attention deficits? What explanations are offered for these behaviour patterns, and how can practitioners facilitate healthy behaviour in young people exhibiting such disturbances? What behaviours displayed by John in the opening case might be indicators of these disorders? This chapter will summarize the major characteristics of disruptive behaviour disorders identified in the DSM-5. It will also examine explanations and approaches to intervention for such disturbances from both a psychological and a CYC perspective.

It is certainly a truism that, more than any other issue, child and youth "disturbances of conduct" are defined "in the eye of the adult beholder." The concerning troublesome behaviours we introduce in this chapter range from general, consistent "minor" acting out behaviours, including noncompliance, defiance, and tantrums, to the far more serious and dangerous acting out behaviours of aggression, extreme violence, criminal activity, sexual acting out, fire setting, and cruelty to animals and people (Fonagy et al., 2002). As noted in Chapter 1, the CYC perspective on disruptive behaviour disorders is in opposition to the DSM model used to categorize and explain them. CYCPs will likely not find the DSM diagnostic label very helpful in practice. In dealing with externalizing behaviours, then, CYCPs look to understand them through a *relational lens* and then develop supportive and strength-based intervention strategies.

WHAT IS DISRUPTIVE BEHAVIOUR?

Disruptive behaviour is associated with difficulties in self-regulation of emotions and behaviour. These difficulties include defiant, aggressive, antisocial, and/or criminal behaviour as well as social maladjustment. Although deficits in emotional and behavioural self-regulation can be a part of other diagnoses in the DSM, disruptive behaviours are grouped together because of the way in which these patterns of behaviour are associated with the violation of the rights of others, including aggressive and violent actions toward others and destruction of property.

The DSM-5 also notes that some disruptive behaviour disturbances are more associated with poorly controlled emotions than behaviours. For example, *Intermittent Explosive Disorder* is characterized by "poorly controlled emotion, outbursts of anger that are disproportionate to the interpersonal or other provocation or to other psychosocial stressors" (APA, 2013, p. 461). As a result, the criteria for this disorder are focused on the emotional aspects of the disturbance rather than related to specific behaviours.

Before turning to a discussion of specific disruptive behaviour disorders, examine your own experiences of difficulties in self-regulation by trying the *Think About It!* exercise.

WHAT IS A DISRUPTIVE BEHAVIOUR DISORDER? THE PSYCHOLOGICAL PERSPECTIVE

From a psychological perspective, disruptive behaviour disorders are characterized by deficits in emotional and behavioural regulation that lead to the violation of the rights of others. Specifically, the DSM-5 identifies abnormalities in at least one of the following general areas:

- *emotional self-regulation or self-control* (e.g., feeling uncontrollably angry)
- *behavioural self-regulation or self-control* (e.g., defiance or argumentativeness)

Thus, the term **disruptive behaviour disorder** refers to disorders that are defined by disturbances in one or more of these general areas and result in impairments in daily functioning and the ability to achieve important goals. You'll notice that many of these

---

Think About It! Exercise: *Experiences of Disruptive Behaviour*

It is not uncommon for behaviours associated with disruptive disorders to be judged harshly by others. Can you imagine what it would be like to experience some of the symptoms associated with these disturbances? For example, have you ever . . .

Stayed out at night without permission? Broken a rule in the classroom? Skipped school? Told a lie? Stolen something from a store or an individual? Been in a physical fight with another person? Engaged in physical cruelty toward an animal or another person? Sexually abused an animal? Used a weapon (e.g., a knife, gun) to harm someone?

Become so enraged that you've damaged property? Purposefully set a fire with intent to harm someone?

These are just a few of the behaviours that are associated with disruptive behaviour disturbances. While some of these behaviours are common among many youth, especially youth at risk, and associated with less harm to others, others (e.g., using a weapon to harm someone, cruelty to animals) are more likely to be a concern for most members of society. So the degree of severity of behavioural symptoms is a critically important consideration in the assessment and treatment approaches used with youth displaying these behaviours.

symptoms are not unlike experiences most of us have had at some point or in some situation or another. As is true in the case of all disorders, it is often the degree, frequency, or extent to which the behaviour interferes with functioning that distinguishes disordered behaviour from normal behaviour. We now turn to a discussion of specific diagnostic criteria to better understand what distinguishes these universal experiences from those that define disruptive disorders.

DSM-5 Categories

The DSM-5's disruptive, impulse-control, and conduct disorders are considered not only as *externalizing* disorders; they're also associated with *disinhibition* and negative emotionality (APA, 2013). As cited above, what these disorders have in common is the underlying deficit in emotional and behavioural regulation.

Disruptive, Impulse-Control, and Conduct Disorders   In its general grouping of Disruptive, Impulse-Control, and Conduct Disorders, the DSM-5 identifies seven diagnostic categories associated not only with deficits in emotional control but also with defiant, aggressive, antisocial, and/or criminal behaviour leading to social maladjustment. The diagnoses in this chapter are grouped together owing to their high rates of comorbidity and the fact that each is considered an *externalizing disorder* (that is, characterized by undercontrolled behaviour and emotion directed outward rather than inward). Box 5.1 provides an overview of the specific diagnoses in this category.

Notice that the DSM-5 includes a category called Other Specified Disruptive, Impulse-Control, and Conduct Disorder; these are diagnosed when the symptoms of a disruptive, impulse-control, or conduct disorder may be present but don't meet the disorder's formal criteria. For example, a youth may demonstrate recurrent behavioural outbursts without meeting the criteria for any of the other diagnostic categories. Accordingly, the mental health practitioner may feel that noting relevant symptoms could be useful to other professionals working with that individual. Under these circumstances, the youth would be diagnosed with *Other Specified Disruptive, Impulse-Control, and Conduct Disorder* and an explanation would be provided as to why another diagnosis doesn't apply (e.g., insufficient frequency of outbursts). In instances where symptoms are present and causing significant impairment but the individual doesn't meet all criteria for a specific disorder and no explanation is provided as to why or what criteria aren't met, the category of *Unspecified Disruptive, Impulse-Control, and Conduct Disorder* would be applied.

Box 5.1

DSM-5 Disruptive Disorders

Oppositional Defiant Disorder

Intermittent Explosive Disorder

Conduct Disorder

Pyromania

Kleptomania

Other Specified Disruptive, Impulse-Control, and Conduct Disorder

Unspecified Disruptive, Impulse-Control, and Conduct Disorder

Disruptive Disorders: Diagnoses and Criteria

CYCPs are likely to encounter several of the seven diagnoses summarized in Box 5.1, particularly Oppositional Defiant Disorder and Conduct Disorder, which are frequently diagnosed in the youth population. Although less likely to be encountered by CYCPs, we also include an overview of the symptoms of Intermittent Explosive Disorder, Pyromania, and Kleptomania. Let's review the specific diagnostic criteria for these disorders.

Oppositional Defiant Disorder Oppositional Defiant Disorder (ODD) is exemplified by defiance, disobedience, and hostile behaviour toward figures of authority. Note that there's a difference between *noncompliance* (not complying with adult requests) and *defiance* (more extreme and active refusal to comply with requests). Noncompliance is commonly demonstrated by children and adolescents for various reasons (e.g., forgetting to comply, being distracted) and is more passive than outright defiance, which may include aggressive and active refusals to comply with requests. To be diagnosed with ODD, one must exhibit signs of hostile and defiant behaviour for a period of at least six months that results in impairment in social or academic functioning. Characteristic symptoms include losing temper, arguing with adults, refusal to comply with adult demands, and hostility toward adults or peers. If aggression is present, it's typically verbal rather than physical. Generally, the young people exhibiting such behaviours view them and their emotional responses as appropriate and the result of unfair requests. What distinguishes ODD from expected noncompliance seen in all children? While all children demonstrate some or all of these symptoms on occasion, the diagnosis requires that the pattern of behaviour be persistent, repetitive, impairing, and developmentally inappropriate given the chronological age of the individual.

The symptoms of ODD are usually seen in a home setting but may not be observed in other environments (e.g., school, community). This is consistent with the finding that these behaviours are more likely to occur in interactions with adults or peers who are well known to the diagnosed individual. Also note that if a child or adolescent meets the criteria for Conduct Disorder or Antisocial Personality Disorder (two diagnoses associated with more severe disruptive behaviours), the diagnosis of ODD is not applied.

Intermittent Explosive Disorder Intermittent Explosive Disorder is characterized by impulsive, anger-based, aggressive outbursts that appear suddenly and often in response to insignificant stressors. The outbursts usually last for less than 30 minutes and illustrate a lack of self-control in both emotion and in behaviour. The underlying deficit of self-control is emphasized in this diagnosis, as indicated by the requirement that aggressive outbursts are not premeditated. Note that both verbal aggression and behavioural assaults are considered in this diagnosis.

Conduct Disorder According to Costello and Angold (1994), Conduct Disorder is considered to be "the oldest described problem condition among children and adolescents" (Olsson, 2009, p. 102). The central aspect of **Conduct Disorder (CD)** is a pattern of behaviour

Rule violations associated with conduct disorder are associated with arrests and criminal convictions.

that violates rules or fundamental age-appropriate societal norms as well as the basic rights of others. The DSM-5 groups these violations into four major categories: aggression toward others (people or animals), destruction of property, deceitfulness or theft, and serious rule violations. Three or more of the symptoms must be observed in the past year, with at least one behaviour being observed in the past six months and resulting in disrupted social, academic, or occupational functioning. Unlike ODD, acts of physical aggression are common and include physical fights, use of weapons, and physical cruelty toward others (e.g., assault, sexual assault, homicide). Rule violations are also prevalent, and are often observed prior to age 13. Compared with ODD, CD is associated with clearly delinquent behaviour that directly violates specific rules or laws (e.g., stealing, truancy, arson). Compared with the diagnostic criteria for ODD, it's likely easier to see how behaviours associated with CD are different from expected age-appropriate activities and might disrupt the daily lives of the child and/or adolescent. The diagnostic criteria for CD are presented in Box 5.2.

On the basis of age of onset, the DSM-5 distinguishes between different subtypes of CD: a *Childhood-Onset Type*, an *Adolescent-Onset Type*, and an *Unspecified Onset*. The

Box 5.2

DSM-5 Criteria for Conduct Disorder

A. A repetitive and persistent pattern of behaviour in which the basic rights of others or major age-appropriate societal norms or rules are violated, as manifested by the presence of at least three of the following 15 criteria in the past 12 months from any of the categories below, with at least one criterion present in the past 6 months:

Aggression to people and animals

1. often bullies, threatens, or intimidates others
2. often initiates physical fights
3. has used a weapon that can cause serious physical harm to others (e.g., a bat, brick, broken bottle, knife, gun)
4. has been physically cruel to people
5. has been physically cruel to animals
6. has stolen while confronting a victim (e.g., mugging, purse snatching, extortion, armed robbery)
7. has forced someone into sexual activity

Destruction of property

8. has deliberately engaged in fire setting with the intention of causing serious damage
9. has deliberately destroyed others' property (other than by fire setting)

Deceitfulness or theft

10. has broken into someone else's house, building, or car
11. often lies to obtain goods or favours or to avoid obligations (i.e., "cons" others)
12. has stolen items of nontrivial value without confronting a victim (e.g., shoplifting, but without breaking and entering; forgery)

Serious violations of rules

13. often stays out at night despite parental prohibitions, beginning before age 13 years
14. has run away from home overnight at least twice while living in parental or parental surrogate home (or once without returning for a lengthy period)
15. is often truant from school, beginning before age 13 years

B. The disturbance in behaviour causes clinically significant impairment in social, academic, or occupational functioning.

C. If the individual is age 18 years or older, criteria are not met for Antisocial Personality Disorder.

Childhood-Onset Type is applied when at least one symptom is observed prior to age 10, the *Adolescent-Onset Type* is characterized by the absence of symptoms prior to age 10, and *Unspecified Onset* is applied when the age of onset of symptoms is not known. Of particular interest are some of the differences between those diagnosed with Childhood-Onset versus Adolescent-Onset. Specifically, those with early onset are more often male, and more likely to demonstrate physical aggression, have a comorbid ADHD diagnosis, and have a previous diagnosis of ODD. Those with Adolescent-Onset are less physically aggressive and have fewer disturbances in peer relationships. Although they're still more likely to be male, more females are diagnosed in this category than in the Childhood-Onset subtype. In addition to the three subtypes, the DSM includes *severity specifiers*, distinguishing between *mild* (e.g., lying, truancy, causing minor harm to others), *moderate* (e.g., vandalism, theft without victim confrontation, causing intermediate harm to others), and *severe* problems (greater number of disordered behaviours that cause significant harm to others, including physical cruelty, use of a weapon).

The DSM-5 includes a similar specifier in relation to *limited prosocial emotions*. Specifically, a diagnosis of *Conduct Disorder With Limited Prosocial Emotions* is applied when two of the following were demonstrated for over 12 months and in multiple settings and relationships: lack of remorse or guilt (e.g., doesn't feel guilty after hurting someone); callousness/lack of empathy (e.g., appears unconcerned and cold with respect to the consequences of their behaviour for others); lack of concern about performance (e.g., demonstrates little effort and little concern about performance at school or work); shallow or deficient affect (e.g., does not express feelings or emotions to others except to manipulate or intimidate others). Consideration of this lack of emotional expression is important, as those displaying this feature tend to be more likely than others diagnosed with CD to engage in intentional aggression against others (APA, 2013).

Pyromania   Compared with ODD and CD, **Pyromania** is less understood and less often diagnosed. However, the multiple episodes of deliberate fire setting that occur in the context of this disorder raise significant concerns, given the damage to property and danger to life that it presents. Like the other disorders in this general category, Pyromania is associated with fire setting in response to feelings of tension and emotional arousal; thus, similar to Intermittent Explosive Disorder, the impulsive behaviour (i.e., fire setting) occurs in relation to an inability to emotionally regulate or manage feelings of distress and emotional discomfort, which is then followed by an inability to control the behavioural impulse. The impulsive nature of the disorder is also evidenced by the fact that the fire setting occurs in the absence of any monetary gain or other clear motive.

Kleptomania   **Kleptomania** is a rare disorder associated with repetitive acts of stealing of items that are not needed for personal use or for monetary value or gain. Similar to Pyromania, these behaviours occur in the context of a rising sense of emotional tension followed by positive feelings of pleasure and a sense of relief when the act of theft is committed. Again, it's easy to see that deficits in emotional regulation underlie the maladaptive behaviours in this syndrome.

Before turning to a discussion of development, incidence, and comorbidity, try the *Test Your Understanding* exercise to review your understanding of the core symptoms of disruptive, impulse-control, and conduct disorders. Can you identify the appropriate disorder for each case example?

When Christian was six, he found some matches on the street. While playing with them in the garage, he lit some paper on fire, and that fire spread to other items. Although he was punished severely for this incident, Christian can't stop thinking about a lighter he took from his brother. He stares repeatedly at its flame, thinking about lighting up the garbage bin in the alley.

Marty's parents report that they're at their wits' end with respect to their son's behaviour. Although he's now nine, temper tantrums are not uncommon for Marty: when he's frustrated, he often throws objects and hits those around him. When his video game didn't work yesterday, he smashed it into the mirror on the wall, breaking the video game unit and the mirror.

Tran has been arrested for attacking his grandfather with a knife. When asked about the incident, he displayed little emotion; laughing, he remarked that the "old man" needed some "fear put into him." His grandfather reported that similar acts of aggression have occurred before, and that they usually subside when he gives Tran money or other things he asks for.

Lidia's teachers feel as if they're walking on eggshells in their interactions with her. Lidia is easily annoyed by others' requests and actions, including those of teachers and peers. Her teachers have also commented on how she seems to intentionally engage in actions that she knows will upset others. And when Lidia makes an error on a test or assignment, she's quick to blame the teacher.

Julia feels frightened by her own behaviour. She can't understand why she continues to steal little items from stores she visits, even though she can easily afford them. In fact, she often doesn't even really want what she takes! Despite her fear, however, Julia finds it difficult to resist the impulse to steal an item after the thought enters her mind. And after she takes it, she feels extreme relief.

Allen's caregivers have grown increasingly concerned about his behaviour. Although as a child Allen was mild-mannered and not one to disobey or break the rules, ever since he turned 14 he's been skipping school, drinking alcohol, and sneaking out through his window at night. Last night, at 3 A.M., he was arrested for stealing from the nearby convenience store with two of his friends.

A CYC APPROACH TO EXTERNALIZING BEHAVIOUR: UNDERSTANDING DISRUPTIVE BEHAVIOUR DISORDERS

> So, according to Harvard researchers, we now have "IED" (Intermittent Explosive Disorder). It seems over twelve percent of high school kids now suffer from this mental illness that makes them violent. Not to worry, pharmaceutical help is on the way. When, if ever, are we going to speak out as a profession and scream *ENOUGH*? (Fewster, 2012)

As noted earlier, many of the young people CYCPs engage with exhibit some of the troublesome behaviours and attachment relationship difficulties described in the DSM-5 symptom clusters for ODD and CD. One of CYCPs' primary criticisms of the DSM is that it's *deficit-based* and doesn't identify the individual strengths of these young people. Further, as Fewster (2012) and many others argue, the Disruptive Behaviour Disorder diagnoses can often lead to the use of psychotropic medications as behaviour management tools, especially with youth in the care system.

> Any perusal of a case file on a troubled young person is likely to turn up multiple DSM diagnoses. As one youth exclaimed "I must be really messed up because they say I have five disorders" . . . [A]re these kids drowning in disorders or is something amiss with the labeling scheme? (Foltz, 2010b, p. 26)

The discussion of ODD, Intermittent Explosive Disorder, and CD prompts relationally based CYCPs to argue that these disorders are "not a solo performance" by youth, but rather a "dance with multiple partners" (Brendtro & Shahbazian, 2004, p. 71). Not only does the DSM fail to identify the resiliencies or strengths of the young people it labels, it doesn't discuss the etiology (causes) of the disorders or provide any real direction for interventions (Foltz, 2010b).

In January 2012, a researcher posted a query to the CYC-Net discussion group asking for examples of how CYCPs might work best with children diagnosed with ODD. One responder, Jeremy Miller (2012), questioned whether CYCPs should recognize it as a "real condition" in the first place. After summarizing the DSM's ODD symptoms, Miller remarked that he'd exhibited at least four of them throughout his child and adolescent years, and that in the 1970s this was considered normal teenage behaviour; he went on to ask whether ODD as a psychiatric diagnosis was perhaps more a symptom of an increasingly controlling adult world in which young people became understandably angry and obstructive with adults trying to tell them what was in their best interests (Miller, 2012).

The question presents food for thought. CYCPs recognize that most disturbed behaviour in children results from discord in the ecology rather than any so-called disease in the child. When a significant adult person in a child's world can no longer tolerate the behaviour, the youth is labelled "at risk," "emotionally disturbed," "delinquent," or "sick," then diagnosed with a disorder and medicated accordingly (Brendtro & Shahbazian, 2004).

ODD is the DSM diagnostic label for children and youth "who engage in adversarial encounters with authority figures" (Brendtro & Shahbazian, 2004). The DSM characterizes ODD as "a pattern of negativistic hostile and defiant behaviour that has lasted a minimum of 6 months" and includes behaviours such as the following: often loses temper, argues with adults, refuses to comply, breaks rules, intentionally annoys people, and blames others (Kendall & Comer, 2010). On the other hand, CD is the clinical DSM diagnosis ascribed to youth who "externalize conflict and violate the rights of others." An important distinction to keep in mind is that while the label ODD is used to describe its main feature, oppositionality, CD refers more to the violation of societal rules and the basic rights of others, and includes such behaviours as cruelty to other people and animals, sexual aggression, fire setting, bullying, and theft. If you think these behaviours sound a lot like those associated with an attachment disorder, you would be correct.

Regardless of whether we agree with the diagnostic labelling of these behaviours as disorders, children who display disruptive behaviours and/or aggression and conduct problems at a young age are at higher risk for developing other, related difficulties later in life, including violent behaviours, mental health problems, early school leaving, chemical dependency, occupational difficulties, marital and family difficulties, and, all too often, criminal offending (Bloomquist & Schnell, 2002).

Young people who display angry, oppositional, or acting-out behaviours (externalizing disorders) that disrupt others in the social context invariably also experience tormented inner lives; they are living in despair or extreme emotional pain, "if not because of their own inner personal turmoil, then perhaps because of the punishment, ridicule, or unwanted attention that their externalizing behaviour generates" (Kendall & Comer, 2010, p. 55). In describing pain-based behaviours earlier in the text, we noted that for some children in the child welfare system, "despair turns into rage." We highlight this phenomenon again because it is so relevant to our practice and might be overlooked in

Consider the case of John, presented in the beginning of the chapter. Identify all the reported behaviours that are associated with the diagnostic categories of ODD, CD, Pyromania, Kleptomania, and IED.

John is now involved in the juvenile justice system as well, since the boys involved in setting the fire have been charged with arson. What do you think? Does his behaviour warrant a diagnosis? Do you need more information? The probation officer will be interviewing the program's CYC staff to make a recommendation to the judge for sentencing. Do you think John should be incarcerated for this crime? Why or why not? Discuss the pros and cons of diagnosing John with CD as well as the pros and cons of having him serve time in custody.

the context of behaviours that are often noted because of the ways they disrupt the lives of those around them.

Before turning to a discussion of prevalence, development, and comorbidity, consider the details of the opening case in relation to the psychological and CYC views of disruptive disturbances in *John's Case: Revisited*.

HOW MANY YOUNG PEOPLE STRUGGLE WITH DISRUPTIVE BEHAVIOUR?

The prevalence of ODD is estimated to be between 2 and 16 percent (APA, 2000). This wide range in estimates seems to be a function of the type of population (e.g., general versus clinical) and the methods used to diagnose the child or adolescent (e.g., clinical assessment, questionnaires, rating scales). In childhood, ODD is more often diagnosed in males, whereas females are equally likely to be diagnosed in adolescence. Despite these commonalities, males are more likely to display more severe confrontational behaviour and more persistent symptoms.

As in the case of ODD, estimates of the prevalence of CD vary widely, ranging from less than 1 percent to greater than 10 percent (APA, 2000). Yet despite this variation, it is generally agreed that "CD is one of the most frequent childhood problems that present for treatment in community clinic settings" (Evans, 2010, p. 145). Moreover, there is evidence that disruptive behaviours are on the increase (Fonagy et al., 2002). ODD and CD are both more prevalent among lower socioeconomic status groups (Fonagy et al., 2002), and not surprisingly, CD is more common in neighbourhoods characterized by social disorganization and high crime rates ("Oppositional Defiant and Conduct Disorders," n.d.).

If we include bullying in the definition of a school-based conduct problem, the prevalence is 10–23 percent of children as either victims or perpetrators of bullying behaviour (Fonagy et al., 2002). School-based violence and bullying are, of course, a serious concern for CYCPs when discussing conduct disturbances.

Unlike in ODD, persistent sex differences are observed in CD, with this disorder being diagnosed significantly more often and earlier in males than in females (Modestin, Matutat, & Würmle, 2001; Nock et al., 2007). Other sex differences appear in relation to the symptoms displayed, with females more likely to engage in truancy, substance use, being sexually exploited, lying, and running away. Males are more likely to exhibit confrontational aggression, including fighting, stealing, and vandalism (APA, 2000). The gender gap is closely rapidly, though, with young women becoming more involved in gangs and assaultive bullying behaviour. "Similar to other countries reporting data related to gender and violence, Canada too shares an increasing violent crime rate for adolescent girls. Recent evidence from Statistics Canada suggests that the violent crime rate for girls has doubled over the past ten years, currently reflecting approximately eight percent of the officially reported total adolescent violent crime rate" (Leschied, 2008, p. 31).

Examining gender difference in her studies on female violence, Sibylle Artz has established that approximately 10 percent of all violent acts are perpetrated by young women. These young women report that they involve themselves in violence for a variety of reasons, including to establish power and authority in their social groups, in response to being victims of violence themselves, and to please their boyfriends (Artz, 2000, Conference Proceedings). However, girls who behave aggressively do report higher levels of depression and suicidal ideation than do boys. In addition, studies suggest that when girls behave violently, it's important to assess for the presence of an underlying mental health concern.

> While males are involved in the majority of incidents of *physical* aggression, the increase of female violence reflects a broadening of the definition of what constitutes violence. And, as the definition of what constitutes violence is broadened, the data begins to reflect something quite different in terms of the representation of girls in violence categories. It is suggested that while girls are lower in rates of school violence when compared to boys when violence is defined as overt aggression, girls are proportionally more likely to appear in the data when verbal threats and intimidation are included. (Leschied, 2008, p. 29)

Young people who live in communities with fewer resources can be exposed to stressful circumstances often associated with gang activity, neglect, and poverty—risk factors that are in turn associated with the occurrence of CD and ODD. Conversely, there is much evidence that strengths, resources, and protective factors related to positive community and family environment lower the prevalence of the disruptive disorders (Leschied, 2008).

Prevalence rates can also be affected by cultural factors related to the degree to which acting out and disruptive behaviours are tolerated or considered unacceptable. For example, suppression of aggression, anger, and strong emotions is part of the pan-Asian culture. This cultural suppression may lead families to maintain a lower tolerance threshold for acting out or disruptive behaviours and to extinguish this behaviour more often than in other cultures. Young people who experience either maltreatment or exposure to violence in their families of origin are nearly twice as likely to report clinically significant elevations of mental health issues, including emotional and behavioural difficulties, compared with children and youth who don't report maltreatment (Leschied, 2008).

Concerns about each of these externalizing disorders have been forwarded in the literature. The fact that each has been increasingly diagnosed in younger and younger populations over the years has led some to question the methods by which children and adolescents are assessed and how the diagnostic categories are applied. Typically, symptoms checklists, medical examinations, and interviews with parents, teachers, and others are part of the assessment process and provide information on which the diagnosis is based. Because there is no one single test for these disorders, and given that behaviour can change significantly from one day to the next, it's been argued that the increasing prevalence rates reflect overdiagnosis rather than actual changes in incidence. Where do you stand with respect to this issue?

DISRUPTIVE DISORDERS AND DEVELOPMENT

Although the specific behaviours associated with disruptive disorders may be observed into adulthood, these behaviour patterns are generally acknowledged as beginning early in development. ODD is most often diagnosed prior to age eight and not later than early adolescence, with symptoms developing gradually over a period of months or years. Not all children diagnosed with or showing evidence of ODD will go on to exhibit the more serious symptoms of CD, but the high number of those with Childhood-Onset CD who were previously diagnosed with ODD has been interpreted as suggesting that ODD is a *developmental antecedent* to CD (APA, 2013). As noted in the DSM, CD symptoms emerge in the context of developmental gains in physical, cognitive, and sexual domains and progress from mild symptoms (e.g., physical fights, lying) to more severe (e.g., assault). The earlier the emergence of severe symptoms, the more likely the pattern is to continue through to adulthood.

Olsson (2009) notes that "CD is considered the most stable form of all psychosocial disorders during childhood and adolescence" (p. 103), especially in cases of early onset. Consistent with this view, Moffitt (1993) distinguishes between *life-course-persistent* and *adolescent-limited* patterns of CD. Although those with early onset don't always continue such behaviours through to adulthood, such perseverance represents the life-course-persistent pattern. In this case, the child who exhibits oppositional behaviour associated with noncompliance and lying gradually becomes a child or adolescent who moves to more severe behaviours, including theft and vandalism, and later an adult who continues to violate the rights of others and exhibits a pattern of manipulative and irresponsible behaviour. This pattern tends to be observed earlier and is generally associated with more severe disturbance than the adolescent-limited pattern, which emerges in early adolescence and ends as the individual enters early adulthood. The earlier antisocial behaviour occurs in development, then, the more likely it is to persist into adulthood.

Families play a powerful role in shaping children's behaviour and values. It is within a developmental perspective, then, that we need to examine what family influences at what ages and stages of their children are predictive of future violent behaviour (Leschied, 2008).

The DSM-5 considers the adult pattern of conduct-disordered behaviours within the personality disorders grouping (see Chapter 1 for a description of this grouping). Specifically, the Antisocial Personality Disorder (APD) diagnosis is applied to those who, since at least 15, have displayed a persistent pattern of violating the rights of others (i.e., Conduct Disorder). The individual must be at least 18 and display a persistent pattern of deceitfulness, impulsivity, irritability, and aggressiveness associated with physical aggression, irresponsible behaviour, and reckless behaviour that can put the safety of self or others at risk (APA, 2013). It has been estimated that half of those diagnosed with CD will later be diagnosed with APD (Powell, Lochman, & Boxmeyer, 2007).

COMORBIDITY

As we've seen, attention deficits are frequently observed with disruptive behaviours. Several studies have found high rates of comorbidity between ADHD and ODD (e.g., Biederman & Faraone, 2005; Costello et al., 2003), particularly in the case of the Combined Presentation of ADHD, although recent research suggests there is also an association between ODD and the Inattentive-Type ADHD (Acosta et al., 2008). Similarly, ADHD is often comorbid with CD (APA, 2013; Thapar, Harrington, & McGuffin, 2001).

Aggression is not uncommon in young people, and is a serious concern in the context of Conduct Disorder.

Monkey Business/Fotolia

ODD is often comorbid with ADHD (14 percent), learning disorders and communication disorders, and mood disorders. Comorbity with anxiety and ODD is reported at 14 percent and with depressive disorders at 9 percent (Fonagy et al., 2002). It's also common to observe low self-esteem (although this may appear in the form of overly inflated self-esteem), swearing, frequent conflicts with others, and substance use. When ADHD and ODD occur together, ODD symptoms are more likely to capture the attention of teachers and parents. Generally, when ODD occurs with ADHD the prognosis is less favourable than in ADHD alone (Hazell, 2010).

In the case of CD, comorbid conditions include ADHD, learning disorders, anxiety disorders, substance-related disorders, and mood disorders (APA, 2013). The comorbidity with ADHD and CD is most significant, given that ADHD often precedes a diagnosis of CD. "In two separate well-controlled studies, children with ADHD were significantly more likely to meet criteria for CD or antisocial personality disorder at age 16 (27–32% vs. 8%)" (Fonagy et al., 2002, p. 109). Impulsivity and hyperactivity are theorized as driving the early onset of conduct disturbances, especially in boys (Fonagy et al., 2002).

CD is also associated with below average verbal intelligence (i.e., reading, writing) and higher than average rates of suicidal thoughts, attempts, and completed suicide. Additional manifestations include lack of empathy for others, lack of guilt or remorse for inappropriate actions, low self-esteem (often accompanied by inflated self-esteem and projections of strength), irritability, and reckless behaviour. Early onset of substance use, sexual behaviour, and risk taking is typically observed, often resulting in exclusion from class or school, sexually transmitted infections, unplanned pregnancy, and physical injury. Consequences for the child/adolescent diagnosed with CD also include increased risk of parental abuse, rejection by peers, and academic problems (Larsson et al., 2009). Aggression is common, and is often used to respond to the actions of others that are misperceived as intentionally hurtful or threatening. The DSM

Box 5.3

Common Myths About Disruptive Behaviour Disorders

MYTH: *Kids who exhibit ODD just need more discipline.*

FACT: Arbitrarily enforced restrictions aren't going to solve ODD; in fact, they're most likely to exacerbate the condition. Treating ODD involves using consistent (and consistently enforced) rules, balanced by warmth and caring.

MYTH: *The ODD and CD labels are primarily used to pathologize youth who misbehave. Youth with CD are just bad kids.*

FACT: While CYCPs may agree that there's some truth to this myth, most youth given the CD label are unusually aggressive and cruel, and do exhibit a conspicuous disregard for the feelings of others, bullying, hurting animals, theft, vandalism, and arson. But, as Charles Applestein has noted, "there is no such thing as a bad kid"; CD is caused by a combination of biology and environment, including an abusive or unsupportive home situation.

MYTH: *Caregivers use psychotropic medications for youth with CD so that they'll be manageable and docile.*

FACT: Medication is not a treatment option recommended for use with CD.

Source: "Common Myths About Disruptive Behavior Disorders" from Myths About Oppositional Defiant Disorder. Used by permission of Childmind Institute.

emphasizes that since the CD label wouldn't be applied in situations where aggressive acts may be necessary for survival (e.g., war or conflict-ridden contexts), the social and economic context in which the behaviours are occurring must be considered (APA, 2013).

Before turning to a discussion of the explanations and treatment of ODD and CD, read the statements in Box 5.3 and examine your own feelings about these behaviour patterns. How might your position on these issues relate to your behaviours toward someone diagnosed with such disorders?

EXPLAINING DISRUPTIVE BEHAVIOUR: PSYCHOLOGICAL PARADIGMS

What are some of the most common explanations for ODD and CD? As with all disorders, the best explanation will vary in relation to one's theoretical framework. From a psychological perspective, predominant explanations of disruptive behaviour disorders include those proposed from the biological and sociocultural paradigms. However, we'll also consider psychodynamic, behavioural, and cognitive factors. As we've noted in earlier discussions, the best explanations for these behaviour patterns are likely to emerge from consideration of biological, psychological, and social factors, and although some explanations have greater empirical support than others, there is no single cause for any of these diagnoses.

Biological Paradigm   The relationship between biological factors and ODD and CD has been evaluated in many scientific investigations. From a biological paradigm, the role of genetics, brain structures, and biochemical processes have been considered.

Heredity and Genetics. ODD and CD appear to run in families. Patterson (1992) conducted a longitudinal study and found that antisocial behaviours are stable across generations. In the case of the disruptive disorders, *temperament* and *aggression* have been the focus of investigations of genetic influence where these characteristics are part of a general "antisocial personality" (Lahey & Waldman, 2003). **Temperament** (stable, individual differences in cognitive, emotional, and behavioural tendencies that appear in infancy) has been found to be moderately influenced by genetics, as supported by twin and family studies (Bouchard, 2004; Caspi & Shiner, 2006). Of particular relevance in the case of ODD and CD, *difficult temperament* (associated with intense negative reactions to stimuli, irritability, impulsivity, restlessness, and difficulties adapting to new routines and experiences), observed as early as ages one to three, has been found to predict conduct problems in childhood (Bates et al., 1991; Powell, Lochman, & Boxmeyer, 2007) and involvement in criminal activity and Antisocial Personality Disorder in adulthood (Caspi et al., 1996).

Genetic influence appears to be more significant in *life-course-persistent* conduct problems than in the *adolescent-limited* pathway (Simonoff, 2001; Taylor, Iacono, & McGue, 2000), where environmental and social influences likely play a greater role. Similarly, genetics appear to be more relevant in *aggression-related* conduct problems than in *non-aggressive* conduct problems (Eley, Lichtenstein, & Moffitt, 2003). Consequently, numerous studies examining the heritability of **aggression** (acts intended to harm or destroy others) have found higher rates of similarity between identical than fraternal twins, supporting the role of genetic influence (Miles & Carey, 1997; Rowe, Almeida, & Jacobson, 1999).

Note that we haven't distinguished between ODD and CD; this is consistent with findings that suggest they reflect the same "genetic liability" (Eaves, Silberg, & Maes, 2005, p. 332). However, recent twin research (Gelhorn et al., 2005) has found that some CD symptoms (lying, stealing, weapon use, vandalism) may be more heritable than others (truancy, breaking and entering). Genes regulating dopamine are being investigated in relation to these behaviours (Beaver et al., 2007).

Brain Structures. Neurobiological factors have been implicated in CD. Children and youth exhibiting conduct-disordered behaviour have higher rates of birth complications and head injuries (McBurnett & Lahey, 1994) and demonstrate impaired executive functioning as well as lower verbal intelligence (Moffitt & Lynam, 1994). Both structural and functional abnormalities in the **prefrontal cortex** (the foremost part of the frontal lobes) have been related to conduct-disordered behaviour (Nigg & Huang-Pollock, 2003; Raine et al., 2000).

As we saw in Chapter 4, Gray (1987) proposed that two brain systems (composed of different neural structures and regulated by different neurotransmitter systems) explain motivation and behaviour: a *behavioural activation system* (BAS) and a *behavioural inhibition system* (BIS). The BAS *stimulates* behaviour (particularly in the context of possible reinforcements) and is associated with seeking rewards and pleasure; the BIS *inhibits* behaviour (particularly in the context of possible punishments) and is associated with the experience of fear and avoiding pain. Quay (1993) suggested that life-course-persistent conduct problems might be a function of an *overactive BAS* (resulting in reward-seeking behaviour) and an *underactive BIS* (resulting in low levels of fear and anxiety). Together, these two systems characterize the child or adolescent with CD as one who will engage in behaviour (antisocial or aggressive if necessary) in order to achieve desired outcomes but lacks the ability to inhibit or prevent actions that violate rules or the rights of others. Consistent with Quay's (1993) proposal, children exhibiting conduct-disordered behaviour show a greater sensitivity to rewards (Frick et al., 2003) and lower sensitivity to punishments or threats of punishment (Fowles, 2001). Consequently, disciplinary strategies that use punishments (or threats of punishment) don't have the anticipated effect of reducing undesirable behaviour. With respect to aggression, low levels of autonomic reactivity (Raine, 2002) and general low levels of cortical activity (Magnusson, 1988) have been observed and might further explain the inability of those diagnosed with CD to acquire appropriate avoidance responses in relation to punishment.

Neurotransmitters. Relevant to the diagnosis of CD, aggression has been associated with higher levels of the hormone testosterone (Archer, 1991) and low levels of serotonin (Dabbs et al., 2001). How might these two chemicals contribute to aggressive behaviour? Low levels of serotonin are associated with increased sensitivity to negative stimuli, which may result in feelings of frustration in various contexts; high levels of testosterone may increase motivation to exert dominance, particularly in the context of frustration. Interestingly, the DSM-5 notes that "neurotransmitter pathways associated with behavioural addictions, including those associated with serotonin, dopamine, and opioid systems, appear to play a role in Kleptomania as well" (APA, 2013, p. 478).

Although relationships between genetics, brain structures, brain function, neurotransmitter activation, and ODD and CD diagnoses have been observed, it can't be assumed that these biological factors *cause* these behaviours or that they alone explain their development. Rather, it may be that any of a long list of possible factors (e.g., birth trauma, prenatal exposure to toxins, and physical trauma in childhood) creates subtle damage to the developing brain, increasing the likelihood of one or more of the behaviours that characterize ODD or CD. The extent to which functioning is affected, however, will also depend on the social and environmental context in which the child or adolescent is developing. Accordingly, it's best to think of disruptive behaviours as emerging from a complex interaction of biological and environmental influences (Reif et al., 2007).

Psychodynamic Paradigm   The first person to consider disruptive behaviour from a psychodynamic perspective was psychiatrist William Healy (1915). In *The Individual Delinquent* he argued that the primary causes for antisocial behaviour in children included mental abnormality, abnormal physical conditions, and defective home environments (Snodgrass, 1984). Psychoanalyst August Aichhorn (1935) also viewed disruptive behaviour from a psychodynamic perspective, arguing that while all children are born "asocial" because they want immediate gratification, they learn to regulate their wants and desires and to delay gratification. Although Aichhorn recognized the role that unfavourable environments play in impulsive and disruptive behaviours, his primary emphasis was on "psychic forces" in the development of these abnormalities. Other psychodynamic explanations have included the idea that noncompliant and defiant behaviour results from an unconscious attempt to reject the control that high moral standards (often unrealistic and unattainable) and authority figures attempt to impose on the individual (Neill, 1926).

Behavioural Paradigm   Behavioural explanations for disruptive behaviour consider the role of basic learning processes (e.g., operant conditioning principles) in establishing conduct-related problems. For example, if a child pushes down his brother and gets the fire truck he's playing with, this desirable consequence for the child will serve to strengthen the aggressive behaviour and increase the likelihood of its occurring in the future—a simple example of positive reinforcement.

In addition to such learning through direct experience, social learning theory emphasizes the fact that children can learn to behave aggressively by observing others. Research in this area considers how the societal context provides youth with *role models* for behaviour. After observing a role model perform an aggressive act, children are more likely to engage in a similar act, particularly if the role model's behaviour was followed by a desired consequence or outcome. For instance, if Jacob watches a bully at school kick another child and then get that child's money and candy, Jacob is more likely to engage in similar behaviour himself in the future. Studies on how violent role models may impact the development of aggressive behaviour have found that children can and do learn such behaviour by observing it in others. For example, children who exhibit excessive aggressive behaviour are significantly more likely to have family members with records of aggression (Farrington, 1987; Waschbusch, 2002). Other studies show that children exposed to aggressive and/or violent peers in the classroom (Barth et al., 2004) and in the neighbourhood (Guerra, Huesmann, & Spindler, 2003) demonstrate an increase in aggressive behaviour. Moreover, research focusing on aggressive and/or violent role models in the media suggests that television violence serves as a "how-to" course in aggression (see Anderson et al., 2003, for a review). Thus, although biological factors may predispose some toward aggressive acts more than others, the idea that social messages regarding aggression and violence are factors in the development of such behaviour patterns is well documented.

Cognitive Paradigm   In this paradigm, the symptoms of disruptive behaviour disorders are considered in relation to cognitive processes. "To fully understand the nature of human aggression and violence, we must understand how it functions at the level of cognition" (Sestir & Bartolow, 2007, p. 158). Consistent with this view, deficits in executive functions have been found to distinguish children with CD from those not diagnosed with the disorder (e.g., Toupin et al., 2000).

Other cognitive approaches emphasize the role of *cognitive distortions* in aggressive acts and behaviours that violate the rights of others. For example, Wallinius et al. (2011) found that self-serving distortions were related to self-reported antisocial behaviour and were more common in incarcerated adults. What are self-serving cognitive distortions? Consider the model introduced by Gibbs and Potter (Gibbs, 1991; Gibbs, Potter, & Goldstein, 1995), according to which there are four types of distorted thinking that help explain aggressive and violating behaviour. *Self-centred* cognitive distortions are thoughts that emphasize the importance of one's own needs and rights to such an extent that those of others aren't considered or respected. *Blaming others* involves cognitive schemas that blame one's own bad behaviour on everything but one's self (e.g., other people, circumstances). In *minimizing*, aggressive and/or disruptive behaviour is viewed as acceptable or even necessary in order to achieve important goals. Finally, *assuming the worst* involves perceiving the intentions of others as hostile, or the worst-case scenario as inescapable, or one's own behaviour as something that can't be changed or improved.

To illustrate how such distortions might impact antisocial behaviour, consider this quote from a male burglar: "My idea in life is to satisfy myself to the extreme. I don't need to defend my behaviour. My thing is my thing. I don't feel I am obligated to the world or to nobody" (Samenov, 2004, p. 86). It's not hard to imagine how such beliefs that one is above the law might predict behaviours associated with disruptive behaviour disorders.

Sociocultural Paradigm   Although biological factors appear to play a role in disruptive behaviour and impulse-control disorders, it's clear that there is no single *cause* for any of these disorders. Instead, it's more realistic to view their development in relation to the diathesis–stress model discussed in Chapter 1. Accordingly, biological factors create a predisposition for developing the disorders, but social and cultural factors both contribute to the likelihood of their manifestation and impact the severity of symptoms and occurrence of comorbid conditions. From the sociocultural paradigm, explanations for externalizing behaviour patterns have included cultural factors (including societal models of aggression and violence) as well as the immediate family environment of the child and/or adolescent.

Culture and Externalizing Disorders. It has been argued that the externalizing disorders of ODD and CD are significantly more prevalent in industrialized societies, including Canada, the United States, Australia, Japan, and South Africa (APA, 2000). More recent investigations, however, bring this general conclusion into question. Specifically, cultural variability has been observed for ODD and CD (Canino et al., 2008), suggesting that social factors play a significant role. Investigations have found that the nature of the parent–child relationship, maternal style, and family values might explain why incidences of ODD and CD are lower for some cultural populations than others (Bird et al., 2006; Canino et al., 2004), with positive characteristics of these social factors serving as protective factors.

Family Influences. The immediate social environment has been considered extensively in relation to ODD and CD. Early psychological trauma (including exposure to stressors associated with various family factors) may affect the developing brain, with consequences for later executive functions (Perry, 2009) and levels of aggression (Anda et al., 2006). Family factors have been found to be associated with ODD and CD. Specifically, parents of those diagnosed with disruptive behaviour disorders tend to have lower socioeconomic status, higher levels of psychopathology, and marital disruption (Frick et al., 1994; Waschbusch, 2002) and are more likely to display antisocial behaviour (Kotler & McMahon, 2005). Of particular interest in the case of ODD and CD is the role of parenting styles. Patterson, Reid, and Dishion (1992) distinguish between **parental discipline** (a set of skills that includes appropriate identification of problem behaviours and the use of effective consequences) and **parental monitoring** (tracking and supervising activities of the child or adolescent). Parents of children with disruptive behaviours demonstrate differences in both of these areas. For example, they tend to issue a greater number of commands and to do so in a way that is more likely to be angry, nagging, and humiliating (Kuczynski & Kochanska, 1995; Loeber, 1990) as well as harsh and punitive, with little warmth and involvement (Loeber, Burke, & Pardini, 2009; Mulford & Redding, 2008). They also tend to exhibit difficulties administering consistent and effective discipline, often rewarding undesirable behaviour (e.g., giving in to yelling/tantrums) and failing to notice and/or reward desired behaviours (Brinkmeyer & Eyberg, 2003; Patterson, Chamberlain, & Reid, 1982). Another difference relates to the types of commands they issue to their children. Specifically, they're more likely to use **beta commands** (vague, interrupted requests that the child is not given time to comply with) than **alpha commands** (specific requests that identify an appropriate and realistic response). For example, rather than the *alpha command* "Pick up your clothes and make your bed!," the *beta command* "Clean up your mess!" is made and the parent proceeds to make the bed and pick up the child's clothes. With respect to parental monitoring, children and adolescents exhibiting higher levels of antisocial behaviour spend more time unsupervised by parents.

While it may be tempting to conclude that these findings suggest that parents are to blame for their child's disorder, keep in mind that multiple factors explain the development of parenting styles associated with these disorders. Rather than merely being a choice that parents make, discipline strategies and other parenting approaches result from various influences, many of which are beyond the control of the parent. For example, stressors, social disadvantage, temperament of the child, parental psychopathology, education, and parenting strategies used in the parent's family of origin all play a role in determining one's approach to discipline and supervision of children (Capaldi et al., 2002). Sensitivity to potential contextual factors that influence parenting styles, then, will help CYCPs avoid inappropriately blaming caregivers' choices for their child or adolescent's disruptive behaviour.

A CYC LENS ON THE PSYCHOLOGICAL PARADIGMS: A HOLISTIC CONCEPTUAL MODEL

From the CYC ecological perspective, it's important to keep in mind that although genetic factors have been shown to play a role in the development of disruptive or aggressive behaviours, these factors must interact with contextual psychosocial influences (risk factors) to produce such behaviours (Austin & Sciarra, 2010). Hormones, neurotransmitter dysfunction, and prenatal toxins like alcohol and nicotine have all been identified as contributing risk factors, yet it's noteworthy that the research relates such factors not to ODD behaviours specifically, but rather to behavioural difficulties in general (Austin & Sciarra, 2010).

Emotional dysregulation and family influence have been found to be two of the most important factors influencing the development of disruptive behaviours. Among the most common family characteristics representing risk factors are behavioural limits that are either too harsh or too lax or applied inconsistently; rules that lack clear structure; poor boundaries; "discipline" (punishment) that is uncertain and inconsistently applied; highly authoritarian parenting; low levels of parental warmth and supervision; insecure attachment; one parent modelling oppositional behaviour; one parent being emotionally or physically unavailable; and overt marital conflict (Austin & Sciarra, 2010; Kendall & Comer, 2010). Another factor is parents' **irritable explosive discipline**, characterized by a high rate of commands, yelling, hitting, threatening, and using humiliating and derogatory statements (Austin & Sciarra, 2010).

Along with a lack of capacity for emotional regulation, other internal characteristics of the child are thought to play a role in the onset of ODD. These include a low frustration tolerance, a lack of problem-solving skills, and a lack of adaptability in shifting from the expectations of one situation to another. And as we've seen, children with ODD have difficulty with cognitive distortions, often exhibiting a tendency to misinterpret and mistakenly ascribe hostile intentions to others in their social environment.

Thus, research in this area hasn't identified one isolated causal factor; rather, there is a known constellation of risk factors that can put a young person at risk for developing a conduct behavioural difficulty. These risk factors relate to youths' biology, personality, and temperament as well as to their social context (Frick, 2004; Mack, 2004). Austin and Sciarra (2010) suggest that there are three methods for calculating the end risk from multiple risk factors: cumulative, interactionist, and multiple pathways. "The most common method of taking into account the multiple risk factors that can lead to conduct disorder is to consider them from a cumulative risk perspective. From this perspective, the number of risk factors present is more important than the type of risk factor" (Frick, 2004, p. 824). The **interactionist pathway** model considers the significance of certain risk factors interacting with others, and the **multiple pathways** model suggests that different causal processes are involved, each with a different set of risk factors (Austin & Sciarra, 2010).

Evidence suggests that in some youth, CD may be caused by abnormal neurological functioning (Mack, 2004). We know that child maltreatment can negatively affect the brain functions related to behavioural and emotional regulation. Problems with regulating emotion have been identified with conduct problems and aggression; emotional dysregulation can impair the development of social cognitive skills that allow a child to effectively process information and respond appropriately in social situations (Frick, 2004). As well, prenatal and perinatal toxin exposure have both been associated with behavioural difficulties in general.

One of the most significant negative impacts upon youth with CD is a **lack of empathy**, also known as "callous disregard" (Mack, 2004). Young people with a lack of empathy tend to feel superior, lack awareness of social expectations, and have a tendency to be disrespectful, intolerant, unkind, and impatient toward others. Anger and rage are also common personality characteristics, and are thought to develop as a result of punitive relationships and negative experiences in the youth's life (Mack, 2004). Those with CD who show a lack of empathy toward others also appear to display a more severe and aggressive pattern of conduct problems than other youth with CD. More specifically, they're more likely to show a pattern of behaviour that includes reactive, impulsive aggressive acts as well as instrumental, premeditated aggressive acts (Frick, 2004).

Another risk factor for CD, as for ODD, is difficult temperament. A child with a difficult temperament related to either genetic or prenatal factors can be very challenging to a parent. If the primary caregiver isn't able to cope with the challenges, attachment processes can be disrupted, which can alter the child's developmental pathway and create a negative internal working model. We discuss the role of attachment and the negative internal working model elsewhere in the text, and specifically as a risk factor for CD in more detail below (Frick, 2004).

Cognitive functioning is also impaired in young people with CD, specifically their problem-solving skills, role-taking skills, and self-control. Youth with CD are limited in all three areas of cognitive functioning; they have limited insight into their own behaviour and in seeing different ways to solve problems (Mack, 2004). Role taking is particularly important, because without the ability to take into consideration another person's perspective, these young people remain in an egocentric state, preoccupied with their own feelings; most significantly, they're unable to have empathy for others or feel remorse for their actions. The lack of internal controls to prevent aggressive responses and the related cognitive distortions about others' intentions prompts aggressive responses to others' harmless comments or actions. As a result, these youth are engaged in a repeated cycle of cognitive distortions and consequent negative—and sometimes violent—reactions (Mack, 2004).

Considerable research shows that the family can be a major risk factor in the development of CD. As with ODD, there are four known common patterns in the families of youth diagnosed with CD: parental deviance, parental rejection and coerciveness, lack of discipline and/or lack of supervision, and marital conflict (Kendall & Comer, 2010). The same pattern of inconsistent discipline is observed as well: the parents of children with CD tend to reward positive and negative behaviours inconsistently. Specifically, they tend to positively reinforce inappropriate or coercive child behaviours (e.g., yelling and arguing) by laughing or giving in, whereas positive behaviours are largely ignored or responded to inappropriately. Consequently, these children are rewarded for their antisocial behaviour and don't learn appropriate adaptive behaviour (Kendall & Comer, 2010). As noted above, irritable explosive discipline is also a risk factor for CD; as well, exposure to parental violence and marital discord increases the risk for later violence. As with intergenerational trauma, there is an intergenerational transmission of CD, although it's not known whether this is primarily caused by learned behaviour (modelling) or by heredity.

A comprehensive means for assessing young people in the context of their family is therefore needed, given that children and adolescents with behaviours related to CD have often been exposed to neglect, abuse, poverty, addictions, and family violence (Mack, 2004). Frequently, they also have coexisting problems related to other mental health concerns, including ADHD, depression, anxiety, expressive and receptive language disorder, and neurological abnormalities (Mack, 2004). Social disadvantage, homelessness, low socioeconomic status, poverty, overcrowding, and social isolation are broader risk factors that can predispose children to CD. Children with CD are more likely to come from poverty and troubled neighbourhoods in urban areas; they're also more likely to be involved in gangs and in other criminal offending behaviours.

In summary, CYCPs must keep in mind that the risk factors for CD overlap in multiple domains and across the individual, family, school, and community systems. Refer to Figure 5.1 for an illustration of how these multiple risk factors may interact across contexts.

When children or adolescents are diagnosed with severe Conduct Disorder, practitioners and others run the risk of identifying the young people themselves as the problem rather than focusing on the complex risk factors (listed above) that likely influenced the development of the troublesome behaviours. Although it's classified as such in the DSM-5, we suggest that CYCPs view CD not as a *diagnosis* but rather as a *descriptor* of a cluster of problematic behaviours. If we use the label as a diagnosis, there are implications or guidelines for treatment based on knowing definitively what causes CD, which we do not know. Moreover, a young person presenting with chronic school absences, running away, and staying out late at night and a young person who sexually assaults, injures others, and uses weapons in criminal activity both fit the DSM-5 criteria:

> It is clear that these are two very different types of behaviors and it is inappropriate to assume these youngsters somehow cluster together. As we look at the other conditions for diagnosis, they also do not apply. As we have seen, there are multiple causes for these behaviors, the course of CD is highly variable, and treatments will vary considerably depending on many other characteristics of the youth than the observed behaviors. (McMains, Maynard, & Conlan, 2003, p. 3)

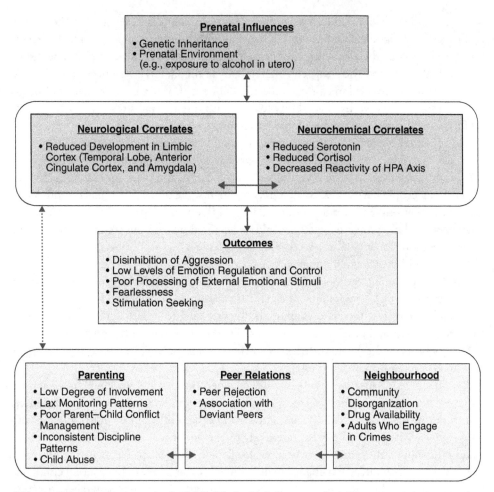

Figure 5.1 The Interaction of Multiple Risk Factors for CD

Neurobiological, genetic, and social risk factors interact and influence the development of behaviours associated with a diagnosis of CD.

Source: From "Contextualizing the Neurobiology of Conduct Disorder in an Emotion Dysregulation Framework" by M. Catherine Cappadocia et al. from Clinical Psychology Review, Vol 29 (09), 2009, pp: 506–518. Copyright © 2009 by Elsevier Ltd. Used by permission of Elsevier Ltd. via Copyright Clearance Center.

Recent research in the three related domains of neuroscience, attachment, and resilience has greatly enhanced our understanding of how risk and protective factors interact to shape outcomes for all children. This information can assist in our understanding of what causes CD and can guide our interventions (Kiro, 2009).

Neuroscience has shown that only the brainstem is fully developed at birth. During the first three years of life the brain develops rapidly, establishing the neural pathways that allow the more complex structures to develop (Perry, 2009). This developmental process is sequential; different areas of the central nervous system are in the process of organizing at different times. Any disruptions of experience-dependent neurochemical signals during these critical periods of brain development can lead to abnormalities or deficits in neurodevelopment (Kiro, 2009). Thus, the environment's role in brain development is critical—and the primary caregiver is known to be the major provider of the environmental cues necessary to this development (Kiro, 2009).

Children's resilience is also a significant factor in their development. "In the context of exposure to significant adversity, resilience is both the capacity of individuals to navigate their way to the psychological, social, cultural, and physical resources that sustain their well-being and their capacity individually and collectively to negotiate for these resources to be provided in culturally meaningful ways" ("What is resilience?," n.d.).

Resilient children have an ability to cope with the internal stresses of their vulnerabilities and the external stresses of their environment. They usually have an easy temperament, high self-esteem, an internal locus of control, and a sense of autonomy. They have a supportive family environment and a supportive person or agency outside the family. A strong cultural connection is also important (Ungar, 2012). "The most resilient children and young people have access to all four components, but any one can make a difference. It is clear that resilience is not an isolated individual characteristic and it is difficult to see how any of these protective factors could be acquired outside the context of secure and consistent attachment" (Kiro, 2009, p. 20).

Some children have a number of risk factors known to be associated with a likely chance of developing acting-out behaviours and yet don't go on to develop the behaviours associated with CD. Longitudinal research has shown that resilient children have the ability to elicit positive responses from others, are engaging to other people, and have good communication and problem-solving skills. They tend to have a high IQ, good dispositions, hobbies, and parents with good caregiving skills, leading to the child's feelings of competence and increased self-esteem ("Conduct Disorders," n.d.).

Attachment patterns become established when the internal working models formed in the early years are reinforced by experiences in the world outside the home. The **internal working model** is the child's view of the world and his or her place in it. Children with insecure and disorganized patterns are likely to encounter rejection from peers, teachers, and other adults they encounter as a result of their behaviours. But negative outcomes aren't always inevitable, and change in attachment patterns is possible. During childhood and adolescence, however, change must be facilitated through the repeated experience of positive relationships that will provide different experiences from those that gave rise to the insecure and disorganized attachment patterns in the first place (Kiro, 2009).

We know that children and youth with a history of secure attachment are clearly at an advantage when presented with life challenges (Kiro, 2009). They have a positive internal working model in that they trust that the world is a safe place; they have positive expectations of themselves and others; and they have access to supportive adults and connections that extend beyond the family, creating a sense of belonging. All of these factors enhance resilience. Children with avoidant and ambivalent attachment patterns lack self-confidence, may have low self-esteem, and have difficulties negotiating social relationships. But many have developed effective coping strategies. They may not be as resilient as securely attached children, but they'll be more resilient than those with a history of disorganized attachment, or attachment disorder, who are the most vulnerable (Kiro, 2009). Note that the behaviours associated with attachment disorders reflect the same behaviours we see associated with CD.

It's clear, then, that CD is extremely complex. Apart from the direct link between attachment, low socioeconomic status, and child behaviour difficulties, other factors, including maternal depression, exposure to violence, and poor parenting practices, act as risks. (Refer to Table 5.1 for a summary of risk factors associated with CD.) Yet neuroscience, attachment

Table 5.1 Risk Factors Associated with CD	
✓ **Individual Child/Youth Risk Factors**	✓ **Environment and Social Context Risk Factors**
Neurochemical abnormalities	Prenatal exposure to toxins
CNS abnormalities	Birth complications
Autonomic irregularity	Parental psychopathology
Difficult child temperament	Family conflict
Parent–child attachment difficulties	Inadequate parental supervision and discipline
Preference for dangerous and novel activities	Lack of parental involvement, neglect
Positive peer group rejection	Association with a deviant peer group
Affiliation with negative peer group	Low socioeconomic status: poverty
Low verbal intelligence	Exposure to violence
Academic underachievement	Access to weapons
Deficits in processing social information	
Genetics	

Source: Adapted from Bloomquist & Schnell, 2002, p. 60; Frick, 2004, p. 824.

research, and resilience research have shown us ways in which we can build on young people's strengths and thus intervene to influence positive outcomes for youth with CD.

As we saw earlier, research and clinical experience suggest that CD follows two courses: one is life-course persistent and the other is limited to adolescence. The life-course-persistent pattern is associated with an earlier presentation of antisocial behaviours and more serious criminal activity in adulthood, whereas the adolescence-limited pattern (by far the most common) has its origins in the social environmental context and discontinues in early adulthood (Kendall & Comer, 2010). The behaviours related to CD also exist along a spectrum; most fall within the mild to moderate range and are very amenable to treatment (McMains, Maynard, & Conlan, 2003). In practice, then, it's important that CYCPs try to distinguish young people with less serious, transient problematic behaviours from those with more serious and entrenched behaviours.

WHERE DO YOU STAND?

Consider the psychological and CYC perspectives summarized above. Where do you stand? Most psychologists and CYCPs alike agree that there is no single cause of ODD or CD. Without question, there is great debate with respect to the best practice in the treatment of ODD and CD. Clearly, each case of an externalizing disorder must be considered individually.

Before turning to a discussion of approaches to treatment, read Janelle's case in the *Take Action!* exercise to evaluate your understanding of the psychological and CYC explanations of disruptive behaviours.

Thirteen-year-old Janelle was brought to the mental health outpatient referral clinic by her foster mother, who explained that Janelle had been suspended from school for throwing a chair and pushing a teacher. Before she could return to school, Janelle needed an assessment and recommendation from a doctor. In the interview, the psychiatrist learned that this was Janelle's sixth school suspension in the past two years: she had been suspended for fighting, carrying a knife to school, smoking marijuana, and stealing money from other students' lockers. When asked about her behaviour at home, Janelle told the psychiatrist that her foster mother "gets on my nerves," and that during those times, she leaves home for several days and hangs out with friends. The social history indicates that when Janelle was an infant her birth mother abandoned the family, and that when she was seven her gang-involved father was incarcerated for auto theft and assault. Child and Family Services had apprehended Janelle and placed her in the foster home

five years before. She had been very stable until relatively recently, when family visits with her father were reinstated.

1. What explanations for Janelle's behaviour might be offered from the psychological perspectives discussed previously?

2. What factors in her home environment might be contributing to her behaviour?

3. What specific interventions might be recommended from a psychological approach?

4. How might Janelle benefit from receiving a diagnosis?

5. As a CYCP in this case, what information might you pursue in your assessment?

6. Describe how you would approach your work with the psychologist and her assessment.

Source: Adapted fr om Searight, Rottnek, and Abby, 2001, in Scarlett, Ponte, and Singh, 2009, p. 229.

HELPING CHILDREN AND ADOLESCENTS WITH DISRUPTIVE BEHAVIOUR DISTURBANCES
Psychological Approaches to Treatment

Following diagnosis, what is the most effective way to support young people whose externalizing behaviours disrupt their daily functioning and negatively impact their relationships with others? As with all disorders, the best approach to treatment will vary in relation to one's theoretical framework. From a psychological perspective, predominant treatments of disruptive behaviour disorders include those proposed from the behavioural and sociocultural paradigms; these consider biological, psychological, and social factors. And while there is no single treatment for any of these diagnoses, some approaches to intervention have greater empirical support than others.

John's Case: *Revisited*

Although John's teachers described him as very bright, they noted that he sometimes seemed sad or depressed. He was very impulsive, constantly interrupted them, seemed distracted, and was inattentive in the classroom. He had difficulty getting along with his peers, including being aggressive and "mouthy" toward them, and was often seen playing on his own or with younger

children. As mentioned earlier, John had recently been skipping school.

John's teachers are very concerned about him, and believe he should be referred for a psychiatric assessment. Mostly, though, they're relieved that he's been enrolled in an alternative school program affiliated with a group home that specializes in working with children with disruptive behaviours.

Biological Paradigm   Considering the high rates of comorbidity between ADHD, ODD, and CD, it's not surprising that the same medications used for ADHD have also been used to treat those with ADHD and comorbid ODD and CD. In the treatment of ODD and CD alone, however, no specific class of drugs is consistently used. Most often used are medications that target the symptoms of existing comorbid conditions or reduce specific symptoms; these medications include stimulants (for ADHD symptoms), antidepressants (for depressive symptoms), and lithium and anticonvulsants (mood stabilizers that can decrease aggressiveness). Risperidone (an antipsychotic discussed in Chapter 9) has also been found to be effective in decreasing symptoms of CD in those with below average IQ (Snyder et al., 2002). Clonidine (which decreases blood pressure by inhibiting the release of norephinephrine) generally reduces sympathetic nervous system activity and has also been found to reduce aggression (Hazell & Stuart, 2003) in those with CD. As in the case of biological treatment of ADHD, however, efficacy, side effects, and long-term consequences are a serious concern (e.g., lightheadedness, low blood pressure). See Table 5.2 for an overview of common medications used to treat disruptive behaviours.

Without question, significant controversy exists over the use of biological treatments for ODD and CD. A major reason for this controversy is the observation that medications for aggression and conduct problems are associated with only small to moderate changes in behaviour (APA, 2006). Psychosocial interventions (discussed below) are associated with more significant changes in behaviour. And yet despite existing concerns, medication is still used to manage disruptive behaviour in some cases. What is your position on the use of such treatments?

Psychodynamic Paradigm   The general emphasis of psychodynamic therapy is to increase individuals' capacity to experience feelings and their responses to those emotions (Lanza et al., 2002). In the context of disruptive behaviour, one general category of application for psychodynamic therapy has been in relation to anger and aggression. From a psychodynamic perspective, aggressive behaviour is viewed as an expression of unconscious conflict. By using various psychodynamic techniques (e.g., hypnosis, dream interpretation), this conflict can be brought into consciousness and dealt with in the context of current reality.

Although some research has demonstrated such approaches to be effective in decreasing aggressive behaviour in youth (e.g., Lanza et al., 2002) and in decreasing anger and confrontation in youth relationships (Tishby et al., 2005), critics argue that, given the length and costs of treatment, investigations of its effectiveness are limited (Glancy & Saini, 2005). Other research suggests that such approaches to treatment are less effective with externalizing than internalizing disorders (Midgley & Kennedy, 2011). Accordingly, much more research with

Table 5.2 Common Medications for Disruptive Behaviour Disorders

Drug	Intended Outcomes for Children/Adolescents
Lithium	Reduces aggressive behaviour
Haloperidol	Reduces aggressive and disruptive behaviour
Risperidone	Reduces disruptive behaviour
Divalproex sodium	Reduces conduct disorder symptoms
Clonidine	Reduces aggression

youth exhibiting disruptive behaviours is needed before conclusions can be reached about the effectiveness of psychodynamic approaches in the treatment of these disorders.

Behavioural Paradigm   Behavioural principles are frequently applied in treatments for ODD and CD. Studies have found that such strategies can be effective in improving classroom behaviour and academic/study skills (Kozioff et al., 2000; Nelson, 1996). Home-based contingency management interventions (i.e., providing rewards for desired behaviour, withdrawing reinforcers after undesirable behaviour) have been associated with improvements in compliance and decreased disruptive behaviour and aggression (e.g., Walker, Colvin, & Ramsey, 1995). However, these techniques are less effective for adolescents than for children and aren't typically generalized to other situations or environments. Moreover, decreasing noncompliance and reducing aggression aren't the only treatment goals; enhancing social-communication and problem-solving skills are also considered important goals, and these are less effectively achieved through strictly behavioural strategies (Gelfand & Drew, 2003).

In addition to being used alone, behavioural strategies serve as the basis for *parent training programs* and *classroom management interventions* (directed toward educators). They've also served as the basis for more intensive *behaviour modification programs* (e.g., the Summer Treatment Program by Pelham and colleagues) provided in a summer-camp context in which the child receives individualized instruction from trained staff.

Cognitive Paradigm   In general, cognitive-behavioural interventions for externalizing disorders encourage young people to increase their awareness of thoughts that occur in the context of day-to-day life, to notice how these thoughts relate to inappropriate behaviour (e.g., aggression), and to alter their cognitions in order to modify their actions. For example, if a child becomes violent when he's teased by peers on a playground, therapy might involve identifying the thoughts he has following such an event (e.g., "They think I'm stupid") and then encouraging him to identify other possible explanations (e.g., "They tease everyone") or identify adaptive ways of coping with the event (e.g., notify a teacher or parent). Such *problem-solving skills training* has been used to help young people effectively manage challenging social situations. Here, the child is trained to approach social situations in a step-by-step approach through the use of games, stories, and activities and is then encouraged to apply these to real-life situations (Kazdin, 1996).

Although cognitive-behavioural interventions are considered likely to be effective (Roberts et al., 2003), particularly with children, and some research suggests they may be beneficial (Kazdin & Wassell, 2000b; Toplak et al., 2008), they're not currently considered to be evidence based. There is little empirical support for their effectiveness, suggesting that observed effects don't last and that the skills aren't likely to be generalized beyond the therapeutic context to real-life settings (Pelham & Fabiano, 2008). Of particular note is their lack of effectiveness with adolescents. More promising is the use of CBT for those with ODD or CD when combined with Parent Management Training or PMT (Kazdin, 2003; Kazdin & Wassel, 2000b).

Sociocultural Paradigm   From a sociocultural standpoint, the treatment of disruptive behaviour disorders involves changing variables in the social environment of the child or adolescent. Most of these interventions focus on the family and the classroom, although other approaches are directed more specifically toward the young person. Numerous programs have been developed and evaluated in an attempt to decrease the symptoms of externalizing disorders and their negative consequences. While each has its own unique approach, they do share similarities, with most combining elements of behavioural and/or cognitive-behavioural therapy with medication (referred to as *multimodal treatment*). Here, we consider some of the basic components of such programs and the evidence supporting their effectiveness.

Parent Training. Parent training programs generally aim to teach parents of youth with a diagnosis of ODD or CD how to effectively use specific child management techniques (Anastopoulos & Farley, 2003). Typically, these programs consist of 8–12 sessions and are considered appropriate for parents of children between 4 and 12 years of age (Seligman & Reichenberg, 2012). While the specific goals of such programs may vary, their general objectives are focused on effective use of behavioural strategies to improve parental discipline and monitoring, increase family unity, and improve parent–child communication and problem solving.

Parent training has been recommended as the "first line approach" of treatment for young children with ODD and CD (Eyberg, Nelson, & Boggs, 2008) based on its demonstrated effectiveness in decreasing oppositional and defiant behaviours (Kumpfer, Moolgaard, & Spoth, 1996; Roberts et al., 2003), including tantrums, aggression, and emotional upset. As in the case of PMT for ADHD, however, there are challenges associated with this mode of intervention. First, parents may be reluctant to explore how their parenting style plays a role in the disrupted behaviour pattern (Evans, 2010). It's also unclear whether parent training for ODD and CD is effective when comorbid conditions (e.g., depression, substance use) are present (Roberts et al., 2003) and whether these benefits persist over time. Also, it appears that PMT alone is less effective for adolescents, with additional interventions required for older youth (Eyberg, Nelson, & Boggs, 2008). One such intervention includes *multisystemic therapy* (which involves the child, parent, family, peers, and school staff as well as therapists, teachers, and physicians). This approach (discussed later in this chapter) acknowledges that each case of antisocial behaviour is different, related to different causal factors, and "embedded in powerful social and family networks" (Karnik & Steiner, 2007, p. 157). Accordingly, treatment must be specifically designed for each individual, using a combination of behavioural approaches, cognitive-behavioural approaches, parent training, and medication. Clearly, the amount of resources required for such treatment is substantial, limiting its accessibility (Evans, 2010). Despite these challenges, research supports long-term benefits associated with this approach—including fewer arrests, lower rates of recidivism, and fewer days of imprisonment over a 10-year period following treatment (Curtis, Ronan, & Borduin, 2004; Schaeffer & Borduin, 2005)—although other findings fail to conclude that MST is superior to other treatments (Littell, Popa, & Forsythe, 2005). Nevertheless, studies evaluating these programs indicate that parent training is among the most successful approaches to decreasing antisocial and aggressive behaviours in youth.

Additional Psychosocial Approaches. A long list of other treatment approaches have been recommended and evaluated in the literature. For example, interventions for ODD and CD include *anger control* and *anger-coping training* for adolescents and *assertiveness training* focusing on teaching the adolescent acceptable ways to express feelings (Roberts et al., 2003). None of these is considered evidence based at this time.

Generally, psychosocial treatments are more effective with children than with adolescents. For youth, strategies that emphasize problem solving and parent–adolescent communication may be preferred (Zisser & Eyberg, 2010).

CYC Approaches for Youth Struggling with Disruptive Behaviour Disturbances

Most CYCPs work with children and youth who struggle with conduct difficulties and oppositional, rule-violating behaviours. Remembering the distinction between internalizing and externalizing behaviours and the gender differences in their occurrence is important. Boys and young men are often labelled as oppositional and rule-breaking or as ODD and CD. Children and youth with oppositional behaviours and/or conduct problems are typically described by adults in their social environment as "argumentative, disobedient, demanding, and defiant" (McMahon & Kotler, 2008).

According to child development theorists, one of the main distinctions between a successful child and a child who struggles with troublesome behaviour is the ability to move successfully from one stage of development to another (Bloomquist, 2006). All children must master each major developmental task at each stage to be successful. The following child development stages, as outlined by Bloomquist (2006), are simple, straightforward, and easy to conceptualize: *self-control development*, *social development*, *emotional development*, and *academic development*. The self-control aspect of development is central to managing anger and obeying and following rules. Social development applies to a child's ability to maintain appropriate social relationships with peers and adults. Emotional development is the understanding of and expressing feelings, thinking helpful thoughts, and having good self-esteem. Children with conduct disturbances and oppositional behaviours often struggle in all these areas of development (Bloomquist, 2006). For CYCPs, then, the key to helping these young people is to identify, and intervene at, the appropriate developmental level, identifying the area of need and work with families to help their children develop successfully. And, of course, we must also recognize what's going right in the family and work with their strengths.

Strength-Based Relational CYC Practice   As always, the key to successful intervention with youth who struggle with conduct difficulties is the therapeutic relationship. Research has clearly established that punitive measures such as boot camps, shock treatment, incarceration, isolated medication trials, and psychiatric hospitalization are ineffective at best and can be injurious at worst. For young people with CD, evidence indicates that relational interventions need to be applied over long periods of time.

As noted above, CYCPs need to be sensitive to the ways in which developmental level might influence their choice of intervention. Effective interventions for conduct difficulties in pre-school-age children, for example, include Head Start types of programming that address both child temperament and parental effectiveness. Again, we must stress that medications have not been shown to be effective.

Assessment

The term *aggressive/conduct problem* (ACP) has been used by Bloomquist and Schnell (2002) to describe the conduct problems of children "who manifest some form of early-onset aggressive behaviour and who also display or who are at risk for displaying covert antisocial actions" (p. 3). Categorizing aggressive conduct problems along various dimensions can help CYCPs consider the different motivations for various aggressive acts and focus their interventions accordingly.

The relevant categories include **overt aggression**, defined as harmful verbal and physical acts of aggression toward others, self, or property (e.g., fighting, assault, robbery); **reactive/proactive aggression**, meaning either unplanned and responsive (e.g., a child is pushed and reacts by punching) or planned and goal oriented (e.g., a child plans to beat someone up after school); *violence*, involving the infliction of serious physical harm to others (as compared with aggression, which inflicts mild to moderate physical or psychological harm); *child delinquency*, associated with rule violations; and **psychopathy**, referring more to the lack of remorse and empathic emotions than to the commission of violent, manipulative, or aggressive acts themselves. These are all serious behaviours of concern to CYCPs, especially those who work with street youth, youth in care, youth in school settings, and youth involved in the criminal justice system.

While some suggest that ODD and CD behaviours stem from the same underlying cause or "disorder," others maintain that the two follow different developmental pathways altogether (Austin & Sciarra, 2010). Quite often ODD is seen as a less serious expression of acting-out behaviour than CD, or a "younger" version of it (Kendall & Comer, 2010). Only about one-third of children and adolescents with ODD will "progress to" or develop CD, meaning that many adolescents with CD were never diagnosed with ODD in the first place (Austin & Sciarra, 2010). Some suggest that when CD behaviours are evident, the behaviours associated with ODD are also likely to be present, with the CD diagnosis "preempting" an ODD diagnosis (Kendall & Comer, 2010, p. 63). Again, not surprisingly, this "progression" from ODD to CD appears to be related to various risk factors, including child characteristics, parenting practices, and family disorganization: "Early onset, greater severity, frequent physical fighting, parental substance abuse, and low socioeconomic status are factors that increase the risk of ODD progressing to CD" (Austin & Sciarra, 2010, p. 61). Nonetheless, the presence or absence of these risk factors does not fully explain the complex interaction of variables involved in the progression to CD in any child diagnosed with ODD ("Disruptive Behavior Disorders," 2015).

CYCPs should be aware of the relationship between CD and the adult diagnosis of Antisocial Personality Disorder (APD). According to the DSM, if a young person's antisocial behaviour associated with CD continues into adulthood, he or she qualifies as having an APD. This disorder is diagnosed when an individual aged 18 or older displays a pattern

Monkey Business Images/Shutterstock

It's important to consider the motivation for aggressive acts in the context of ODD and CD. What might be motivating this youth to hurt the other?

of behaviour characterized by repeated criminal behaviour, recklessness, impulsivity and irresponsibility, deceitfulness, and lack of remorse.

Typically, there are multiple areas of difficulties and "co-occurring" problems for children and youth who present with disruptive behaviours. In order to plan an intervention for each area of concern, CYCPs must conduct a thorough assessment of all potential problem areas as well as the strengths and protective factors in the child's ecology. Only a thorough understanding of young people's life experience, internal working model (how they interpret the world), and past and present relationship experiences will provide a complete picture of their actual needs (Foltz, 2008a). Moreover, these needs may be related to the more common co-occurring conditions, including ADHD, mood/anxiety disorders, PTSD, and substance abuse (Fonagy et al., 2002; McMains, Maynard, & Conlan, 2003).

Clinical assessments of young people's disruptive behaviours need to include multiple sources of observation as well as discussion with all the relevant informants. Keep in mind that children and youth interpret their stories differently from the adults in their lives. CYCPs should rely too on their own observations to guide their assessment, whether they're in a primary or a supportive role in the assessment process. As always, a meaningful relationship with caring adults in the life space has been shown to be effective in mitigating difficult behaviours. And given that children and youth with conduct difficulties are often distrusting of adults in general, the traditional CYC relational approaches to establishing trust and caring will go a long way toward helping them.

As we've noted, one recommended starting point for CYCPs' assessment is examining the overall development of the young person, including the level of family functioning. Assessing areas in which development is lacking and identifying the need that underlies the problem behaviour will help guide intervention. If young people are struggling with self-control, for example, they're also likely to be having difficulties with social and emotional skills. Self-control difficulties, oppositional behaviours, and rule-breaking can all lead to social rejection, academic failure, emotional difficulties, family breakdown, and criminal behaviour (Bloomquist, 2006). Strength-based relational practice, as outlined in Chapter 1, will guide CYCPs in their work with children and youth who are struggling with oppositional and disruptive behaviours.

Clinical Rating Scales. We noted earlier that although most CYCPs don't typically use rating scales in their assessments of youth, other professionals rely on these extensively, so it's helpful to be aware of them. In addition to a structured interview process, behaviour rating scales are used to assess ODD and CD. For example, CYCPs can readily employ the Achenbach Child Behavior Checklist to track behaviours of concern and the success of interventions over time; this checklist is used for individual clinical evaluations as well as for an aggregated treatment-program evaluation. Another clinical rating scale is the National Initiative for Children's Health Quality (NICHQ) Vanderbilt Assessment Scales; these are designed for the assessment of children with suspected or diagnosed ADHD but contain questions that aid in the identification of ODD. The SNAP-IV Teacher and Parent Rating Scale for children with ADHD may allow enhanced detection of ODD as well as other psychological concerns. Broad screening tools such as the Pediatric Symptom Checklist aren't specific to ODD but can screen for cognitive, emotional, or behavioural problems, thereby identifying children who require additional investigation (Hamilton & Armando, 2008).

Table 5.3 Behavioural Indicators Checklist: ODD and CD

✓ Signs of ODD	✓ Signs of CD
Frequently throws temper tantrums	*Aggression:* bullying, hitting peers or instructors, stealing from classmates
Talks back to teachers and/or aides	*Destruction:* destroying of classroom materials without remorse, showing no real care for books or materials needed for homework, marking on walls and otherwise defacing public spaces
Refuses to comply with rules set by teachers or administrators	
Deliberately annoys peers or instructors	*Lack of conscience, lack of right and wrong:* lying to teachers, peers, and others to get his or her own way; cheating in games; cheating on assignments and exams
Seeks revenge and is overly spiteful of peers and authority figures	
Blames others for his or her misbehaviour	*Rule violation:* constant truancy or tardiness; violent reaction to discipline; extreme resistance to following set rules; sexual acting out, cruelty to animals, fire setting, cruelty to children, offending behaviours, criminal behaviours

Source: From APPROACHES TO BEHAVIOR AND CLASSROOM MANAGEMENT: INTEGRATING DISCIPLINE AND CARE, VOLUME 01 by W. George Scarlett, Iris Chin Ponte, Jay P. Singh. Copyright © 2009 by Sage Publications. Used by permission of Sage Publications via CCC.

Indicators to Recognize It's important for CYCPs to understand the primary behavioural differences between ODD and CD. Young people with ODD are known to exhibit an *attributional bias*, meaning that they react aggressively as a result of a perceived threat, while those with CD tend to be more proactively aggressive. Some behaviours associated with ADHD are also seen in CD and ODD, but whereas the former are unintentional, they're considered to be purposeful and intentional in CD and to some extent in ODD (Austin & Sciarra, 2010). Barkley (2013) theorizes that given the emotional dysregulation involved in ADHD, it's actually a cause of ODD. The concordance rate for ADHD and ODD diagnoses range between 25 and 60–80 percent depending on the research, but ODD is known to be the most common coexisting condition with ADHD.

Table 5.3 provides a summary of behavioural indicators for ODD and CD in the classroom.

Intervention

Depending on the young person's unique strengths and needs, countless outside-the-box psychosocial and relational intervention approaches may be effective. Interventions should be implemented as soon as possible after the onset or identification of the behavioural difficulties, since evidence indicates that early intervention is key to success with this population.

Behavioural and Cognitive-Behavioural Techniques for CYCPs As we've emphasized throughout the text, **cognitive-behavioural interventions (CBIs)** are based on techniques that promote self-control skills and teach reflective problem-solving strategies. CBIs combine elements of behaviour therapy (modelling, feedback, and reinforcement) with cognitive approaches (problem solving, self-monitoring, self-instruction, communication skill building, relaxation, and situational self-awareness training) to teach youth to recognize difficult situations, take the time to think of possible alternative solutions, and select the most appropriate response (Robinson, Smith, & Brownell, 1999). In short, it involves teaching young people to "*stop, think, and act*" (Lorraine Fox, personal communication, 2003).

Social skills training and problem-solving skills training are the two most effective CBI tools for adolescents with conduct issues. Anger management programs are still used, although they've been criticized for not being able to generalize learned skills outside the therapy sessions. "It is likely that anger, as a target for intervention, is not sufficiently central to problems of aggression for its control to be an appropriate goal on its own" (Fonagy et al., 2002, p. 167).

According to Fonagy et al. (2002), evidence-based treatment options include teaching assertiveness, teaching relaxation techniques, teaching self-instruction, and challenging perceptions of social situations. Not surprisingly, CBT works better with older youth than with children (Fonagy et al., 2002). There are a number of successful social skills training programs available (Kendall & Braswell, 1993), including the school-based Peer Coping-Skills Training program.

An effective CBT method for adolescents with CD is **rational emotive behaviour therapy (REBT)**. Originally developed by psychologist Albert Ellis, this solution-oriented approach focuses on resolving emotional, cognitive, and behavioural problems. Fundamental to REBT is the idea that emotional and psychological suffering result primarily, though not completely, from our interpretation of negative events, not from the events themselves. REBT intervention focuses on first building a relationship between the practitioner and the young person, followed by challenging distorted thinking and teaching problem-solving strategies. REBT is thus entirely fitting with a CYC approach. Cognitive change is brought about through a process of teaching young people to systematically examine their thoughts and beliefs in order to assess the degree to which they're true, logical, and helpful (Gonzalez et al., 2004). Past negative experiences are validated but not permitted to be used as an excuse for poor choices (Ellis & Bernard, 2006).

The Role of Medication

No medications have demonstrated effectiveness in treating CD (Foltz, 2008a). Psychostimulants have been shown to be effective in reducing antisocial behaviours in children and adolescents with comorbid ADHD and ODD/CD. Awareness and observation of prescribed medications' potential side effects is, of course, critical for CYCPs. However, the evidence indicates that "medication cannot be justified as the first line of treatment for conduct problems" (Fonagy et. al, 2002). (See the end-of-chapter list of online resources relating to the use of psychotropic medications as a behaviour management tool for youth in care.)

Psychoeducation and Individual Counselling

Individual psychodynamic psychotherapy has been shown to be ineffective with disruptive behaviours (Fonagy et al., 2002; McMains, Maynard, & Conlan, 2003). Available evidence suggests that the use of psychodynamic therapy for children with disruptive behaviour disorders is unfavourable and not recommended (Dunnachie, 2007).

The literature indicates that teaching pro-social skills and challenging antisocial behaviours need to be addressed separately. *Problem-solving skills training* (PSST) is known to be effective in decreasing conduct-disordered behaviours (Fonagy et al., 2000). It has been repeatedly shown that children and youth with conduct problems have difficulty generating alternative solutions to interpersonal difficulties. As we've seen, they also tend to misinterpret others' intentions and fail to see the consequences of their choices and actions. PSST teaches interpersonal and cognitive problem-solving skills, and assists in challenging cognitive distortions (Fonagy et al., 2002).

Family Support Interventions

A family-focused approach is an integral part of any successful CYC intervention plan. After all, we've established that the family system is a major influence in the formation of attachment strategies and in the child's development, both from a positive and a negative perspective. It's also been well established that family conflict and poor parenting skills are most often characteristic of the families of youth with conduct disturbances. "Family dynamics and the ability of the child's external environment to meet the child's developmental needs have a central role in the development of CD" (Mack, 2004, p. 107).

Family-focused support interventions and parenting skills training are effective for both ODD and CD. The effectiveness of parent training in producing changes in parent–child behaviour has been established since the mid-1970s (Dunnachie, 2007). Parent management or parent skills training programs are well established as evidence-based treatments for disruptive behaviour disorders (Fonagy et al., 2002), and the younger the child, the greater the opportunity for success. As with other treatment programs, cultural competence must be honoured in the design and the delivery of these programs. Parent training models are based on social learning theory, where parents are encouraged to focus on positive rather than negative behaviours; CYCPs can use such strategies as role-playing, behavioural rehearsal, and structured homework exercises to teach the requisite skills.

For adolescents already involved in the justice system as a result of their criminal involvement, families need to share responsibility for their supervision outside of custody and agree to the treatment plan. Family group conferencing has been found to be highly successful, especially in the child welfare or justice systems, as it's based on principles of restorative justice. A family group conference brings together all the family members and other stakeholders to find a solution to a problem, usually an offending behaviour ("An introduction to family group conference," n.d.).

Two other approaches are *action-oriented family therapy* and *multisystemic therapy*. In **action-oriented family therapy**, parents are taught behaviour management skills with the aim of undermining the coercive family interactions associated with antisocial behaviours. As with parent effectiveness training approaches, through training by CYCPs and assigned homework tasks, the family learns to identify the young person's problem behaviours, to stop unknowingly rewarding them, and to reward the positive behaviours (Hartman & Bush, 1975). **Multisystemic therapy (MST)** fits with the family group conferencing approach; it has been shown to strengthen family relationships and reduce recidivism and aggression (Foltz, 2008a), and is "arguably the most promising intervention for serious juvenile offenders" (Fonagy et al., 2002, p. 161). MST recognizes the multiple factors involved in serious antisocial behaviour and makes use of multiple interventions in combination (Dunnachie, 2007). And since MST is both ecologically and relationally based, it fits well with the CYC perspective. It's an intensive treatment that addresses conduct disturbances and antisocial behaviour; it targets chronic, violent, or substance-abusing young offenders and their families who are at high risk of out-of-home placement. The major goal of MST is to teach parents the skills and resources needed to successfully parent adolescents and to empower youth to cope with family, peer, school, and neighbourhood problems. MST services are delivered in the home, school, or community, and the treatment plan is family rather than therapist driven. Evaluations of MST have demonstrated reduced long-term rates of criminal offending in serious juvenile offenders, improvements in family functioning, and decreased mental health problems for serious juvenile offenders (Rechichi & Baglivio, 2011).

CYC interventions for ODD and CD undoubtedly require consideration of numerous factors. Although the alternatives for CYCPs working with a child or adolescent exhibiting

Techniques for CYC Intervention

Identify the strengths and resiliency factors of the youth, family, and community.

Use strengths and resiliencies to build successful intervention strategies.

Use a multi systemic or ecological approach.

Identify each problem area domain and plan specific interventions for *all* areas.

Early intervention should be emphasized; maintain interventions for a long period of time.

If the youth is in and out of home care, maintain long-term caregiving relationships in the life space.

Treatment plans should be broadly based to cover the range of needed skills, services, funding, and supports.

If youth is involved in the justice system, treatment case planning should include collaterals from corrections and juvenile justice.

Include cognitive-behavioural therapy, but not individual psychodynamic psychotherapy.

All good CYC treatment plans should be designed to change and demonstrate progress over extended period of time. As with all treatment plans, the goals should be SMART: specific, measurable, attainable, realistic, and timelined.

A family-focused approach is an integral part of any successful CYC intervention plan.

Teaching parents parenting skills can be beneficial.

The Roots of Empathy program (see below) is effective for all school-aged children.

If the child is an adolescent, multi systemic therapy (MST) is suggested.

CYCPs must always use a culturally competent, family-focused approach.

The family will need to share the responsibilities for the youth's supervision and agree to the treatment plan.

Family group conferencing is a highly successful method for CYC work with families.

disruptive behaviours are many, some are more evidence based than others, and as such fit best with a CYC approach. Refer to Box 5.4 for a summary of guidelines for CYC interventions that might be considered in your practice.

Prevention: Advocacy, Community, and School-Based Strategies

Prevention programs are sometimes directed at youth who've already been identified as being vulnerable or at risk for antisocial behaviours and/or have committed crimes or acts of violence. Some programs aimed at gangs, for example, serve as useful examples of "prevention" intervention. Effective programs in this area include positive adult-role-model mentoring, focused skill development, teaching problem solving and non-violent conflict-resolution skills, implementing substance- and alcohol-abuse education programs, and providing academic and vocationally focused upgrading and recreation programs to all youth. These types of universal programs serve as an effective deterrent to gang membership and involvement in other antisocial activities (Leschied, 2008).

Generally, the treatment of conduct problems in the classroom or community hasn't received as much attention as interventions for conduct problems in the home. Factors associated with communities, schools, and students with lower levels of problem behaviours overall include strong, positive leadership; high expectations; close monitoring of students; good opportunities to engage in school and community life and take on responsibility; well-functioning incentive, reward, and consequence systems; high levels of parental involvement in activities; and a focus on learning (Dunnachie, 2007).

As we've described elsewhere in this text, contingency management programs are school-based behavioural programs focused on social learning principles, usually with an emphasis on decreasing disruptive behaviours or reducing aggression with peers. Programs where parents are involved in offering reinforcement are very effective (Dunnachie, 2007). An appropriate role for CYCPs in the classroom is to closely observe and monitor behaviour and to support and help young people refocus on learning.

Other effective interventions for conduct problems include positive peer culture (PPC) programs and skills training in learning how to build peer relationships. Teaching empathy and appropriate social skills at a young age helps children develop healthy peer and adult relationships. Roots of Empathy (ROE), a school-based Canadian program developed by Mary Gordon, has been shown to have a dramatic effect in reducing levels of aggression among school-aged children by raising their social and emotional awareness and increasing empathy. The internationally acclaimed ROE has shown dramatic effects in increasing positive social behaviour and decreasing aggression and bullying. The organization's mission is to create a caring, peaceful, civil society through the development of empathy in children and adults. The program could be facilitated by trained CYCPs. (For more information, see www.rootsofempathy.org.)

Alternative Healing Some nutritional supplements are purported to be effective in ameliorating ODD symptoms: according to Dr. Sandy Newmark (2010), supplementation with omega-3 fatty acids may help improve the behavioural symptoms associated with ODD. Omega-3 fatty acids are essential for the normal functioning of the brain and for the production of certain brain chemicals; dopamine, for example, helps regulate mood and emotions (Newmark, 2010). Further, vitamin E may act as an antioxidant in the brain, protecting brain cells from free radicals that may contribute to cognitive disorders. Vitamin E can also enhance the absorption and effects of omega-3 fatty acids by preventing the oxidation of omega-3 in the brain, which may further help enhance the ability of both vitamin E and omega-3 to treat ODD (King, 2013).

According to some sources, melatonin can be taken as a nutritional supplement for a variety of brain-related disorders, including ODD. Melatonin supplementation can help

Roots of Empathy (ROE) is a Canadian school-based program that has been shown to reduce aggression among children by increasing empathy.

Monkey Business Images/Shutterstock

control the sleep–wake cycle and thus work to balance brain hormones, including serotonin, which regulates mood, aggression, anxiety, and depression. There is, however, some controversy about the use of melatonin for ADHD and ODD; CYCPs should investigate these issues prior to encouraging its use for youth (King, 2013).

It appears that a zinc deficiency may play a role in the severity of some of the neurological and behavioural symptoms associated with ODD. According to naturopaths, zinc promotes the production of the brain chemicals that neutralize hyperactivity and impulsivity (King, 2013).

Exercise is absolutely critical; swimming is considered best, but all exercise is key, including yoga. As well, relaxation techniques, meditation, and MBSR are all known to be highly effective healing interventions for many young people struggling with ODD and CD behavioural concerns.

Relational CYC Practice   It is only with a thorough understanding of young people's life experience, strengths, internal working model, and past and present social relationships can we gain an accurate picture of their needs (Foltz, 2008a).

> Ultimately even the diagnosis of conduct disorder itself is problematic, as there is considerable overlap between the diagnoses of ADHD, ODD and CD. Of significant concern, a study exploring the diagnostic reliability of CD yielded very poor agreement among experts . . . [O]nly 45.5% of clinicians polled endorsed the diagnosis accurately. (Foltz, 2008a, pp. 7–8)

Refer to Box 5.5 for a summary of specific communication strategies that could be used in your work.

Box 5.5

CYC Communication Strategies

Set firm limits for behaviour, using short, clear directives.

Ensure that you have the youth's full attention by making eye contact; if the youth is upset, give him or her ample time to calm down.

Provide one clear direction at a time (alpha command); don't use vague or chained directions.

Be firm, unemotional, specific, and direct; tell the youth what to do, don't ask (e.g., "It's time to brush your teeth," not "It's time to get ready for bed"); avoid "stop" and "let's" commands (e.g., "Lower your voice, please," not "Stop shouting!").

Give the youth at least 5–10 seconds to comply.

Give warnings or reminders (e.g., "In five minutes it'll be time to go brush your teeth").

Have the youth repeat back instructions to ensure that he or she has understood.

Use "when–then" commands, going from less to more pleasant activities whenever possible (e.g., "When you finish your dinner, then you can have dessert").

Praise compliance to let youth know that you appreciate his or her cooperation, and use attachment strategies.

Avoid all power struggles, but be clear, consistent, and firm.

Use a non-emotional tone of voice.

Challenge all cognitive distortions and thinking errors.

Validate feelings, but do not allow rationalization or excuses.

Respond, don't react, to behaviours.

Source: Excerpt from Abnormal Child and Adolescent Psychology by J. E. Dumas and W. J. Nilsen. Published by Allyn and Bacon, Inc., © 2003.

WHERE DO YOU STAND?

Consider the approaches to treatment and intervention summarized above. Where do you stand? Most psychologists agree that the best interventions involve an approach that is sensitive to the needs and strengths of the individual. As you can see, there is great debate with respect to the best practice in the treatment of ODD and CD. Although behavioural and parent-training approaches have demonstrated efficacy, they're expensive and thus often not accessible to those with limited resources (Evans, 2010). Complicating matters further is the fact that different treatments are effective for some symptoms but not others (Schachar & Tannock, 2003). Clearly, each case of an externalizing disorder must be considered individually. There is no best treatment for all children with any of these diagnoses. Interventions must be adapted to fit the needs of each individual youth.

As we conclude our discussion of ODD and CD, evaluate your understanding of CYC interventions for disruptive behaviours (and how these compare with the psychological approach) by revisiting John's and Janelle's cases in the *Viewpoint Challenge* exercise.

John's and Janelle's Cases: *Viewpoint Challenge Exercise*

Reread the excerpts of John's and Janelle's stories presented in this chapter. Identify specific strategies you would recommend as CYCPs for each. How would your recommended strategies be similar to those recommended from a psychological approach? How would they differ?

CHAPTER SUMMARY

- Disruptive behaviour disorders are characterized by deficits in emotional and behavioural regulation that can lead to the violation of the rights of others.

- ODD is exemplified by defiance, disobedience, and hostile behaviour toward figures of authority, while CD is a pattern of behaviour that violates rules or age-appropriate fundamental societal norms as well as the basic rights of others.

- Although the CYC view of disruptive behaviour isn't based on a pathology-focused approach as in the DSM, understanding the differences between the diagnostic categories as well as risk factors and effective approaches to interventions will enable CYCPs to better support the young people (as well as their families, teachers, and other professionals) they assist in various settings.

- From a psychological perspective, explanations for disruptive behaviour include the heritability of temperament and aggression, an overactive BAS and underactive BIS, deficits in executive functions and cognitive distortions, societal models of aggression, and the immediate family environment.

- From a CYC perspective, emotional dysregulation, attachment patterns, socioeconomic issues, and various family factors are emphasized in understanding the development of ODD and CD.

- Psychological interventions emphasize changing variables in the social environment of the child or adolescent and include behavioural and cognitive-behavioural interventions as well as parent training.

- Assessments for ODD and CD should be relational and ecological, and need to include multiple sources of observation and discussion with relevant informants. Effective strategies include problem-solving skills training, social skills training, and empathy-building programs.

Critical Thinking Questions

1. Is it helpful for CYCPs to use diagnostic labels such as Oppositional Defiant Disorder and Conduct Disorder? Why or why not?

2. How do social environment risk factors influence the development of the disruptive behaviour disorders? How would you explain these disorders using a relational theoretical model?

3. How can we modify the larger sociocultural context that contributes to disruptive behaviour disorders in our day-to-day work with youth?

4. What do you think about the following statement? "Conduct Disorder is an easy out for psychologists and psychiatrists. Get a good mental health assessment. I have never found a pure CD youth" (CYC-Net, n.d.).

5. Consider the estimates of prevalence of ODD and CD in the Canadian population. What implications might these estimates have for your CYC practice? Do they reflect what you've seen in your practice to date?

6. What is the role of resiliency or protective factors with the behaviours associated with Conduct Disorder?

7. Do you think "untreated" ODD leads to CD? Why or why not? Do you think untreated CD leads to Antisocial Personality Disorder in adults? Why or why not?

Key Terms

action-oriented family therapy, 217

aggression, 198

alpha commands, 201

beta commands, 201

cognitive-behavioural interventions (CBIs), 215

Conduct Disorder (CD), 188

disruptive behaviour, 186

disruptive behaviour disorder, 186

interactionist pathway, 203

Intermittent Explosive Disorder, 188

internal working model, 206

irritable explosive discipline, 202

Kleptomania, 190

lack of empathy, 203

multiple pathways, 203

multisystemic therapy (MST), 217

Oppositional Defiant Disorder (ODD), 188

overt aggression, 213

parental discipline, 201

Supplemental Readings

Barkley, R. (2012). *Executive functions: What they are, how they work, and why they evolved.* New York: Guilford.

Herbert, M., & Wookey, J. (2004). *Managing children's disruptive behaviour: A guide for practitioners working with parents and foster parents.* Chichester, UK: Wiley.

Knapp, S. E. (2005). *Parenting skills homework planner.* New York: Wiley. (Features specific exercises for working with parents with children exhibiting disruptive behaviours.)

Tolan, P. H., & Leventhal, B. (2013). *Disruptive behavior disorders.* New York: Springer.

Ziegler, D. (2002). *Traumatic experience and the brain: A handbook for understanding and treating those traumatized as children.* Phoenix, AZ: Acacia Publishing.

Online Resources

Drugs in Our System: An Exploratory Study on the Chemical Management of Canadian Systems Youth—Full Report, www.youthincare.ca/drugs-in-our-system

Social skills worksheets, http://specialed.about.com/od/integration/ss/friends.htm

Mary Gordon discussing Roots of Empathy, https://www.youtube.com/watch?v=glgLGt4hZuY

Conduct Disorder Resource Center, www.aacap.org/aacap/Families_and_Youth/Resource_Centers/Conduct_Disorder_Resource_Center/Home.aspx

Russell Barkley discussing ADHD, ODD, and emotional impulsiveness, www.youtube.com/watch?v=rcwp9T3zNcM

Disruptive Behavior Disorders in Children, www.childrenshospital.org/conditions-and-treatments/conditions/disruptive-behavior-disorders

Oppositional and Aggressive Behaviors, www.brightfutures.org/mentalhealth/pdf/bridges/oppositional.pdf

Chapter 6
Anxiety, Obsessive-Compulsive, and Related Disturbances

A diverse range of symptoms characterize the various Anxiety Disorders identified in the DSM-5.

hikrcn/Fotolia

Case Example: *Alena*

Twelve-year-old Alena's school-based CYCP referred her for a psychological assessment because she had been avoiding class, not completing her homework, and was generally noncompliant. According to the Child and Family Services referral the CYCP received when she began working with Alena, she had witnessed significant domestic violence in childhood. Just before she started kindergarten, her sister was hit by a car. Following the accident, Alena would cry and become extremely fearful when she had to go to school. When Alena was at home, she cried most of the time, complained of dizziness, headaches, and other symptoms. Consequently, Alena's mother allowed her to stay home from school often. In grade 1, however, Alena made a friend and began to do better in her studies, a trend that continued into Grade 5. When she changed schools for Grade 6, though, Alena was bullied by a group of older girls after which her physical symptoms returned as did her avoidance of the classroom and it was at that point that her school-based CYCP referred her for a psychological assessment. That same year, Alena threatened to commit suicide and was hospitalized on an emergency basis. During this time she received a diagnosis of severe Major Depressive Disorder with Generalized Anxiety Disorder.

Source: Based on Joshua M Hamilton, Case Example: Alena from Anxiety Disorder in Adolescence: A Case Study, JOURNAL OF CHILD AND ADOLESCENT PSYCHIATRIC NURSING, Vol: 21(03), pp: 186–190, Wiley Publishing, Inc., 2008.

Learning Objectives

1. Distinguish between anxiety and fear.

2. Distinguish between the six anxiety and five obsessive-compulsive and related disorders identified in the text and summarize their primary symptoms.

3. Summarize the CYC perspective regarding child and youth anxiety issues.

4. Explain Foxman's theory regarding the cause of anxiety in children and youth.

5. Describe differences in prevalence rate of anxiety disorders by gender, socioeconomic status, Aboriginal status, and newcomer status.

6. Compare and contrast primary psychological explanations (biological, behavioural, cognitive, psychodynamic, and sociocultural) for anxiety and obsessive-compulsive and related disorders.

7. Describe the psychological treatment approaches used in treating anxiety disorders.

8. List the behavioural indicators for the most common child and adolescent anxiety and obsessive-compulsive and related issues.

9. Describe a relational-based approach to CYC interventions for child and youth anxiety difficulties.

Chapter Overview

The topic of anxiety—including how feelings of worry and apprehension can affect one's sleeping, eating, relationships, physical health, and overall well-being—is being discussed more and more by researchers, practitioners, and the general population (Muris & Broeren, 2008). What exactly is anxiety, and how does it differ from fear? What are the different types of anxiety disorders and what are their most prominent symptoms? Are some individuals more likely to develop symptoms of anxiety that disrupt general functioning? From a psychological perspective, this chapter identifies the anxiety disorders outlined in the DSM-5 and summarizes their major symptoms and characteristics. It considers a second group of disorders, *Obsessive-Compulsive and Related Disorders*, that are similar in some of their symptoms of distress and anxiety but distinct in their emphasis on preoccupation and repetitive behaviours. The chapter will introduce psychological explanations and approaches to intervention for those diagnoses that CYCPs are most likely to encounter in the field.

From a CYC perspective, this chapter explores how to recognize whether young people's anxiety responses are of concern or are normal responses to an abnormal situation. We emphasize the CYCP's need to understand the complexity of anxiety in children and youth and to recognize that anxiety symptoms exist on a continuum. Whereas the psychological perspective focuses on the various anxiety symptoms as defined by the DSM-5, the CYC perspective highlights explanations as to why youth anxiety issues have become so prevalent in today's society. We consider whether their increasing diagnoses constitute an emerging epidemic, as some have identified (Foxman, 2010). Has the anxious young person today become the norm rather than the exception (Straus, 2007)?

WHAT IS ANXIETY?

Did you know that there are significant differences between fear and anxiety? Although the terms are often used interchangeably, their meanings are distinct. **Fear** generally refers to a response to current danger. Accordingly, it is *adaptive* (i.e., facilitates survival), *realistic* (because it occurs in relation to an actual threat), and oriented toward the *present* (i.e., immediate danger in the current environment). For example, fear is an expected response when confronted by a dog that's growling and baring its teeth. By comparison, **anxiety** is a negative emotional state characterized by the worry, fear, and bodily reactions related to *thoughts* of an actual or potential event, object, or situation. Thus, anxiety is typically oriented toward the *future* and is generally considered to be an *unreasonable or excessive* emotional reaction because it occurs in the absence of any immediate severe threat. For example, anxiety is the worry and distress someone experiences before he even leaves his house because he thinks he might encounter a growling dog on his way to school. Although some level of anxiety is expected in particular situations and might occasionally motivate productive action (e.g., you study for a test because you're anxious about failing), high levels of anxiety interfere with social and occupational functioning and are the basis of the anxiety disorders.

Thus, anxiety can be defined as an unpleasant *tension state*, which resembles fear in certain circumstances but need not be associated with a specific stimulus and perhaps not with any external event. Some researchers view anxiety as a uniquely human emotion and fear as more common to nonhuman species. In any case, it's easy to see how fear is an *adaptive response* to a realistic threat, whereas anxiety is sometimes an unreasonable or excessive emotional reaction to current or future perceived threat (Evans et al., 2005).

Before turning to a discussion of anxiety from a psychological perspective, examine your own experiences of anxiety by trying the *Think About It!* exercise.

Think About It! Exercise: *Experiences of Anxiety*

In order to better understand the experience of anxiety, track your own episodes of anxiety for the next three days. Take note of the following in relation to each episode of anxiety:

1. What specific experience triggered the anxiety?
2. What bodily symptoms did you experience?
3. What thoughts ran through your mind during the experience? How did these affect your feelings of anxiety?

4. What behaviours did you engage in as a result of the anxiety?
5. How did you manage the experience of anxiety? Were your coping strategies effective?
6. How can you use insights from this exercise in your work with others?

WHAT IS AN ANXIETY DISORDER? THE PSYCHOLOGICAL PERSPECTIVE

According to the psychological perspective, disorders grouped as **Anxiety Disorders** are characterized by motor tension, hyperactivity, apprehensive thoughts, and fearful expectations. More specifically, there are three general areas of anxiety symptoms:

- *physical* (e.g., nausea, dizziness, increased heart rate)
- *cognitive* (e.g., thoughts of being hurt, difficulty concentrating, sense of uncontrollability)
- *behavioural* (e.g., crying, screaming, fidgeting, immobilization, avoidance)

Although these symptoms aren't necessarily uncommon and are typical of human experience, their persistence, severity, and resulting interference in daily functioning are associated with various anxiety disorders depending on how the symptoms are expressed and those areas of functioning that are impaired.

DSM-5 Categories

While symptoms of anxiety are observed in the context of many psychological disorders, they're most prominent in the group the DSM-5 refers to as *Anxiety Disorders* and includes together in one chapter. A second group of disorders, known as **Obsessive-Compulsive and Related Disorders**, is also associated with significant anxiety symptoms; the DSM-5 includes this group in a separate chapter so as to emphasize the role of obsessional thinking and repetitive behaviours in creating distress and disruption in functioning for those diagnosed with these disturbances. Let's briefly overview these two general categories of disorders before considering the specific symptoms of those diagnoses you're most likely to encounter in your CYC practice. We'll also review criteria for **Panic Attack Specifier**, which might be observed in the context of any disorder.

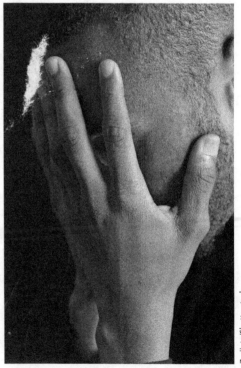

Anxiety Disorders The DSM-5 identifies 11 different anxiety disorders and organizes them according to the order in which they're likely to appear over the course of an individual's development. As noted above, the most pronounced symptoms in these disturbances are physical, cognitive, and behavioural indicators of anxiety that are persistent and severe enough to interfere with daily functioning. Anxiety disturbances are considered *internalizing* disorders, which are characterized by overcontrolled behaviour and emotion that is directed inward rather than outward. The avoidance of the object, thought, and/or situation associated with anxiety is often more significant in creating impairment than the experience of anxiety itself.

Obsessive-Compulsive and Related Disorders Although included in a separate chapter in the DSM-5, obsessive-compulsive and related disorders consist of those diagnoses that are associated with the anxiety disorders in that anxiety symptoms are often observed in their

The distress associated with the avoidance of what is feared is often considered the basis of an anxiety disorder.

Box 6.1

DSM-5 Anxiety Disorders	DSM-5 Obsessive-Compulsive and Related Disorders
Separation Anxiety Disorder	Obsessive-Compulsive Disorder
Selective Mutism	Body Dysmorphic Disorder
Specific Phobia	Hoarding Disorder
Social Anxiety Disorder	Trichotillomania (Hair-Pulling Disorder)
Panic Disorder	Excoriation (Skin-Picking) Disorder
Agoraphobia	Substance/Medication-Induced Obsessive-Compulsive and Related Disorder
Generalized Anxiety Disorder	
Substance/Medication-Induced Anxiety Disorder	Obsessive-Compulsive and Related Disorder Due to Another Medical Condition
Anxiety Disorder Due to Another Medical Condition	Other Specified Obsessive-Compulsive and Related Disorder
Other Specified Anxiety Disorder	Unspecified Obsessive-Compulsive and Related Disorder
Unspecified Anxiety Disorder	

expression. However, they're set apart from the anxiety disorders in the DSM-5 in order to highlight the greater relevance of obsessional thoughts and repetitive behaviours in creating distress and impairment for those diagnosed with these disturbances. Refer to Box 6.1 for an overview of the nine diagnostic categories specified in the DSM-5.

Panic Attack Specifier   In addition to criteria for each of these disorders, the DSM-5 specifies criteria for *Panic Attack Specifier* in the Anxiety Disorders chapter. Although not considered a specific disorder, panic attacks can occur in the context of a number of anxiety disorders. A **panic attack** is a discrete period during which the individual experiences a severe and sudden onset of intense apprehension, fearfulness, or terror, typically associated with feelings of disaster. Physical symptoms (including shortness of breath, heart palpitations, chest pains, dizziness, sensations of choking) and psychological symptoms (thoughts of losing control or "going crazy," intense fear) are associated with the attack. A panic attack can occur in the context of other disorders as well, including mood disorders, substance-related disorders, and general medical conditions (e.g., heart, respiratory).

The DSM-5 distinguishes between *unexpected* and *expected* panic attacks. **Unexpected panic attacks** are those that occur spontaneously and are unrelated to a specific triggering situation, object, or thought (e.g., experiencing symptoms of panic while you shop for groceries or ride the bus). **Expected panic attacks** are those that occur in relation to a specific triggering event, object, or thought (e.g., experiencing symptoms of panic every time you get into a car). Given the severity of the symptoms, it's not surprising that many people experiencing a panic attack (whether unexpected or expected) will seek out emergency medical assistance, believing their life is in jeopardy.

Anxiety Disorders: Diagnoses and Criteria

As we've seen, the DSM-5 identifies 11 anxiety disorders. In this section, we summarize the criteria for those disorders that are most likely to be encountered by CYCPs in their practice.

Separation Anxiety Disorder   **Separation Anxiety Disorder** is characterized by intense fear or anxiety in relation to actual or anticipated separation from significant others. Although in a healthy attachment relationship it might be expected that children would exhibit some distress upon being separated from important caregivers, the degree of fear or anxiety is developmentally inappropriate (i.e., most of their peers don't exhibit similar symptoms) and associated with persistent thoughts that some harm will come to their caregivers. Nightmares and physical symptoms of distress (e.g., headaches, vomiting) are also observed.

Separation Anxiety Disorder may be observed as early as the preschool years and is most frequently evident during childhood (although onset, on occasion, can develop in adolescence and continue into adulthood). Avoidance of separation from caregivers can result in clinging behaviour, refusing to leave the attachment figure's side, and as a result missing school and other expected and developmentally expected activities (e.g., playing with peers, exploring of environment).

Selective Mutism   Developmentally, children speak more frequently as they acquire language skills. **Selective Mutism** is associated with a failure to speak in specific social situations in which one is expected to speak, even though the individual speaks fluently in other situations. For example, a child might speak as expected at home with parents but fail to respond to the communications of peers and teachers or speak in school. As you might expect, this can result in significant impairments in social relationships and academic achievements, as well as in occupational settings when exhibited by adolescents or adults (although after childhood the disturbance usually takes the form of Social Anxiety Disorder). It's worth noting that the failure to speak is often associated with significant levels of anxiety and shyness, and those diagnosed with this disorder are often diagnosed with Social Anxiety Disorder as well.

Specific and Social Phobias   A **Specific Phobia** is defined by impairing anxiety that is related to a specific object or situation. The extreme fear associated with the object or situation results in avoidance of what is feared, which in turn typically results in the greatest disturbance in functioning. For example, if someone has a phobia of spiders, he or she may refuse to leave the house or to play outside. Usually, the individual recognizes that his or her fear is out of proportion to any actual threat posed by the relevant stimulus (although children may lack such awareness). Notice that although many individuals refer to their fears of spiders, snakes, and heights as a *phobia*, this diagnosis is formally applied only when the fear, distress, or avoidance of the feared object or situation results in significantly impaired functioning (i.e., disrupted daily routine, inability to interact with peers or perform tasks associated with academic schooling).

The DSM-5 identifies several specifiers in this classification in relation to the nature of the feared stimulus. Specifically, the nature of the phobic stimulus is noted during the diagnostic process, distinguishing between *Animal* (including animals or insects), *Natural Environment* (e.g., storms, heights), *Blood-Injection-Injury* (e.g., seeing blood, receiving an injection), *Situational* (e.g., public transportation, elevators, driving), and *Other* (e.g., fear of vomiting, falling down if unsupported, costumed characters). Any one individual may have a phobia in relation to one or more of these specific objects or situations.

Specific phobias are distinguished from **Social Anxiety Disorder (SocAD)** (also referred to as **Social Phobia**), which is characterized by impairing fear and anxiety associated with specific types of social or performance situations (e.g., meeting new people at a social gathering, giving a presentation at the front of class). As in the case of Specific Phobia, the affected individual avoids the feared situation or performance (e.g., skips class to avoid giving a presentation), resulting in significant impairment in one or more areas. The average age of onset is 13 (APA, 2013), with most onsets occurring between 8 and 15 years of age. Accordingly, it is one of the anxiety diagnoses that CYCPs are most likely to encounter in their work.

Panic Disorder   The most obvious symptom of **Panic Disorder** is the incidence of repeated and unexpected panic attacks accompanied by at least one month of continuous concern about the occurrence of another panic attack and related consequences (e.g., embarrassment) or significant behavioural changes (e.g., quitting one's job). Those diagnosed with this disorder may experience expected or unexpected attacks. In the event of expected attacks, the cue or trigger may be *external* (e.g., a crowded bus) or *internal* (e.g., heart racing after running for the bus).

It's important to note that a single panic attack doesn't necessarily warrant a diagnosis of Panic Disorder. Although the frequency and severity of panic attacks in those diagnosed with Panic Disorder vary significantly (e.g., once a week to two a month), it is the pattern or recurrence of such attacks that is associated with this diagnosis. Accordingly, one cannot assume that an isolated panic attack is a consequence of Panic Disorder. For those experiencing recurrent attacks, there is greater likelihood of such impairments as disrupted interpersonal relationships, feelings of failure and shame, persistent beliefs that minor physical symptoms are a reflection of a life-threatening condition, and avoidance of objects and situations (e.g., school, work) that can have negative and lasting consequences for the individual (e.g., dropping out, unemployment).

Agoraphobia   **Agoraphobia** is associated with worry about and avoidance of situations that individuals fear they'll be unable to escape should they experience a panic attack or related symptoms. Agoraphobia typically develops when an individual experiences an attack in a particular situation and consequently experiences anxiety when exposed to a similar situation (or thoughts about a similar situation). For example, if an individual has experienced an unexpected panic attack at a local movie theatre, he or she may avoid going to that movie theatre. This avoidance might later generalize to all movie theatres or even all public places. It is this avoidance that typically results in the greatest impairment of functioning for the individual, resulting in loss of employment, relationships, and life satisfaction.

Generalized Anxiety Disorder   We saw in Chapter 2 that symptoms of anxiety in PTSD and ASD are associated with a specific and/or extreme event. By comparison, **Generalized Anxiety Disorder (GAD)** is characterized by intense anxiety and worry about a variety of events or activities; this anxiety occurs for more days than not for at least six months. A central feature of this disorder is that individuals find it difficult to control their worry, which occurs together with symptoms of restlessness, fatigue, irritability, sleep disturbance, muscle tension, and/or difficulty concentrating. In order for this diagnosis to be applied, these symptoms must create significant impairment in daily functioning. Note that GAD is the most common of the anxiety disorders (Lenze & Wetherell, 2011).

Typical events associated with symptoms of worry and anxiety in GAD include everyday and routine activities and responsibilities (e.g., being late for appointments, household chores, finances), with the duration, frequency, and intensity of the anxiety or worry being far greater than the actual likelihood or potential impact of the feared event. In the case of children and adolescents, typical events include concerns about competence or efficacy of performance. The focus of the anxiety may alter from one event to another. Indicators associated with this disorder include muscle tension, trembling, shakiness, sweating, nausea, diarrhea, dizziness, increased heart rate, and exaggerated startle response. Children and adolescents may present as being overly conforming, seeking excessive reassurance and approval from others, lacking confidence, and being perfectionistic in their approach to tasks. It's worth noting that the DSM (APA, 2013) acknowledges that GAD may be over-diagnosed in children and encourages thorough assessment before applying this diagnosis so as to rule out other possible explanations (e.g., Social Phobia, OCD).

Obsessive-Compulsive and Related Disorders: Diagnoses and Criteria

We mentioned earlier that the DSM-5 identifies nine obsessive-compulsive and related disorders. Let's consider the criteria for those disorders that CYCPs are most likely to encounter in the field.

Obsessive-Compulsive Disorder   Obsessive-Compulsive Disorder (OCD) is characterized by *obsessions*, which result in considerable distress and anxiety, and/or *compulsions*, which function to decrease that anxiety. An **obsession** is a persistent, recurrent, and intrusive thought that can include images (e.g., of throwing a pet into a fire) or ideas (e.g., a fear that parents will be hurt). Typically, these cognitions are focused on unrealistic events, are excessive and irrational, and result in significant distress and fear. Although the individual usually recognizes the illogical nature of the obsession (although this may be less common in children), he or she is unable to decrease the occurrence of the thought and associated fear. The most common obsessions in children and youth include thoughts of contamination, bodily preoccupations, harm to self or significant others, and concerns about order and symmetry.

In order to reduce the distress and anxiety associated with an obsession, the individual engages in one or more **compulsions**, which refer to repetitive, purposeful, and intentional behaviours (e.g., hand washing) or mental acts (e.g., counting to 100 by twos silently). Typically, these acts are typically time-consuming (i.e., they take more than one hour per day), may be recognized as excessive or unreasonable, and create distress for the individual.

Notice the relationship between obsessions and compulsions. The *obsessional thought* creates anxiety and distress; the *compulsive act* serves to decrease this distress (even if for only a moment). For example, if someone has an obsessional thought about having germs on her hands, the compulsion may be to wash her hands. Engaging in this compulsive act serves to decrease the fear associated with the thought for a short time. Refer to Table 6.1 for a summary of common obsessions and compulsions in children and adolescents.

Rituals and repetitive actions (e.g., inflexible bedtime practices, concerns about imperfections) are not uncommon in young children (Peleg-Popko & Dar, 2003), but in the case of OCD, these thoughts and actions are *repetitive and excessive* (e.g., washing one's hands

Table 6.1 Common Obsessions and Compulsions in OCD	
Obsessions	**Compulsions**
Concerns with dirt, germs	Excessive hand washing, bathing, grooming, etc.
Concerns about symmetry, order, exactness	
Concern of disgust with bodily wastes/excretions	Repeatedly moving objects for symmetry, order, etc.
Concerns about potential events (fire, death, illness)	Repetitive checking (locks, doors, stove, homework)
Persistent self-doubt	Ritualistic touching, tapping, counting
Frightening mental images (e.g., seeing parent dead)	Repeating (in and out of door, up and down from chair)
Fears of harm coming to family members or self	Asking repeated questions for reassurance
	Needing to confess things

repeatedly until they're raw and bleeding). Although the compulsion to wash hands after a thought of contamination seems to make sense, such logical relationships between obsessions and compulsions are not always present. For instance, a boy might have an obsessional thought that his parents will be hurt and his compulsion will be to flick the light switch off and on numerous times. In many cases, the obsessions and compulsions are multiple and change over time, making their identification over the course of treatment difficult.

Body Dysmorphic Disorder   **Body Dysmorphic Disorder** is associated with intense concerns about perceived flaws and imperfections in one's physical appearance followed by repetitive acts (behavioural or mental). For example, someone might have persistent thoughts that her nose is exceptionally large and as a result spend hours in the mirror examining her nose and using makeup to try to alter its appearance. Although the perceived flaws are slight or unobservable by others, excessive grooming, reassurance seeking, or comparisons to others are engaged in to address the distress and anxiety associated with the preoccupation.

Note that in both OCD and Body Dysmorphic Disorder, although anxiety symptoms and distress are associated with obsessional thinking and bodily preoccupations, it is the fixation on specific thoughts and their associated repetitive, uncontrollable actions that are the foundation of the disturbances. This is also the case in Hoarding Disorder, Trichotillomania, and Excoriation Disorder, which are discussed next.

Hoarding Disorder   Those diagnosed with **Hoarding Disorder** exhibit great difficulty in throwing away unnecessary or unneeded personal possessions. Although the objects may be of little to no value, the thought of discarding them results in significant distress, associated with a strong belief that they should be saved. Generally, this difficulty in discarding items is long-standing and persistent and creates impairment in a variety of ways (e.g., interferes with the use of living space, incurs health and safety risks).

Although the disorder is more common in adults older than 55, the DSM notes that "hoarding symptoms may first emerge around ages 11–15 years, start interfering with the individual's everyday functioning by the mid-20's, and cause clinically significant impairment by the mid-30's" (APA, 2013, p. 249).

Trichotillomania   As with other obsessive-compulsive and related disorders, **Trichotillomania** is associated with a repetitive act; in this case, the pulling out of one's own hair. Despite repeated attempts to stop or reduce such pulling, those diagnosed with this disorder continue to pull hair from various parts of the body, which leads to hair loss. Significant distress results from this recurrent behaviour, including feelings of shame and embarrassment and avoidance of social situations in which the hair loss may be observed by others. As noted in the DSM, the disorder usually emerges at the onset of puberty. Emotional states (e.g., boredom, anxiety) can precede the hair pulling, and a state of tension is often associated with efforts to resist the pulling. Feelings of relief or pleasure may follow the hair pulling, serving to reinforce the repetitive behaviour.

Excoriation Disorder   **Excoriation (Skin-Picking) Disorder** is associated with repeated picking of one's skin, resulting in skin wounds. As in the case of Trichotillomania, the individual may feel anxious or bored prior to skin picking, followed by an increased sense of tension and inability to prevent the behaviour. Feelings of gratification, pleasure, or relief follow the skin picking. Significant distress results from feelings of shame and embarrassment and avoidance of social situations in which wounds may be observed by others. As noted in the DSM, symptoms of Excoriation Disorder typically emerge during adolescence and (similar to Trichotillomania) coincide with the onset of puberty. Symptoms typically persist, although they can come and go or lessen or worsen over time (APA, 2013).

As you can see, the list of anxiety and obsessive-compulsive and related disorders is long. And as you might expect, it's often difficult to determine which diagnosis is most appropriate for a child or youth.

Before turning to a discussion of anxiety from a CYC perspective, test your understanding of the diagnostic categories we've discussed by trying the *Test Your Understanding* exercise. Can you identify the disorder that most closely matches the description of each case?

Test Your Understanding: *Case Examples of Anxiety and Obsessive-Compulsive Disorders*

One day, Sam noticed a popping sound when she accidentally pulled out one of her eyelashes. Now she finds herself feeling a sense of comfort whenever she pulls out hairs on her head. Sam is getting worried about pulling out so many of her hairs, but she can't seem to stop thinking about the act or prevent herself from doing it.

Alice is petrified of spiders. Ever since her mother saw a spider and started yelling until she killed it, Alice runs away if she sees one and feels sick and nervous even when she sees a picture of one. She's stopped playing outside and in her basement so that she can avoid coming into contact with them.

Carl is a healthy five-year-old who refuses to speak to anyone when he's left at daycare. He has few friends, and his mother is worried that this behaviour will continue when he begins school. Carl's mother doesn't understand his behaviour because he speaks to her all the time at home as well as to his friends next door.

Thad lives with his mother on the tenth floor of an apartment block. His mother is worried about him because he doesn't have many friends and doesn't seem to like people. Thad refuses to take the elevator when he's alone so that he can avoid people he doesn't know. He often skips school, particularly on those days when he's expected to make a presentation to the class.

Sandra thinks of herself as a worrier. Each and every day she feels anxious about her appearance, her school performance, whether people like her, and whether or not she'll arrive at school safely. As soon as one worry disappears, another comes in to take its place. Sandra is noticing that her worries keep her awake at night and distract her from her schoolwork.

Each morning before Tim goes to school he notices that he has upsetting thoughts about something bad happening to his parents. To ease his worry, he flips the light switch on and off exactly 23 times; he notices that he feels less anxious for a short time but that the upsetting thoughts soon return. Tim is often late for school as a result of this daily ritual.

A CYC APPROACH TO ANXIETY DIFFICULTIES: UNDERSTANDING ANXIETY DISTURBANCES

We all know what it's like to experience anxiety, whether it occurs before an exam, when starting a new job, or when meeting new people. Often we can recognize that our anxieties are irrational and we learn to identify and manage them. CYCPs must be able to determine when young people are experiencing real and troubling anxiety, or whether they are perhaps overreacting to perceived stresses, or becoming fearful in everyday situations. Our role is to help youth learn to respond to these stressors in ways that are functional and healthy.

> What are diagnosed as psychiatric disorders are most often the result of some kind of stress, and the kinds of stress children are subject to is well documented, be it the myriad types of dysfunction at home (divorces, abuse, alcoholism, lack of parental attention, etc.), unyielding school systems that refuse to tolerate or acknowledge the diversity of human temperament, abilities, interests and learning styles, or simply living in an uncertain world that grows more threatening and complex. (Baughman, 2006, p. 176)

In his book *The Worried Child*, Paul Foxman (2011) distinguishes between fear, anxiety, fright, and stress, whereby *fear* is an instinctive reaction to a clear and present danger or threat; *anxiety* is a state of apprehension or worry about a danger or threat that might occur; *fright* is a state of fear when danger or threat catches us by surprise; and *stress* is any situation (positive or negative) that requires adjustment or change. Foxman suggests that anxiety—the fear reaction triggered by the *possibility* of danger where none exists—can be explained to children by asking them to imagine being a small animal, such as a mouse, living in nature where there are predators. When the mouse is threatened, it senses danger and hides; when all is safe, the mouse relaxes and resumes normal activities. But if the mouse can't relax, we'd say that it's suffering from anxiety, because the immediate threat and danger has passed (Foxman, 2011).

> In children . . . dangers and threats consist of anything that jeopardizes emotional security or physical dependency. They can include sexual or physical abuse, witnessing violence, divorce of parents, being bullied, losing a parent, injury or serious illness, and other stresses. The high rate of such stresses and threats facing today's children is the main reason why anxiety disorders have become so prevalent. (Foxman, 2011, p. 22)

Whether CYCPs support or refute the DSM-5's defining of severe anxiety responses as pathology, our role is to recognize, respond, and assist whenever the behaviours associated with anxiety are seriously interfering with young people's mood and their ability to successfully function in daily life. Regardless of the system we work in, when excessive anxiety responses are associated with severe distress or impaired functioning, CYCPs need to know how best to support the young person.

So, is anxiety in children and youth a disorder or a normal response to an abnormal situation? Young people's difficulties with anxiety have become so prevalent in Western society that some clinicians and authors refer to it as an "emerging epidemic" (Foxman, 2010); being an anxious child or adolescent in what many refer to as the Age of Anxiety seems to be the norm rather than the exception.

Is fear shaping our children? "Why," asks California-based child psychologist Madeline Levine, "are the most advantaged kids in this country running into unprecedented levels of mental illness and emotional distress?" "Parents are genetically programmed to protect their children from threats," she says. "Thankfully, the more recent historical threats to our children's well-being—malnutrition and devastating childhood illnesses—have been eradicated, or greatly reduced. Yet, levels of parental anxiety remain extraordinarily high." We worry about our children, which makes them worry, and then—surprise!—we treat their worries as a health crisis and medicate them. (Pearson, 2006)

Following Hurricane Katrina, it was reported that 22–55 percent of children and youth in Louisiana experienced serious emotional difficulties. Moreover, concerns about the safety of these children actually worsened over time after the hurricane (Overstreet & Burch, n.d.). Similarly, after September 11, most North American children reported being concerned about their safety; in New York City, 85 percent of children reported that "their sense of security had been shaken" (Kendall & Comer, 2010, p. 100). Children's reported anxiety and safety was highest in the lower socioeconomic areas of New York (Grant et al., n.d.).

While some argue that increased rates of anxiety disorders in today's youth is the result of increased expectations and stressors, others argue that they're more a function of how children and adolescents *perceive* the world and society's readiness to apply pathological labels to youth.

External Events. We've learned that regular exposure to news media can lead to elevations in reported feelings of anxiety in children and adolescents; this relates to information overload. Perceived threats of war and terrorism, the failing economy, pandemic illnesses, and so on have contributed to a heightened sense of fear and worry in adults as well as in children and youth (Foxman, 2010). Yet some authors point out that the increase in child and youth anxiety doesn't correlate with such external events: "Rates of anxiety and depression among children and adolescents were far lower during the Great Depression, during World War II, during the Cold War, and during the turbulent 1960's and early '70s than they are today. Interestingly, the changes seem to have much more to do with the way young people view the world than with the way the world actually is" (Gray, 2012). (Of course, the exposure to media was significantly different in those days as well.)

Sense of Control. Young people's anxiety and depression correlate significantly with their sense of control over their own destinies. Research shows that those who believe they're in charge of their own fate (**internal locus of control**) are less likely to become anxious or depressed than those who believe they're victims of circumstances (**external locus of control**). *Locus of control* refers to one's perception of the underlying main causes of events in one's life, which in turn guide what kinds of attitudes and behaviours one has. Those with an internal locus of control are more likely to believe that failures or successes result from their own efforts, whereas those with an external locus of control believe these can be explained by luck, other people, or unfairness rather than hard work or character (Neil, 2006).

Some might think that young people's sense of personal control has increased over the last several decades, given Western society's improvements in overall comfort and in the prevention and treatment of physical disease, and its decline in the acting out of serious prejudices relating to race, gender, and sexual orientation. Yet the data indicate that young people's belief in their control over their own destinies has declined sharply over the past 40 years (Gray, 2010). According to a recent study at San Diego State University (Twenge et al., 2010), from 1960 to 2002, average scores on the external/internal locus of control scale for children aged 9 to 14 shifted dramatically away from the *internal* toward the *external* end of the scale. The shift was so great that in 2002 the average young person believed more in an external locus of control than over three-quarters of all young people tested in the 1960s. Interestingly, this increase follows the same linear trend as the rise in depression and anxiety among children and youth.

> It is reasonable to suggest that the rise of Externality (and decline of Internality) is causally related to the rise in anxiety and depression. When people believe that they have little or no control over their fate they become anxious. "Something terrible can happen to me at any time and I will be unable to do anything about it." When the anxiety and sense of helplessness become too great people become depressed. "There is no use trying; I'm doomed." (Gray, 2012)

Thus, it appears that young people's beliefs that anxiety-related events and sensations are *uncontrollable* is part of what makes anxiety a problem for them. It would seem then that "non-pathological" anxiety in children and youth is differentiated, in part, from "pathological" anxiety in that the latter is characterized not only by heightened levels of anxiety in response to threatening situations but also by the belief that threatening events are uncontrollable.

Freedom to Play. Another theory used to explain the increase in anxiety among children and youth relates to the decline in children's freedom to play and explore on their own, independent of direct adult supervision, guidance, and direction. Free play and exploration are the means by which children learn to solve their own problems, control their own lives, develop their own interests, and become competent. Play, by definition, is activity controlled and directed by the players; and play, by definition, is directed toward intrinsic rather than extrinsic goals (Gray, 2010). Many middle-class parents face increasing demands in their everyday lives, which contributes to making their children's leisure-time schedules move way too fast.

> Children today can be as rushed and stressed as their parents, and this is often *because* of their parents' stress. In an effort to provide opportunities and to jump-start their children's success in life, many parents are overloading kids with extracurricular activities such as sports, music, art, and various other social, religious, educational, and recreational activities. The net result is stress in children who have too little personal time for relaxation and stress recovery. Chances are high that if the parents are feeling stressed and overwhelmed, their children are also feeling the same way. (Foxman, 2011, p. 15)

By depriving children of opportunities to play on their own, away from direct adult supervision, we may be depriving them of opportunities to learn how to take control of their own lives. While we may think we're protecting children, some say that in fact we're reducing their opportunities to experience joy, diminishing their sense of self-control, preventing them from discovering and exploring the endeavours they might love, and worse, actually increasing the chance that they'll suffer from anxiety, depression, and various other mental health concerns (Gray, 2010).

On the other hand, in his book *Hold On to Your Kids*, Gabor Maté (2004) points out that too little adult involvement leads to an increase in peer influence, which is also unhealthy for children. Lacking a meaningful relationship with adults in their lives, children and youth in North American society today have lost their "moorings" (Brendtro, Brokenleg, & Van Bockern, 2002; Neufeld & Mate, 2004). That young people no longer seem to listen to the adults in their lives or embrace their values isn't a coincidence, these writers suggest. Children and youth have little sense of who they are, nor are they self-directed; on the contrary, they're increasingly alienated, lacking in direction and self-control, less teachable, and more aggressive.

Diagnostic Labelling. According to Gerry Fewster, Fred Baughman, and other clinicians (Baughman, 2006; Fewster, 2002, 2004), the increase in diagnoses of anxiety disorders among children and youth can be seen not just as evidence of an emerging societal epidemic, but also as another major growth opportunity for psychiatric diagnostic labelling and for the use of prescription psychotropic medication as a primary or adjunct treatment approach to helping young people struggling with anxiety issues.

> Unprecedented numbers of children and adolescents are now being prescribed medications for depression, anxiety or a host of other diagnoses. The crisis of the young has manifested itself ominously in the growing problems of bullying in the schools and at its very extreme, in the murder of children by children. Such tragedies, though rare, are only the most visible eruptions of a widespread malaise, an aggressive streak, rife in today's youth culture. (Neufeld & Mate, 2004, p. 5)

Baughman (2006) argues that, contrary to the prevalent psychiatric disorder reference literature (i.e., the DSM), emotional pain, angst, and worry are all normal components of the human experience and are expected to be present in the life of a child or adolescent. When worries and angst become troublesome, as when youth are struggling with ongoing feelings of major depression or serious anxiety, they're usually in response to something gone awry in the youth's environment. This, Baughman contends, is ignored by the DSM and its wide-ranging diagnostic labelling: "So here we have another expansion in the territory over which disease is trumping difficulty, another area where children experiencing very real emotional distress are called mentally ill and their symptoms damped down with medications" (Baughman, 2006, p. 136).

Anxiety plays an important role in normal adolescent development. It's a survival signal, suggesting that something is not right or unsafe. Contrary to defining anxiety as a disorder, we can understand it as a feeling state that is expressed in our physical, emotional, and behavioural responses to perceived threats in the environment, as a normal response to stress, and as an expected part of daily life, especially for youth who have survived disrupted lives that may include trauma and/or maltreatment.

Before turning to a discussion of prevalence, development, and comorbidity, consider the details of the opening case in relation to the psychological and CYC views of anxiety disturbances in *Alena's Case: Revisited*.

HOW MANY YOUNG PEOPLE STRUGGLE WITH ANXIETY?

Recent estimates indicate that between 8 and 22 percent of all children and adolescents suffer from symptoms associated with an anxiety disorder (McLoone, Hudson, & Rapee, 2006; Miller, 2008). Community-based surveys in many countries, including Canada, have found that anxiety disorders are the most common mental disorder in children (Waddell et al., 2004), with an estimated prevalence rate of 6.4 percent (Waddell et al., 2004). In 2009, 4 percent of young adults in Canada (aged 12–19) reported being diagnosed with an anxiety disorder (Statistics Canada, 2009).

Studies of prevalence consistently report sex differences in the rates of anxiety disorders. Although the extent of difference depends on the particular disorder, higher rates of occurrence for females are observed across all age groups, with these differences arising prior to adolescence (e.g., Shear et al., 2005).

> During their lifetimes, women are twice as likely as men to have panic disorder (5.0% versus 2.0%), agoraphobia (7.0% versus 3.5%), PTSD (10.4% versus 5.0%), or GAD (6.6% versus 3.6%). Social anxiety disorder (15.5% versus 11.1%) and OCD (3.1% versus 2.0%) also are more common in females than in males, but differences in prevalence rates are less pronounced. (Shear et al., 2005, p. 2)

We know that unresolved severe anxiety difficulties in childhood and adolescence can lead to an elevated risk of anxiety and depression in adulthood. Given the large number of children diagnosed and the established link between child and adult difficulties, according to the mental health literature, the social costs associated with unresolved or ongoing anxiety difficulties may be very high.

As well, it's important to consider the effects of anxiety on Aboriginal and newcomer youth in Canada. Data are extremely limited, but they do indicate high rates of mental health difficulties, including anxiety, depression, and suicide, among youth in many Aboriginal communities. Suicide is one of the most dramatic indicators of extreme distress, whether related to intergenerational trauma, PTSD, complex trauma, depression, anxiety, or other mental health concerns. Newcomer youth frequently experience race-based discrimination in Canada, which contributes to mental health difficulties. Studies have examined the relationships between perceived discrimination, mental health well-being, and the ethnic/racial identity of newcomer youth populations. Race-based discrimination has been found to result in negative physical and mental health outcomes, including elevated stress, lowered self-esteem, increased anxiety, depression, and behavioural concerns (e.g., violence and substance misuse) (Shakya, Khanlou, & Gonsalves, n.d.).

Research indicates that it is the children and youth of intact families from predominantly middle classes or from higher socioeconomic status groups that are accessing treatment for anxiety disorders. However, not surprisingly, lower socioeconomic status appears to contribute to the development of generalized anxiety.

> The higher incidence of GAD in women has been linked to the diffuse yet comprehensive expectations of women as caregivers. . . . Persons of lower socioeconomic status . . . have fewer resources for dealing with minor stressors and so appear to be at greater risk for generalized anxiety. It would be particularly problematic for a woman who does not truly have anxiety to be treated with medication. . . . Instead of medication, social workers could provide financial support, food stamps, assistance getting a job, and free day care, the researchers suggested. ("Generalized anxiety disorders," n.d.)

The most common diagnoses applied to children and youth are GAD, OCD, Panic Disorder, and Specific Phobia (Straus, 2007); we'll review each of these in our discussion below. Specifically, we'll look at the behavioural indicators, theoretical causes and risk factors, and selected intervention approaches for the most commonly seen anxiety and obsessive-compulsive and related disorders in young people. Data consistently suggest that lower socioeconomic status groups have a higher prevalence of panic attacks, all types of phobias, and GAD. Research also indicates that low occupational status is a risk factor for panic attacks and Panic Disorder and that low educational level is a risk factor for Agoraphobia, Social Phobia, and OCD. This is an important issue for CYCPs to consider.

ANXIETY DISORDERS AND DEVELOPMENT

Classic studies have shown that children experience a large number of fears (Jersild & Holmes, 1935; Macfarlane, Allen, & Honzik, 1954) and that, as might be expected, these change over the course of growth in relation to advances in cognitive and social development. Specifically, children become better able to distinguish between fantasy and reality; they begin to think about the future, and they become more aware of their abilities and skills in relation to others as well as the expectations others have for them. Fears of physical and tangible objects in childhood become less common over the course of development while fears of future events and those associated with self-presentation, performance, and relationships increase. See Table 6.2 for a summary of common fears in childhood and adolescence.

It's normal and expected for children and adolescents to have specific fears. Given that fears and avoidance of animals, objects, and situations aren't unusual in childhood, the DSM requires that symptoms of Specific Phobia and Social Phobia must persist for at least six months to ensure that they're not transient or fleeting.

Anxiety is also common during childhood and adolescence, beginning as early as age four (Eley et al., 2003). In general, however, almost all fears decrease with age (Barrios & Hartmann, 1997), although social fears may increase. Interestingly, it's been argued that youth diagnosed with anxiety disorders don't necessarily have more fears or worries but

Table 6.2 Common Fears in Childhood and Adolescence

Age	Common Fears
0–6	Loss of support, loud noises
7–12 months	Strangers, sudden movements, large/looming objects
1 year	Separation, toilet, strangers
2 years	Separation, dark, animals, loud noises, large objects, changes in the house
3–4 years	Separation, masks, dark, animals, noises at night
5 years	Separation, animals, "bad people," bodily harm
6 years	Separation, thunder and lightning, supernatural beings, dark, sleeping or staying alone, bodily injury
7–8 years	Supernatural beings, dark, fears based on television viewing, staying alone, bodily injury
9–12 years	Tests, school performance, physical appearance, thunder and lightning, bodily injury, death
14–15 years	Family and home issues, political concerns, preparation for the future, personal appearance, social relations, school

Source: From The Worried Child: Recognizing Anxiety In Children And Helping Them Heal" by Paul Foxman. Copyright © 2004 by Turner Publishing. Used by permission of Turner Publishing.

rather differ in the *intensity*, *duration*, and *frequency* of their worry (Weems, Silverman, & La Greca, 2000). A diagnosis of any anxiety disorder will thus require that the anxiety symptoms are creating significant impairment for the child or youth (e.g., refusing to go to school). For children, anxiety symptoms may interfere with the ability to achieve expected normative milestones, while for adolescents, impairments in social and academic performance are more likely indicators of dysfunction.

Although symptoms of anxiety disorders may be observed at any age and many childhood symptoms resemble those in adolescents and adults, there can be differences in the way they're expressed and experienced across the lifespan (Kendall & Pimentel, 2003). This variation in symptom presentation according to developmental stage is acknowledged in the DSM-5, which identifies specific age-related differences in symptoms for some disorders. For example, in Specific Phobia and Social Phobia, children may be less able than adolescents or adults to identify the nature of their anxiety and less likely to recognize that their fear is excessive or unreasonable. In addition, anxiety in children may be expressed by clinging, inhibited interactions, freezing, tantrums, crying, and physical symptoms rather than through the emotional symptoms and direct reports of distress that are typical of adolescents and adults. Due to limitations in cognitive capacities, children may be unable to verbalize a loss of interest in activities, and report physical symptoms (e.g., aches and pains) instead.

According to the DSM-5, some anxiety and obsessive-compulsive and related disorders are more likely to arise in childhood (i.e., Separation Anxiety Disorder), while others are more likely to appear in late childhood or adolescence (i.e., GAD, Social Phobia, OCD). Specific Phobias are equally likely in childhood or adolescence. Lenze and Wetherell (2011) note that anxiety disorders associated with significant autonomic arousal (e.g., symptoms of panic) are more common in childhood than in adulthood, likely due to changes in the nervous system. Although anxiety disturbances that emerge in childhood and adolescence may be temporary (Last et al., 1996), for some youth these disruptions continue to cause distress and impair functioning for many years (e.g., Kessler et al., 2005).

COMORBIDITY

After reviewing the symptoms of the various anxiety disorders, it's probably not surprising to learn that many youth have comorbid anxiety disturbances. As summarized in the DSM-5, for example, GAD is often comorbid with Specific Phobia and also co-occurs with OCD. Anxiety disorders are also often comorbid with other non-anxiety disorders, including mood disorders, eating disorders, and personality disorders. As well, anxiety predicts more general impairments, including inattention, disrupted social relations, low self-esteem, and substance abuse (Farrell & Barrett, 2007; McLoone, Hudson, & Rapee, 2006). Refer to Table 6.3 for an overview of the most common comorbid conditions for children and youth diagnosed with anxiety disorders.

In addition to comorbid conditions, children and adolescents diagnosed with an anxiety disorder are likely to display various cognitive, physical, social, and emotional disturbances. Cognitive disturbances include deficits in memory and attention, and it's not surprising that high levels of anxiety can result in decreased academic performance and achievement (e.g., Ialongo et al., 1995; Van Ameringen, Mancini, & Farvolden, 2003). In addition to somatic complaints, common physical disturbances include disrupted sleep patterns (Garland, 2001). Social and emotional impairments are also frequently observed, as well as include general difficulties in interactions with peers (Fox, Barrett, & Shortt, 2002). From a psychological perspective, it's worth noting that in North America, youth diagnosed with anxiety disorders tend to be viewed by most adults as socially maladjusted (Chansky & Kendall, 1997; Krain & Kendall, 2000).

From a CYC perspective, it's important to be aware of the likelihood that difficult anxiety responses for young people are highly likely to coexist with depression, eating difficulties, substance misuse, and complex trauma. Before moving on to a discussion of explanations for anxiety and obsessive-compulsive and related disorders, review some common myths of these diagnoses, as presented in Box 6.2.

Table 6.3 Anxiety Disorders and Common Comorbid Diagnoses

Disorder	Comorbid Diagnoses and Other Correlates
Panic Disorder	Any other anxiety disorder, major depression, alcohol and substance use/abuse
Specific Phobia	Any other anxiety disorder
Social Phobia	Specific Phobia, Panic Disorder, major depression, alcohol and substance use/abuse
OCD	Any other anxiety disorder, depressive disorders, disruptive behaviour disorders, substance-use disorders, learning disorders, eating disorders, social and motor tics
GAD	*For younger children:* Separation Anxiety Disorder, ADHD *For older children:* Specific Phobia, major depression

Common Myths About Anxiety and Obsessive-Compulsive Related Disorders

MYTH: *Anxiety disorders are caused by stress and trauma.*

FACT: Although anxiety symptoms can arise from specific experiences (including stressful and traumatic events), a complex interaction of biological, environmental, and psychological variables coalesce to create a vulnerability to anxiety disorders.

MYTH: *The compulsive acts of those diagnosed with OCD could be overcome with willpower.*

FACT: Obsessional thoughts and compulsive acts are more than signs of emotional weakness. Research

shows significant differences in brain activity associated with specific symptoms of OCD.

MYTH: *Excoriation (Skin-Picking) Disorder is a form of self-mutilation.*

FACT: Some aspects of picking feel good (although this is different for each person). These behaviours serve a particular function and might be considered adaptive in that they help manage distressing emotions.

EXPLAINING ANXIETY DISTURBANCES: PSYCHOLOGICAL PARADIGMS

Although everyone experiences anxiety, not everyone develops a pattern of symptoms associated with a formal anxiety diagnosis. What causes anxiety disorders and why do some develop these patterns of symptoms while others do not? What's the best way to support a child or adolescent exhibiting symptoms of anxiety? Answers to these questions vary and are associated with the specific theoretical framework from which the pattern of symptoms is observed. From a psychological standpoint, the leading explanations for anxiety disorders include those from the biological, psychodynamic, behavioural, cognitive, and sociocultural paradigms. Although we'll consider each of these independently, predominant models of anxiety disorders today generally acknowledge that it is a combination of biological, behavioural, cognitive, and social factors that results in an increased risk of developing any anxiety disorder (Muris, 2007; Vasey & Dadds, 2001). Accordingly, the best approach to explaining and treating anxiety disturbances will be based on some combination of strategies associated with multiple paradigms. Thus, it's important to view each paradigm as part of the explanation for anxiety disorders rather than as competing views. Our greatest understanding of these disorders and the most effective approaches to treatment will be achieved by considering the insights offered from each of these viewpoints.

Biological Paradigm   An extensive body of research demonstrates important relationships between biological processes and anxiety disorders. Specifically, from a biological paradigm, the role of genetics, biochemical processes, and neurobiological factors have been explored.

Heredity and Genetics. The role of genes in anxiety disorders is supported by a large number of family, twin, and adoption studies (Hettema, Neale, & Kendler, 2001). Research suggests that some individuals may be genetically predisposed to respond with greater fear to unfamiliar events and less able to manage these fear responses (Lonsdorf et al., 2009). Although specific genetic markers associated with any one disorder have yet to be consistently identified (Smoller, Block, & Young, 2009), there appears to be a biological diathesis, or predisposition, to respond with heightened anxiety to stressors and everyday events. Any one individual may not be predisposed to develop a particular anxiety disorder, but rather an anxiety disorder in general. This is supported by the observation that although identical twins have higher rates of concordance for anxiety disorders than fraternal twins, the former don't necessarily exhibit symptoms of the same anxiety disorder (Eley, 1999). Similarly, family studies reveal that children are five times more likely to develop an anxiety disorder if their biological parents have been diagnosed with a disorder, but that these disorders aren't necessarily the same as their parents' (Mancini et al., 1996). Recent research suggests that heritability can explain up to 50 percent of the variation in anxiety disruptions (Eley & Gregory, 2004). Thus, it is a *general predisposition* that is inherited rather than a disorder-specific diathesis, and environmental factors may then influence the way in which this general tendency is expressed. Other research suggests that genes seem to have greater influence in the development of some anxiety disorders than others. For example, genetic influence seems particularly relevant in OCD and social anxiety (Eley et al., 2003; Silberg et al., 2001) and in Panic Disorder (e.g., Straub et al., 2002). By comparison, environmental experiences seem to be especially influential in the case of Specific Phobias and Separation Anxiety Disorder (Muris & Merckelbach, 2001).

Brain Structures. The amygdala is an important brain structure in the experience of emotion (see Appendix 2 to see its location in the human brain); unsurprisingly, then, this structure has been found to play a role in the experience of anxiety. For example, greater activity in the amygdala is associated with the experience of anxiety in GAD (Etkin et al., 2009). In another study, youth with anxiety disorders showed greater activity in the amygdala than did non-anxious participants when viewing fearful faces (Beesdo, Knappe, & Pine, 2009). Other research suggests that activity in the amygdala activates neurons in the *locus ceruleus* (a group of neurons in the pons), which is associated with the symptoms of panic attacks (Goddard, Dritschel, & Burton, 1996). Some of the most consistent neurobiological findings have been observed in the case of OCD. Specifically, higher levels of activity in the *orbital frontal cortex* appear to be associated with obsessional thoughts, while compulsions have been associated with abnormalities in the *basal ganglia*, which fail to inhibit repetitive behavioural responses (Baxter et al., 2000; Szeszko et al., 2008). The location of these structures is shown in Appendix 2.

How might activity in brain structures relate to stable differences in anxiety responses? One theory argues that *temperament* (defined in Chapter 5) creates a readiness to react to unfamiliar or unexpected events in such a way that predisposes an individual to developing an anxiety disorder. Specifically, some infants are inclined to respond more intensely to novel stimuli, and this serves as the basis for the development of persistent fears and anxieties. Such heightened sensitivity to unfamiliar events is a reflection of increased sensitivity of the amygdala and other brain structures that activate the sympathetic nervous system; it results in an exaggerated fear response, overexcitement, and withdrawal when encountering new stimuli, which may put the individual at risk for developing later anxiety disorders.

One specific temperament trait that appears to be associated with increased risk of later anxiety disorder is **behavioural inhibition**, a tendency to stop ongoing behaviour and react intensely with vocal restraint, caution, and withdrawal when encountering unfamiliar situations or people (Kagan, 1994). When encountering new people, behaviourally inhibited individuals tend to respond in a fearful and shy manner (Kagan, Reznick, & Snidman, 1988). Children who demonstrate high levels of this trait have a higher rate of anxiety disorders (Hirshfeld-Becker, Biederman, & Rosenbaum, 2004; Hirshfeld-Becker et al., 2008), are more likely to be diagnosed with anxiety disorders in the future (Fox et al., 2005), and are at greater risk for developing social anxiety symptoms (Muris et al., 2011). A longitudinal study by Biederman et al. (1993) found that behaviourally inhibited children were significantly more likely to develop anxiety disorders three years later than uninhibited children. Another temperament trait that may underlie anxious symptoms is general **negative affectivity (NA)**, which characterizes the extent to which one feels distress (e.g., sadness, guilty, worry) rather than calm and relaxed (Barlow, 2000). This trait is also believed to have its basis in nervous system responses.

Neurotransmitters. From a biological approach, one explanation for the symptoms of anxiety disorders is an atypical level or activity of certain neurotransmitters in the brain. As discussed in Chapter 1 neurotransmitters are chemicals in the nervous system that are responsible for communication between neurons. Gamma-aminobutyric acid (GABA) is an inhibitory neurotransmitter that generally works to decrease activity in the central nervous system and reduce bodily response to stress; if GABA activity is low, it can result in feelings of anxiety and increased tension. Goddard et al. (2001) observed low levels of GABA associated with Panic Disorder. Evidence that further supports the role of GABA in anxiety symptoms comes from research demonstrating the effectiveness of benzodiazepines (e.g., Valium and Xanax) in decreasing anxiety symptoms; these drugs increase the sensitivity of receptor sites to GABA, resulting in decreased tension and arousal (Davis, 2002; LeDoux, 2002).

Serotonin also works to regulate emotional states (Weisstaub et al., 2006), and can decrease the symptoms of OCD (Pogarell et al., 2003). Findings demonstrating the effectiveness of medications that enhance serotonin activity in decreasing anxiety symptoms support the role of atypical levels of this neurotransmitter in the experience of anxiety.

Hormones, another group of body chemicals, also play a role in the experience of anxiety. As discussed in Chapter 2, *corticotropin-releasing hormone* (CRH) is released when an individual perceives a threat, which then stimulates the release of *cortisol*, a stress hormone that has been associated with generalized anxiety (Lang, Davis, & Öhman, 2000).

Psychodynamic Paradigm   From a psychodynamic standpoint, anxiety and its associated behaviours are best explained in relation to the contents of the unconscious. For example, traumatic or stressful experiences during childhood that have been repressed into the unconscious result in the ego using defence mechanisms in order to protect one from the painful memories. This results in a transformation of the original memory (i.e., distortion of reality) into a behaviour associated with the symptoms of anxiety. According to this view, anxiety is functional because it informs the ego that a danger (i.e., recalling the traumatic memory) is present (Freud, 1933/1964).

The ego's use of defence mechanisms (see Chapter 1 for a summary of these mechanisms) represses the memory or unacceptable thought/image, which reduces the pain of anxiety. Without such defences, the ego would be overwhelmed by the pain and distress associated with anxiety. "In psychodynamic terms, the use of worry as a way to avoid thinking about other troubling issues would be labeled a defense mechanism" (Crits-Christoph, 2002, p. 81).

Other psychodynamic perspectives of anxiety have focused on the importance of early human relationships. Horney (1950), for instance, suggested that a child might emerge from early childhood with "basic anxiety" as a result of interactions with caregivers who were overprotective, indifferent, or dominating. Such experiences lead to a lack of trust that one can rely on others or oneself, resulting in feelings of helplessness and isolation, the source of basic anxiety. More recently, Crits-Christoph (2002) identified multiple sources of anxiety, with the primary basis being a "persistent fear of not obtaining what one needs in relationships" (Crits-Christoph, 2002, p. 82). Anxiety symptoms (e.g., persistent worry about life events, bodily symptoms) serve to defend the individual from such fears by creating a distraction from the real source of the distress (i.e., the fear of not having needs fulfilled in relationships) and related emotions. This is supported by research that finds insecure attachment to primary caregivers to be higher in those diagnosed with GAD than those not diagnosed with an anxiety disorder.

Behavioural Paradigm   Learning experiences have been found to play a significant role in the development of anxiety disorders. It has long been recognized that a neutral stimulus in the environment (e.g., sight of a dog) that precedes and/or occurs with a fear-provoking stimulus (e.g., a bite) can later acquire the ability to elicit the fear response (Wolpe, 1962). You'll likely recognize this as the process of *classical conditioning* reviewed in Chapter 1. The classically conditioned fear response that develops as a result of such associations is *anxiety*. Mowrer (1948; 1960) proposed, in his **two-factor theory**, that while conditioned fears are first *established* through classical conditioning, *operant conditioning* processes explain the *maintenance* of such fears. Specifically, once a conditioned fear of an object has been established, the feared object (e.g., dog) is avoided. This **avoidance response**, or moving away from the feared stimulus, is accompanied by a *decrease in anxiety and discomfort* (i.e., a negative reinforcement for the behaviour). As a result, avoidance responses continue, and the fear and avoidance cycle becomes stable and persists.

Such conditioning experiences can have long-lasting consequences on emotion and behaviour. Consider the personal experience of one of the authors of this text. Growing up, she was unafraid of insects in general, collecting spiders, ladybugs, beetles, and grasshoppers in a glass jar for closer examination. One day, walking home from school, she noticed that a very large water bug was on her pant leg. Unsure of what to do, she began yelling for help, and thought she was saved when an adult neighbour came running down the street. Upon seeing the giant water bug, however, the adult began screaming, took off her shoe, and began to hit the bug (and your author's leg!). As a result of this early experience (Grade 3!), this author developed a classically conditioned fear of water bugs. Specifically, the water bug (initially neutral) was paired with a frightening stimulus (adult yelling, screaming, and being hit with a shoe), resulting in an intense feeling of fear whenever she sees a water bug. Furthermore, through the process of **generalization**, any stimulus that closely resembles the original conditioned stimulus (e.g., small beetles, any bug with antennae) will send a chill

It has long been recognized that a neutral stimulus (e.g., a spider) that precedes and/or occurs with a fear-provoking stimulus (e.g., sudden appearance of the spider) can later acquire the ability to elicit the fear response.

Jaimie Duplass/Fotolia

of fear down your author's spine and provoke an avoidance response which is accompanied by the relief of decreased tension and distress!

From these examples, it's easy to see how classical and operant conditioning processes explain the development and maintenance of Specific Phobias. In fact, such traumatic conditioning experiences appear to be the basis of many persistent phobias, including fear of closed-in spaces, or claustrophobia (Rachman, 1997); accident phobia (Kuch, 1997); and dental phobia (Kent, 1997). Other research suggests that **vicarious conditioning**, in which you observe another person react in a fearful manner to a particular object, can also result in the development of a conditioned fear response. Accordingly, watching your mother run in fear to avoid a dog might result in your developing a fear of dogs (and exhibiting a similar avoidance response). Notice the relationship of vicarious conditioning to the process of observational learning discussed in Chapter 1.

Other anxiety disorders might also be explained in relation to behavioural processes. For example, Social Phobia has been found to be associated with a personal or vicarious experience of humiliation or criticism (Mineka & Zinbarg, 2006; Tillfors, 2004). In the case of Panic Disorder, symptoms such as increased heart rate and dizziness (originally neutral symptoms) that precede a full-blown panic attack (severe and intense panic response) become conditioned stimuli that can serve to perpetuate future attacks. After such experiences, any experience of increased heart rate (even after running for the bus) becomes a trigger that can elicit severe panic and anxiety symptoms. Even in OCD, in which biological factors have been found to play a significant role, conditioning processes can serve to trigger and maintain obsessional thoughts and compulsive acts. Specifically, through classical conditioning, exposure to a stimulus that has previously been associated with an obsessional thought (e.g., sight of a doorknob) can trigger new obsessional thoughts (e.g., repetitive thoughts of contamination), which produce distress. Engaging in a compulsive act (e.g., washing hands) serves to decrease distress and anxiety, a powerful negative reinforcer which, through operant conditioning, increases the likelihood of the compulsive act occurring in the future. In fact, in the case of all anxiety disorders, *thoughts* of feared objects, events, or situations might become conditioned stimuli that can trigger significant anxiety reactions.

It should be noted that not all children and adolescents exposed to such traumatic conditioning experiences develop an anxiety disorder. In addition to possible genetic predispositions that may play a role in these differences, other factors (such as a number of positive experiences with the conditioned object) might serve to protect one from developing a conditioned fear despite negative traumatic experiences. This *exposure* to what is feared serves as the basis for behavioural approaches to treatment for anxiety disorders, which we consider later in this chapter.

Cognitive Paradigm   Experiencing physiological reactions in fear-provoking situations is common to everyone. When faced with a stressor, our palms sweat and our heart rate and breathing accelerate. According to the cognitive paradigm, however, a major determinant of our experience is the *thoughts* we have in relation to these physiological changes. **Anxiety sensitivity** refers to the extent to which people experience fear in relation to their bodily stress responses. For example, feeling your palms and forehead sweat together with an increase in heart rate may be interpreted by some as excitement and expected tension. By others, however, these symptoms may be viewed as a sign of impending disaster and serious danger (e.g., heart attack, stroke), which can further enhance their physiological arousal, leading to a full-blown panic attack. What makes the difference in the experience of anxiety, then, is how one *thinks* about these physical changes.

A cognitive approach to explaining anxiety disorders therefore emphasizes the role of *maladaptive styles of thinking* (e.g., Beck, 1976; Ellis, 1962). Specifically, anxiety stems from **distorted beliefs** that overestimate, exaggerate, or misinterpret the physical and/or psychological threat posed by various stimuli and result in an increased feeling of personal vulnerability (Beck, Emery, & Greenberg, 1985). These thoughts promote additional fear and threat responses, which result in continued and intensified fear and anxiety.

Various distorted beliefs or *cognitive biases* play a role in the development and continuation of anxiety disorders. For example, an **attentional bias**, where potential threats are focused on with increased intensity and interest, is more likely to be observed in children with anxiety disorders (Vasey & MacLeod, 2001). Youth diagnosed with anxiety disorders are also more likely to demonstrate an **interpretation bias**, perceiving ambiguous situations and people as threatening (Ladouceur et al., 2005).

Consistent with this emphasis on thoughts in relation to feelings of anxiety, research demonstrates that negative cognitions and information-processing errors (e.g., rumination, worry, catastrophizing) characterize anxiety (Dozois & Beck, 2008). For example, those who are high in social anxiety tend to explain personal failures in social situations as stemming from internal, stable, and global causes (Alfano, Joiner, & Perry, 1994). When negative social events occur, they're more likely to relate these events to negative expectations for future interactions, which in turn negatively impacts their sense of self-worth (Stopa & Clark, 2000). Interestingly, these cognitive styles that create anxiety in childhood may increase young people's risk of depression later in their development (Garber & Weersing, 2010). As we've seen, cognitive factors also play a role in the experience of panic (Casey, Oei, & Newcombe, 2004), with those suffering from panic symptoms demonstrating increased attention to bodily sensations (e.g., increased heart rate) and an increased likelihood of interpreting these as signs of serious danger or catastrophe. In the case of GAD, individuals are more likely to expect that negative events will occur in the future

(MacLeod et al., 2004; Richards, 2004) and increase their search for potentially threatening cues accordingly (MacLeod et al., 2004). Cognitive biases play a role in OCD as well, with those diagnosed demonstrating an increased attention to stimuli associated with their fears (McNally, 2000) attempts to *suppress* negative thoughts, which serves only to increase the anxiety experienced in relation to these thoughts (Purdon, Rowa, & Antony, 2005).

Without question, how young people think about various stimuli (internal and external)—including their perception of the *threat* posed by the stimulus, their interpretation of how *vulnerable* they are to specific dangers, and their beliefs about how well they'll be able to *cope* with the threat—will play a role in their experience of anxiety and impact how they attempt to manage their fears. A cognitive approach to therapy, then, attempts to alter dysfunctional beliefs and maladaptive thoughts in order to reduce anxiety.

Sociocultural Paradigm   As we saw in Chapter 2, early psychological trauma may affect the developing brain, with consequences for levels of anxiety and risk of anxiety disorders. In addition to trauma, however, other experiences in the social environment are associated with an increased risk for anxiety disturbances—particularly exposure to stressful life events and factors in the immediate family environment.

Stressful Life Events. Early psychological trauma predicts psychological disorders in general and some anxiety disorders in particular. Indeed, research suggests that children diagnosed with anxiety disorders have experienced significantly higher numbers of negative life events than non-anxious children (Legerstee et al., 2008). However, exposure to stressors alone doesn't explain the increased rate of occurrence of anxiety disturbances: those diagnosed with anxiety disorders are also more likely to use less effective coping strategies (e.g., rumination, catastrophizing) than non-anxious children, who tend to use more adaptive strategies (e.g., positive reappraisal, problem solving). Nevertheless, stressful events are an important consideration in the development of anxiety symptoms.

Family Influences. In general, agreement that the foundation of adult anxiety disorders is developed during childhood is increasing (Craske, 2003), and parenting behaviours appear to play a significant role in the onset and stability of anxiety symptoms (McLeod, Wood, & Weisz, 2007). For example, recall our earlier discussion of the role of temperament (the readiness to react to unfamiliar or unexpected events) in anxiety, and note that not all youth with this predisposition (e.g., behavioural inhibited temperament) develop anxiety disturbances. Other socially based vulnerability factors interact with biologically based predisposing factors to determine one's overall risk. For example, the nature of the child–parent attachment relationship has been found to be a risk factor for later anxiety disturbances (Dadds, 2002). Specifically, **insecure attachment** relationships have been associated with anxiety disorders (Davila et al., 2005; Warren et al., 1997). For example, Warren et al. (1997) found that *ambivalent attachment* (an insecure style defined by fear of strangers, little environmental exploration, and high distress when separated from caregiver that does not diminish quickly upon the care giver's return) in infancy was associated with anxiety disorders 16 years later! Other research supports the idea that the combination of behaviourally inhibited temperament with insecure attachment is associated with the highest levels of anxiety disturbances (Muris & Meesters, 2002; Shamir-Essakow, Ungerer, & Rapee, 2005).

themselves (Bernstein, 2010). Emotional neglect in childhood is a typical characteristic of people with depression, Dysthymia (depression in a mild form), and/or Social Anxiety Disorder later in life.

We've seen that the children of anxious parents are more likely to experience difficulties with anxiety. Whether this correlation is primarily due to heritability or to the family system's dynamics and/or learned behaviour is not known. Research evidence supports the view that social anxiety and severe shyness are highly inherited traits. We've also seen that the majority of adolescents diagnosed with anxiety disorders are female: "Genetic contributions may explain a greater percentage of the variance in male vs. female SocAD (social anxiety disorder)" (Kendall & Comer, 2010, p. 209). Alternatively, girls and women may be more inclined to express anxiety because it's more socially acceptable for them to do so.

According to one theory in the *biomedical model*, GAD is thought to stem from an imbalance in the loop between the brain's cortex and the more primitive areas of sensory input and emotion, meaning that the emotion centres are triggered without the conscious part of the brain being aware of it—providing one explanation for why we may feel nervous but not know why (Kutscher, 2005). Indeed, in adolescents, responses of the more primitive parts of the brain are known to override the cortex. Understanding that anxiety is a neurological process that affects physical, emotional, and behavioural responses helps CYCPs realize that assisting young people in developing control over their responses to external stimuli should be the focus of treatment and management rather than the use of psychotropic medications (Bernstein, Borchardt, & Perwien, 1996).

The *cognitive explanation* for the development of anxiety disorders is based on the idea that those who suffer from anxiety have a dysfunctional or unhealthy worldview, maintain a negative internal working model, and engage in negative self-talk. Such cognitive distortions contribute to the development of faulty thinking, feeling, and behaving. Constant worrying, for example, is the hallmark feature of *Overanxious Disorder*, a term which some use to refer to the children's version of GAD (Foxman, 2011). Other potentially anxiety-producing cognitive distortions include perfectionism, the *shoulds* or *musts*, catastrophizing, and black-and-white thinking. Anxious children tend to perceive threats in various situations; such statements as "I thought I was going to do something wrong" or "I feel as if they were all staring at me and laughing" are common. Anxious youth also anticipate negative outcomes and experience a sense of uncertainty, which can be very troubling. In fact, "it has been proposed that a general intolerance of uncertainty is a cognitive vulnerability for several anxiety disorders" (Kendall & Comer, 2010, p. 109).

Behavioural theory proposes that developing anxiety is a part of avoidance learning, in which the relief of successfully avoiding something anticipated as "bad" or unpleasant serves as its own natural reward and is negatively reinforced. For example, having experienced teasing or embarrassment at a party, an adolescent may avoid the next party entirely and thus avoid the anticipated unpleasant feelings; over time, it becomes easier and easier to avoid all social gatherings with peers. *Modelling* is another important factor in the learned behaviour of anxious responses. Parental reactions to situations are observed and modelled, and children may also learn avoidance behaviour through vicarious experience (Kendall & Comer, 2010).

Finally, *family systems theory* suggests that parents of children with anxiety may be typically more controlling and intrusive, especially in an anxiety-provoking situation. They're also unlikely to grant autonomy easily. "It appears that parent–child interactions contribute to the development and/or maintenance of children's problems with anxiety" (Kendall & Comer, 2010, p. 110). Research has shown that negative parental behaviours, including rejection and maltreatment, are correlated with the development of anxiety in children. There are also indications that youth who experienced parental maltreatment early in life are at increased risk for elevated rates of aggressive and anxious symptomatology in adolescence. Additionally, cross-cultural research indicates that the use of physical discipline has been linked to anxious behaviour in children.

According to Foxman's (2010) **three-ingredients model**, the factors that coalesce in the development of an anxiety disorder are the youth's biological sensitivity, personality traits, and reactions to stress overload. Figure 6.1 illustrates this developmental theory.

The first aspect, the biological component, involves a child's inherited characteristics or temperament, which is observed to be sensitive. A **sensitive temperament** includes high emotional reactivity, and often a heightened sensitivity to many stimuli, including lights, sounds, and the feel of clothes against the skin. These biological characteristics seem to be a risk factor for anxiety. The second aspect, a child's unique personality, is formed when her temperament interacts with her early life experience, especially within the family environment. When her temperament includes a biological sensitivity and she also has certain early life experiences, she's likely to develop what Foxman (2010) refers to as **anxiety personality traits**. These include a strong sense of responsibility, high standards of achievement, difficulty in relaxing, a need to please others, difficulty being

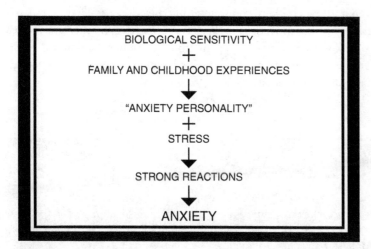

Figure 6.1 Foxman's Developmental Theory of Anxiety Disorders

Biological sensitivity may interact with early experience and individual personality factors to create strong reactions to stressful events that increase the risk of developing anxiety-related disturbances.

Source: Foxman, 2010.

assertive, oversensitivity to criticism or rejection, and an overall tendency to worry. The third aspect, the impact of stress on the child, can involve extreme reactions, with much worrying and little recovery. Thus, her personality traits can make a bad situation even worse, and the impact is cumulative.

Foxman's (2010) three-ingredients model helps highlight anxiety as being a developmental process that occurs over the course of childhood and is likely to carry on into adulthood. If this model sounds familiar, you might be reminded of the diathesis–stress model discussed in Chapter 1. Although Foxman's model is consistent with that more general model, it specifically relates to anxiety disturbances.

WHERE DO YOU STAND?

Since normal and abnormal expressions of anxiety exist on a continuum (Vasey & Dadds, 2001), discussions of anxiety are relevant to all young people, not just those diagnosed with a specific anxiety disorder. Although biological factors clearly play a role in anxiety disturbances, no single cause can explain their occurrence. Rather, as emphasized in Foxman's (2010) model, these factors seem to create a predisposition that then interacts with environmental (e.g., stressors, learning experiences) and personal factors (e.g., resiliencies, temperament) to ultimately determine whether any disruptions are manifested. Interestingly, different factors may exert different levels of influence depending on the developmental stage. For example, Feng, Shaw, and Silk (2008) found that temperament (shyness) was strongly associated with anxiety levels in early childhood, but a greater contributor to anxiety in middle childhood and preadolescence was parenting style (high control), even in those children who weren't initially anxious. After considering anxiety disturbances from both a psychology and a CYC perspective, try the *Take Action!* exercise and apply your knowledge of both explanations for anxiety difficulties to Brad's case. Where do you stand when it comes to the explanations for anxiety difficulties? Do you consider anxiety to be a disorder?

Take Action! Exercise: *Brad's Case*

Brad is a 12-year-old in middle school in Calgary. He's described by his adoptive caregivers as a worrier; they say he's "always been that way." When Brad was much younger he was afraid to go on camping trips or to summer camp because "everything" in the woods frightened him: spiders, the dark, poison ivy, "wild" animals, and so on. In school, he now refuses to participate in sports because they're "too dangerous." He doesn't hand in his assignments on time because he's afraid they're not good enough, and as a result he's failing several classes. The CYCP is working on helping Brad be less self-critical and more accepting of criticism, but so far things seem to be getting worse. Brad is now refusing to attend school altogether.

Explain how Brad's symptoms/diagnosis might be explained and treated from each of the following paradigms: biological, behavioural, cognitive, sociocultural, and holistic. For each paradigm, what additional information about Brad's history would you need to know more about?

HELPING CHILDREN AND ADOLESCENTS WITH ANXIETY DISTURBANCES

Alena's Case: *Revisited*

After Alena was released from hospital, conflicts with her mother increased and she started to get into physical fights with her sister and friends. Her peers stopped calling her which led to further avoidance of school and greater noncompliance in the classroom. In Grade 8, she came to the attention of police when she was seen smashing windows in cars and bus shelters. At that point, was taken into custody at the Manitoba Youth Centre. During a session with the forensic psychiatrist, Alena revealed that she had been experiencing suicidal thoughts since her release from hospital. When asked to describe her experiences in greater detail, Alena shared that she often felt so anxious it felt like her heart was pounding out of her chest and this sensation was accompanied by dizziness and chest pains, and an intense fear that she was out of control and might die. After these experiences, Alena reported feeling exhausted, unmotivated, and worthless which then seemed to trigger feelings of anger, rage, and deep sadness. Alena was diagnosed with Major Depressive Disorder, School Phobia, Generalized Anxiety Disorder, and Conduct Disorder.

Source: Based on J. M. Hamilton, 2008.

Psychological Approaches to Treatment

Various methods associated with the major psychological perspectives (summarized in Chapter 1) are used in an attempt to decrease symptoms of anxiety and restore healthy functioning for those diagnosed with anxiety and obsessive-compulsive and related disorders. Those treatments that have received the most attention in psychological research and practice are discussed below.

Biological Paradigm Pharmacotherapy has been found to be effective in reducing anxiety symptoms in children and youth (Reinblatt & Riddle, 2007; RUPP Anxiety Study Group, 2001). SSRIs—medications that increase the activity of serotonin by preventing the reuptake of this neurotransmitter in the central nervous system—reduce these symptoms in general (Bridge et al., 2007) and in OCD (Flament & Cohen, 2000; Geller et al., 2003). SSRIs are also used to treat depression; however, lower doses are typically required for anxiety disorders (although this doesn't apply to the treatment of OCD) (Garber & Weersing, 2010). Similar effectiveness and side effects are observed in both anxiety and depression (Bridge et al., 2007). (Refer to Chapter 7 for a more detailed consideration of SSRIs.)

Benzodiazepines have also been found to reduce anxiety symptoms and increase overall relaxation, decrease tension, and induce feelings of calmness and sleepiness. This group of medications enhances the sensitivity of receptor sites to GABA (the inhibitory neurotransmitter discussed above) and are fast-acting (decreasing anxiety within an hour, whereas SSRIs typically take one to two weeks to demonstrate effects). But because benzodiazepines can be habit forming, their use (particularly with children and adolescents) is avoided. If they are used, it's for short-term and immediate effects only (e.g., they can induce immediate relaxation in someone who's highly panicked or someone exposed to a sudden trauma) and/or until other interventions can be employed and begin to demonstrate effects.

Table 6.4 Common Anti-Anxiety Medications

Drug	Mechanism of Action	Intended Outcomes for Children/Adolescents	Side Effects
Benzodiazepines Alprazolam (Xanax) Clonazepam (Klonopin) Diazepam (Valium) Lorazepam (Ativan) Oxazepam (Serepax)	Enhances the activity of GABA	Effectively reduces anxiety symptoms immediately; most often used in Panic Disorder, GAD, Specific Phobias; not typically used in treatment of youth due to side effects	Concerning side effects (sedation, habit formation, withdrawal); anger, irritability
Selective Serotonin Re-uptake Inhibitors (SSRIs) Citalopram (Celexa) Fluoxetine (Prozac) Fluvoxamine (Luvox) Paroxetine (Paxil) Sertraline (Zoloft)	Inhibits reuptake of serotonin	Improves anxiety symptoms in various anxiety disorders, including GAD, SocAD, OCD (and excluding Specific Phobias)	Fewer side effects, greater efficacy overall, less lethal/toxic; excitation, agitation, disinhibition, headache, nausea
Other Medications Buspirone (BuSpar)	Binds to serotonin receptor sites	Unknown effectiveness; little controlled research for youth populations but used in GAD, Social Phobia	Nausea, headache, weakness, tremors, insomnia, sleepiness, dependency
Propranolol (Inderal)	Decreases activation of sympathetic nervous system		Decreased heart rate, skin rashes, sleep disturbances
Venlafaxine (Effexor)	An SNRI (inhibits reuptake of serotonin and noradrenaline)		Agitation, suicidal thoughts, decreased appetite, confusion, tremor

See Table 6.4 for an overview of common anxiety medications, outcomes, and side effects.

As we'll see later in this chapter, despite some evidence of the efficacy of medications in the treatment of anxiety, they're not the first line of intervention for youth; in fact, their use with young people is highly controversial.

Psychodynamic Paradigm   A psychodynamic approach to therapy assumes that the source of anxiety is unknown to the individual. The memories or painful conflicts that are the actual cause of the anxiety symptoms lie below one's level of awareness in the unconscious. The goal of therapy, then, is to help bring this unconscious content into awareness where the individual can consider the information in the context of reality and a safe environment created by the therapeutic relationship.

Look back to Chapter 1 (p. 42) for a description of the seven features that distinguish psychodynamic therapy from other intervention approaches (Blagys & Hilsenroth, 2000). The self-exploration and personal discovery that occurs in the context of such relationships has been found to be effective in reducing symptoms of anxiety, panic, and physical symptoms (Leichsenring, 2005; Milrod et al., 2007). Although there are few reviews of

(Moulds & Nixon, 2006), many individuals (your author included!) refuse to participate in such an intervention due to the high level of distress it would elicit.

It's worth noting that both flooding and the more *gradual exposure* process associated with systematic desensitization often occur naturally in the course of daily life. For example, your author has been in public places where beetles have flown or crawled by, and because they were simply passing through, no avoidance response occurred. With repeated exposure in these natural settings followed by the experience of anxiety and the absence of a negative consequence, extinction may occur in the course of these naturally occurring events. Exposure can also take place in **virtual reality** environments, where individuals wear a helmet and gloves connected to a computer that creates a virtual world in which they can be exposed safely to a wide variety of feared objects and situations. This approach has been successful in decreasing fears of flying and heights (Coelho et al., 2009; Parsons & Rizzo, 2008), and may be even more effective than actual exposure treatments (Powers & Emmelkamp, 2008).

In addition to effectively decreasing the anxiety in Specific Phobia and Social Phobia, exposure techniques are used in treating other anxiety disorders. For OCD, for example, those treated through **exposure with response prevention** are presented with cues or situations that result in obsessive thoughts (which create anxiety) and then refrain or prevent themselves from engaging in the compulsive act (which is typically engaged in to reduce their anxiety). Thus, by touching a dirty doorknob, feeling the anxiety, and then having it followed by nothing bad happening, the anxiety associated with the obsessive thought is gradually diminished. This strategy has been found to be effective in treating OCD symptoms (Abramowitz, 2006; Hassija & Gray, 2010). In the case of Panic Disorder, exposure techniques have also been used successfully by exposing the individual to anxiety-provoking sensations (e.g., dizziness by spinning in a circle or heart racing by running in place) followed by the absence of negative consequences (i.e., panic attack).

We've seen that *thoughts* of feared objects, events, or situations can become conditioned stimuli that trigger significant anxiety reactions in the context of any anxiety disorder. Therefore, situations in which individuals are exposed to feared thoughts can also be effective in reducing anxiety reactions. This type of exposure typically occurs in the context of *cognitive therapy*. In fact, most of the behavioural approaches discussed so far are usually combined with cognitive elements of treatment when treating an anxiety disorder. Accordingly, we now examine the role of cognitive factors in anxiety disorders.

Cognitive Paradigm   From a cognitive standpoint, one reason exposure therapy is effective is that it gives individuals information about how dangerous a stimulus (object or situation) actually is, resulting in the correction of their faulty beliefs about risk with respect to the feared stimulus (Foa & Kozak, 1986). Given this relationship between thoughts and emotional responses, identifying distorted cognitions and changing beliefs and cognitive tendencies is the key element in decreasing the symptoms of anxiety.

Nonetheless, most cognitive interventions also include a behavioural component. As we saw in Chapter 1, *cognitive-behavioural therapy* (CBT) combines cognitive and behavioural elements in its approach to treatment. For children and adolescents diagnosed with anxiety disorders, cognitive therapy is combined with the exposure procedures discussed above (Silverman & Kurtines, 1996). Youth diagnosed with Panic Disorder, for example, are exposed to situations that trigger feared sensations (e.g., dizziness, sweating) and then encouraged to think differently about them (e.g., to view them as passing sensations rather than indicators of disaster). Replacing such thoughts as "I'm going to die" with "I'm just feeling a bit dizzy and it will soon pass" is combined with relaxation techniques in the context of controlled exposure trials. In the case of SocAD, individuals may be instructed to test their irrational beliefs (e.g., "If I ask to play basketball with the group at recess, everyone will laugh at me") by initiating interactions that allow them to evaluate the validity of these thoughts. Through such **cognitive restructuring**, children and adolescents are encouraged to identify maladaptive beliefs and replace them with alternatives that are reality based (i.e., supported by evidence).

CBT manuals for anxiety include strategies and techniques focused on enhancing problem solving, assertiveness training, cognitive restructuring, family communication skills training, relaxation, exposure, and increasing pleasant activities (Weersing, 2004). The primary focus of these techniques is on the relationship between thoughts, feelings, and behaviours and on teaching effective coping responses for stress and negative emotions (Garber & Weersing, 2010). For example, Silverman and Kurtines (1996) emphasize cognitive self-control strategies in their STOP method.

> Youth learn to first identify when they are feeling anxious or Scared (S), then to identify their anxious Thoughts (T). Then they learn to modify or restructure their anxious thoughts by generating Other alternative coping thoughts and behaviours (O). Finally, youth learn to evaluate their performance in confronting their fears during exposure tasks, and to reward or Praise themselves for confronting their fears (P). To help modify irrational thoughts (or change T's to O's), youth are taught to look for evidence for their anxious thoughts and to identify a more realistic thought based on the evidence or lack of evidence. (Rey, Marin, & Silverman, 2011, p. 1141)

In general, then, cognitive approaches to treatment combine elements of exposure techniques with strategies that focus on identifying irrational beliefs and enhancing problem-solving skills to help individuals better cope with stress and negative emotions (Weersing et al., 2008). Although evidence suggests that pharmacotherapy is effective in treating anxiety symptoms, there is even greater evidence that CBT is effective in reducing anxiety symptoms; as such, it's been recommended as the treatment of choice for childhood and adolescent anxiety (Muris & Broeren, 2009). So it's not surprising that CBT is the primary approach to intervention for anxiety disorders in children and youth (Compton et al., 2004), demonstrating positive effects for various anxiety disorders both in the short term (Nevo & Manassis, 2009) and perhaps even in the long term, with benefits extending into adulthood (Saavedra et al., 2010).

You may be wondering whether cognitive strategies are superior to exposure techniques in their effectiveness. Unlike the comparisons that have been made between biological treatments and CBT, few studies have examined the impact of cognitive strategies alone. This is because most of these strategies also include a behavioural (exposure) component, meaning that it's not possible to draw conclusions about the effectiveness of cognitive strategies alone (Deacon & Abramowitz, 2004).

Despite the effectiveness of CBT, not all youth demonstrate positive change after therapy. Young people demonstrating particularly severe symptoms or high levels of negative self-talk prior to treatment, as well as those with comorbid diagnoses, are less likely to benefit from CBT interventions (McKay & Storch, 2009; Silverman, Pina, & Viswesvaran, 2008).

In addition, other social and environmental factors appear to be related to the severity of symptoms and the effectiveness of treatment, including family and parental factors. Accordingly, we now turn to a discussion of the sociocultural paradigm.

Sociocultural Paradigm Given the role that parenting strategies might play in the development and/or maintenance of child and adolescent anxiety symptoms, it's not surprising that treatments for anxiety disorders that are directed toward the family context (rather than the affected child alone) demonstrate greater and longer-lasting effects (Barrett & Shortt, 2003). Specifically, family interventions that focus on the dynamics of interactions, communication, problem solving, and managing emotions have been found to predict positive short-term outcomes as well as long-term benefits (Barrett, Dadds, & Rapee, 1996). For example, in the case of OCD, all family members are educated about the disorder, and coping with feelings is emphasized (e.g., sibling jealousy, parental disappointment that their child is "abnormal"). Together with individual treatment efforts, such interventions have demonstrated effectiveness in decreasing OCD symptoms (Barrett, Healy-Farrell, & March, 2004).

CYC Approaches for Youth Struggling with Anxiety Disturbances

There's no question that CYCPs will be assisting young people who are struggling with issues related to anxiety. When a diagnosis has been made, CYCPs work with the mental health clinician or team. Within the interdisciplinary team approach, CYCPs help design and implement the most helpful intervention plan for the young person and his or her family.

Strength-Based Relational CYC Practice We've seen that the most common anxiety and obsessive-compulsive and related disorders diagnosed in young people are GAD, OCD, Panic Disorder, and Specific Phobia (Straus, 2007). We'll review these below, examining the behavioural indicators, theoretical causes, risk factors, protective factors, and selected intervention approaches.

Assessment

When concerned about any signs or symptoms related to mental health, CYCPs' first response is to *collaborate*, *consult*, and *refer*, where appropriate. Anxiety-related issues are no exception to this standard of practice. It's important to first refer to a medical practitioner in order to rule out any medical conditions, as there are illnesses and reactions to prescribed medications that can mimic the physical responses and behaviours associated with many anxiety disorders. Next, CYCPs use the behavioural indicators we've described in this chapter as observational guidelines, ensuring that they document their observations precisely and accurately.

CYCPs' assessments should also include the protective factors in youths' life space. We've seen that anxiety disorders stem from an intricate web of interacting risk factors, and yet in relational CYC practice, we also recognize the role of protective factors, or strengths, in moderating the impact of these risk factors and allowing young people to develop resilience in the face of potentially adverse events.

Resilience turns victims into survivors and allows survivors to thrive. Resilient individuals can get distressed, but they are able to manage the negative behavioral outcomes in the face of risks without becoming debilitated. Such resilience should be viewed as a relational concept conveying connectedness to family, schools, and community. One can speak of resilient families and communities and not just resilient individuals. (Meichenbaum, n.d., p. 4)

Other protective factors that help young people successfully navigate stressful situations and avoid developing issues with anxiety include having healthy feelings of self-worth, an internal locus of control, a secure attach[ment]; problem-solving coping strategies; involvement in c[ommunity]; availability of constructive recreation; good family su[pport]; vention programs; pro-social peers and activities; an[d] substance abuse prevention programs ("Anxiety: Risk[...]

Indicators to Recognize   Here we look at t[hese]: GAD, panic attacks and phobias, OCD, Hoarding D[isorder], riation Disorder.

> *Handwritten note:*
> generalized Anxiety Disorder
> being worried, anxieous, over whealmd
> Out of control environment, self-
> asteem, confidence is low
> Noor l ehlah
> it is strong associated with Major
> Depressive D Border and Bipolar Dis

Generalized Anxiety Disorder (GAD). A number of behavioural criteria can help CYCPs recognize when young people's anxiety has become serious enough to warrant support and possible referral to a mental health practitioner. Some youth may express feelings of overwhelming nervousness, anxiety, or stress; others may describe an inability to sleep, vague bodily pains, headache, dizziness, stomach upset, or other somatic symptoms. Sleep difficulties are a hallmark feature of anxiety issues (Kutscher, 2005), but since they're also common with depression, it's important that CYCPs differentiate between these in their daily observation notes for referral. Generally speaking, whereas other anxiety difficulties are more specific and focused, GAD is pervasive—with its characteristic feature being excessive worry in all aspects of a youth's life, from health, safety, and school to relationships and future planning. When they face stressful situations, children and youth with GAD may become extremely oppositional and may engage in negative self-talk, making it very difficult to engage them in a rational discussion (Austin & Sciarra, 2010). GAD rarely presents as an isolated condition. It's almost always complicated by other comorbid issues; for example, it's known to have a strong association with Major Depressive Disorder and Bipolar Disorder.

Young people struggling with generalized anxiety often present as *perfectionists*. Whereas those with a healthy striving for excellence find healthy ways to successfully overcome life challenges, youth with perfectionist tendencies will seek to avoid most challenges; they attribute any success to pure luck and define failure as their fault or weakness (Kutscher, 2005). Young people with GAD usually know that they worry too much, and may tell their caregivers that they find it annoying, especially when asked about it. As a front-line CYCP in managed care, one of the authors of this text often observed unusual perfectionism and compulsive neatness in young men who had histories of sexual abuse.

This highlights another important point for CYCPs: no one but the young person will really know how much the anxiety is troubling him or her. It's important to ask young people whether they feel as if they worry more than other kids, or if they worry, whether they worry too much, as this will allow them to feel they can talk to you about it. Whatever CYCPs can do to reduce young people's anxiety about discussing their feelings will be of assistance. Always ask and listen.

Panic Attacks and Phobias. CYCPs need to appreciate the overwhelming and debilitating physical effects of a panic attack, as described earlier. Anyone who has experienced a panic attack can testify to its terrifying effects. According to the Canadian Mental Health Association, the physical symptoms of both phobias and panic attacks include a racing pulse, heart palpitations and chest pain, shortness of breath, panting, dry mouth, blushing, nausea and/or vomiting, trembling and shaking, muscle tension, dizziness, hot flashes, and sweating or chills, and, as with GAD, difficulties with sleep and an inability to concentrate ("Phobias and Panic Disorders," 2015).

Unlike Panic Disorder, phobias have identifiable triggers. Young people with phobias can have an overwhelming, irrational fear of various objects, situations, or animals. It's theorized that phobias develop from situations, events, or people that influenced the individual earlier in his or her developmental years. A history of family breakup, parental aversion to socializing, an influential adult's phobia, or a traumatic event can be linked to the development of a phobia in a child or youth. CYCPs should be aware of the common fears of childhood and adolescence at each stage of development in order to know which are to be expected and which may be cause for concern. For example, it's normal for six- and seven-year-olds to fear thunder and lightning, the dark, and monsters in the closet or under the bed. Normal worries for those aged 7–15 include school performance, appearance, social acceptance, death of a parent, friends, and global issues (e.g., poverty, hunger, violence, terrorism) (Foxman, 2010, presentation notes). Refer back to Table 6.2 (p. 240) for a summary of the common fears in childhood and adolescence.

Obsessive-Compulsive Disorder (OCD). As we've seen, whereas *obsessions* are recurrent, repetitive thoughts that are unwelcome, irrational, and cause distress, *compulsions* are behaviours used to reduce the anxiety caused by the obsessive thoughts. Common obsessions include dirt, germs, doubts, a need for order, and a fear

Some adolescents will begin to use substances to manage anxiety-provoking social situations.

Jetrel/Shutterstock

of violence. Common compulsions include counting, touching, checking, and repeating words. Compulsive rituals often include hand washing, cleaning, arranging, and reordering.

> So obsessions are thoughts, and compulsions are acts to neutralize the obsessions. The adult at some point recognizes that this is all unreasonable or excessive. Children may not reach this realization, and usually do not spell out obsessions or compulsions unless specifically asked about them. (Kutscher, 2005, p. 131)

When CYCPs observe concerning behavioural rituals, they need to use a non-threatening manner in exploring these with young people. If the difficulties associated with such rituals are severe enough to cause **functional impairment**—a noticeable impact on day-to-day functioning—then CYCPs should request a referral to a mental health clinician for a diagnosis. The thoughts associated with OCD are generally more intrusive, more rigid, and less reality based than the repetitive thoughts associated with GAD. Children and youth may believe that their recurrent thoughts might actually cause a worrisome event; for example, that having the recurrent thought "My mom will be killed in a car accident" will actually make it happen (Kendall & Comer, 2010).

Hoarding Disorder. Until they reach late adolescence, young people generally don't engage in problematic hoarding behaviours that negatively affect day-to-day functioning. There is, however, one important exception: food hoarding, which is frequently encountered with children and youth in out-of-home care. Children who've been neglected or have experienced food insecurity don't automatically understand that food is now available or is unlimited in accessibility; they commonly adopt eating-related survival skills that may be very difficult for caregivers to manage. Moreover, it's often difficult for caregivers to understand this disorder, which inadvertently adds to the stress these young people may experience in relation to food. Such issues may be manifested in overeating, extreme pickiness, undereating, and stealing or hoarding food. In addition, ideas about mealtimes may be very different for children who've had to learn to fight for food, were given limited food options, or weren't part of families or settings that had rules about eating (e.g., sitting at a table together).

Trichotillomania (TTM). Trichotillomania is a chronic impulse-control difficulty whereby young people pull out their own hair to the point of alopecia (baldness). While it occurs in people of all ages, TTM is estimated to affect 1–3.5 percent of late adolescents and young adults; rates among younger children are largely unknown. Sufferers of TTM across the developmental spectrum may experience medical complications such as skin irritation, infections, and repetitive-use hand injuries (Franklin, Edson, & Freeman, 2010). Given that the incidence of TTM appears to be increasing, it's important that CYCPs be aware of this condition. In children, several behaviours contribute to the development of TTM: feeling the texture of the hair; rubbing fingers along the hair shaft; biting, sucking, eating, or playing with the hair in the mouth; and rubbing the hair along the cheek, nose, or lip. These behaviours may not be unusual in children, but for many they're motivated by touch, which has a self-quieting effect similar to that achieved by rocking, thumb sucking, rubbing a favourite blanket, or stroking a stuffed animal. The problem arises when increased incidents of hair pulling become a habit, which can easily evolve into a behaviour pattern that has complex emotional and situational influences and is thus difficult to change. Over time, the effects of hair pulling can have negative consequences for an individual's emotions, self-esteem, and social confidence. (If you'd like to read a thread discussion on hair pulling, go to www.cyc-net.org/threads/Pullingeyelashes.html.)

Excoriation Disorder. This disorder is characterized by a type of self-injurious behaviour in which a flaw in the skin, real or imagined, triggers an impulse for the individual to pick at it (Ngan, 2014). The most common coexisting mental health conditions for Excoriation Disorder are depression and anxiety disorders, especially OCD. As with other self-injurious behaviours, skin picking can provide a feeling of relief or pleasure; it can be a conscious response to anxiety or may be an unconscious habit (Ngan, 2014). Since compulsive skin picking usually begins in adolescence, CYCPs need to be aware of it; however, it's important to recognize that skin picking is also associated with methamphetamine or cocaine abuse, meaning its cause can differ. A referral to a physician is always warranted if you suspect that a child or youth is developing a skin-picking habit.

Table 6.6 summarizes the behavioural indicators associated with anxiety disorders.

Table 6.6 Behavioural Indicators Checklist: Anxiety

✓ Expresses many worries repeatedly before approaching many different situations

Shows signs of nervousness and is reluctant to participate in most or all novel situations

Physical symptoms might include muscle tension, inability to relax, restlessness, irritability, and disturbed sleep

May become very quiet or remote in all social situations

Displays behaviours very different from typical demeanour; clings to caregiver or peer in novel situations

Engages in unusual actions to cope with obvious nervousness

Asks many questions about the appropriateness or effectiveness of own actions

Adolescent frequently or always uses substances to calm down before social gatherings

Adolescent avoids newspapers and watching the news

Hesitant or avoidant of situations

Refuses to participate in normal activities as a result of worrying about other people laughing at them

Repetitive behaviours, including checking, counting, excessive hand washing, repeating words softly or silently to self

Continually voices self-critical remarks and gives up in defeat

Spends hours doing a project and then rips it up or doesn't hand it in because it's "not good enough"; schoolwork is full of erasures

Stealing or hoarding food or other items

Hair pulling, skin picking, and/or extreme self-loathing of body

Sources: "Generalized anxiety disorders," 2012; Silva, Gallagher, & Minami, 2006.

Intervention

We begin this discussion of interventions with a brief reminder: it's important to consider your conceptual lens. What is your personal experience with anxiety? How do you perceive anxiety and stress as they may affect the young people you're engaged with? Put another way, how does stress and its resulting anxious responses affect all youth in society today? Might anxiety responses that have been labelled as disorders be better described as dysfunctional coping strategies related to the exacerbating, very real stressors in a young person's life and environment?

Good CYC practice in any setting will aid in treating anxiety difficulties for all children and youth who may be struggling. The intervention plan should include the following: establishing a trusting relationship, letting the young person know that you care and that you understand how painful or scary issues with anxiety can be, providing a safe and supportive environment, celebrating all efforts at achievement (not just the successful ones), educating peers who may be bullying or teasing her, honouring her strengths, accommodating her "quirky" behaviours wherever possible, making a safety plan for escape if and when needed, asking her what she needs and what works for her (Kutscher, 2005).

Combined with relational CYC practice, psychoeducational and cognitive-behavioural approaches work very well. **Psychoeducation** refers to any approach that includes education given to individuals about their mental health situation; it's intended to both inform and empower them, and is believed to help motivate individuals to engage in the change process. It's usually done in groups, but can be used in individual counselling as well. Psychoeducation helps to replace myths and misinformation with knowledge and understanding, and usually helps to reduce fear in individuals ("Psycho-education," 2014).

Psychoeducation about the nature of anxiety, especially for adolescents, is a crucial part of the intervention process; again, it can be conducted either one on one or in a group (Kutscher, 2005; Straus, 2007). As with all psychoeducation, a group is a powerful intervention modality for adolescents. CYCPs can also help young people research and learn about the typical medications used in treating anxiety disorders. This in turn can help them make a well-informed choice about whether to take any medication that may be prescribed.

Behavioural and Cognitive-Behavioural Techniques for CYCPs

We've seen that behavioural and cognitive-behavioural techniques are particularly successful with young children with GAD and phobias (Fonagy et al., 2002). CBT approaches are the gold standard of evidence-based interventions for young people with anxiety issues. Studies have shown that 70 percent of children with anxiety disorders demonstrate marked improvements using a CBT approach without any medication (Kendall & Comer, 2010). CBT approaches include a combination of *education*, *skill building*, and *cognitive restructuring*. An important part of skill building in CYC interventions is teaching problem-solving skills. More formal mental health therapeutic approaches also include *exposure exercises* and *homework*.

One of the first steps in a CBT approach to anxiety involves helping young people develop **emotional literacy** (or *emotional intelligence*). Having good emotional health includes a healthy self-awareness, self-control, the ability to deal with social relationships, communication skills, and self-esteem. Another important aspect of emotional intelligence is the ability to identify the feelings and bodily sensations that precede or accompany anxiety episodes. For example, CYCPs could introduce relaxation methods (which may include MSBR) and then practise them with young people so that they can do the exercises themselves whenever they feel nervousness coming on, whether in the form of butterflies or other bodily sensations.

Cognitive restructuring involves teaching young people how to block or reframe negative thoughts. This approach is based on the idea that psychological health stems from our worldview, or internal working model: we can interpret events in ways that can cause anxiety, anger, fear, or depression, or we can learn to think in ways that result in a sense of well-being. Intrusive negative or distorted thoughts are challenged (reality tested), and over time are substituted with more positive thoughts. Such cognitive distortions as "I'm going to die," "They all hate me," and "This is the worst possible thing that could happen" are replaced with positive affirmations; "I'm safe" is a good example. CYCPs can also teach young people to externalize the anxiety (in order to "talk to it") and to use positive affirmations.

In addition, CYCPs can use *scaling questions* (e.g., asking youth to rate their anxiety on a scale of 1 to 10, with 10 being the worst anxiety ever and 1 being no anxiety at all) or a "fear thermometer" (Foxman, 2010), whereby CYCPs encourage breathing and relaxation exercises and then have young people take their temperature with the thermometer again to see whether they've reduced their anxiety a bit.

Another helpful strategy is to have young people ask themselves four questions—*Is it true? Can you absolutely know that it's true? What happens, how do you react, when you believe that thought? What would it be like without the thought?*—and then help them turn the thought around by encouraging them to consider the validity of statements that oppose the original statement (Katie, 2013). CYCPs can also help young people make a "coping menu" in which they include all the strategies they've learned; in any given anxiety-provoking situation they can then select which strategy to use from their menu.

Assisting youth in developing strategies for relaxation that can be used anywhere, any time, can be very effective in helping young people manage their symptoms of anxiety.

Nataraj/Fotolia

The Role of Medication   As we saw earlier, there has been some evidence of positive outcomes in the use of SSRIs for treating OCD, especially when combined with CBT. Some clinicians have pointed out, however, that as their anxiety decreases with the use of SSRIs, young people are less likely to be invested in the CBT work (Kutscher, 2005). Moreover, in the treatment of generalized anxiety, although very little research has been conducted on the efficacy of benzodiazepines, beta blockers, and SSRIs, they are commonly prescribed (Fonagy et al., 2002). Health Canada has recently issued a warning about such use of SSRIs.

> Health Canada and the U.S. Food and Drug Administration (FDA) have issued advisories to patients, families, and health professionals to closely monitor for warning signs of suicidal behaviour in children and adults who take antidepressants. This is especially important at the beginning of treatment or when doses are changed. (Health Canada and FDA Advisories for Antidepressants, 2013)

Refer back to Chapter 1 for a discussion on the advantages of, and concerns about, the use of psychotropic medications and their fit with a relational CYC approach to practice. And keep in mind that even if the young person struggling with anxiety is using prescription medications, pills don't teach skills (Foxman, 2010).

Psychoeducation and Individual Counselling   Young people with attachment issues often experience a high level of anxiety unrelated to the situation they're in. Reassurance alone isn't helpful. CYCPs can support young people in expressing their anxiety, and in experiencing all the related feelings, by listening carefully, reflecting back emotions, summarizing, and using empathic responses. These are all important counselling skills. As well, journalling can work very well for some.

Externalizing-the-issue practices can be extremely effective in managing young people's anxiety. Externalizing counteracts th[e] whereby it's viewed as a problem residing wit[h] external entity helps to objectify *it* as the pr[oblem] problem exists outside themselves, they can themselves as separate from the problem an[d] ries also work very well to assist in this wa[y] available for work with young people experi[encing] story to a child and perhaps write one with [a]

As a specific intervention for food hoa[rding] n.d.) suggests the following techniques: ack[nowledge] that you understand why he's afraid, and that although he will, he'll get fed predictably, you recognize that it will take time; support the hoarding in the meantime by telling the child that he doesn't have to hide what he's doing; offer to give him extra food to take back to his room; give him a proper place to store the food; make sure there are bountiful snacks and plenty of food available at mealtimes; take him shopping for food, letting him get something for himself and helping him put it away when he returns; and involve him in food preparation as a mastery experience in which he can be instrumental—the dispenser of food rather than the potential recipient ("Hoarding food," n.d.).

[Handwritten note overlaying text: externalizing-the-issue practices — separating the problem from the person so that it can be viewed as a problem they can control. "excoriate person" (skin pulling) A person dealing with excoriation disorder]

Family Support Interventions We've seen that family support is an integral part of an intervention plan for child and youth anxiety issues. Koroll (2006) has suggested that CYCPs can help parents identify areas where they are denying their children opportunities for developing their own resistance and resilience.

> We need to reframe for parents how letting go and allowing their children to struggle is actually a good thing. We need to challenge some of the policies around developing children's self-esteem where everyone is treated as special and receives a reward whether it's deserved or not. These common practices result in a false sense of competence that turns into anxiety and depression when faced with hardships and failures. (Koroll, 2006, p. 1)

Refer to Box 6.3 for a summary of common techniques for intervention with anxiety-related disturbances.

Prevention: Advocacy, Community, and School-Based Strategies

Research indicates that universal, school-based interventions can be very successful in helping reduce anxiety symptoms for all youth, regardless of the level of individual risk. Prevention programs that teach how to use cognitive-behavioural techniques as a coping skill have been found to be very effective. For example, the FRIENDS program has been specifically designed for use in schools as a universal preventative approach. It doesn't involve any clinical assessment or diagnosis, and according to the literature, the labelling of children as anxious or different is avoided (FRIENDS Program, 2012). Another universal prevention approach, the skills-based Cool Kids program, teaches children, adolescents, and their parents how to better manage anxiety ("Cool Kids," 2015). The STEP program,

---

Box 6.3

Techniques for CYC Intervention

CBT approaches include education, skill building, and cognitive restructuring.

Assist youth in reframing negative thoughts or attitudes.

Assist youth in blocking negative thoughts.

Replace intrusive negative thoughts with positive affirmations (e.g., "I'm safe").

Challenge all cognitive distortions.

Increase all physical activity (take a walk, jog, dance).

Use MBSR and other relaxation techniques.

Involve social supports (family, friends).

Identify strengths and facilitate increased access to activities and resources involving strengths.

Teach youth how to externalize anxiety.

Create a safe milieu.

Address underlying trauma issues where and when appropriate.

Teach coping-in-the-moment skills, including the use of positive self-talk.

which uses peer support networks to ease the transition into junior high school, is also reported to be beneficial. Prevention programs like these, which target young people in the general population with elevated anxiety or depression, do seem to work.

If we agree that anxiety is an emerging epidemic among youth, and that this epidemic is at least partly caused by increased parental and societal demands on young people, then our interventions shouldn't be based solely on psychoeducational methods and individual and group cognitive behavioural therapy. CYCPs ought to consider prevention approaches that focus on the macro level, designing their interventions to include the *education and community system levels* such as the ones we've just outlined. It's been well documented that the role of families and parents in the lives of their children has changed so significantly over the past three decades that many families increasingly "struggle with finding the balance between parental protectionism and supporting their children in becoming independent and self-reliant adults" (Koroll, 2006). We also know that children and youth more and more often depend on their parents and caregivers to intervene on their behalf when they find themselves in challenging situations (Koroll, 2006). Whenever CYCPs intervene with anxiety issues, then, family support is both warranted and recommended.

Alternative Healing   Several alternative and complementary therapies have been found to be particularly helpful in supporting and treating young people with GAD. Although not evidence based, much anecdotal evidence suggests that visualization, relaxation exercises, and MBSR are all important tools in assisting with anxiety-related concerns. Many therapists and clinicians have long held that these mind–body techniques are far more beneficial for anxiety and depression than medication—and safer, too. Yoga is another technique that works well. Hypnotherapy, Aboriginal healing ceremonies and other spiritual or religious practices, meditation and guided imagery, biofeedback, and relaxation techniques are also recommended for children and youth with GAD. In addition, massage therapy, hydrotherapy, shiatsu, and acupuncture have been reported to relieve the physical symptoms that are sometimes associated with GAD.

Daily exercise alone helps to drastically reduce anxiety. Exercise relieves stress, tension, and anxiety and rids the body of excess negative emotions and adrenalin, leading to a more relaxed state. It increases blood flow to the brain, releases hormones, stimulates the nervous system, and increases levels of morphine-like substances found in the body (such as beta-endorphin) that have a positive effect on mood. As well, exercise may trigger a neurophysiological high—a shot of adrenalin or endorphins—that produces an antidepressant effect in some, an anti-anxiety effect in others, and a general sense of "feeling better" in most ("Anxiety," 2007).

Relational CYC Practice   As always, relational CYC practice is key. Listening to youth and practising advocacy are critical components of good CYC practice in general and of mental health specifically.

In 2012, a Youth Action Committee in Ontario designed a project centred on encouraging youth to have a voice in mental health services and accessibility. In gathering feedback about whether or not schools provide a positive environment for youth with mental health and addiction issues, it was found that just over 45 percent of youth participants identified stigma as a barrier at their school that prevented them from seeking support for mental health and/or addiction issues. They also reported that a lack of access to resources prevented them from receiving support and that there was insufficient mental health and addiction education in the school curriculum; students recommended that more mental health–related professional-development courses would benefit both teachers and students. Of serious concern was the finding that only 35.1 percent of youth respondents felt that staff at their school had an understanding of youth mental health issues ("Building a better school environment," 2013).

> One of the things my disorder [GAD] challenges me with, is my ability to stay awake in class. [Once] I asked if I could go in the hallway to walk as I read, so I wouldn't fall asleep. [My teacher] said yes! When I went back to the classroom . . . I realized something, everyone else was finishing the article at the same time I was. That had never happened before! In that moment I realized that I could achieve the same level of success as anyone else. I just might need to get there a different way. This realization not only related to my academics, but to my whole life. And it was that teacher, with her willingness to listen to my idea and accommodate, simply by saying yes! (Ontario youth in "Building a better school environment," 2013, p. 14)

Refer to Box 6.4 for a summary of useful communication strategies that can facilitate CYCPs' application of these treatment principles.

Box 6.4

CYC Communication Strategies

Help young people maintain regular routines in daily activities (e.g., sleeping, eating, and exercise).

Provide psychoeducation by sharing (and helping to gather) all the information you have about anxiety and its effects.

Try to see the anxiety from the youth's perspective. (We all feel anxiety at times, but how does it feel for them?)

Validate concerns.

Teach emotional literacy.

Ask open-ended questions to encourage the sharing of feelings and thoughts (e.g., "How have you been feeling since . . .").

Ask the child or adolescent how you can help. Listen, and reflect.

Explore options for healing together (e.g., experiment with youth; accompany them to fearful situations).

Gently encourage and reward gradual exposure to feared objects and situations (after consulting with a clinician).

Provide continuous, genuine support along with reminders of strengths and learned coping options.

Recognize that anger and irritability may be symptoms of anxiety rather than expressions of hostility.

Test the worry. ("If that were true, what would happen?")

Use the four questions (Katie, 2013) outlined earlier.

Focus on and praise accomplishments, however minor.

Avoid criticism.

Encourage as much physical activity as possible to reduce stress (e.g., exercise, meditation, leisure activities).

WHERE DO YOU STAND?

As Martha Straus reminds us, "anxiety disorders feed on isolation and self-condemnation." Young people who are struggling with issues of anxiety are almost always upset about feeling that way, which compounds their sadness and misery. We must explore and build on their strengths and competencies. With strength-based, relational CYC practice and support, young people struggling with anxiety "will come to see themselves as more competent as they become better problem solvers and self-soothers and worthy of the love and admiration of nurturing adults like you" (Straus, 2007, p. 171).

Evaluate your understanding of the CYC explanations and interventions for anxiety disorders, and how these compare with the psychological approach, by revisiting the cases of Alena and Brad in the *Viewpoint Challenge* exercise.

Brad's and Alena's Cases: *Viewpoint Challenge Exercise*

Reread the excerpts of Brad's and Alena's stories presented throughout this chapter. Compare and contrast the psychological and CYC explanations for their respective anxiety symptoms. Specifically, identify both similarities and differences between the two perspectives. What similarities and differences might exist between the psychological and CYC perspectives when it comes to working with Brad or with Alena? What approach would you take as a CYCP with both youth? Defend your approach.

CHAPTER SUMMARY

- Anxiety is a negative emotional state associated with worry, fear, and bodily reactions that are related to *thoughts* of an actual or potential event, object, or situation.

- Anxiety is the basis of both anxiety disorders—a group of disorders characterized by motor tension, hyperactivity, apprehensive thoughts, and fearful expectations—and obsessive-compulsive and related disorders, which emphasize the role of obsessional thinking and repetitive behaviours in creating distress and disruption in functioning.

- CYCPs emphasize that the increased incidence of anxiety diagnoses seen in children and youth has less to do with inherent pathology or even the increase of real stresses, dangers, and uncertainties in society and the world today and more to do with a belief that threatening events are uncontrollable.

- From a psychological perspective, anxiety and related disorders are explained in relation to genetics; specific temperament traits (e.g., behavioural inhibition and negative affectivity); repression of traumatic events; classical, operant, and observational/vicarious conditioning; maladaptive styles of thinking; and various family factors (e.g., insecure attachment relationships, overprotective parenting).

- From a CYC perspective, three essential ingredients contribute to the development of an anxiety disorder: sensitive temperament, "anxiety personality" traits, and reactions to "stress overload."

- Psychological interventions emphasize symptom reduction and improvement in functioning and include medications that alter levels of serotonin and GABA, exposure to feared stimuli, cognitive restructuring, and CBT.

- Externalizing-the-issue practices can be extremely effective in helping young people learn to manage their anxiety. CYCPs ought to regard anxiety symptoms as coping mechanisms or adaptations. Consider youth as survivors, not victims.

Critical Thinking Questions

1. How would you describe your personal experiences of fear versus anxiety? Provide specific examples to illustrate.
2. As a CYCP, how useful do you think might be the *Anxiety Disorder* diagnosis given to a youth you're working with?
3. Why do you think the diagnosis of anxiety has reached "epidemic" levels in Western society today?
4. Why do you think that although more middle-class families access treatment for anxiety disorders, lower socioeconomic groups seem to be more affected by anxiety?
5. Why do you think there are more girls and young women diagnosed with anxiety disorders than boys and young men?
6. Think about all the causal explanations of anxiety outlined in this chapter. Which do you believe have the most validity for you as a CYCP? Explain your position.
7. What do you think about the use of SSRI medications for child and youth anxiety disorders?
8. What are the risks involved when CYCPs don't recognize or underestimate a young person's anxiety symptoms?
9. What personal skills do you believe are most relevant in working with youth coping with anxiety and related symptoms? Provide specific examples to illustrate.
10. Do you think gender is related to locus of control? What do you think the link between overall mental health and locus of control might be?

Key Terms

Supplemental Readings

Burns, D. D. (1990). *The feeling good handbook*. New York: Penguin.

Pincus, D. B., Ehrenreich, J. T., & Mattis, S. G. (2008). *Mastery of anxiety and panic for adolescents riding the wave: Therapist guide*. Oxford: Oxford University Press.

Rapee, R. M., Spence, S. H., Cobham, V., & Wignall, A. (2000). *Helping your anxious child: A step-by-step guide for parents*. Oakland, CA: New Harbinger.

Schab, L. M. (2008). *The anxiety workbook for teens: Activities to help you deal with anxiety and worry*. Oakland, CA: New Harbinger.

Spinazzola, J., Rhodes, A., Emerson, D., Earle, E., & Monroe, K. (2011). Application of yoga in residential treatment of traumatized youth. *Journal of the American Psychiatric Nurses Association, 17*(6), 431–444.

Strong, K. V. (1997). *Anxiety, panic attacks, and agoraphobia: Information for support people, family, friends*. New York: Oakminster.

Wagner, A. U. (2002). *What to do when your child has Obsessive-Compulsive Disorder: Strategies and solutions*. Lighthouse Point, FL: Lighthouse.

Online Resources

American Academy of Child and Adolescent Psychiatry's Anxiety Disorders Resource, www.aacap.org/AACAP/Families_and_Youth/Resource_Centers/Anxiety_Disorder_Resource_Center/Home.aspx

Anxiety Disorders Association of Canada, www.anxietycanada.ca/english/index.php

British Columbia FRIENDS program, www.mcf.gov.bc.ca/mental_health/friends.htm

CBC documentary *The Age of Anxiety*, www.cbc.ca/player/Shows/Shows/Doc+Zone/ID/2210701652

Generalized Anxiety Disorder, www.minddisorders.com/Flu-Inv/Generalized-anxiety-disorder.html#ixzz23SpagcAM

Locus of Control test, www.psych.uncc.edu/pagoolka/LocusofControl-intro.html

Sadness and social isolation are major elements of most descriptions of mood disturbances.

Mitarart/Fotolia

Case Example: *Larry*

Larry came into care through the youth justice system after several incidents of aggravated assault. He says that before this he lived with anger and confusion most of the time. Larry spent most of his childhood on a remote reserve, where life was very traditional. When he moved to a small Mormon town, he says he experienced complete culture shock. In his words,

"Obviously, it's a constant battle to walk both worlds. Where I come from it's nothing but Indian life. I mean, it was a Mormon town, but directly impacted through the religion, I mean in every part of the school, every aspect of it. And . . . being as proud—I mean, I was very proud of where I come

from, I was very aware of my culture and very involved in all walks of it. . . . A lot of it was the racism that goes on really. . . . You could try to be the greatest person at heart, but it's hard to walk the life of non-violence. I guess you get the idea young that to really fight and stop violence, you got to beat it with violence, and that throws you in the whole cycle of, over and over and over, solving every problem through violence."

At the age of 16, Larry was diagnosed with depression.

Source: From Drugs in our system: An exploratory study on the chemical management of Canadian systems youth - Full report by Y. Lambe and R. McLennan. Published by Youth in Care Canada.

Learning Objectives

1. Define and distinguish between mood disturbances, mood disorders, and mood episodes.

2. Distinguish between the three depressive disorders and the three bipolar and related disorders identified in the text and summarize their primary symptoms.

3. Explain how mood disorders differ from expected emotions in children and youth.

4. Describe differences in the prevalence rates of mood disorders with respect to gender and age.

5. Compare and contrast biological, psychodynamic, behavioural, cognitive, and sociocultural explanations for mood disorders.

6. Describe the relationship between trauma/maltreatment and youth depression.

7. Describe psychological treatment approaches used in treating mood disorders from each of the major psychological paradigms.

8. Identify different symptoms of mood disturbances exhibited by infants, preschoolers, school-aged children, and adolescents.

9. Summarize selected approaches to intervention that fit best with a CYC approach.

Chapter Overview

Major depression is often referred to as the "common cold" of mental health because it's one of the most widespread psychological disorders diagnosed around the world. What is major depression? How does it differ from Bipolar Disorder? What behaviours and emotions must Larry have experienced or demonstrated in order to be diagnosed with major depression? This chapter will summarize the major characteristics of mood disturbances identified in the DSM-5. It will then examine explanations of depressive disorders and bipolar and related disorders from both a psychological and a CYC perspective. As you'll see, while the two perspectives share some ideas with respect to these disturbances, they also differ significantly in terms of the approaches considered most useful in assisting young people diagnosed with these disorders.

From a CYC perspective, this chapter will also explore the idea that, for many vulnerable or at-risk young people, symptoms of clinically diagnosed mood disturbances are best understood as components of pain-based behaviours (Anglin, 2002). A strength-based perspective allows us to see these pain-based behaviours as coping mechanisms or attachment strategies that have helped youth navigate and survive dangerous or threatening situations. For CYCPs working with street youth, or with youth in managed or out-of-home care settings, sadness and despair can be seen as normal responses to the real and significant cumulative losses of family, home, culture, and community. The very act of having to come into care often results in deep sadness and withdrawal that would be expected in the face of devastating loss (Anglin, 2002). Mood disturbances can have a significant negative impact upon youths' day-to-day functioning, and can be extremely debilitating for the children, adolescents, and families affected. Thus, this is a very important topic in mental health literacy for CYCPs.

WHAT IS A MOOD DISTURBANCE?

Mood disturbance is a general, non-diagnostic term that refers to some type of mood symptoms (e.g., excessive unhappiness, persistently elevated or irritable mood). Children and adolescents with mood disturbances suffer from extreme and/or poorly regulated emotional states (e.g., excessive unhappiness, mood swings). Everyone experiences varying moods; in fact, the human experience is characterized by a variety of emotional states that are universal and expected. In the case of mood disturbances, however, these emotional states impact the individual to the extent that they interfere with daily functioning and/or create significant distress. For example, if someone is sad for many weeks to the point where she can't get out of bed and begins missing school or work, she may begin failing courses or lose her job.

Although it's easy to imagine how extreme and persistent *depressed mood* might interfere with daily functioning, it may be more difficult to envision how extreme and persistent *elevated mood* (e.g., extreme euphoria or happiness) might interfere with day-to-day life. However, if extreme happiness or elevated mood results in making impulsive decisions (e.g., making purchases one can't afford), the consequences of such actions associated with this subjectively positive emotion might also be considered a mood disturbance.

Before turning to a discussion of depression from a psychological perspective, examine your own experiences of sadness by trying the *Think About It!* exercise.

WHAT IS A DEPRESSIVE DISORDER? THE PSYCHOLOGICAL PERSPECTIVE

According to the psychological perspective, diagnoses grouped as **Depressive Disorders** are characterized by sad mood, feelings of emptiness, and physical and cognitive changes that interfere with one's ability to achieve important goals and function successfully in

---

Think About It! Exercise: *Experiences of Sadness*

In order to better understand the experience of depression, think of three times in your life when you felt sad or what you might have referred to as "depressed." Then answer the following questions:

1. Were there specific incidents that triggered the feelings of sadness? If so, what were they? If not, what was the trigger?

2. If specific events triggered the feeling of sadness, how long after the event was sadness experienced?

3. What thoughts ran through your mind while you were feeling sad?

4. How did you feel physically? Describe specific physical sensations associated with being sad.

5. What impact did your feelings of sadness have on your actions?

6. How did you manage the experience of sadness? Which coping strategies were most effective for you?

7. Identify and describe three specific insights from this exercise that you can use in your work with others.

daily life. Similar to anxiety disorders, symptoms of depressive disorders are observed in three general areas, and these symptoms result from an emotional state:

- *physical* (e.g., loss of appetite, insomnia)
- *cognitive* (e.g., impaired concentration, difficulty problem solving)
- *behavioural* (e.g., loss of motivation, motor agitation or retardation)

Thus, *Depressive Disorder* is a formal diagnostic term that refers to those psychological disorders characterized primarily by a mood disturbance. So although this term is often used interchangeably with *mood disturbance* or *mood disorder*, they are distinct. In reviewing examples of the physical, cognitive, and behavioural symptoms above, you might have noticed that they aren't entirely unfamiliar to you. Indeed, such experiences are not at all unusual: we all feel sad on occasion to the point where it's difficult to concentrate or we've lost the motivation to engage in those activities we typically enjoy. However, it's the severity and persistence of these experiences and the resulting impairment of functioning that are associated with disorders of mood disturbance.

DSM-5 Categories

Disrupted mood can be observed in the context of many disorders. For example, significant fear and apprehension are associated with anxiety disorders, while inappropriate mood (e.g., finding humour in and laughing at a tragic event) is observed in the context of Schizophrenia. However, the DSM-5 identifies two major categories of mood disturbances (each with its own chapter) in which extreme mood and disrupted emotion are the central features of the disorder: Depressive Disorders and Bipolar and Related Disorders. Within each of these categories, the DSM-5 distinguishes among more specific disturbances. Why are depressive disorders and bipolar and related disorders considered separately from one another if they're both associated with mood disturbances? The explanation relates to differences in symptoms (e.g., sad mood versus elation) and causal factors (e.g., family history and genetic factors). For example, the role of genetics appears to be more significant in bipolar and related disorders than in depressive disorders. Consideration of these disorders in separate chapters suggests that depressive disorders should be seen as distinct from bipolar disorders rather than on a continuum.

Yet the diagnostic criteria for both *depressive disorders* and *bipolar and related disorders* do have something in common: mood disturbances in both categories are based on the occurrence of *mood episodes*. A **mood episode** is the experience of some type of mood disturbance defined in relation to specific symptoms that differ from typical emotional experience. For example, a *Major Depressive Episode* is characterized by depressed mood most of the day, excessive fatigue, and insomnia. In order to be diagnosed with Major Depressive Disorder, you must have experienced a Major Depressive Episode. Therefore, although mood episodes aren't diagnosed as distinct entities, they're the foundation on which the criteria for each of the disorders are based. The DSM-5 identifies three distinct types of mood episodes: *Major Depressive Episode*, *Manic Episode*, and *Hypomanic Episode*. Let's briefly overview the two general categories of disorders and their related mood episodes before considering specific symptoms of those diagnoses you're most likely to encounter in your CYC practice.

Depressive Disorders   The DSM-5 identifies eight depressive disorders. We've seen that their most pronounced symptoms are physical, cognitive, and behavioural outcomes that result from sad, empty, or irritable mood and are persistent and severe enough to interfere with daily functioning. The mood episode most prominent in this category of disorders is the *Major Depressive Episode*. Similar to anxiety disorders, mood disturbances are considered *internalizing* disorders characterized by overcontrolled behaviour and emotion that is directed inward rather than outward.

Bipolar and Related Disorders   The DSM-5 identifies seven disorders in the category **Bipolar and Related Disorders**. In addition to symptoms of sadness and emptiness, this group of disorders is associated with varying degrees of **mania**, characterized by elevated mood, high levels of arousal, energy, and irritability that can result in numerous negative consequences and impair functioning. Accordingly, all three of the mood episodes identified by the DSM (*Major Depressive Episode, Manic Episode*, and *Hypomanic Episode*) are relevant to bipolar and related disorders. Refer to Box 7.1 for an overview of the diagnostic categories specified in the DSM-5 for mood-related disturbances.

Depressive Disorders: Diagnoses and Criteria

Of the eight depressive disorders listed in the DSM-5, those most likely to be encountered by CYCPs are *Disruptive Mood Dysregulation Disorder, Major Depressive Disorder*, and *Persistent Depressive Disorder (Dysthymia)*. Let's review the criteria for each and highlight their similarities and differences.

Disruptive Mood Dysregulation Disorder   **Disruptive Mood Dysregulation Disorder** is a new diagnosis that hasn't appeared in previous editions of the DSM. This

---

Box 7.1

DSM-5 Depressive Disorders	DSM-5 Bipolar and Related Disorders
Disruptive Mood Dysregulation Disorder	Bipolar I Disorder
Major Depressive Disorder (including Major Depressive Episode)	Bipolar II Disorder
Persistent Depressive Disorder (Dysthymia)	Cyclothymic Disorder
Premenstrual Dysphoric Disorder	Substance/Medication-Induced Bipolar and Related Disorder
Substance/Medication-Induced Depressive Disorder	Bipolar and Related Disorder Due to Another Medical Condition
Depressive Disorder Due to Another Medical Condition	Other Specified Bipolar and Related Disorder
Other Specified Depressive Disorder	Unspecified Bipolar and Related Disorder
Unspecified Depressive Disorder	

disorder was added in order to "address concerns about the potential for the overdiagnosis of and treatment for bipolar disorder in children" (APA, 2014, p. 155). Characterized by anger, irritability, and frequent occurrences of behavioural dyscontrol (e.g., temper outbursts associated with verbal rages and/or physical aggression) that occur in at least three settings (e.g., home, school), the symptoms of this disorder are distinct from those of Bipolar Disorder in that the individual doesn't meet the criteria for a Manic or Hypomanic Episode (summarized below).

Disruptive Mood Dysregulation Disorder can't be diagnosed together with a variety of other disorders—including ODD, Intermittent Explosive Disorder, and Bipolar Disorder—a fact that highlights the distinction between these syndromes. Comorbidity, however, can occur with this diagnosis and Major Depressive Disorder, ADHD, and other diagnoses.

Major Depressive Disorder   Major Depressive Disorder is commonly referred to as *depression*, *clinical depression*, *major depression*, or *unipolar depression*. The term *mood disorder* is also sometimes used, although this is a more general and non-diagnostic term that could refer to any one of several disorders. **Major Depressive Disorder (MDD)** is characterized by one or more *Major Depressive Episodes*. The diagnostic criteria for Major Depressive Disorder are presented in Box 7.2. Note that Criteria A to C represent a **Major Depressive Episode**.

It's important to note that not everyone with an MDD diagnosis exhibits the same behaviour. Some of the more typical symptoms include a persistent, sad, anxious, or empty feeling, feelings of hopelessness and isolation, fatigue or decreased energy, irritability and restlessness, difficulties concentrating, changes in sleep and/or eating habits, and thoughts of suicide. Although the same criteria are applied to children, adolescents, and adults, some features (i.e., irritable mood, somatic complaints, unexpressed resentment and anger) are more common in children and adolescents than in adults. Hopelessness and suicidal thoughts and actions are rare in children but increase dramatically during adolescence (Gelfand & Drew, 2003; Luby et al., 2002). In order for a diagnosis of MDD to be applied, five or more symptoms must *persist* for at least two weeks, *reflect a change* in behaviour, and *cause impairment in functioning*. Also, the presence of sad mood (or irritability) or loss of interest/pleasure (*anhedonia*) is essential for a diagnosis of MDD. Onset of the symptoms can be gradual or sudden, and the severity and duration of symptoms varies depending on the individual. Because it's an internalizing problem where distress is turned inward toward the self, it's often overlooked (whereas externalizing, disruptive behaviours are directed outward toward others and so are more likely to attract attention). According to the DSM-5, if those diagnosed with MDD don't meet the criteria for a Major Depressive Episode for a period of two months, they're considered to be "in remission." Because MDD can come and go and is typically recurrent, knowledge of previous Major Depressive Episodes is important and may increase the likelihood that subsequent episodes are readily identified.

Persistent Depressive Disorder (Dysthymia)   The DSM-5 distinguishes between MDD and **Persistent Depressive Disorder (Dysthymia)**, a similar but more chronic condition (i.e., lasting for at least one year for children and adolescents) that is associated with less severe depressive symptoms. Youth diagnosed with this disorder have symptoms similar to those of MDD (e.g., poor concentration, insomnia, low self-esteem) that are present for at least one year (for adults, two years are required), with symptoms never remitting for more than two months at a time.

Box 7.2

DSM-5 Criteria for Major Depressive Disorder

A. Five (or more) of the following symptoms have been present during the same 2-week period and represent a change from previous functioning; at least one of the symptoms is either (1) depressed mood or (2) loss of interest or pleasure.

1. Depressed mood most of the day, nearly every day, as indicated by either subjective report (e.g., feels sad, empty, or hopeless) or observation made by others (e.g., appears tearful). (Note: In children and adolescents, can be irritable mood.)

2. Markedly diminished interest or pleasure in all, or almost all, activities most of the day, nearly every day (as indicated by either subjective account or observation made by others).

3. Significant weight loss when not dieting or weight gain (e.g., a change of more than 5% of body weight in a month), or decrease or increase in appetite nearly every day. (Note: In children, consider failure to make expected weight gain.)

4. Insomnia or hypersomnia (oversleeping) nearly every day.

5. Psychomotor agitation or retardation nearly every day (observable by others, not merely subjective feelings of restlessness or being slowed down).

6. Fatigue or loss of energy nearly every day.

7. Feelings of worthlessness or excessive or inappropriate guilt (which may be delusional) nearly every day (not merely self-reproach or guilt about being sick).

8. Diminished ability to think or concentrate, or indecisiveness, nearly every day (either by subjective account or as observed by others).

9. Recurrent thoughts of death (not just fear of dying), recurrent suicidal ideation without a specific plan, or a suicide attempt or a specific plan for committing suicide.

B. The symptoms cause clinically significant distress or impairment in social, occupational, or other important areas of functioning.

C. The symptoms are not due to the direct physiological effects of a substance or another general medical condition.

NOTE: Criteria A–C represent a major depressive episode.

Source: Reprinted with permission from the Diagnostic and Statistical Manual of Mental Disorders, Fifth Edition, (Copyright ©2013). American Psychiatric Association. All Rights Reserved.

Bipolar and Related Disorders: Diagnoses and Criteria

Of the seven bipolar and related disorders listed in the DSM-5, those most likely to be encountered in CYC practice are *Bipolar I Disorder*, *Bipolar II Disorder*, and *Cyclothymic Disorder*. Let's examine the criteria associated with each of these diagnostic categories.

Bipolar I Disorder   **Bipolar I Disorder** is often referred to as *bipolar depression* or *manic depression*. This disorder is generally characterized by dramatic swings in mood, ranging from periods of elation (called *mania*) to periods of sadness that correspond with symptoms of a Major Depressive Episode. Children and adolescents diagnosed with Bipolar I Disorder must have had one or more **Manic Episodes**, during which they present as very happy or euphoric and experience high energy and self-esteem as well as decreased inhibitions. Mania is associated with being very talkative, having rapidly changing thoughts, having little need for sleep, and being highly distractible. Although some of these symptoms may sound positive (e.g., elation, high energy), they often result in negative and devastating consequences (e.g., spending too much money, making impulsive decisions, engaging in dangerous behaviours, violence, and excessive involvement in pleasurable activities).

For children and adolescents diagnosed with Bipolar I Disorder, Manic Episodes are preceded by or followed by one or more Major Depressive Episodes (see Box 7.2), during which the individual feels very sad and is much less active than usual. Mood episodes are intense and usually last a week or two, but sometimes longer. During an episode, the symptoms are experienced every day for most or all of the day. As with depression, the same diagnostic criteria are used with both children and adults. Recall, however, that although children may still be diagnosed with Bipolar I Disorder, the diagnosis of Disruptive Mood Dysregulation Disorder is now included in the DSM-5 in order to avoid an overdiagnosis of Bipolar I Disorder.

Bipolar II Disorder   Although the term *Bipolar Disorder* is used most often to refer to Bipolar I Disorder, the DSM-5 distinguishes between Bipolar I Disorder and Bipolar II Disorder. **Bipolar II Disorder** is diagnosed when an individual experiences one or more Major Depressive Episodes and at least one **Hypomanic Episode**. The diagnostic criteria for a Hypomanic Episode are nearly identical to those for a Manic Episode, with the exception that hypomania is less likely to cause significant impairment in functioning. Therefore, although the euphoric and cheerful presentation of young people with Bipolar II Disorder is recognized as being distinct from their usual presentation, the behaviour associated with it is less bizarre and more organized than those observed in the Manic Episodes associated with Bipolar I Disorder. Refer to Table 7.1 for a comparison of behaviours that might be observed during Major Depressive and Manic Episodes.

Cyclothymic Disorder   The DSM-5 distinguishes between Bipolar Disorder (I and II) and **Cyclothymic Disorder** (sometimes referred to as *cyclothymia*), a similar but more chronic condition (i.e., lasting for at least two years) that is typically associated with less

Table 7.1 Comparison of Behaviours During Manic and Depressive Episodes

Children and adolescents having a Manic Episode may . . .

Feel very happy or act silly in a way that's unusual

Have a very short temper (an unusual irritable mood)

Talk really fast about a lot of different things

Have trouble sleeping but not feel tired

Have trouble staying focused

Do risky things

Children and adolescents having a Major Depressive Episode may . . .

Feel very sad

Complain about pain a lot, like stomachaches and headaches

Sleep too little or too much

Feel guilty and worthless

Eat too little or too much

Have little energy and no interest in fun activities

Think about death or suicide (or exhibited in play themes)

Source: NIMH, 2008.

Twelve-year-old Chad is doing well in school, but for the past three years he's experienced periods of extreme sadness. Last year, though, Chad experienced a period during which he felt unusually euphoric. He enjoyed the feeling, but during that time he traded his Xbox 360 for an old guitar that he doesn't really need.

Beth is eight years old. Her teachers and foster parents have grown increasingly concerned about her because of her frequent angry outbursts. Recently, after she heard that there would be no recess that day, she threw another student's computer across the room. Her peers are beginning to avoid her.

Over the past six months, 14-year-old April has been unable to shake her feelings of sadness. She finds herself crying uncontrollably, often over minor problems, and on other occasions she feels irritable and acts out toward others. She's lost a significant amount of weight and doesn't understand why she has little appetite. April thinks she should speak with someone about her feelings, but she doesn't have the energy or interest to find out where she should go.

For over a year, Laura has been unhappy. She has difficulty sleeping, eats very little, and at times feels as though things will never improve. Despite her sadness, however, she still manages to complete her schoolwork and maintain regular contact with several of her friends. She wonders if she'll ever feel better.

severe depressive and manic symptoms. Note that in the course of Cyclothymic Disorder, an individual may at some point meet the criteria for a Manic or Major Depressive Episode, which would result in additional diagnoses.

Before turning to a discussion of mood disturbances from a CYC perspective, try the *Test Your Understanding* exercise. Can you identify the disorder that most closely matches the description of each case?

A CYC APPROACH TO MOOD DISTURBANCES: UNDERSTANDING DEPRESSION

Before the 1970s, it was thought that depression didn't even exist in children and youth. The literature cites several reasons for this, including the following: clinicians didn't fully explore children's feelings or moods and so wouldn't know whether children were depressed; in the Freudian view, children's unconscious minds weren't developed enough to experience depression; and adolescent depression, confusion, and difficulties with mood ("adolescent angst") were considered a normal part of development. In the 1970s and '80s, childhood depression was thought to be *masked* by other conditions. Today, we recognize that young people's depressive symptoms do exist, and that they exist on a continuum. They may indeed be masked or expressed differently than they are in adults; for example, children and adolescents may express depression through frequent somatic complaints, including digestive difficulties, sleeping difficulties, anxiety, and rage, and by such behaviours as inattentiveness, hyperactivity, tantrums, boredom, withdrawal, and eating problems. Some therapists and clinicians still dispute the idea of masked depression, and view child and adolescent depressive symptoms as basically similar to those of adults.

Many of the young people with whom CYCPs engage struggle with extreme sadness and despair, and may attempt or complete suicide as a result. CYCPs need to know how to recognize clinical depression and what to do when they're concerned about a youth's presentation of depressed mood and affect. However, the effectiveness of using the

DSM-5 mood-disorder categories to assist CYCPs in this role is a matter that warrants discussion. For example, serious concerns have been raised about the addition of Bipolar Disorder to the list of childhood and adolescent psychiatric diagnoses in the 1990s. As a result of this addition, between 1994 and 2003 the diagnosis of Bipolar Disorder in children and youth aged 1–19 in the United States rose by 40 percent (Root, 2009). The concurrent increase in the use of mood stabilizers and antipsychotic medications for young children was so alarming that it was referred to as a "false epidemic." Stuart Kaplan, a clinical professor of psychiatry at the Penn State College of Medicine, suggests that the widespread diagnosis of Bipolar Disorder in children is entirely an American phenomenon, as it's used only rarely in other countries, including Canada, Australia, New Zealand, and Germany. The research indicates that the actual incidence of Bipolar Disorder in children is in fact more accurately considered rare, with a rate of only 1 percent (NIMH, 2008).

We discussed earlier that, in order to address concerns about the overdiagnosis of Bipolar Disorder in children, a new diagnosis, Disruptive Mood Dysregulation Disorder, has been added to the DSM-5; it's used for children up to 18 who exhibit persistent irritability and frequent episodes of extreme behavioural dyscontrol (APA, 2013). Many would agree that this might accurately describe most, if not all, children. According to Allen Francis, the DSM-5 turns temper tantrums into a mental disorder: "We have no idea whatever how this untested new diagnosis will play out in real life practice settings, but my fear is that it will exacerbate, not relieve, the already excessive and inappropriate use of medication in young children. During the past two decades, child psychiatry has already provoked three fads—a tripling of Attention Deficit Disorder, a more than twenty-times increase in Autistic Disorder, and a forty-times increase in childhood Bipolar Disorder" (Frances, 2012, p. 1).

Notwithstanding the increased diagnosing of children, depression in young people is very real. For example, the child or youth experiencing serious depressive symptoms displays persistent sadness that interferes with day-to-day functioning (including daily routines, academic performance, social relationships) and negatively impacts psychosocial development (Lewinsohn et al., 2003). Extreme mood swings can make it very difficult, if not impossible, for a young person to interact with peers and family members, and will

Social withdrawal and peer rejection are often associated with mood disorders.

Bramgino/Fotolia

At the age of 16, Larry was diagnosed with depression. At the time, however, he believed that what he was experiencing was the exact opposite. He says he felt as if he were "on fire," although he admits to deliberately "shutting down" during his psychiatric assessment, and therefore understands how his behaviours were perceived as symptoms of depression. Understandably, the medication prescribed to him never seemed to work, and in his opinion, made him more "on edge" and "moody." The side effects of the prescription drugs caused nausea, and Larry constantly gained and lost weight.

In an effort to improve his state, his medication was changed several times. Larry began to feel that the drugs were harming his body, and that they hadn't provided any emotional benefit. Perhaps more importantly, he believed that the treatment prescribed to him was in direct conflict with his cultural beliefs.

If you were the CYCP working with Larry, how might you approach the issue regarding the medication? Do you think that assisting Larry to access an Elder and/or traditional healing would be helpful? How would you explore the role of trauma in his depression?

Source: Excerpt from Drugs in our system: An exploratory study on the chemical management of Canadian systems Youth by Y. Lambe and R. McLellan. Published by Youth in Care Canada, © 2009.

certainly interfere with academic and work performance. As noted earlier, however, most concerning is the fact that many youth who struggle with mood disturbances also have persistent thoughts of self-harm and/or suicide.

Before turning to a discussion of prevalence, development, and comorbidity, consider the details of the opening case in relation to the psychological and CYC views of mood disturbances in *Larry's Case: Revisited*.

HOW MANY YOUNG PEOPLE STRUGGLE WITH MOOD DISTURBANCES?

Major Depressive Disorder is the fourth leading cause of disability and premature death in the world (Health Canada, 2002). It is predicted that by the year 2020, MDD will be among the leading causes of disability worldwide, second only to heart disease (WHO, 2001b). Not surprisingly, then, mood disorders are one of the most common and disabling conditions in young people.

A nationwide survey of Canadian youth by Statistics Canada found that 6.5 percent—more than a quarter million youth and young adults between 15 and 24—met the criteria for MDD in the prior year (Statistics Canada, 2003). Recent estimates suggest that approximately 2 to 8 percent of all children aged 4 to 18 experience a Major Depressive Episode. Côté et al. (2009) found that 15 percent of preschoolers exhibited significant levels of depressed mood. Although MDD is equally common in boys and girls in childhood, more girls than boys are diagnosed with MDD in adolescence (Rushton, Forcier, & Schectman, 2003). Despite challenges in acquiring accurate estimates of depressive disorders in the population, most would agree that the statistics are cause for alarm and warrant continued development of reliable assessment tools and treatment approaches for these disorders.

In 2014, approximately 5 percent of male youth and 12 percent of female youth aged 12 to 19 experienced a Major Depressive Episode. According to the Canadian Mental Health Association, the total number of 12- to 19-year-olds in Canada at risk for developing depression in 2014 was 3.2 million ("Depression," 2013). Accessing help can make a difference for 80 percent of all youth who are affected, allowing them to get back to their regular activities ("Depression," 2013).

Paying close attention to symptoms of youth depression is critical. While not all depressed youth will contemplate suicide or engage in self-harm, most young people who are suicidal are depressed ("Fast facts," 2015). Canada's youth suicide rate is the third highest in the industrialized world, and suicide is among the leading causes of death in 15- to 24-year-old Canadians, second only to accidents ("Suicide," 2013). Young people with mood disorders are at a particularly high risk of suicide. Lesbian, gay, bisexual, trans, and two-spirited youth, as well as Aboriginal youth, also have a much higher risk of suicide than their peers. Major depression and Bipolar Disorder each account for 15 to 25 percent of all deaths by suicide in youth with severe mood disorders ("Depression and suicide," 2015).

MOOD DISTURBANCES AND DEVELOPMENT

The symptoms of mood episodes are expressed and experienced in varying ways at different ages. These variations are considered to represent the same process over the developmental life course. Some common depressive symptoms observed at various ages are presented in Box 7.3.

Although children can be diagnosed with a Major Depressive Episode as early as three to five years of age, generally, there is an increase in the diagnosis of depressive disorders from preschool to elementary school (e.g., Cohen et al., 1993; Lewinsohn et al., 1993). This is assumed to reflect increased cognitive capacity, self-awareness, and verbal ability as well as an increase in performance stress. It's not until adolescence, however, that a sharp increase in the diagnosis of depressive disorders is observed and reaches adult levels (Costello et al., 2003). This significant change in prevalence has been linked to biological changes in the brain as well as an increase in stressors. The occurrences of Manic Episodes are considered rare and difficult to diagnose in children. Consequently, there is less available information for bipolar disorders at this stage than for depressive disorders (Nottelmann & Jensen, 1995). There is, however, some indication that Manic Episodes are more likely to occur in adolescence (Carlson, 1994; Poznanski & Mokros, 1994) and a

---

Box 7.3

Symptoms of Depression at Various Periods of Development

Infants: sad, passive, unresponsive, sleep disturbance, appetite loss, clinging, excessive crying

Preschoolers: withdrawn, inhibited, tearful, lack of enthusiasm in play, excessive clinging/whining, fear of separation/abandonment, irritability for no reason, physical complaints (stomachaches), negative and self-destructive verbalizations ("I hate myself")

School-age: same as preschoolers—argumentative, disruptive behaviour, greater irritability, temper tantrums, weight loss, headaches, academic and peer problems (e.g., fighting, feeling of "being picked on")

Adolescents: feelings of guilt, hopelessness, loneliness, self-blame, low self-esteem ("Nobody likes me"), eating disturbance, worsening school performance, arguments with parents, negative body image

growing consensus that child mania exists and warrants continued study (National Institute of Mental Health Research Roundtable on Prepubertal Bipolar Disorder, 2001).

COMORBIDITY

Many of the behaviours associated with mood disorders also occur in normal development or in relation to other disorders (Hammen & Rudolph, 2003). In particular, MDD is often comorbid with conduct problems and anxiety disorders in childhood (Garber & Weersing, 2010; Wolff & Ollendick, 2006). In adolescence, MDD often co-occurs with impulsivity, substance use, and unstable relationships (Lewinsohn et al., 1993). A diagnosis of MDD is also associated with an increased risk for delinquency, arrest or conviction, school dropout, and suicidal behaviour. These comorbid conditions can interfere with the recognition of depressive symptoms because the externalizing behaviours (e.g., rule violations, conflict) are more likely to be noticed by others than the internalizing behaviours (e.g., sadness, guilt) associated with a Major Depressive Episode. By comparison, substance use/dependence, disruptive behaviour disorders, and academic failures are most often associated with Manic Episodes in adolescents (Papolos, 2003; Tillman et al., 2004). In addition, mania in adolescents may include psychotic symptoms (refer to Chapter 9), which can result in a misdiagnosis of Schizophrenia (James & Javaloyes, 2001).

Before moving on to a discussion of the DSM-5 criteria for bipolar and related disorders, review some common myths about mood disturbances presented in Box 7.4.

EXPLAINING MOOD DISTURBANCES: PSYCHOLOGICAL PARADIGMS

What causes mood disorders? What is the best way to help a child or adolescent suffering from symptoms of a mood episode? Consistent with our discussion of paradigms (in Chapter 1), the answers to these questions vary in relation to the theoretical framework one adopts. From a psychological perspective, predominant explanations include those

---

Box 7.4

Common Myths About Depressive and Related Disorders

MYTH: *It's normal for youth to be moody; adolescents don't get "real" depression.*

FACT: Depression is more than just being moody, and it can affect people at any age, including adolescents. Any noticeable change in personality or in daily activities needs to be questioned.

MYTH: *Depression is something that happens to everyone at some time in their life.*

FACT: There is a significant difference between feeling sad and lonely and having a clinical depression.

MYTH: *Depression is a sign of personal weakness.*

FACT: Although emotions and personality do play a role in the development of depression, chemical imbalances in the brain and genetic predisposition also contribute to depression.

Source: From Myths and Facts from Teen Depression. Copyright ©2014 by the University Health System. Used by permission of University Health System.

offered from the biological, psychodynamic, and cognitive paradigms. Although each of these approaches is considered independently in our discussion, it's generally believed that there is no single factor that can explain mood disturbances. Instead, a combination of biological, psychodynamic, and cognitive variables interact with one another to produce and sustain the symptoms associated with mood disorders (Stark et al., 1999). The best approach to treatment, then, involves a combination of strategies based on multiple paradigms. Although the paradigms described below might be perceived to be competing explanations for depression, they're best considered as contributing one or more elements to the overall understanding and treatment of the disorder.

Biological Paradigm   The relationship between biological processes and mood disorders has been investigated extensively. Most of the research has focused on identifying biological factors involved in adult MDD, and although we can't assume that the physiological expressions of depressive disorders are the same across the lifespan (Stark et al., 2006), the biological basis of adult MDD and treatment can provide a valuable starting point from which to understand the biological aspects of depressive episodes in children and adolescents. Research based on a biological paradigm of depression has focused primarily on the role of genetic, biochemical, and neurological factors in mood disorders.

Heredity and Genetics. Numerous studies have shown that individuals with greater degrees of genetic relatedness (e.g., identical versus fraternal twins) have higher concordance rates for depressive and bipolar disorders (e.g., Gershon, 1990; James & Chapman, 1975), supporting the notion that these disorders have a genetic component. Generally, results indicate a greater genetic influence in the case of bipolar disorders than for depressive disorders, although adoption, twin, and family studies suggest that genetics also plays a role in the onset of MDD (O'Conner et al., 1998; Silberg, Maes, & Eaves, 2010). What might be inherited that could predispose one to develop a mood disorder? Genes! Although specific genes responsible for genetic influences haven't yet been identified, their influence on the development of the nervous system—including the development of specific brain structures as well as the functioning of neurons and the availability and sensitivity to various chemicals in that system—is currently being explored (e.g., Kendler et al., 2005).

Brain Structures. Various areas of the brain play a role in regulating mood. Specifically, the amygdala, hippocampus, and thalamus have been found to be important brain structures in the experience of emotion. From a biological paradigm, abnormalities in the size or activity of these structures might explain the abnormalities in emotion associated with mood disorders. Refer to Appendix 2 to view the location of these st̶r̶u̶c̶t̶u̶r̶e̶s̶.

  This biological explanation of depressive disorders is̶ relationships between depressive symptoms and structu̶r̶e̶ various brain structures. For example, heightened activity i̶n̶ activating memories and enhancing emotion) has been ass̶o̶c̶ MDD (Drevets, 2001). Other studies have found the hippo̶c̶a̶m̶p̶u̶s̶ ̶smaller in some people diagnosed with MDD (Bridge et al., 2007). According to this line of research, stress may be a significant factor in depressive disorders: it results in the release of the hormone cortisol, which has been found to suppress the production of new neurons in the

[handwritten note]: The amygdala + hippocampus and thalamus play a role of experiencing emotions

hippocampus. Harsh conditions experienced early in life (e.g., prenatal stress, neglect) may produce abnormal stress responses in the brain that can alter brain activity, sensitizing the child to later stress and increasing the individual's risk of a Major Depressive Episode. It's important to note, however, that these neuroanatomical differences aren't observed in everyone diagnosed with depressive symptoms.

Neurotransmitters. From a biological approach, another explanation for the symptoms of mood disorders is an atypical level of certain neurotransmitters in the brain. As discussed in Chapter 1, neurotransmitters are chemicals in the nervous system that are responsible for communication between neurons. It's been suggested that low levels of certain neurotransmitters (including norepinephrine, serotonin, and dopamine) might explain differences in mood for those experiencing depressive symptoms. If so, medications that increase the activation of these neurotransmitters should result in a decrease in depressive symptoms. By comparison, high levels of epinephrine have been associated with symptoms of mania. If so, medications that decrease the activation of this chemical should alleviate the mania observed in bipolar disorders.

Support for these ideas comes from studies in which a decrease of depressive symptoms is observed following the administration of medications that increase levels of certain neurotransmitters. These medications (referred to as *antidepressants*) affect various neurotransmitters. The most studied medications with adults include *tricyclic antidepressants* (TCAs), *monoamine oxidase inhibitors* (MAOIs), and *selective serotonin reuptake inhibitors* (SSRIs).

TCAs (e.g., imipramine, amitriptyline, nortriptyline, desipramine) affect levels of noradrenaline and serotonin but have generally been found to be ineffective with youth (Bostic et al., 2003; Hazell et al., 1995). MAOIs (e.g., phenelzine, tranylcypromine, isocarboxazid) elevate levels of serotonin, norepinephrine, and dopamine by interfering with the activity of enzymes in the synaptic cleft that usually function to eliminate unused neurotransmitter substance. By decreasing the activity of these enzymes, these neurotransmitters can remain in the synaptic cleft and exert their effects for longer periods of time. One of the difficulties with MAOIs, however, is that they can interact with tyramine, a chemical found in many foods, including cheese and pickles. This interaction can cause a sudden increase in blood pressure, which can result in strokes. While these interaction effects can be avoided through diet modification, they're still cause for alarm; consequently, MAOIs are typically not the first choice of treatment.

Instead, SSRIs such as fluoxetine (trade name Prozac) are usually prescribed first. These medications increase levels of serotonin through a different mechanism. Specifically, they interfere with the reuptake mechanisms that are responsible for taking unused neurotransmitter substances back up into the neuron that originally released them (refer to Figure 7.1). SSRIs have been shown to reduce symptoms of depression in children and adolescents aged 7 to 17 (Emslie et al., 1997), and are often the treatment of choice for those of all ages because they're typically associated with fewer side effects than MAOIs or the tricyclics. Other SSRIs (sertraline, or Zoloft; paroxetine, or Paxil) have also shown some effectiveness in youth (Wagner et al., 2003). In the case of

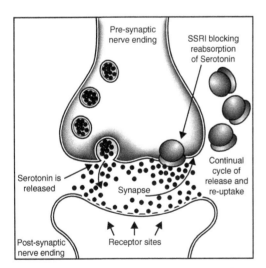

Figure 7.1 How SSRIs Exert Their Effects

SSRIs interfere with the reuptake mechanisms that are responsible for taking unused neurotransmitter substances back up into the neuron that originally released them.

Source: Illustration, "The Brain, Neurons and Synapses" by Dr. Alan Priest. Used by permission. http://www.alanpriest.f2s.com/Depression%20Medication%20p5.htm

bipolar disorders, lithium (often referred to as a *mood-stabilizer*) has been found to be effective in reducing symptoms of mania as well as in decreasing general mood instability (Hirschowitz, Kolevzon, & Garakani, 2010). Although the exact mechanisms by which lithium exerts its effects are unknown, it may result in an increase in serotonin as well as a decrease in norepinephrine and dopamine.

Psychodynamic Paradigm Psychodynamic explanations of mood disorders have primarily focused on explanations for Major Depressive Disorder. From a psychodynamic approach, depressive episodes result from a significant separation or loss, referred to by Freud as "object loss." From Freud's (1965) perspective, the loss could be real (parental death or divorce) or symbolic or imagined (rejection or withdrawal of affection, conflict with a friend, failing in school). Following the loss, the individual experiences ambivalent or angry feelings toward the lost love object. In order to avoid the anxiety associated with harbouring such negative feelings toward the lost "object," the individual directs these aggressive and hostile feelings toward the self. The end result is "anger directed inward" and its associated depressive symptoms. More recently, others have instead emphasized the feelings of helplessness and decline of self-esteem that result from loss (e.g., Kessler, Turner, & House, 1988). This is consistent with the observation that depressed individuals are more likely to experience anger and hostility toward others than toward themselves (Weissman, Klerman, & Paykel, 1971).

The role of loss in depressive symptoms is supported by findings that children diagnosed with MDD have experienced higher rates of early parental loss or separation than children not diagnosed with MDD. For example, Seligman (1974) observed that among 100 adolescent referrals for MDD, 37 percent had experienced a loss of one or both parents, compared with only 11.7 percent of a general public school sample. Although these findings might be interpreted as suggesting that the link between loss and MDD is a direct one, more recent studies support the idea that the link is an *indirect* one in which loss initiates a series of challenging alterations in the environment (e.g., lack of care, socioeconomic difficulties) that can increase the risk for MDD. For example, West and colleagues (1991) examined a sample of 92 families who'd lost a parent within the previous two years; MDD in children aged 8–15 was mediated by the level of parental encouragement, family warmth, and stable positive events rather than being directly related to the loss. Thus, when adequate parental care follows loss and there are few environmental disturbances, an increase in susceptibility to MDD is not observed (Goodman, 2002).

Behavioural Paradigm According to the behavioural paradigm, mood disturbances (particularly depression) result from a lack of positive, reinforcing events (Lewinsohn, 1974; Manos, Kanter, & Busch, 2010). Research findings indeed demonstrate that depression severity is related to fewer positive events and lower levels of environmental rewards (Hopko & Mullane, 2008; Hopko et al., 2003). More recently, behavioural models of depression emphasize the role of *behavioural avoidance* in the development of depression. Specifically, avoiding problems (rather than solving them) has been found to be associated with reduced positive reinforcement, which then predicts depression (Carvalho & Hopko, 2011).

Other research shows that those diagnosed with depression are more likely to use *avoidance coping* when encountering stressful events (e.g., Connor-Smith & Compas, 2002; Ingram et al., 2007) by engaging in maladaptive behaviours such as gambling, binge-eating, or substance abuse. Longitudinal studies have demonstrated that although these avoidance coping strategies serve a short-term purpose in that they allow one to avoid facing a problem, this avoidance is directly associated with the development and continuation of symptoms of depression (e.g., Holohan et al., 2005) because it decreases opportunities to experience positively reinforcing/rewarding events. "Over-reliance on avoidant coping creates an environment where healthy behaviours are not adequately reinforced and reduce in frequency . . . being replaced with passive non-rewarding activity" (Carvalho & Hopko, 2011, p. 160).

Cognitive Paradigm   From a cognitive approach, thoughts and beliefs are considered to be important factors in influencing emotional states. Therefore, rather than emotions being central to understanding mood disorders, how we think and give meaning to our experiences is vital in understanding negative emotions. One of the most influential cognitive theories of MDD was developed by Aaron Beck (1967; 1976; 1983). Beck hypothesized that depressed mood *results from* specific thoughts. For example, *thinking* that no one likes or loves you is likely to result in *feelings* of sadness.

According to Beck, negative experiences such as rejection or conflict with significant others during childhood and adolescence create a vulnerability to developing depressive disorders (Beck, 1967; Scher, Ingram, & Segal, 2005). Specifically, as a result of such negative experiences, one develops *depressogenic* or dysfunctional schemas and beliefs. A *schema* is a general cognitive framework that helps us organize and interpret information. Depressogenic schemas can result in a biased interpretation of stimuli and events around us, and may fuel dysfunctional beliefs.

For example, if a child has been told repeatedly, "You're so stupid" or "You'll never amount to anything," a schema of inadequacy may develop where the child now assumes that he or she is insufficient and a failure. The child develops specific beliefs such as "I don't know how to talk to others" or "I'm ugly." Even in the context of successes (e.g., receiving praise from a teacher for good performance), the child will tend to focus on those events that are consistent with the schema (e.g., he or she did poorly on a quiz) and ignore those events that are inconsistent with the schema. This bias in perception and interpretation of events continues to support the irrational beliefs. See Table 7.2 for examples of common dysfunctional schemas and related beliefs.

Once formed, these dysfunctional schemas may remain inactive for many years. Although a child may be unaware of such schemas and/or beliefs, stressors or life events can activate them, resulting in a pattern of negative automatic thoughts that form what Beck refers to as the **negative cognitive triad**, which consists of negative thoughts about the *self*, one's *experiences and the world*, and one's *future*. For example, the stressor of a

Table 7.2 Common Dysfunctional Schemas and Related Beliefs

Dysfunctional Schema	Related Beliefs
Incompetence	"I'll never amount to anything" or "I can never do anything right."
Worthlessness	"I don't deserve good things in my life" or "No one will ever love me."
Mistrust	"You can't really trust anyone" or "I can expect others to hurt me somehow."

Depressogenic schemas can result in a biased interpretation of stimuli and events around us and may fuel dysfunctional and negative beliefs about oneself.

Suzanne Tucker/Shutterstock

failed academic test m~~ay activate the schema of "inadequacy,"~~ which then results in a pattern of negative thoug~~hts~~

[handwritten note: Cognitive distortions individual alters the perception of events and other self relevant information to make them consistent with underlying negative assumptions and beliefs. making small problems BIG!]

According to Bec~~k~~ ... ~~a~~ttern of negative thoughts that re~~sult in the symptoms~~ of depression. As discussed in ~~...~~ argue that the negative cognitive tri~~ad ... automatic~~ use of various **cognitive distortions** in which the individual alters his or her perceptions of events and other self-relevant information to make them consistent with underlying negative assumptions and beliefs. For example, *magnification* refers to a cognitive distortion in which individuals overly emphasize negative events.

Numerous studies have been conducted to evaluate the validity of various aspects of Beck's theory. A significant amount of research demonstrates that those diagnosed with MDD think more negatively about themselves, the future, and the world around them, confirming Beck's negative cognitive triad (for reviews, see Abela & Hankin, 2008; Dozois & Beck, 2008). Negative cognitive biases are more prominent in depressed individuals and alter the events and information that is focused on as well as what information is best remembered (Clark, Beck, & Alford, 1999). Furthermore, support for Beck's idea that such cognitions *cause* MDD comes from some studies demonstrating that non-depressed individuals with negative cognitive biases were more likely to experience a Major Depressive Episode over the next four years those were those with more positive cognitive schemas (Alloy et al., 2006; 2008).

Sociocultural Paradigm   According to this paradigm, the social and cultural environment influences the expression of mood disturbances. Specifically, researchers have found relationships between depression and various social variables including culture, gender, race, stressors, coping strategies, and social support.

Stressful Life Events. Stressful life events have been found to be associated with depression (Grant et al., 2004). According to the **stress exposure model** (Brown, 1993), exposure to stressful events makes one more likely to develop dep~~ression ...~~ have shown that exposure to stress is followed by the onset of a~~n~~ ~~...~~ sive symptoms (Garber, Keiley, & Martin, 2002) and that bo~~...~~

[handwritten note: stress exposure model   stress = depression]

stressors are associated with depression (Birmaher et al., 1996). For example, changing schools, lack of family resources, or conflict between parents are related to depression in children and adolescents (Goodyer et al., 1997; Kovacs, 1997).

But not all children and adolescents exposed to such stressors will develop depression. One explanation for this is differences in coping strategies used to manage stressful life events. For example, a review by Compas et al. (2001) found that *problem-focused coping* (where one attempts to take action to resolve the stressor) and *engagement coping* (which includes problem solving, viewing the stressor in a positive light, and distraction) are associated with lower levels of depressive symptoms. Coping responses that are more *emotion-focused* (where one attempts to decrease negative emotions associated with the stressor) and that involve *disengagement coping* (which includes avoidance, self-blame and criticism, and rumination) are associated with higher levels of depressive symptoms.

Family Influences. One important source of stress is in relationships with others. In particular, numerous family factors have been explored in relation to mood disturbances. For example, being raised in a household with one depressed family member is associated with problems in various areas, including childrearing practices, harsh discipline, and attachment (Cummings & Davies, 1994; Kaslow, Deering, & Racusin, 1994). Within a family environment, child abuse and maltreatment has also been found to be associated with depression, particularly for females (Weiss, Longhurst, & Mazure, 1999; Whiffen & Clark, 1997), as have maternal hostility and parent–adolescent conflict (Sagestrano et al., 2003). In general, depressive symptoms in youth are significantly related to impaired family functioning (Bond et al., 2005).

Specific factors associated with social relationships in general predict mood disturbances. For example, interpersonal loss, conflict, and a lack of interpersonal skills are among the social problems that may predispose one to developing depressive symptoms (e.g., Eley & Stevenson, 2000; Herzberg et al., 1998). Several studies have found that depressed youth have poorer communication skills and are less supportive and assertive compared with non-depressed youth (Kobak & Ferenz-Gillies, 1995). Such findings support the idea that the relationship between depression and difficulties in relationships are bidirectional, with the youth being both influenced by and influencing those factors that lead to and maintain the symptoms of mood disturbances.

A CYC LENS ON THE PSYCHOLOGICAL PARADIGM: A HOLISTIC CONCEPTUAL MODEL

CYCPs are all too familiar with stories like Larry's; in CYC practice, there are many faces to child and adolescent mood disturbances. Let's review aspects of the psychological perspective and highlight those that have particular relevance for CYCPs.

Depression in children and youth is often overlooked because it's an internalizing problem. Young people struggling with depression aren't "acting out" their pain, they're *acting in*—they're in despair (Lavin & Park, 1999). In fact, some youth who exhibit depressive symptoms can be very compliant with the adults in their life space. It's important to recognize, then, that occasionally CYCPs might inadvertently reinforce some of the behaviours related to depressive symptoms. For example, young people who are socially withdrawn might be perceived as obeying the rules or agreeing with others when in fact they're failing to participate in social exchanges.

Although pain-based behaviours are usually either internalized or externalized, the behaviours related to depression can't necessarily be categorized according to a simple either/or proposition. We've seen that whereas in internalizing disorders the pain associated with past trauma has been turned inward and is expressed toward oneself (e.g., when young people struggle with behaviours related to depression, suicide, self-harm, and anxiety), externalizing disorders are directed outward toward others in the life space. And yet consider, for example, the observed gender differences relating to this distinction: boys, in general, tend to display acting-out behaviours, whereas girls tend to act inwardly. Children and adolescents can display many features of both acting out and acting in—and so for CYCPs, these are not discrete categories. For example, an adolescent female could act out her pain as rage or bullying but still be clinically depressed.

Review the summary of behaviours associated with depression in Box 7.3 (p. 283). Knowledge of the differences associated with specific diagnoses can aid CYCPs in identifying relevant pain-based behaviours. This is particularly important considering that many CYC workers in North America practise in mental health settings and psychiatric centres (Mattingly, Stuart, & VanderVen, 2002). CYCPs need to engage in knowledgeable, meaningful discussions with other professionals and concerned family members. Accountability is key. When required, CYCPs refer to outside resources for assistance; their well-informed documentation will help clinicians in their assessment. Conversely, professional judgments by clinicians can help CYCPs distinguish between, for example, situational depressed behaviours and the serious clinical depressive episodes that in some cases can lead to suicidal behaviours (McGeady, 1999).

Assess which of the psychological paradigms you think fit well within a CYC perspective. As we outlined in Chapter 1, paradigms, or conceptual models, are used in the emotional/behavioural disorders or abnormal psychology literature to explain the development of certain behavioural difficulties seen in children and youth. Since these explanations are based on various theories or theoretical orientations, the paradigms of a particular field depend on that discipline's primary theoretical framework. As we've seen, the primary CYC theoretical and practice approach is referred to as the *ecological* or *relational model*.

While this approach might consider various aspects of all the psychological paradigms, some are better suited to the CYC perspective in explaining mood difficulties. For example, the cognitive paradigm, which emphasizes the role of perception and learned helplessness in the development of depression, is consistent with a CYC understanding of the impact of childhood experiences on thought patterns and behaviours. The ecological model (see Chapter 1), which considers patterns of relationships and the interaction between young people and other individuals in their ecosystem, is also a good fit, as it helps CYCPs see depressive symptoms as resulting from problematic interactions rather than residing in the young people themselves. An ecological model also looks for strengths in interactions and in the environment.

Since there is no one single model that can explain what causes depression in young people in any field of practice, we suggest using a CYC perspective to examine the interaction of the many variables or risk factors, including the youth's genetic makeup, brain functioning, and environment. An ecological view can incorporate most, if not all, aspects of the psychological paradigms. For example, we know that if a youth's parent has depression, there is a 25 percent likelihood that the youth will develop depression in his or her lifetime, and that if both parents have been diagnosed, the risk increases to 75 percent (Boesky, 2002). CYCPs need to also understand the role of the brain neurotransmitters in depression, whereby an imbalance in serotonin results in impairment in sleep, aggression, and motor activity. As well, we know that family difficulties or dysfunction appear to be related to child and adolescent depression: although dysfunctional families don't cause adolescent depression, high parental conflict, overcontrolling parents, and emotionally distant parents are all implicated. Perhaps our best understanding of depression will be achieved by considering biological, psychological, and environmental variables associated with depressive symptoms, as presented in Figure 7.2.

Many CYCPs also employ aspects of the behavioural model in their work by using consequences in responding to related behaviours. An understanding of the CBT model is important, as it incorporates both the cognitive model and the behavioural model. Another approach that fits well with a CYC perspective is Crittenden's (2004) dynamic-maturational model (DMM), which explores the role of attachment in the development of depressive symptoms. In this view, depression is seen as a coping mechanism or strategy that is developed over time as a response to dangers in the environment: a survival strategy, if you will.

Regardless if which conceptual model CYCPs use to explain the development of depressive symptoms, they always operate from a strength-based perspective. There are, of course, major differences in perspective between the traditional medical model of treatment for children with emotional and behavioural issues and the more recent

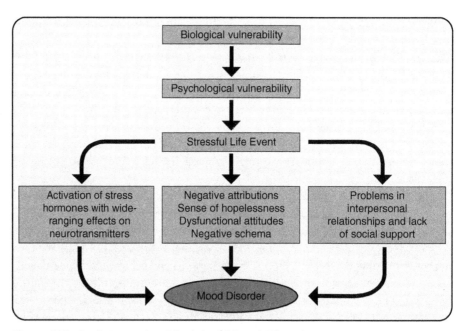

Figure 7.2 An Integrative Model of Mood Disorders

Mood disturbances are likely best explained by considering biological, psychological, and environmental factors.

Source: Adapted from Abnormal Psychology: An Integrative Approach by David H. Barlow, Vincent Mark Durand. Copyright © by Cengage Learning. Used by permission of Cengage Learning via CCC.

strength-based, relational, and brain-based corrective approaches. This was apparent when the widespread prescribing of psychoactive drugs became a substitute for interpersonal therapeutic interventions. Medications and therapeutic relationships both impact the brain, but in very different ways. Whereas medications affect the brain in ways that facilitate the short-term management of behaviour, lasting and positive changes develop as a result of repetitive, corrective interpersonal relationships that serve to rewire the brain. Moreover, as Foltz (2006) argues, there is evidence that commonly used psychotropic drugs interfere with oxytocin or vasopressin, the human trust and bonding hormones. Thus, psychotropic drugs *may actually impair* the development of healing interpersonal relationships and directly impede the forming of a therapeutic alliance.

What CYCPs intend to do to assist youth in changing troublesome behaviour (the intervention) needs to be based on their theory about what caused the behaviour in the first place. As we described in Chapter 1, a CYC approach often combines aspects of all the psychological models, depending upon the practitioner's lens, her employing agency's culture or function, the young person's life space, and the major system in which the CYC works—whether it's mental health, community-based services, justice, education, family services, or managed care.

WHERE DO YOU STAND?

Think about both the psychological perspective and the CYC perspective summarized above. Where do you stand? Most psychologists, clinicians, and CYCPs agree that a combination of biological, psychodynamic, and cognitive variables interact with one another to both produce and maintain the symptoms of depression (Stark et al., 1999). Specifically, genetics and early learning experiences may predispose an individual to developing negative core beliefs, which, together with stressful, activating events like trauma, results in depressed emotions and related behaviours. What do you think? Try the *Take Action!* exercise and apply your knowledge of psychological explanations for mood disorders to Stacey's case. What is your position on these views?

Take Action! Exercise: *Stacey's Case*

Stacey, a 12-year-old Korean girl who lives in a western Canadian suburb, has recently been struggling in school. Over the past six weeks her behaviour has been very different from usual: she's been exhibiting severe withdrawal, her grades are dropping, she's sleeping in class, and she won't talk to the teacher. A referral was made to the school psychologist, who diagnosed Stacey with Persistent Depressive Disorder (Dysthymia) and recommended a CYC in-class support worker for her. Stacey's mother is a busy interior designer with a history of depression herself, and her father is absent on business during most of every week. Stacey has been teased daily by the other girls at school because of her acne and her weight. One morning she was found huddled on the bathroom floor in the fetal position, sobbing uncontrollably. She told the CYCP, who'd been looking for her, that her cat had been hit by a car that morning, and that she couldn't go on anymore: the teasing was unbearable, she felt as if her family wasn't there for her, and she was contemplating suicide.

Explain how Stacey's diagnosis might be explained from each of the following paradigms: biological, psychodynamic, cognitive, and ecological. For each paradigm, what additional information about Stacey's history would you like to learn more about?

Larry tried several times to refuse taking his medications, saying that "they weren't doing anything positive." Despite his protests, the staff working with Larry wouldn't make any changes without a physician's approval. However, Larry's access to his doctor was limited. In his words,

"It's not how I heal. It went against my entire, I mean, every part of my belief. When encountering a situation or a phase, or whatever it is in life, you know you fully experience it . . . you know that it is there for a reason. There are lessons in the process.

There's so many better ways, that you've got to stop thinking that it's going to take this one thing to do it.

You come here to life to learn lessons and to gain tools. You don't have tools when you're taking a pill. It

doesn't teach you anything to take a pill when you're taught to work through your problems . . . if it's through your culture, it's through your culture. If it's through a treatment form or a structure of healing, it's through that. But we've got to get the processes back. We've got to return the responsibility. I think so often the biggest problem in care—and why so many kids choose the streets compared to anything else—is you're in control."

Source: From Drugs In Our System: An Exploratory Study On The Chemical Management Of Canadian Systems Youth - Full Report by Y. Lembe and R. McLennan. Published by Youth in Care Canada, 2009.

HELPING CHILDREN AND ADOLESCENTS WITH MOOD DISTURBANCES

Psychological Approaches to Treatment

The psychological approach to treating mood disturbances incorporates various strategies, with those effective in reducing depressive symptoms often differing from those used to alleviate symptoms of mania. Let's review the approaches to treatment that have received the most attention in psychological research and practice.

Biological Paradigm   The use of antidepressant medication for treatment of child and adolescent depressive disorders is controversial for many reasons. In particular, the effectiveness and safety of such medications used with younger populations is uncertain (Vitiello & Swedo, 2004). Despite these concerns, antidepressants, including TCAs and SSRIs, have been widely used with children and youth. Since TCAs aren't as effective and have been associated with severe side effects, SSRIs are more likely to be used today in the treatment of children and adolescents (Birmaher & Brent, 2003). However, although evidence supports the effectiveness of such medications in adult MDD, there is limited research clearly supporting their effectiveness in treating children and youth (McClellan & Werry, 2003). Overall, controlled research shows mixed results for antidepressants' effectiveness in treating young people's depressive symptoms, with some studies demonstrating only partial or no improvement in response to medical treatment. Consequently, there is a lack of clear guidelines for the administration with children and youth. See Table 7.3 for an overview of common antidepressants, outcomes, and side effects.

Additional concerns have been raised about the use of antidepressants with children and adolescents. First, the effects of medication on the developing brain are unknown. In

Table 7.3 Common Antidepressants

Drug	Mechanism of Action	Intended Outcomes for Children/Adolescents	Side Effects
Tricyclics (TCAs)	Increase levels of action of various neurotransmitters (serotonin, norepinephrine)	Likely ineffective or harmful	Take a while to work, higher toxicity (overdose concerns), heart problems, sedation, dry mouth, weight gain, dietary restrictions (interacts with wine, cheese, caffeine, etc., and other drugs)
Monoamine Oxidase Inhibitors (MAOIs)	Block enzyme that breaks down neurotransmitters, increasing their level of activity	Unknown effectiveness	Not tolerated as well (strong drug and food interactions, stimulant effects); thus, not used as frequently as other two classes
Selective Serotonin Reuptake Inhibitors (SSRIs) (*most common*)	Inhibit reuptake of serotonin	Improve remission rates, prevent relapse	Fewer side effects, greater efficacy overall, less lethal/toxic; excitation, sexual dysfunction, headache, nausea

addition, although SSRIs have fewer side effects than other antidepressants, they can still result in restlessness, headache, insomnia, decreased appetite, and increased aggression. In particular, alarm has been expressed regarding the possible side effects of suicidal thoughts and self-harm (Vitiello & Swedo, 2004). For example, in Canada and Great Britain (and later in the United States as well), government regulatory bodies for health matters issued a warning that antidepressants, including SSRIs, weren't recommended for use with children and youth (Health Canada and FDA Advisories for Antidepressants, 2013). This advisory was based on research indicating that tricyclic antidepressant medications did not improve depressive symptoms and frequently caused side effects, including suicide ideation. According to Waddell et al. (2004), "selective serotonergic reuptake inhibitor antidepressant medications demonstrated small improvements in depressive symptoms but were also associated with significant side effects including increased suicidal ideation" (p. 4). After conducting a comprehensive review of pediatric trials conducted between 1988 and 2006, Bridge et al. (2007) concluded that the benefits of antidepressant medications likely outweigh their risks to children and adolescents with MDD. Specifically, it was found that among nearly 2200 children treated with SSRI medications, no completed suicides occurred. However, approximately 4 percent of those taking SSRIs experienced suicidal thinking or behaviour, including actual suicide attempts, compared with 2 percent of those taking placebo or sugar pills. In light of such findings, continued apprehension about the use of antidepressants with youth is understandable. It also points to the need for close monitoring of any child or adolescent taking SSRI medication for a worsening of symptoms, suicidal thinking or behaviour, and unusual changes in behaviour (e.g., sleeplessness, agitation, social withdrawal), particularly during the first four weeks of treatment. Clearly, additional research investigating these concerns is warranted.

Although antidepressants aren't addictive and can be taken on an ongoing basis, they're normally prescribed for a four- to six-month period. Most individuals experience some reduction in depressive symptoms after two to four weeks, and full benefits after four months. As a result of the observed effectiveness of antidepressants in alleviating such symptoms, MDD is viewed by some as an "illness." As with other medical conditions, however, even though symptoms can be treated successfully through biological mechanisms, other approaches to treatment are also effective, including exercise, healthy diet, and cognitive or talk therapy to help the individual work through external causes of depressive symptoms. In fact, when individuals are treated through solely medical means, repeated episodes of depression are significantly more likely. It's important to recognize that medications don't change behaviours. However, together with other approaches to treatment that encourage individuals to explore and make changes in the relational and societal contexts in which the depression occurs, medication can optimize the likelihood of a depressed individual exploring these options. Where do you stand on the issue of medications and treatment for mood disorders?

Psychodynamic Paradigm Traditionally, psychodynamic approaches to treatment involved in-depth exploration of unconscious and early childhood memories, including perceptions of past relationships with significant others. This *psychodynamic psychotherapy* was typically directed at adults and generally involved many years of treatment. However, a more modern approach, *interpersonal therapy (IPT)*, focuses on the *interpersonal* aspects of MDD (rather than intrapsychic aspects of psychodynamic psychotherapy). This short-term approach to therapy is based on Coyne's (1976) interpersonal theory of MDD and emphasizes the relational aspects of the individual's experience. According to Coyne, those diagnosed with MDD exhibit negative interpersonal behaviour that results in others rejecting them. In an escalating cycle, those suffering from depressive symptoms desperately seek reassurance from others and begin to make an increasing number of requests for reassurance. This results in others negatively evaluating the depressed person and then avoiding and rejecting him or her. Consequently, the depressed person experiences worsening symptoms followed by further attempts to obtain reassurance, which results only in further rejection and avoidance by others.

IPT seeks to interrupt this cycle by focusing on *emotions* and exploring ways in which a person's *current relationships and social context* cause or maintain symptoms (rather than exploring the subconscious source of the symptoms). The goals of IPT include *symptom reduction* and *improved social adjustment*, resulting in more satisfying relationships. Mufson et al. (1999) evaluated the effectiveness of IPT for adolescents diagnosed with MDD (aged 12–18) and found that, when compared with a control group, those who received IPT reported significantly greater decreases in depressive symptoms and greater improvement in overall functioning and interpersonal problem-solving skills. More recent investigations have also shown that IPT is effective in treating MDD (Hollon, Thase, & Markowitz, 2002; Weissman, 2006) and might also have applications in treatment of bipolar disorders (Craighead et al., 2002; Frank, 2005).

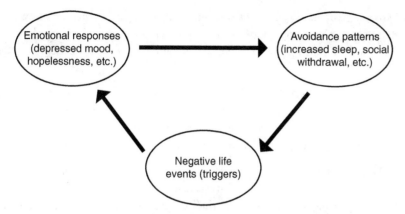

Figure 7.3 The Behavioural Activation Approach to Treating Depression

By reducing avoidance behaviour (that results in passivity, withdrawal), opportunities to experience environmental rewards increase as individuals are encouraged to engage in goal-oriented behaviours that are likely to be met with successful outcomes.

Source: Reprinted with permission from Rachel C Leonard, PhD, Rogers Memorial Hospital, adapted from content in Depression in Context: Strategies for Guided Action [Martell CR, Addis ME, Jacobson NS. (2001) Depression in Context: Strategies for Guided Action. New York: Norton.] and published by Medscape Drugs & Diseases (http://emedicine.medscape.com/), 2015, available at: http://emedicine.medscape.com/article/2094696-overview.

Behavioural Paradigm Given that the behavioural explanation for mood symptoms are explained in relation to low levels of positive, rewarding experiences, it's not surprising that the aim of behavioural approaches to treatment is to increase levels of such events in daily life. **Behavioural activation (BA)** (Martell, Addis, & Jacobson, 2001) seeks to change behaviours in such a way that one experiences positively reinforcing events and activities. By reducing avoidance behaviour (which results in passivity, withdrawal), opportunities to experience environmental rewards increase as individuals are encouraged to engage in goal-oriented behaviours that are likely to be met with successful outcomes. These rewarding experiences reduce feelings of passivity and depression. Figure 7.3 illustrates this model.

Although some support for BA's effectiveness has been observed (Jacobson & Gortner, 2000; Turner, Ward, & Turner, 1979), approaches to treatment using related techniques also often include attempts to alter cognitions. We now turn to a discussion of approaches to treatment for mood disturbances from a cognitive approach.

Cognitive Paradigm The goals of cognitive therapy include increasing awareness of personal cognitive biases and how these negative thoughts contribute to emotional reactions, as well as challenging dysfunctional cognitive beliefs. As discussed in Chapter 1, individuals might be asked to keep a "thought record" in order to more readily identify the relationship between specific situations, automatic thoughts, and resulting emotions. The therapist then encourages the individual to identify alternative interpretations for such situations, thereby challenging his or her negative beliefs and assumptions.

We've seen that since these cognitive approaches usually include behavioural exercises, they're often referred to as *cognitive behavioural therapy* (CBT). An abundance of research documents the effectiveness of CBT with both depressive disorders (Hollon, Stewart, & Strunk, 2006; Hollon, Thase, & Markowitz, 2002) and more recently, with

Bipolar Disorder (Lam et al., 2003). Despite generally favourable outcomes, however, the effectiveness of cognitive approaches in assisting depressed individuals with comorbid conditions as well as non-European-American adolescents requires further investigation (Rohde, 2005).

Sociocultural Paradigm Sociocultural approaches to the treatment of mood disturbances focus on addressing the social and cultural factors that are associated with symptoms of mood disturbances. In particular, programs for treatment developed from this paradigm emphasize enhancing coping and communication skills.

Stressful Life Events. In order to decrease the impact of stressful life events, several prevention programs that teach youth to use successful coping strategies in managing life events have been developed. For example, the Resourceful Adolescent program (Shochet et al., 2001) teaches youth relaxation strategies together with cognitive restructuring and problem solving. Other programs help youth deal with specific stressors, including loss and grief (Sandler et al., 1992), parental divorce (Wolchik et al., 1993), and parental substance abuse (Roosa et al., 1989).

Family Influences. In order to address the role of dysfunctional family factors in youth mood disturbances, programs combining several approaches have been developed to facilitate communication skills in children, adolescents, and their family members. Some research supports the effectiveness of such strategies in reducing mood symptoms. For example, the Resourceful Adolescent program combined CBT and IPT (which focuses on enhancing family harmony and building/accessing support networks) and found that depressive symptoms were lowered for those receiving the program compared with others not receiving the intervention (Shochet et al., 2001). Depressive symptoms were also found to be reduced in the Penn Prevention Program (Jaycox et al., 1994; Reivich, 1996), which focuses on developing problem-solving and decision-making skills and strategies for coping with family conflict (this program is discussed further in the CYC section that follows). Although these studies support the effectiveness of addressing youth challenges in coping with family stressors, such approaches incorporate multiple strategies derived from many paradigms. As Cottrell (2003) notes, rather than a single strategy, approaches to treating mood disturbances typically incorporate multiple strategies, making it difficult to compare the efficacy of one strategy with another's.

CYC Approaches for Youth Struggling with Mood Disturbances

In assessing young people's mood disturbances, CYCPs must observe their behaviour through a relational approach and in the context of their ecology—their relationships with family, significant others, peers, school, and community. In this way we explore the potential causes of the difficulty, identifying the needs underlying the observed behaviour while honouring young people's strengths and their capacity for resiliency.

Strength-Based Relational CYC Practice CYCPs must carefully consider what a young person says about his or her experience of mood difficulties, and then respond after considering what's been expressed and what they know about the youth's strengths. It's important that when CYCPs observe for behavioural difficulties they take into account the differences in symptoms at each age and stage of development, and assess the level of impact of these depressive symptoms on day-to-day functioning. And as we've seen, CYCPs also need to know when to refer youth for a clinical assessment and ongoing therapy.

In both assessment and intervention processes, cultural and gender differences must be considered. For example, in Larry's case, his depressive symptoms were linked to his cultural context—his placement in a mainstream culture facility and away from his First Nations home community, where spirituality, ceremony, and traditional healing and medicines were part of the healing approach. Larry's symptoms were exacerbated, or perhaps even partly caused by, the trauma of this separation from community. CYCPs must respect the fact that culture and often spirituality are a large part of who young people are; they must ensure that youth are offered opportunities to participate in their traditional cultural healing approaches. Also observe for gender differences in the expression of depressive symptoms: as we mentioned previously, girls and young women, as well as bisexual, gay, transgendered, and two-spirited youth, may demonstrate more traditional "female" or "male" expressions of depression. Some youth may exhibit tearfulness and others may behave in aggressive ways.

It's been well established that depression is far more widely diagnosed in Western society than elsewhere in the world. Is this owing to an actual higher prevalence, or is depression viewed differently in other cultures? In Western society, we associate depression with a lowered mood accompanied by distinct physical symptoms. However, in Asian cultures, for example, depression is rarely reported, and yet the physical symptoms we associate with depression are still common. That there's an unwillingness to report psychological distress in Asian cultures may be due to the stigma associated with illnesses of the mind and the discrimination families may face as a result ("Culture and depression," 2008). Young people in other cultures might express only somatic complaints; for example, that they're having headaches or feeling "nervous" (Boesky, 2002). Moreover, stress and depression are known to be closely correlated, and in most Aboriginal, Asian, and Hispanic cultures, extended families provide the social support that can alleviate stress-related problems ("Culture and depression," 2008).

Jose Gil/Shutterstock

The Hopi have no word for depression. Do you think this means that there's no depression in their culture?

Best Practice Considerations. Best practice dictates that CYCPs need to be accountable for the interventions they choose and be able to demonstrate whether they're effective; thus, whenever possible, these interventions need to be evidence based (although some writers in the CYC field dispute this tenet). The two main types of empirically supported interventions for young people with depressive symptoms are talk therapy (counselling, psychotherapy) and pharmacotherapy (use of psychotropic medications). The two kinds of psychotherapy known to be most effective for young people are cognitive behavioural therapy (CBT) and interpersonal therapy (IPT). We've seen that CBT concentrates on changing the negative attributional biases or negative schemas associated with depression by challenging the associated negative thinking and cognitive distortions. IPT focuses on changing young people's self-concept and improving their relationships with peers and family. The more unstructured and general day-to-day support and caring that CYCPs offer, while they may not be evidence based per se, are of course still absolutely key to healing.

Assessment

When CYCPs assess young people for mood disorders, in addition to changes in behaviours, they may note serious changes in overall attitude. It's often the change in overall presentation that is most noticeable; such a change can be sudden and dramatic, but may also be subtle and gradual. A change in eating habits and sleeping too much or too little are usually quite apparent to others. There may be feelings of worthlessness and inadequacy expressed; low self-esteem and a pervasive "What's the use in trying?" attitude may be observed. Young people may be preoccupied with inner thoughts and stresses, self-critical (blaming themselves for any bad outcomes), and more self-conscious. They may also exhibit slowed thought, distorted reasoning, pessimism about the future, and difficulty in concentrating, remembering, and making decisions. Physical changes to watch for besides disruptions in eating and sleeping include somatic complaints like headaches, stomachaches, nausea, and other aches and pains. An awareness that these symptoms are often accompanied by behaviours usually associated with Disruptive Behaviour Disorders such as ADHD or CD, by substance-related disorders, and/or by internalizing behaviours such as anxiety, eating disorders, and self-harm can further help CYCPs in accurately identifying and responding to such behavioural concerns.

It's important, of course, to assess these observed behaviours in the context of normal sadness as well as age and stage of development. As well, it's important to consider attachment issues, as this will help in designing the intervention. We've seen that despair, hopelessness, withdrawal, and sadness may well be attachment coping strategies developed in response to trauma and neglect (Crittenden, 2006), and so CYCPs might ask themselves how the young person's behavioural, cognitive, and emotional responses may be serving a specific function.

Knowledge of the areas of functioning by age and stage affected by depression is crucial (refer to Table 7.4 for a comprehensive checklist). Exaggerated, persistent feelings of sadness are often observed; irritability, guilt, and shame are common. The young person may display restlessness and agitation, and there may be reduced activity, slowed speech, excessive crying, decreased social contact, verbal sarcasm, screaming and destructive behaviour, and increased substance use. The child or adolescent may be much more argumentative than usual. While many young people act out in order to avoid feelings of depression, such acting out is often overlooked as a sign of depression. The young person's oppositional or antisocial actions may very well warrant an in-the-moment response, but it's important to recognize that depression is often the catalyst behind such externalizing behaviour—their "despair has turned into rage" (Lavin & Park, 1999, p. 18).

CYCPs can ask clear, direct questions to explore with young people how they're feeling. The more precise the questions, the more information can be obtained. Here are some examples: How many hours did you sleep last night? The night before? Is this the same or different from a few weeks ago? Do you usually wake in the night? How often? How hard is it to fall back asleep? How is your appetite? Better or worse than before? How is your concentration? Any differences? How much time do you spend alone? How much time do you spend crying? Are you sadder than usual? Are you grumpy with friends and family? (Straus, 2007, pp. 152–153).

Assessment and Referral Resources. CYCPs should be familiar with the clinical assessment tools used by psychologists and other clinicians to assess depression; these include the Beck Depression Inventory, the Hamilton Depression Rating Scale, and the Children's Depression Inventory. We've seen that although CYCPs don't use paper-and-pencil assessment measures, they do need to be familiar with them, as they can help guide assessments.

An assessment by a collateral mental health service provider will be required if CYCPs have observed the symptoms of depression as described in the DSM-5. CYCPs need to assess suicide risk, and in most jurisdictions, a mental health status check will be warranted to provide safety and reduce risk. (Suicide risk and assessment is discussed in Appendix 1.) It's also important to assess, in a nonjudgmental way, how a young person may be using illicit or harmful substances and whether this might indicate a pattern of self-medicating for depression or anxiety; be aware, too, of any potential harmful side effects from combining alcohol or non-prescription substances with prescribed psychotropic medications.

Indicators to Recognize   Although similar DSM-5 criteria for mood disorders may be used with adults and youth, some features are more common in children and adolescents than in adults. As well, depressive symptoms exhibited in children can be quite different from those seen in adolescents: "Children commonly display irritable mood rather than depressed mood, somatic complaints and social withdrawal; depressed adolescents typically display psychomotor retardation and hypersomnia" (McWhirter et al., 2013, p. 107).

The distinction between mood disturbances and normal emotions is key. We've seen that expressions of extreme sadness, grief, and loss are expected responses to overwhelming life circumstances and may be common among the young people CYCPs work with. So when watching for the potential signs and symptoms of mood disturbances, CYCPs should instead focus on whether the sadness is overwhelming, persistent over time, significantly affecting the youth's ability to function on a day-to-day basis, and interfering with his or her ability to experience success or joy in daily living. In addition, such signs should represent an observable or noticeable change in the pattern of the youth's usual behaviour. For example, a "loss of interest or pleasure in daily activities consistently for at least a two-week period" must represent a *change in the pattern* of the young person's usual mood. If CYCPs are uncertain about the nature of the concerning behaviours, a referral to a physician or other clinician for assessment is always warranted. And, of course, if a youth is expressing suicidal ideation, the CYCP must use appropriate suicide intervention techniques. See Table 7.4 for a summary of behavioural indicators of depression for various age ranges.

Table 7.4 Behavioural Indicators Checklist: Depression

✓ Elementary School (6–8 yrs.)	✓ Middle School (9–12 yrs.)	✓ Adolescence (13–18 yrs.)
Lethargy	Lethargy	Somatic complaints
Sleep problems	Irritability	Social withdrawal
Irritability	Expressions of hopelessness, self-deprecation	Hopelessness
Prolonged unhappiness		Irritability
Poor school performance	Low self-esteem	Expressions of pessimism, worthlessness, apathy
Accident-proneness	Depressed mood	
Phobias	Sad expression	Suicide attempts
Separation anxiety	Aggression	Substance abuse
Attention-seeking behaviours	Guilt	Eating disorders
Decreased socialization	Poor school performance	Antisocial behaviour
Somatic complaints	Phobias	Restlessness
Enuresis	Separation anxiety	Temper tantrums
Psychomotor agitation	Suicidal ideation	Running away
	Hallucinations	Anhedonia
	Self-destructive behaviours	Hypersomnia
	Somatic complaints	Weight change (loss or gain)
	Enuresis	

Source: From Handbook of Child Psychopathology by T. H. Ollendick and M. Hersen. Copyright © 1997 by Springer. Used by permission of Springer.

Intervention

Thom Garfat (1998) defines intervention as "an intentional caring action, taken into one of the daily life systems of which the youth is a part, which facilitates a change in that system such that a context is created for the youth to have a different experiencing of herself and/or the meaning that she gives to her experiencing" (p. 168).

It's painful to be with young people who are experiencing profound sadness and depression. We're often inclined to distract them, and to avoid any activities or conversations that might exacerbate their mood difficulties. However, frank and direct conversations and a supportive, caring relationship are crucial. Prescribing one specific model for implementing interventions for every young person experiencing a mood disturbance is antithetical to a CYC approach. Regardless of which paradigm informs your intervention, it should be designed to meet the unique needs of young people in the context of their life space and considering their special circumstances. We recognize young people's past context and their historical risk factors as well as recognizing their strengths and their capacity for resilience. We must also continually assess and evaluate the risk for suicide and self-harm. (Again, refer to Appendix 1 for a specific discussion of suicide.)

Behavioural and Cognitive-Behavioural Techniques for CYCPs   We've seen that CBT is the best behavioural intervention technique for helping children and youth who are experiencing a depressive episode (Stuart, 2009a). CYCPs are all too familiar with the cycle of despair that vulnerable young people can engage in, whereby bad thoughts (distorted thinking, negative cognitions) can lead to depressed mood and bad feelings (Jongsma, Peterson, & McInnis, 1999).

> Depression carries with it a negative cognitive style: depressed individuals see themselves and the world more negatively than nondepressed individuals do. This negative style is sometimes referred to as *depressive realism* and often remains after the episode has remitted. (Oyserman, 2004, p. 265)

Examples of cognitive distortions include *black-and-white thinking*: viewing situations, people, or oneself as entirely good or bad, with nothing in between; *exaggerating*: self-critical or other critical statements using "never" or "always"; *filtering*: ignoring the positive and focusing on the negative; *discounting*: rejecting positive experiences as unimportant; *judging*: being critical of oneself or others; using statements such as "should have," "ought to"; *mind reading*: making negative assumptions about people's motivations; *forecasting*: predicting that events will turn out badly; *self-blame*: holding oneself accountable when event was not entirely in one's control; and *labelling*: calling oneself or others a name when unhappy with a behaviour (Jongsma, Peterson, & McInnis, 1999). The literature suggests that children who've been maltreated develop pervasive *negative plot lines* or a *negative internal working model* whereby they perceive the world to be a dangerous place and adults in general to be unsafe. As a result of repeated negative attachment cycles, they've developed such perceptions as "I'm unsafe," "I'm unlovable," "the world is unsafe," and "adults are dangerous and not to be trusted" (Delaney, 1998).

In challenging cognitive distortions, providing alternative "plot lines" (i.e., teaching positive self-talk techniques and providing opportunities for success) is an effective strategy. Using a CBT approach, youth are taught to "stand back, talk to themselves to guide their thoughts and/or actions, and only then act out their thoughts"; in short, to *stop, look, listen* (self-talk), *think* (think aloud), and then *act* or *do* (Fox, personal communication, 2003).

CYCPs can also use evidence-based training techniques that focus on social, problem-solving, and coping skills (Stuart & Sanders, 2008). The key depression deficits unique to the individual (Maag, 1993) are first identified, and then the appropriate intervention is applied. For example, does the youth lack the requisite social skills to manage in a social context? If so, CYCPs would focus on teaching social skills. Another important area is that of self-control deficits: Does the youth engage in selectively monitoring negative events while excluding positive events? Does she habitually make negative attributions for her behaviour (Maag, 1993)? Does she engage in negative self-talk (the negative plot)? In all these instances, CYCPs can teach self-monitoring techniques and challenge negative distortions. Refer to CYC resources (e.g., www.cyc-net.org; the suggested readings list at the end of this chapter) for more ideas about incorporating CBT techniques into your CYC practice with youth who are depressed.

Keep in mind, however, that correcting cognitive distortions is not an easy task. Even though establishing a relationship with youth who distrust adults is the foundation of CYC practice (Brendtro et al., 2002), CBT may be difficult to use with some of the young people CYCPs work with (Lavin & Park, 1999). Challenging the negative internal working model through which maltreated children interpret events can be very difficult, given that these children's experience has verified as accurate their perceptions of the world (that adults are not to be trusted, that bad things happen often). CBT may also be less effective when the parent is depressed as well (often seen in cases of intergenerational trauma) (Kendall & Comer, 2010).

Nonetheless, challenging cognitive distortions and thereby breaking the cycle of despair is the main focus when working with youth who are depressed, and has a very good chance of being successful. From a CYC perspective, CBT will be much more effectively accomplished in the context of a trusting, positive relationship. In addition, we've seen that, notwithstanding our concerns about the use of SSRI medications with children and youth, recent research has demonstrated that CBT combined with SSRI medication therapies may hold the most promise as the overall preferred treatment approach (Kendall & Comer, 2010).

The Role of Medication   Fluoxetine (Prozac) is the only antidepressant specifically approved by Health Canada for the treatment of depression in children aged eight and older. Although antidepressant medication therapy in combination with CBT is the first choice as a treatment option for adolescent depression, such medication does carry serious risks, especially with younger children. These include increased suicidal thoughts and an increased risk of mania in some youth. And since children and adolescents who first experience a Major Depressive Episode may, over time, be predisposed to Bipolar Disorder, reviewing any family history of Bipolar Disorder and being mindful of this possibility is a good idea when treating a child or adolescent experiencing a Major Depressive Episode.

CYCPs must be aware of warnings and precautions associated with medications prescribed for mood disorders.

As outlined in Chapter 1, CYCPs must carefully examine a number of issues when administering psychotropic medications to youth in general—and particularly when considering prescription medications for young people diagnosed with mood disorders. CYCPs must be up to date with all warnings and precautions issued in their jurisdictions; follow Gerry Fewster's guidelines (summarized in Chapter 1) when working with youth who've been prescribed antidepressants (notwithstanding the controversy, young people are still prescribed these medications to treat depression); become informed by conducting your own research; consider alternative approaches, including natural remedies, diet, and exercise; and, where appropriate, help young people make decisions about these medications. Let the statistics we presented earlier regarding psychotropic drugs and young people in the system guide you—in this instance, CYCPs' role as advocate may be critical.

Psychoeducation and Individual Counselling   Psychoeducation involves teaching young people about their depression. Through psychoeducation, CYCPs can help youth learn about the role of genetics and changes in brain structure; the role of stress; appropriate treatment options; and how to recognize signs of relapse so that they can get the necessary treatment before the depression worsens or occurs again. Support groups for young people and families dealing with mental health difficulties are becoming more widely available; in these groups, young people share their frustrations and successes, their referrals to qualified specialists and community resources, and their information about what works best when trying to recover.

We've seen that interpersonal therapy for adolescents (IPTA) is an effective treatment approach for young people struggling with depression. Whereas CBT attempts to challenge the automatic negative thinking that contributes to depression, IPTA aims to improve young people's self-concept as well as their relationships with peers and family. It focuses attention on some of the common developmental issues of adolescence that may be triggering depression: loss and separation, relationships with parents, peer pressure, and intimate relationships. The premise of the IPTA approach is that the effects of depression are greatest in young people's social relationships. As their relationships diminish, life in general becomes more and more difficult and overwhelming.

It has long been recognized that low self-esteem is associated with depression. The Compassionate Mind Training approach challenges low self-esteem by teaching young people a different style of coping with their internal relationship with themselves. In group, young people role-play how they'd support a good friend who's undergoing the sort of crisis they're currently experiencing, and then apply this to themselves. The participants work together, encouraging each other to develop the new coping style and apply it to behavioural change (Clarke, 2009).

Family Support Interventions   In contrast to past mental health approaches that treated young people apart from their family and community, the CYC approach is grounded in relational practice and risk and resilience concepts; the focus of intervention is social relationships and other aspects of the environments in which young people function (Steele & Roberts, 2005).

In CYC family-focused practice, young people are served within the context of their family and other caregiving environments. Services are designed according to family needs, goals, and preferences, and include attention to the family's cultural and ethnic values. This is a capacity-building model in which families are supported in securing the resources and skills that will allow them to create nurturing environments, facilitate social competence, and ameliorate challenging behaviours and emotional problems; the professional's role thus shifts from that of expert to that of collaborator and facilitator (Steele & Roberts, 2005, p. 26). And since parental criticism often reflects the habits of the caregiver and can contribute to the youth's pessimism (McWhirter et al., 2007), parents can be taught optimism as well. Learned helplessness, as the name suggests, is learned in families.

CYCPs can engage with families using psychoeducation, which can significantly reduce distress, confusion, and anxieties within the family and can help youth recover. Family psychoeducation has been shown to have positive effects on family interactions, and these effects are thought to mediate the clinical course of MDD in youth. Research has also demonstrated that an adjunct multi-family psychoeducation group for families of children with mood disorders improves family relations by increasing knowledge, child-perceived support from the parents, and treatment adherence. Integrating family psychoeducation with other psychosocial interventions such as social skills training and other evidence-based cognitive-behavioural strategies will further improve outcomes for youth and families affected by mood disorders ("The evidence: Family psychoeducation," 2009).

Refer to Box 7.5 for a summary of guidelines for CYC interventions that might be considered in your practice.

Prevention: Advocacy, Community, and School-Based Strategies

Vulnerable children and youth who are struggling with depression usually also struggle with related risk factors or negative thinking patterns, including low self-esteem, negative self-concepts, and lack of self-efficacy. Youth at risk for developing depression generally have poor coping skills, an external locus of control, and a general pessimism about life and events.

One of the earliest and most successful prevention approaches was developed by Seligman and his associates: known as the Penn Prevention Program (PPP), it aims to prevent future depressive symptoms from developing in children who are at risk. Although it's based in cognitive therapy, it's used as a universal prevention/intervention program in schools and other organizations. The program has two main components: cognitive (which encourages children to develop a flexible thinking style and learn to evaluate the accuracy of their beliefs) and social problem solving (which teaches children skills such as goal setting, perspective taking, and decision making). PPP also provides direct training in coping with family conflict and other stressors, and addresses the lowered academic

---

Box 7.5

Techniques for CYC Intervention

Increase enjoyable activities (play a game, cook or bake together).

Increase physical activities (e.g., take a walk, jog, play catch, swim, get involved in a sport).

Encourage consistent sleep habits (e.g., by developing a before-sleep ritual such as reading, bathing, relaxation).

Encourage consistent and healthy eating (plan together, consider likes/dislikes and healthy options, schedule regular mealtimes).

Assist with daily problem solving (help define the problem, generate alternatives, take action, and follow up).

Assist with goal setting (help discover short-term and long-term goals, check for appropriateness, develop action plans).

Facilitate concentration (develop daily checklists and schedules, ensure appropriateness of expectations).

Involve all social supports wherever possible and appropriate (family, friends, peers, counsellors, CYCPs).

Explore cultural beliefs and traditional-healing alternative persons and activities.

Teach and use relaxation and MBSR techniques together.

Teach CBT to challenge cognitive distortions.

Help young people make well-informed choices about taking SSRIs if these are prescribed.

Explore alternative interventions.

Use interpersonal therapy.

Develop and assist with homework treatment strategies.

Ensure trust and sharing of feelings every day.

Create opportunities for one-to-one support and attention.

achievement, poor peer relations, lowered self-esteem, and behavioural problems that may result from pessimistic thinking.

Children are taught coping strategies to counteract cognitive distortions and deficiencies, specifically their chosen explanatory style. The cognitive component of the program teaches children how to interpret problem situations in more adaptive ways by identifying negative beliefs, evaluating the evidence for those beliefs, and generating alternatives. The problem-solving component focuses on children's actions for solving their problems by teaching social problem solving and adaptive coping. Children are encouraged to think about their goals before acting, generate solutions, and weigh the pros and cons of these solutions. They're also taught skills for managing parental conflict and behavioural techniques to enhance assertiveness, negotiation, and relaxation (Gillham et al., 1995).

Identifying automatic negative thoughts, looking for evidence, generating alternative explanations, and not catastrophizing are all important techniques to teach young people optimistic thinking and lessen their overall risk for pessimism and consequent depression (McWhirter et al., 2007). These skills can be taught in schools: CYCPs and teachers can initiate class discussions to help students learn to identify their thoughts in response to common negative experiences; the class can then examine sample thoughts as a group and generate alternative explanations (McWhirter et al., 2007, p. 266). CYCPs can function as advocates by helping school-based and other programs reduce the stigma of depression and by helping young people access resources when needed.

Alternative Healing   Exercise and social support are also necessary elements of any good intervention plan to address youth depression. While these types of interventions alone may fail to address more serious symptoms, they remain important components throughout the course of treatment. In fact, research is demonstrating that exercise combined with mindfulness-based stress reduction techniques (MBSR) has had as much success in managing depression as medication. MBSR, a psychoeducational training program that applies the principles of mindfulness to daily life, is described by Kabat-Zinn (2003) as the awareness that emerges through paying attention—on purpose, in the present moment, and nonjudgmentally—to the unfolding of experience. Specifically, mindfulness involves giving close attention to stimulus inputs that enter awareness without engaging in judgmental thoughts about them. "Studies to date have shown mindfulness-based practices seem to reduce stress, anxiety and emotional reactivity among youth, and that mindfulness-based stress reduction practices improve adjustment among chronically stressed adolescents" ("University child/adolescent counselor," 2013, p. 1). As direct reports from children and youth suggest, MBSR facilitates increased understanding of one's emotional experiences, enhances one's feelings of control over emotions and subsequent behaviour, and can be used to decrease anxiety that is interfering with one's social and academic performance (Saltzman, 2015).

Relational CYC Practice   In interventions with young people who may be depressed, relational CYC practice should involve thinking outside the box—including humour and non-mainstream ways of healing. Whenever possible, include the young person in all intervention planning. Consider simple solutions for mood difficulties, including the therapeutic use of animals, increased play, exercise and recreation activities, and a change in diet. Challenge cognitive distortions in humorous ways, increase social support, create opportunities for success, use the young person's strengths, and have fun. Refer to Box 7.6 for a summary of useful communication strategies.

Box 7.6

CYC Communication Strategies

Ask open-ended questions to encourage sharing of feelings and thoughts (e.g., "How have you been feeling since . . .?").

Ask closed-ended questions when you require specific information (e.g., "What did you have for dinner today?").

Ask precise questions about every possible symptom.

Offer support (e.g., "How can I best help you right now?").

Offer honest communication (e.g., "I don't know exactly how you feel, but I do care about how you're feeling").

Don't minimize distress, and always validate feelings (avoid using familiar sayings such as "Everyone goes through this," "Try to see the silver lining here," "Things will be better tomorrow").

Be a positive role model (e.g., maintain a positive outlook, sleep and eat well yourself).

Gently challenge maladaptive beliefs and cognitive distortions.

Model, practise, and teach social skills and problem-solving techniques.

Maintain and model a positive outlook.

Use humour where appropriate: watch a comedy show or a funny movie with the young person.

WHERE DO YOU STAND?

Since mood disturbances are one of the general categories of mental health diagnoses CYCPs are likely to encounter, familiarity with their explanations and intervention approaches will figure prominently in their practice. CYCPs' effectiveness in this area will also depend on awareness of their own perspectives on these disturbances. Revisit the cases of Larry and Stacey one final time in the *Viewpoint Challenge* exercise to help you evaluate your understanding of both CYC and psychological interventions. Where do you stand with respect to treatment approaches to mood disturbances?

Larry's and Stacey's Cases: *Viewpoint Challenge Exercise*

Reread the excerpts of Larry's story that were presented throughout this chapter. Do you think he views mood disorders (causes and treatments) from a psychological perspective or more from a CYC perspective? Explain your answer, making reference to specific statements in his story and relevant concepts highlighted in the text. How does your view of mood disorders compare with Larry's? What similarities and differences can you identify with respect to intervention issues in the cases of Larry and Stacey? Compare and contrast the CYC and psychological approaches in relation to Stacey's case.

CHAPTER SUMMARY

- *Mood disturbance* is a general, non-diagnostic term that refers to some type of mood symptoms (e.g., excessive unhappiness).

- The DSM-5 considers mood disturbances under the general categories of Depressive Disorders (associated with depressive episodes) and Bipolar and Related Disorders (associated with depressive and manic episodes).

- CYCPs should be aware that a young person's struggle with depressive disorders may be overlooked because he or she is *acting in*.

- Psychological explanations for mood disturbances include a consideration of levels of neurotransmitters, separation or loss, and dysfunctional schemas and beliefs.

- The ways in which pain-based behaviours are expressed according to young people's age and stage of development, as described in the psychological approach, are critical for CYCPs to consider in their observations, assessment, and intervention planning.

- Psychological approaches to treatment include antidepressants, traditional psychodynamic psychotherapy, interpersonal therapy (IPT), and cognitive behavioural therapy (CBT).

- CYC planned interventions for youth with mood difficulties are based on the unique needs of the young person in the context of his or her life space. Such interventions take into account his or her special circumstances and explore strengths, capacity for resilience, context, and both the immediate circumstances and historical risk factors. The risk of suicide and self-harm must also be evaluated.

Critical Thinking Questions

1. Explain how major depression is an internalizing rather than an externalizing problem.

2. Compare and contrast criteria for childhood and adult mood disorders in the DSM-5. Do you think these disorders should be distinguished more specifically than they are currently? Explain.

3. What do you think the relationship is between depression and suicide in our client population?

4. How important do you believe cognitive distortions are in mood disturbances? How likely are you to pick up cues of such distortions in your CYC practice? Explain, providing specific examples to illustrate.

5. Think about the causal explanations of depression outlined in the chapter. Which ones have the most validity for you as a future CYCP? Defend your decision.

6. What are the pros and cons regarding the use of psychotropic medications for children and adolescents diagnosed with depression?

7. What are the risks involved when CYCPs underestimate or don't recognize a young person's depressive symptoms?

8. Why do you think combining CBT with SSRI medication has been found to be the most promising treatment approach for child and adolescent depression? Do you agree or disagree with such an approach? Why or why not?

Key Terms

behavioural activation (BA), 297

Bipolar and Related Disorders, 276

Bipolar I Disorder, 278

Bipolar II Disorder, 279

cognitive distortions, 289

Cyclothymic Disorder, 279

Depressive Disorders, 274

Disruptive Mood Dysregulation
   Disorder, 276

Hypomanic Episode, 279

Major Depressive Disorder (MDD), 277

Major Depressive Episode, 277

mania, 276

Manic Episode, 278

mood disturbance, 274

mood episode, 275

negative cognitive triad, 288

Persistent Depressive Disorder
   (Dysthymia), 277

stress exposure model, 289

Supplemental Readings

Frank, E. (2005). *Treating bipolar disorder: A clinician's guide to interpersonal and social rhythm therapy.* New York: Guilford. (This book discusses applications of interpersonal and social rhythm therapy in the treatment of Bipolar Disorder and considers the role of stabilizing social rhythms in treating mood episodes.)

Mufson, L., Dorta, K., Moreau, D., & Weissman, M. M. (2004). *Interpersonal psychotherapy for depressed adolescents* (2nd ed.). New York: Guilford. (An overview of adolescent depression, a detailed summary of the application of IPT for adolescents, and extensive case examples illustrating the IPT process.)

Seligman, M. E. P., Reivich, K., Jaycox, L., & Gillham, J. (1995). *The optimistic child: A proven program to safeguard children against depression and build lifelong resilience.* New York: HarperCollins. (Ideas for building optimism and developing resilience.)

Strom, D., Randall, K., & Bowman, S. C. (2007). *102 creative strategies for working with depressed children and adolescents: A practical resource for teachers, counselors, and parents.* Chapin, SC: YouthLight. (Worksheets, activities, and handouts that help practitioners teach young people practical ways to handle negative emotions.)

Online Resources

Mood Disorders Society of Canada, www.mooddisorderscanada.ca

Youth in Care Canada resources, www.youthincare.ca/resources

Canadian Mental Health Association, British Columbia Division, www.cmha.bc.ca/get-informed/mental-health-information/depression

Depression in Children and Youth, www.ementalhealth.ca/Winnipeg-Regional-Health-Authority/Depression-in-Children-and-Youth-Information-for-Parents-and-Caregivers/index.php?m=article&ID=8879

Depression Hurts, http://depressionhurts.ca/en/default.aspx

Chapter 8
Eating Disturbances

Psychological and behavioural aspects are central to a diagnosis of an eating disorder.

Umpalumpas/Fotolia

Case Example: *Jasmine*

Fifteen-year-old Jasmine is in Child and Family Services care, living in a six-bed, community-based group home. Jasmine had settled into the program in that she'd stopped running away, had disassociated herself from the street youth crowd and the risky behaviours she'd been involved in, and was attending school regularly. The group-home staff were aware that when had Jasmine moved in she'd been engaged in some self-injurious behaviour, and so they were working with her in a variety of ways to decrease or eliminate these actions. Jasmine was also being seen by an agency therapist. All members of the treatment team were pleased with Jasmine's progress, as the indications were that she'd successfully stopped self-cutting. But as time went on the CYC staff observed that Jasmine was losing a lot of weight, and that she was more and more often refusing to join the group for meals. At first they thought she was depressed, but then noticed that after dinner she'd spend long periods of time in the bathroom. The CYC staff became increasingly concerned, and began to observe for other evidence of a problem with food or disordered eating. When they eventually searched Jasmine's room, they discovered hidden caches of chips and chocolate bars under her bed. After about two months Jasmine began to look alarmingly thin, and yet she refused to be weighed and even to discuss her weight; she was also withdrawing from her relationship with her key worker in the home. One day after school, Jasmine fainted. She was rushed to emergency, where she was later diagnosed with Bulimia. The CYC staff was shocked to learn that five-foot-eight Jasmine weighed only 99 pounds. Following a clinical and physical assessment, Jasmine was referred to an inpatient eating disorders program at the hospital.

Learning Objectives

1. Summarize the DSM criteria for Pica, Rumination Disorder, Avoidant/Restrictive Food Intake Disorder, Anorexia Nervosa, Bulimia Nervosa, and Binge Eating Disorder.

2. Describe the CYC perspective regarding child and youth eating disturbances.

3. Compare and contrast biological, psychodynamic, behavioural, cognitive, and socio-cultural explanations for eating disorders.

4. From a CYC perspective, summarize and distinguish between sociocultural, developmental, personality, trauma-related, and familial risk factors for eating disturbances.

5. Describe psychological treatment approaches used in treating eating disorders for each of the major psychological paradigms.

6. Describe the role of CYCPs in the assessment of eating disorders.

7. Describe specific indicators of the major eating disorders.

8. Explain various treatment methods and describe ways in which you might use them in your CYC practice with youth with eating disorders.

Chapter Overview

Eating disorders have been a popular topic in the media for some time now, but it's important to examine how common knowledge about these disturbances compares with the formal diagnostic criteria and research findings. Eating disorders, like most mental health concerns, are often observed together with one or more additional diagnoses that can make them difficult to recognize. What are the different types of eating disorders and how can their symptoms be identified? Why do some people develop eating disorders while others do not? What were the key symptoms displayed by Jasmine and what interventions might be used to support her? From a psychological perspective, this chapter will summarize the major characteristics of those eating disorders in the DSM that are most likely to be encountered by CYCPs. It will then examine explanations and approaches to intervention for such disturbances from a psychological perspective.

Regardless of the system within which CYCPs practise, they're likely to encounter young people struggling with eating difficulties. These disturbances can be serious—affecting medical, emotional, and social day-to-day functioning—and sometimes even life-threatening. Supportive care and effective interventions, however, do lead to favourable outcomes (Binford et al., 2003), particularly with early identification and treatment. From a CYC perspective, this chapter will examine CYCPs' role in identifying eating disturbances and the ways they can support youth exhibiting these disorders.

WHAT IS DISORDERED EATING?

Everyone must eat in order to survive. Clearly, the act of eating itself is necessary and associated with healthy functioning. How can we distinguish healthy eating from disordered eating? Generally, disordered eating is associated with specific behaviours; for example, restricting food intake, bingeing (ingesting large amounts of food in short time periods), skipping meals, and eating to soothe emotional distress. Underlying these actions are extreme concerns about body weight and shape (Gowers & Bryant-Waugh, 2004) resulting in preoccupation with food and eating. Disordered eating is a serious concern given the potential negative consequences it can have on physical health as well as social, emotional, and cognitive development (Striegel-Moore, Seeley, & Lewinsohn, 2003). Because these disorders can be life-threatening (Gowers & Bryant-Waugh, 2004), it's important to be aware of their indicators so that these patterns can be identified and interrupted in order to prevent long-term effects on physical health and emotional well-being. Before reading about the various eating disorders, consider your own experiences associated with food and eating in the *Think About It!* exercise.

WHAT IS AN EATING DISORDER? THE PSYCHOLOGICAL PERSPECTIVE

According the DSM-5, **feeding and eating disorders** are "characterized by a persistent disturbance of eating or eating-related behaviour that results in the altered consumption or absorption of food" (APA, 2013, p. 329). The behaviours associated with these disturbances result in significant physical and/or social-emotional impairments. One important component of such disturbances relates to their *psychological features*, including distorted thoughts, feelings of distress, and persistent thoughts about food and/or body shape and weight. A second central factor of such disturbances relates to the *harmful behavioural strategies* or **compensatory behaviours** (Binford & le Grange, 2005) that are used in attempt to decrease body weight, including fasting, self-induced vomiting, laxative misuse, and extreme exercise. Together, these psychological features and compensatory behaviours put the youth at risk for a number of negative physical and mental health outcomes.

DSM-5 Categories

Eating disturbances are included in the DSM-5 in a single chapter entitled Feeding and Eating Disorders (APA, 2013). It should be noted that the DSM-5 doesn't consider *obesity*—defined as a condition in which an individual is 20 percent or more in excess of recommended body weight (Health Canada, 2003a)—in its discussion of eating disorders. In fact, "obesity is not included in DSM-5 as a mental disorder" (APA, 2013, p. 329). The American Medical Association designated obesity as a disease in 2013, and so obesity's non-inclusion in the DSM-5 is in recognition of the various genetic, physiological, and environmental influences that contribute to its development. The DSM-5 does, however, acknowledge the relationship between obesity and other mental disorders (e.g., Binge Eating Disorder, depression), and we'll consider some of these associations in this chapter.

Feeding and Eating Disorders   The specific eating disorders identified in the DSM include *Pica, Rumination Disorder, Avoidant/Restrictive Food Intake Disorder, Anorexia Nervosa, Bulimia Nervosa,* and *Binge Eating Disorder.* In addition, the DSM-5 includes a diagnostic category called **Other Specified Feeding or Eating Disorder**, which summarizes disturbances of eating behaviour that might be of concern but that don't meet the formal criteria of any specific eating disorder. For example, a youth may meet all criteria for Anorexia Nervosa except that she has a normal weight. In this instance, although a diagnosis of Anorexia couldn't be applied, this pattern of behaviour might be clinically significant. Consequently, documenting such a behaviour pattern might be particularly relevant to the health and well-being of the adolescent as well as useful for any professional working with her. Accordingly, the mental health professional would note the disturbance under the *Other Specified Feeding or Eating Disorder* heading to ensure that it's considered by anyone working with the youth as well as to specify why the diagnosis doesn't meet the criteria for a specific eating disorder (e.g., the individual is of normal weight). In instances where symptoms of eating disturbances are present and causing significant impairment but the individual doesn't meet all criteria for a specific disorder and no explanation as to why or what criteria are not met, the *Unspecified Feeding or Eating Disorder* diagnosis would be applied. Refer to Box 8.1 for an overview of the diagnostic categories pertaining to eating disturbances as specified in the DSM-5.

Feeding and Eating Disorders: Diagnoses and Criteria

To better understand the differences between various feeding and eating disturbances, let's review the DSM-5 diagnostic criteria for those disorders that CYCPs may encounter in their work with youth.

Box 8.1

DSM-5 Feeding and Eating Disorders

Pica	Bulimia Nervosa
Rumination Disorder	Binge Eating Disorder
Avoidant/Restrictive Food Intake Disorder	Other Specified Feeding or Eating Disorder
Anorexia Nervosa	Unspecified Feeding or Eating Disorder

Pica

[handwritten: eating items]

...ion of nonnutritive substances (e.g., glass, string, dirt, [...] ...month and at an age in which this behaviour is inconsistent with the individual's development (Kariholu et al., 2008). The DSM-5 recommends that those younger than two not be diagnosed with Pica, given that it's not uncommon for infants to mouth and/or ingest nonfood objects. Although this disorder is more frequently diagnosed in the context of intellectual disabilities, it's not unusual for young children to engage in behaviours associated with Pica. In addition, these actions may be observed in the context of other disorders.

Pica is of concern because the ingestion of nonfood items may be associated with dangerous health outcomes (e.g., damage to intestines, poisoning). In light of the fact that these behaviours may occur in the context of normal development, a diagnosis of Pica "should be made only if the eating behaviour is sufficiently severe to warrant additional clinical attention" (APA, [...]

Rumination Disorder

[handwritten: chewing and swallowing food, bring swallowed food back up into the mouth and a chewing again]

...erized by chewing and swallowing food followed by reg[...]...partially digested food back up into the mouth). The regurgitation is not associated with disgust or nausea, and the food may then be re-chewed, re-swallowed, or spit out (Rajindrajith et al., 2012). Symptoms must persist for at least one month, and the DSM-5 requires that the behaviour occur at least several times per week and usually daily. The regurgitation is not associated with flu or other medical conditions.

Although Rumination Disorder is more likely to be observed in those with intellectual disability (e.g., Rogers et al., 1992), symptoms have been observed in groups of all ages and abilities (Lee et al., 2007). Concerns about mineral and vitamin deficiencies, weight loss, and dental problems are associated with Rumination Disorder. Social consequences include avoiding eating in public (given the negative reaction of others to regurgitation). It should be noted that regurgitation may occur in the context of other disorders (e.g., Generalized Anxiety Disorder), in which case a diagnosis of Rumination Disorder would be applied only if the symptoms are severe enough that they wouldn't be addressed by treatment of the other disorder.

Avoidant/Restrictive Food Intake Disorder

[handwritten: 2. avoiding food or fluid intake, avoiding colour, taste or texture of food, early trauma with breast feeding]

Restrictive Food Intake Disorder (ARFID) is res[...] Restricted intake may be due to (a) the individual avoiding food based on colour, taste, texture; (b) emotional disturbances surrounding the feeding context (e.g., relationship with caregiver associated with conflict during feeding times); and/or (c) avoidance of ingesting food due to a previous negative experience (e.g., choking, vomiting) associated with eating. In order to be diagnosed with this disorder, weight loss, nutritional deficiencies, and/or impaired psychosocial functioning must be observed. Given the large number of possible explanations for appetite loss and food avoidance, ARFID may be observed in the context of numerous physical and mental disorders. The diagnosis of ARFID is made only if the severity of symptoms requires specific attention and/or intervention.

Anorexia Nervosa

[handwritten: doing whatever they could to maintain their body weight]

orexia Nervosa (AN) is the refusal to maintain body ... ically, to be diagnosed with AN one must be significantly below the recommended weight for one's age, height, sex, and build. Although there is disagreement as to what should quality as *significantly underweight*, body mass index (BMI) is typically used for children and adolescents, with those scoring in the lower range compared with their peers being defined as significantly underweight.

A less obvious but important feature of AN is an intense fear of gaining weight. This fear motivates the individual to use unhealthy and extreme strategies to decrease body weight and avoid weight gain. Such strategies can include extreme restriction of caloric intake (referred to as *dieting* or in the case of not eating at all, *starving* or *fasting*) or excessive exercise. As a result of excessive weight loss, menstruating females will lose significant amounts of body fat, which can result in *amenorrhea*, a condition in which menstruation ceases. Another feature of the disorder is a distorted *body image* or inaccurate perception of the size and/or shape of one's body. For example, an adolescent diagnosed with AN may see her body as being larger than it actually is and see fat where there is none. The diagnostic criteria for AN are presented in Box 8.2.

The DSM-5 distinguishes between two subtypes of AN: a *Restricting Type* and a *Binge-Eating/Purging Type*. Most discussions of AN in the media focus on the *Restricting Type*, which is characterized by the use of excessive exercise or restrictive eating to

---

Box 8.2

DSM-5 Criteria for Anorexia Nervosa

A. Restriction of energy intake relative to requirements, leading to a significantly low body weight in the context of age, sex, developmental trajectory, and physical health. *Significantly low weight* is defined as a weight that is less than minimally normal or, for children and adolescents, less than that minimally expected.

B. Intense fear of gaining weight or of becoming fat or persistent behaviour that interferes with weight gain, even though at a significantly low weight.

C. Disturbance in the way in which one's body weight or shape is experienced, undue influence of body weight or shape on self-evaluation, or persistent lack of recognition of the seriousness of the current low body weight.

Source: From DIAGNOSTIC AND STATISTICAL MANUAL OF MENTAL DISORDERS. Reprinted with permission from the Diagnostic and Statistical Manual of Mental Disorders, Fifth Edition, (Copyright ©2013). American Psychiatric Association. All Rights Reserved.

achieve weight loss. The *Binge-Eating/Purging Type*, however, is diagnosed when binge-eating and/or purging have occurred in the context of other symptoms of AN. **Binge-eating** generally refers to eating a large amount of food (greater than what most would eat) in an isolated time period (usually less than two hours). **Purging** refers to strategies used after eating to eliminate ingested food from the body in order to avoid weight gain. These *compensatory strategies* can include self-induced vomiting and the use of laxatives, enemas, or *diuretics* (water pills that remove fluid from the body). In the case of AN, then, one may binge-eat followed by purging or only purge even after a small amount of food is ingested. Given these two subtypes, it's clear that not everyone with a diagnosis of AN will exhibit the same behaviour.

Although the same criteria for AN are applied to children, adolescents, and adults, the DSM-5 does consider how symptoms might relate to a failure to make expected weight gains during developmental growth (rather than weight loss)—an important consideration for children and younger adolescents who display disrupted eating behaviours.

It's worth noting the relevance of psychological aspects of AN. For example, the fear of gaining weight doesn't decrease with weight loss, but actually *increases*, highlighting the irrational nature of these motivating emotions. Similarly, those diagnosed with AN typically deny or fail to recognize the serious medical consequences associated with their disordered eating behaviour, illustrating a lack of insight into their condition. Distortions in perceptions of the size and shape of one's body and of the amount of fat believed to be present further illustrate the role of perceptual and psychological factors in this diagnosis.

Purging is a compensatory strategy in which the individual self-induces vomiting or uses laxatives or enemas after eating as a way to eliminate the ingested food from the body.

Bulimia Nervosa

[handwritten: binge eating followed by risky behaviours to compensate for the binge]

...ssociated with **Bulimia Nervosa (BN)** is repeated ... by maladaptive behaviours that attempt to compensate for the binge (i.e., self-induced vomiting, ingestion of laxatives, excessive exercise, restricted eating). Current severity is indicated in relation to the number of compensatory episodes that occur. Specifically, *mild severity* is associated with 1–3 episodes of compensatory behaviours per week, *moderate severity* by 4–7 episodes, *severe* by 8–13 episodes, and *extreme* by 14 or more. Notice that one of the most significant differences between BN and AN is that the individual with Anorexia is significantly underweight. Those with BN may be slightly underweight but are often of average or sometimes above average weight. The diagnostic criteria for BN are presented in Box 8.3.

As with AN, psychological factors are relevant to a diagnosis of BN. Those diagnosed with BN overemphasize the significance of body shape and weight in their self-evaluations, which has a negative effect on self-esteem. Accordingly, fears of gaining weight and body dissatisfaction are common. Binge-eating, when present, is typically triggered by negative emotions or interpersonal stressors. A profound sense of lack of control over eating is also a unique feature of BN, and during binge-eating episodes, feelings of dissociation may be

Box 8.3

DSM-5 Criteria for Bulimia Nervosa

A. Recurrent episodes of binge eating. An episode of binge eating is characterized by both of the following:

(1) Eating, in a discrete period of time (e.g., within any two-hour period), an amount of food that is definitely larger than most people would eat during a similar period of time and under similar circumstances.

(2) A sense of lack of control over eating during the episode (e.g., a feeling that one cannot stop eating or control what or how much one is eating).

B. Recurrent inappropriate compensatory behaviour in order to prevent weight gain, such as self-induced vomiting; misuse of laxatives, diuretics, enemas, or other medications; fasting; or excessive exercise.

C. The binge eating and inappropriate compensatory behaviours both occur, on average, at least once a week for three months.

D. Self-evaluation is unduly influenced by both shape and weight.

E. The disturbance does not occur exclusively during episodes of Anorexia Nervosa.

Source: From DIAGNOSTIC AND STATISTICAL MANUAL OF MENTAL DISORDERS. Reprinted with permission from the Diagnostic and Statistical Manual of Mental Disorders, Fifth Edition, (Copyright ©2013). American Psychiatric Association. All Rights Reserved.

experienced (e.g., feeling numb or spaced out). Following a binge, overwhelming feelings of guilt are common, and the resulting distress is often what motivates purging. In addition, the distortions in body image associated with AN are also observed in those diagnosed with BN.

It's worth emphasizing that the specific behaviours associated with the diagnostic criteria for AN and BN are not uncommon. For example, Neumark-Sztainer et al. (2002) found that 20 percent of overweight girls and 6 percent of overweight boys reported using inappropriate compensatory behaviours (i.e., vomiting, laxatives, diuretics) in attempts to lose weight. Sometimes, although disrupted eating behaviours are exhibited (e.g., occasional binge-eating, weight loss followed by restricted eating, occasional purging), the disturbance doesn't meet the criteria for either AN or BN. In such instances, as we've seen, the behaviour may be categorized as an "Other Specified Feeding or Eating Disorder." For example, an adolescent may meet all the criteria for Anorexia but not be significantly underweight; in another example, someone may meet all the criteria for Bulimia, but the bingeing and purging occur less than once a week.

Binge Eating Disorder   Binge Eating Disorder (BED) is characterized by recurrent binge-eating episodes where compensatory strategies are not regularly used, distinguishing this disrupted eating pattern from BN. Binges are accompanied by feelings of significant distress, and following the binge episodes (which must occur at least once a week for at least three months), emotional distress associated with guilt, disgust, and depression is experienced. Current severity is indicated in relation to the number of binge episodes that occur. Specifically, *mild severity* is associated with 1–3 episodes of binge-eating episodes per week, *moderate severity* by 4–7 episodes, *severe* by 8–13 episodes, and *extreme* by 14 or more. The criteria for Binge Eating Disorder are presented in Box 8.4.

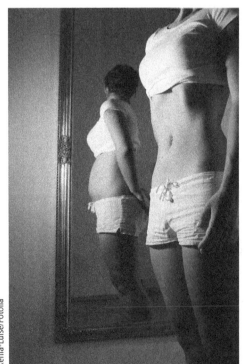

Xenia-Luise/Fotolia

Distortions in perceptions of body image are common in both Anorexia Nervosa and Bulimia Nervosa.

DSM-5 Criteria for Binge Eating Disorder

A. Recurrent episodes of binge eating. An episode of binge eating is characterized by both of the following:

(1) Eating, in a discrete period of time (e.g., within any two-hour period), an amount of food that is definitely larger than what most people would eat in a similar period of time under similar circumstances.

(2) A sense of lack of control over eating during the episode (e.g., a feeling that one cannot stop eating or control what or how much one is eating).

B. The binge-eating episodes are associated with three (or more) of the following:

(1) eating much more rapidly than normal

(2) eating until feeling uncomfortably full

(3) eating large amounts of food when not feeling physically hungry

(4) eating alone because of being embarrassed by how much one is eating

(5) feeling disgusted with oneself, depressed, or very guilty after overeating

C. Marked distress regarding binge eating is present.

D. The binge eating occurs, on average, at least once a week for three months.

E. The binge eating is not associated with the recurrent use of inappropriate compensatory behaviour as in Bulimia Nervosa and does not occur exclusively during the course of Bulimia Nervosa or Anorexia Nervosa.

Source: From DIAGNOSTIC AND STATISTICAL MANUAL OF MENTAL DISORDERS. Reprinted with permission from the Diagnostic and Statistical Manual of Mental Disorders, Fifth Edition, (Copyright ©2013). American Psychiatric Association. All Rights Reserved.

Unlike AN and BN, which tend to be observed in adolescence, Binge Eating Disorder is more often observed in obese women of older ages. Recent research demonstrates that binge-eating is precipitated by feelings of distress, including depression and anxiety. Others report a dissociative quality to the binge episodes while they take place. Feelings of self-disgust and self-loathing are common. Comorbid conditions include Major Depressive Disorder and substance-related disorders. Those who meet the criteria typically have a history of dieting, and most are overweight. Initial estimates suggest that females are twice as likely to display this disrupted eating pattern (APA, 2013).

Before moving on to a consideration of eating disturbances from a CYC approach, test your knowledge of the primary differences between the various DSM-5 diagnostic categories in the *Test Your Understanding* exercise. Can you identify the disorder that most closely matches the description of each case?

Test Your Understanding: *Case Examples of Eating Disorders*

Belinda eats large amounts of calories at least three times per week, followed by feelings of guilt and shame. In order to help herself feel better, she'll self-induce vomiting to relieve herself of her guilty feelings. Although Belinda is of average weight, she is very concerned about her body and weight.

Allen frequently manipulates food in his mouth with his tongue for long periods of time while he's chewing his food. Following a visit to his dentist, the parents were informed that Allen has significant tooth decay; they were asked if they'd noticed any unusual eating behaviours.

(continued)

Following an argument with her friend, Fiona went home and quickly ate several packages of cookies and potato chips, and all the leftovers in her refrigerator. Although she felt disgusted and embarrassed by this behaviour, she felt as if she wasn't in control of her actions.

Madison takes great pride in her cooking skills, and enjoys making food for others. But she eats very little herself, and lately she's been eating only calorie-free foods. She wants to lose weight, even though her friends and family are worried about how thin she is. Madison wears baggy clothing that hides her weight loss so that she can avoid their questions and criticisms.

Leah frequently finds herself eating unusual things, including sand from her sandbox and clay from her toy box. Although her mother has scolded her for eating these things, Leah continues to ingest these nonfood items. This past week her stomach has been feeling different, and she's wondering whether she should ask her mother to take her to the doctor to see what's wrong.

Patrick has been losing weight, and his mother is concerned. Although she's been encouraging Patrick to eat, he doesn't feel hungry and tries his best to avoid food. When his mother asked why he isn't eating, Patrick said he didn't know—but later that day he began wondering if he didn't like eating anymore because of the fights his mom used to have with his father at the dinner table before he moved out.

A CYC APPROACH TO EATING DIFFICULTIES: UNDERSTANDING EATING DISTURBANCES

Given the likelihood that CYCPs will engage with young people diagnosed with an eating disorder, it's important to be aware of the potential health consequences associated with these diagnoses. Approximately 10–15 percent of young people diagnosed with Anorexia Nervosa may eventually die from it as a result of such medical complications as heart failure, electrolyte imbalance, and suicide (Kearney, 2003). Individuals with Bulimia Nervosa seldom die from it, but they may live with the disorder for the rest of their lives. Yet despite these concerning outcomes, there is much hope for recovery.

Western society's preoccupation with thinness and glamour has contributed to this "new age of eating disorders" (Wilmshurst, 2004, p. 187). Although full recovery is possible, it can be difficult. The factors associated with poorer outcomes include substance abuse and the existence of other mental health concerns, such as Borderline Personality Disorder, Obsessive-Compulsive Disorder, Dissociative Identity Disorder, anxiety, depression, and severe disturbance in the perception of body size. Such comorbidity can make it very difficult to identify the relevant behavioural indicators (Kearney, 2003). There is no one factor that will help determine whether a young person has an eating disorder, and the secrecy or denial involved can make identification very difficult. If CYCPs are concerned that a young person may be struggling with an eating disorder, they must first refer to a medical professional. Clinical diagnoses are made based on multiple reports and observations from direct care providers, including foster parents, CYCPs, parents, teachers, and health care providers, and from the youth themselves.

Before turning to a discussion of prevalence, development, and comorbidity, consider the details of the opening case in relation to the psychological and CYC views of eating disturbances in *Jasmine's Case: Revisited.*

HOW MANY YOUNG PEOPLE STRUGGLE WITH EATING DIFFICULTIES?

One national study found that 1.5 percent of Canadian women between the ages of 15 and 24 had an eating disorder (Government of Canada, 2006). Hoek (2007) found the rates of BN to be slightly higher in adolescents and young adults than AN (1.0 percent for BN compared with 0.3 percent for AN). Despite its lower prevalence, concerns about AN continue in light of reports that of all psychiatric illnesses, Anorexia has the highest mortality rate. Sullivan (2002), for example, reports that approximately 10 percent of those diagnosed with Anorexia die within 10 years following onset of the disorder. Moreover, the subclinical levels of eating disorders, which include a fear of fatness, dieting, and fasting, all occur much more often in the general population (McClure & Teyber, 2002). For example, some research indicates that as many as 38 percent of 11-year-olds have a distorted body image, and that 58 percent think they're overweight (Mellin, Irwin, & Scully, 1992, as cited in McClure & Teyber, 2002). The actual numbers of those affected may be even higher.

There are also indications that the incidence of eating disorders appears to be increasing in industrialized societies (Pike & Borovoy, 2004). Furthermore, research suggests that these disorders are now seen in developing as well as developed countries and may even manifest themselves in the face of apparent starvation. It's believed that this increase is in part due to the increased exposure to Western media and its influence on perceptions of desirable body characteristics (WHO, 2003).

Studies of prevalence consistently report sex differences in the rates of eating disorders, with the lifetime prevalence for AN, BN, and BED significantly higher for females than for males (e.g., Hudson et al., 2007). Theorists suggest that eating disorders are more common in women because, in general, boys tend to be less concerned with body image and weight. However, recent studies have found that the incidence and prevalence rates are increasing among boys and men. Statistics show that there is approximately 1 male case to 10 female cases, and that 1 in 4 children referred for Anorexia is a boy. Boys with eating disorders have the same characteristics as their female counterparts: low self-esteem, the need for acceptance, an inability to cope with emotional pressures, and family and relationship issues (Agency for Healthcare Research and Quality, 2010).

It's apparent, then, that in the general Canadian population many young people are engaging in undereating and overeating, whether due to underlying stress, poor nutritional habits, or peer, media, and societal pressures. Body image problems and eating difficulties in adolescence are now relatively common, and young people struggling with complex trauma needs and pain-based behaviours will be even more vulnerable. The prevalence of eating disorders in the high-risk youth with whom CYCPs work is unknown, but CYCPs should recognize that other, indirect self-harm behaviours are often associated with eating disorders, and that sexual abuse often appears in the histories of affected youth. Thus, many young people in our care may be vulnerable to this area of concern.

EATING DISORDERS AND DEVELOPMENT

Eating disorders are most often diagnosed in adolescence, although cases of children diagnosed with these eating disturbances have been reported (Bryant-Waugh & Lask, 2002). Consequently, most of the research examining eating disorders is based on adolescents and young adults. The DSM-5 does, however, acknowledge that symptoms may be observed in children, and so in such instances it includes a consideration of failure to demonstrate expected weight gain.

It's unclear whether early feeding and eating disturbances are associated with later diagnosis of eating disorders. However, in contrast to later disturbances, early conditions tend to lack the core *psychological features* of fear of weight gain, distorted body image, and extreme emphasis on body weight as an indicator of self-worth (Gowers & Green, 2009). This is likely a reflection of the level of cognitive development of the individual and the fact that concerns about physical appearance become particularly relevant only in middle childhood and adolescence (Shapka & Keating, 2005).

As is the case for most psychological disorders, early recognition of disrupted eating patterns is important. In one study of 14- and 15-year-old girls, those who had used restrictive eating as a means of controlling weight were 18 times more likely to be diagnosed with an eating disorder six months later than were non-restrictors (Patton et al., 1999). Another study found that the risk of later obesity is 324 percent greater for adolescent girls who use restrictive eating practices to control their weight (Stice et al., 1999). Clearly, early recognition of such eating behaviours is important and may allow appropriate supports to be put in place to prevent long-term negative outcomes.

COMORBIDITY

Diagnoses of eating disorders often occur in the context of other psychological disturbances. Pica, for example, most commonly occurs with ASD and intellectual disability. Other comorbid conditions include Trichotillomania and Excoriation Disorder. Comorbid conditions for ARFID include anxiety disorders, OCD, and neurodevelopmental disorders (including ASD, ADHD, and intellectual disability). BED is most often comorbid with depressive and bipolar disorders as well as anxiety disorders (APA, 2013). As we noted above, the presence of any accompanying condition negatively affects treatment outcomes.

In the case of AN, symptoms may be accompanied by depressed mood, social withdrawal, irritability, insomnia, and decreased sex drive in adults. Comorbid conditions may include Major Depressive Disorder and personality disorders. Obsessive-compulsive features are common, as exhibited by preoccupation with thoughts of food and relevant compulsive behaviours (e.g., collecting recipes, hoarding food). It's possible that some of these symptoms/conditions may result from the physical consequences of starvation

Common Myths About Eating Disorders

MYTH: *Eating disorders are a choice.*

FACT: No one chooses to have an eating disorder. A complex interaction of biological, environmental, and psychological factors are associated with the development of eating disorders.

MYTH: *You can tell if a person has an eating disorder simply by appearance.*

FACT: Although Anorexia can be easier to identify, individuals may wear loose clothing to hide their weight loss. Bulimia is less obvious, as it's typically associated with normal or above normal weight. Other symptoms may be actively hidden.

MYTH: *Eating disorders are an attempt to seek attention.*

FACT: Typically, those diagnosed attempt to conceal the disorder and associated symptoms from others. Although it may be perceived as "attention seeking" by others, an eating disorder is best interpreted as an indicator that the person is experiencing serious difficulties and requires support.

Source: Excerpt from Educator Toolkit. Published by National Eating Disorders Association.

associated with AN. Specific physical symptoms may include constipation, abdominal pain, cold intolerance, lethargy or excess energy, skin dryness, and *lanugo* (fine downy body hair). If purging is used as a compensatory strategy, damage to teeth or scars on hands from self-induced vomiting may result. In the case of AN, cardiovascular problems are common. Interestingly, an increased risk of depression, bipolar disorders, and Substance Use Disorders is observed in those with the Binge-Eating/Purging Type of BN (APA, 2013). In the case of BN, comorbid conditions include mood disorders, symptoms of anxiety, substance use, and Borderline Personality Disorder (APA, 2013).

Trauma is a major contributing factor to the development of co-occurring disorders in young people. In fact, co-occurring disorders, particularly in children with histories of trauma, might be *expected* rather than considered an exception, and are especially prevalent in child welfare systems, juvenile justice systems, and community-based organizations serving vulnerable youth (Hendrickson, 2009, p. 5). Although self-harming and obsessive-compulsive behaviours are frequently seen in youth with eating disorders, there is some evidence that eating disorders may also coexist with ADHD. Research has shown that women who live with undiagnosed ADHD (but do in fact meet the criteria) are much more likely to develop an eating disorder.

Before examining explanations for eating disorders, consider some common myths of eating disturbances presented in Box 8.5. Are you surprised by any of these myths? Are your beliefs about eating disturbances consistent with the facts?

EXPLAINING EATING DISTURBANCES: PSYCHOLOGICAL PARADIGMS

What explanations have been forwarded for eating disorders? Why do some develop these disturbances but not others? As emphasized in previous chapters, the answers to these questions vary in relation to the theoretical framework one adopts. From a psychological perspective, predominant explanations of eating disorders include those proposed from the biological, psychodynamic, behavioural, cognitive, and sociocultural paradigms. Accordingly, we will examine these frameworks in relation to the development of eating disorders. As you'll see, the research suggests that the best explanation for eating disorders arises from a consideration of biological, psychological, and social factors. You might also notice that most of the research reviewed discusses causal explanations for AN and BN. This reflects the fact that most of the research in this area has focused on these diagnoses and less is known regarding the causes of other eating disturbances.

Biological Paradigm   A significant number of investigations have explored the relationship between biological factors and eating disturbances. Research based on a biological paradigm of eating disorders has focused primarily on the role of genetic and biochemical factors.

Heredity and Genetics. It has been observed that eating disorders are likely to run in families (e.g., Bulik & Tozzi, 2004; Hitti, 2006), suggesting that genetics may play a role in these disturbances. Accordingly, other investigations have found that individuals with greater degrees of genetic relatedness (e.g., identical versus fraternal twins) have higher concordance rates for both AN and BN (Kendler et al., 1991; Strober et al., 2000). Of particular interest is the suggestion that precise genes may be related to the onset of eating disorders. Specifically, sections of *chromosome 1* (recall from Chapter 1 that a *gene* refers to a particular segment of DNA along a chromosome) are suspected to be related to AN, restrictive type (Bergen et al., 2003; Brown et al., 2007). In the case of BN, genes located on chromosome 10 have been linked to the disorder, and more specifically to the compensatory behaviour of self-induced vomiting (Bulik et al., 2003). Although these findings are preliminary, it seems quite possible that the influence of genes on the developing nervous system may very well predispose some individuals to developing AN and BN.

Neurotransmitters. Genes organize the nervous system and determine the availability and sensitivity to neurotransmitters. If there is a genetic influence in the role of eating disorders, perhaps it's associated with abnormalities of a neurochemical nature. Supporting this idea, low levels of serotonin have been associated with both AN and BN (Kaye et al., 1998; 2001). It's interesting to note that serotonin has been found to regulate appetite and feeding behaviour; this neurotransmitter is also associated with mood disturbances (recall our discussion of the role of serotonin in MDD in Chapter 7) as well as impulsivity and obsessional thinking. Disruptions in the serotonin system, then, would also explain some of the other features of AN and BN.

eating disorders, it's important to recognize recall the *diathesis–stress model* discussed in eloping a disorder is based on an interaction (environmental or psychosocial disturfluences represent a possible diathesis. ined by this diathesis alone; rather, this onmental factors (stresses) to affect the ting disorders, genetic factors may alter ses resulting in obesity, perfectionism, and/or impulsivity. Together with environmental variables (e.g., cultural norms, beliefs about food and weight), a tendency toward certain relevant behaviours is created (e.g., dieting) and a corresponding risk for developing the symptoms of AN and/or BN results.

Psychodynamic Paradigm   You may recall that from a psychodynamic perspective, mental disturbances result from unresolved childhood conflicts and traumas. In order to reduce anxiety associated with these early experiences, the individual uses defence mechanisms that distort reality. From this perspective, current behaviours can reflect unconscious attempts to resolve these early concerns and issues.

Various psychodynamic explanations for eating disorders have been proposed. For example, Bruch (1962; 1973; 1974) argued that those diagnosed with AN are struggling to obtain control and achieve their own identity, which is reflected in their struggle for thinness. If parents didn't show an awareness of and sensitivity to their child's independent needs over the course of development, and family relationships didn't support the child in her development of a sense of identity, young girls might feel that their needs were second to those of their mother. Consequently, symptoms of eating disorders (particularly AN) reflect an attempt to achieve a sense of control, autonomy, and self-respect. This is consistent with findings that show those diagnosed with eating disorders perceive their parents to be less caring and more controlling than those not diagnosed with an eating disorder (De Panfilis et al., 2003).

More recently, other researchers have discussed the possibility that eating disorder symptoms are adaptive in that they provide the individual with a way to self-soothe and to maintain an attachment to (as well as separate from) needed and loved attachment figures (Barth, 2008). Other studies in the area of attachment are consistent with Bruch's view that early family relationships may predispose one to eating disturbances. For example, Canetti et al. (2008) found that grandfathers' controlling behaviour predicted more controlling behaviour and less caring in their sons, which then predicted AN in these sons' daughters.

Behavioural Paradigm   According to Crisp (1997), eating disorders such as AN are a form of phobia. Specifically, the individual fears normal adult body weight and shape as well as other outcomes associated with the transition into adulthood (e.g., increased responsibility, choices, decision making). Other behavioural explanations suggest that perfectionism and rigid behavioural style may be associated with a predisposition toward developing conditioned fears while at the same time being resistant to the extinction of fears (Strober, 2004).

In the case of other eating disorders, the reinforcers and punishers that play a role in maintaining unhealthy eating behaviours are examined. In BN, for example, bingeing can alleviate the distressing emotions associated with psychosocial stressors. Following the binge, the guilt and shame that result are alleviated by compensatory behaviours (e.g., self-induced vomiting), which serve as a negative reinforcer for the behaviour. Similar forces are at work in the case of ARFID and BED.

Cognitive Paradigm   From a cognitive paradigm, eating disorders are explained in relation to irrational thoughts and beliefs and their resulting distressed emotional states. Cahill (1996) defines AN as the "self-imposed starvation resulting from a distorted body image and an intense and irrational fear of gaining weight" (p. 36). This definition clearly illustrates the role of thoughts and beliefs in determining negative emotions and subsequent eating-disordered behaviour.

Numerous illogical beliefs have been explored in the context of eating disorders. For example, irrational beliefs regarding **perfectionism** (the need to be perfect, exact, and avoid errors) are consistently observed in those diagnosed with both AN and BN, but not in BED (Lilenfeld et al., 2006; Sassaroli, Gallucci, & Ruggiero, 2008). Accompanying this desire to be perfect is the self-imposed pressure to achieve the "ideal body," resulting in the establishment of extremely strict and inflexible dieting standards. In the case of AN, adherence to such strict diet standards results in feelings of control, accomplishment, and autonomy. For those with BN, perfectionism in addition to "black or white" dichotomous thinking is observed (Fairburn et al., 1997). Specifically, deviation from the unrealistic standards results in a perception of self as a complete failure. Binge-eating episodes result in significantly harsh self-criticism and guilt, often motivating subsequent purging.

Negative experiences such as childhood sexual abuse may create a vulnerability to eating disorders (Connors, 2001; Fairburn et al., 1997); however, this association has been found to be weak (Smolak & Murnen, 2002). Although the means by which such experiences may precipitate an eating disorder is uncertain, one possibility is that these early events structure young people's schemas and beliefs about their body. Consistent with this view and as noted in the DSM diagnostic criteria, distorted body image and views of the self are common in those diagnosed with both AN and BN (Jacobi et al., 2004). These distorted perceptions and beliefs result in body dissatisfaction, an established risk factor for eating disturbances (Lynch et al., 2008; Stice, 2002). This general cognitive framework can result in a biased interpretation of stimuli and events that continues to fuel the dysfunctional beliefs. Consistent with this idea, those diagnosed with eating disorders have been found to exaggerate the negative consequences of gaining weight (Poulakis & Wertheim, 1993) and generally evaluate the self negatively (Fairburn et al., 1997). See Table 8.1 for examples of common dysfunctional beliefs associated with eating disorders.

Feelings about the self and the world are significantly impacted by these irrational beliefs. Consistent with this idea, those with BN tend to have lower self-esteem compared with others (Jacobi et al., 2004). Comorbid depression and anxiety in the context of eating disorders further supports the relationship between irrational thoughts and negative affect. This is particularly concerning given that negative affect predicts later eating disorders (Johnson et al., 2002) and seems to maintain binge-eating episodes (Stice, 2002).

Sociocultural Paradigm   As discussed in Chapter 1, the *sociocultural paradigm* emphasizes the role of social and cultural factors in explaining abnormal behaviour. From this perspective, explanations for eating disorders consider conditions *outside* the individual

Table 8.1 Common Dysfunctional Beliefs in Eating Disorders

"If only I were thin, I'd be happy."

"No one will love me if I'm overweight."

"Gaining weight is a sign of failure."

"Any deviation from my diet puts me at great risk for gaining weight."

"Eating is a sign of weakness."

"I'm fat."

exhibiting such disturbances, including cultural ideals for body size, societal emphasis on the importance of physical appearance, and acceptance of extreme dieting as a means for achieving weight loss. The more immediate environment of the family is also considered to be particularly relevant in the case of eating disorders in childhood and adolescence.

Culture and the "Ideal Body Type."

As highlighted in the DSM-5, both AN and BN are significantly more prevalent in industrialized societies, including Canada, the United States, Australia, and Japan (APA, 2013). What might explain these differences across societies? One factor that has been emphasized is a culture's ideal or standard for beauty. It has been documented that the ideal body size of models presented in North American media (e.g., magazines, television advertisements, billboards) has become significantly thinner in the past 20 years (Sypeck, Gray, & Ahrens, 2004). Even children's toys and books convey a message regarding thinness.

The extent to which one internalizes the standards of beauty conveyed in the media and cultural objects (e.g., toys) may be an important precipitating factor in the development of eating disorders.

The extent to which a child or adolescent internalizes this standard for beauty has been found to predict body dissatisfaction and dieting (Stice, 2002; Vartanian, Herman, & Polivy, 2005), both correlates of later eating disorders. In fact, Pinhas et al. (1999) found that Canadian female university students were more depressed and angry after viewing pictures of models portraying the thin ideal than were students who viewed pictures without human figures. Based on such observations, it is argued that such images have a profound and immediate effect on viewers and represent a precipitating social factor in the onset of both AN and BN (Stice, 2001).

One of the most fascinating illustrations of the impact of such media messages is provided in a study by Becker et al. (2002). Before the introduction of American television programming to Fiji, being overweight was valued and associated with such positive qualities as strength, kindness, and generosity. By comparison, being thin was seen as a reflection of illness and incompetence. In the context of such views, eating disorders were virtually nonexistent. Following the introduction of American television programs, however, these researchers noted a significant increase in dieting, body dissatisfaction, and weight concerns. Although not a controlled study, it's clear that images in the media that encourage thinness should be cause for alarm. What images can you identify in your environment that portray messages about standards of beauty?

Family Influences.

Social relationships in a child or adolescent's immediate environment have also been the focus of investigations attempting to identify causes of eating disorders. Although there is no characteristic "family profile" associated with eating disturbances, self-report studies have found that a significant number of those diagnosed with AN consider dysfunctional family relationships to be a significant factor in their disorder (Tozzi et al., 2003). Consistent with this finding, family behaviours including parental overprotectiveness, a focus on control, and marital conflict have been associated with greater risk for the disorder (Strober, 1997). It has been hypothesized that AN develops in such an environment as an attempt to gain a sense of autonomy, and that the distraction created by the child or adolescent's disorder allows the unstable family relationships to be precariously maintained (Minuchin, Rosman, & Baker, 1978). These family dynamics are discussed in greater detail later in this chapter.

Parents of those diagnosed with both AN and BN tend to score higher on measures of perfectionism (Woodside et al., 2002) and acknowledge a history of concerns with weight, dieting, and physical appearance (Garner & Garfinkel, 1997). In the case of BN, high parental standards and critical comments from family members about weight and eating are significant predictors of the disorder (Crowther et al., 2002; Fairburn et al., 1997). It's easy to imagine how such variables might influence the beliefs and emotional states of children and adolescents.

A CYC LENS ON THE PSYCHOLOGICAL PARADIGMS: A HOLISTIC CONCEPTUAL MODEL

CYCPs must be aware of the underlying issues and risk factors that may influence the development of eating disorders in young people. Perfectionism, peer pressure, media images, and family history all play a role in the development of difficulties around food in adolescence and early adulthood ("Preventing and treating," 2005). As noted earlier, neurochemical imbalances have also been implicated in the development of eating disorders.

The sociocultural paradigm fits well with a CYC holistic perspective. Within this paradigm, for example, is the *dual pathway model* (Stice, 2001). In this model, sociocultural factors—the social pressure to be thin and the idealizing of thinness—promote body dissatisfaction. This leads to caloric restriction, which produces hunger, irritability and frustration, negative affect, and a lowering of self-esteem. The theory is that this then leads to binge-eating, which in turn leads to more guilt and purging (Weisz, 2004). The model is based on the understanding that society places unrealistic demands on girls and young women to be thin. Most adolescent girls internalize this ideal, and are reinforced positively by their peers when they conform to it and punished when they violate it. As we know, praise and teasing by peers are powerful consequences for adolescents.

According to the *tripartite model*, originally suggested by Thompson, Coovert, and Stormer (1999), three factors influence the development of disturbed eating behaviours: peers (e.g., through teasing), parents (through criticizing their own or their daughter's weight), and the media (in which women featured in movies, magazines, and TV are very thin). These three factors lead to eating disturbances in three ways: instilling a motivation to diet, internalizing of unrealistic standards, and a tendency to compare one's appearance with others' (Weisz, 2004). The model assumes that body dissatisfaction has a direct effect on the development of restrictive eating and bulimic behaviours. This theory has received support from studies with adolescent and adult female populations and with boys (Johnstang, 2009).

In the *developmental risk factors* theory, adolescence is acknowledged as a time of experimentation and self-expression. One of the most accepted theories proposed to explain the acting-out seen in adolescence suggests that individuals are searching for love and structure not only in the outside world but in their inner worlds as well (McKenzie, 2008). Neuroscience supports this idea. Specifically, we know that if an infant doesn't satisfactorily develop the capacity to self-soothe, the capacity to successfully manage strong emotions like anger and frustration later in adolescence may also be impaired or compromised (McKenzie, 2008). This may become increasingly evident when the onset of adolescent development exacerbates the expression of all emotions. Some of the dysfunctional ways a youth may use to express strong emotion are through self-injurious behaviours, including cutting, harmful substance use, and eating disorders (McKenzie, 2008). The onset of puberty, academic demands, and relationship changes are all stressful events that can precipitate concern with body image, thinness, and perfectionism, leading to disordered eating (Allen-Meares & Fraser, 2004). As well, eating disorders may reflect underlying struggles with identity, self-worth, and intimacy (McClure & Teyber, 2002). Adolescence and early adulthood are the developmental stages in which the primary tasks are to establish a sense of identity and develop close relationships with peers. For many, these tasks are challenging and even overwhelming, and eating behaviours may be one way to manage feelings of stress and inadequacy (McClure & Teyber, 2002).

The cognitive-behavioural view of eating disorders stresses the cycles of emotions and obsessive thinking involved in the development of disturbed eating habits. For example, stressful situations, low self-esteem, and concerns about body image lead to anxiety; binge-eating relieves the anxiety temporarily, but the guilt and shame that follow influence purging, and a repetitive cycle develops (Kearney, 2003). The feelings of stress, inadequacy, and anxiety are made worse in a painful spiralling effect that occurs with many risk behaviours. In this case, the attempt to control the food becomes symbolic of controlling or managing difficult emotions.

> It seems like I spend every waking hour consumed with thoughts about food, wanting it but feeling I shouldn't have it or not wanting it but knowing I'll have it anyway. . . . I feel like I am fighting this battle to control food and my weight and everything related to it, but really it all controls me. The thing that's really scary, though, is that when I manage not to think about food or my weight for just a little while. . . . I feel more scared . . . or even worse, totally empty, so I end up going back to obsessing about food. (McClure & Teyber, 2002, p. 19)

The **personality risk factors** associated with the development of eating disorders include negative or low self-esteem, perfectionism, a perception of ineffectiveness, negative self-appraisal, negative emotionality, dissatisfaction with body image, and a general expression of negative affect. One of the most commonly known and widely accepted explanations for the development of eating disorders is the need for control. The belief is that if one can control one's food intake, one can control others as well. Low self-esteem and poor body image lead to distorted perceptions about body weight and image. The distortion feeds the insecurity and low self-esteem, and eating is further restricted in an effort to exert control over self. Consequently, the spiralling cycle is repeated over and over again. For youth with AN, they can never be thin enough because the issue is not ultimately with their bodies but rather their lack of identity or sense of self (McKenzie, 2008). Young people demonstrating bulimic behaviours usually have the same type of distorted body image but also have an extremely poor self-concept or self-esteem. "Bingeing serves to feed the self and purging expels and punishes the self for that soothing. In many ways this is similar to cutting" (McKenzie, 2008, p. 140).

More specifically, however, the personality risk factors used to explain the development of AN differ from those used to explain the risk of developing BN. For AN, relevant personality factors include a tendency to be compliant, conforming, obsessive, and stoic. For youth who engage in bingeing and purging, the risk factors appear to include a tendency to require approval from others, to experience mood swings, to be more extroverted, to be more likely to use alcohol, to show signs of impulsivity, and to like novel situations (Kearney, 2003; McClure & Teyber, 2002).

CYCPs need to be aware of the relationship between self-harm and eating disorders. There are two types of self-harming behaviours: indirect and direct. **Indirect self-harm** refers to behaviours where the damage to self is generally cumulative rather than acute or immediate. In addition, the intent to actually hurt oneself may be somewhat ambiguous (Walsh, 2006). Two of the most common indirect self-harming behaviours are eating disorders and substance abuse, particularly when damage to physical and emotional health occurs as a result (Walsh, 2006). In fact, clinicians and researchers report that with eating-disordered and self-harm behaviours, if one pattern of behaviour has been eliminated, the other will increase.

> Simone worked hard in therapy, her perfectionism spurring her to be my "best" patient.
> . . . As her cutting subsided, the anorexia re-emerged, which I had expected as it was her original diagnosis. Again our work centered on dispelling Simone's ideas about the need for perfection, which had trapped her in two isolating behaviours, though fortunately not forever. (Levenkron, 1998, pp. 81–82)

With both eating disorders and substance abuse, the young person may lack awareness and deny or justify the self-destructive intent. There is much shame associated with both disorders; indeed, denial and secrecy are a hallmark characteristic of all eating disorders. Given these disorders' many layers of dynamics, CYCPs need to understand that intervention is complex and multifaceted and will almost always require clinical therapeutic resources and support.

Direct self-harm, also known as **self-inflicted violence (SIV)**, can be understood as a coping mechanism. Some youth use SIV because they find it easier to deal with real physical pain than their emotional pain. Others may feel emotionally numb, and using SIV reminds them that they're alive. Refer to Table 8.2 for an overview of self-harming behaviours and associated lethality.

Also important are the **trauma-related risk factors** that may lead to eating disorders and other indirect self-harming, pain-based behaviours; these factors include sexual abuse, parental discord and violence, and physical abuse (Allen-Meares & Fraser, 2004). Experienced clinicians are attuned to looking for a history of sexual and other trauma, especially when

Table 8.2 Classification of Self-Harming Behaviours and Lethality

Direct Self-Harming Behaviour	Indirect Self-Harming Behaviour	Level of Lethality
Suicide, single episode	Risk-taking single episode	High
Suicide, multiple episodes	High-risk episodes, late phase Anorexia	Medium-high
Major self-injury, single episode	Sexual risk taking, major intoxication, single episode	Medium-low
Self-injury, multiple episodes	Chronic substance abuse, Bulimia, discontinuation of psychotropic medications, multiple episodes	Low

Source: Adapted from Walsh, 2006, p. 22.

In addition to enmeshment, rigidity, and overprotectiveness, denial of family conflict is one of the four main characteristics found in families with a youth diagnosed with AN.

eating disorders are present in very young children (Weller & Weller, 2000). Some research examining data on children with a history of maltreatment found that compared with the general population, a history of sexual abuse is five times as likely to appear in the background of children who have BN. This research also explored whether eating disorder symptoms would correlate with trauma symptoms: 40 percent of girls with sexual abuse in their histories and 29 percent of boys with the same histories were found to experience eating problems, anxiety, and PTSD later in their development (Weller & Weller, 2000). Other research exploring the relationship between eating disorders and sexual abuse has not been as conclusive. The greatest continuity appears to be between sexual abuse and BN (Austin & Sciarra, 2010), with a small but significant relationship between sexual abuse and eating disorders. "It may be that sexual abuse has more of an indirect effect because of its association with other risk factors and is part of a complex interaction" (Austin & Sciarra, 2010, p. 202).

Many widely accepted theories suggest that **familial risk factors** are related to the development of eating disorders. These factors include **familial over-enmeshment** (meaning that family members are overinvolved in one another's lives to the point that even small decisions or events have a great deal of attention paid to them; Kearney, 2003), maternal overprotectiveness, mother's dieting and preoccupation with weight concerns, father's stated preference for thinness, direct parental comments regarding weight, and a family history of an eating disorder (Allen-Meares & Fraser, 2004). Within these family system theories, other factors include rigidity or rules and an overall denial of family conflict. In families with a youth struggling with BN, the risk factors that appear to indicate the youth's "pre-disorder" include heavy conflict with parents; greater family pathology, including substance abuse or depression; and more intense family conflict (Wilmshurst, 2004a).

WHERE DO YOU STAND?

Although the psychological explanations for eating disturbances differ somewhat from those emphasized from a CYC perspective, CYCPs can benefit from an understanding of the psychological models. Specifically, an awareness of the potential underlying issues (e.g., self-esteem, body image) and various risk factors (e.g., trauma, personality characteristics) that may cause eating disorders to develop in young people might help CYCPs better identify eating disturbances in the youth they support in practice. Try the *Take Action!* exercise and apply your knowledge of both the psychological explanations and the CYC perspectives for eating disorders to Phillip's case. How do your thoughts about this case reflect your position on the causes of eating disturbances?

Historically, family therapists such as Salvador Minuchin and Jay Haley have long theorized that eating disorders are a symptom of family dysfunction—that enmeshed families have more and stronger family rules, and that they tend to strictly prohibit the demonstration of such intense emotions as anger, sadness, or fear (McClure et al., 2002). These therapists don't contend that dysfunctional families *cause* eating disorders, but rather that such dysfunction (e.g., forced compliance with family norms, especially when enforced through withdrawal of affection or other means) can be a risk factor for eating disorders to develop.

> The child in such a family grows up unable to express strong emotion and lacks a firm sense of personal identity. Who is she? What are her likes/dislikes? What are her needs? . . . For this child, the family system has not equipped her to launch into adolescence. Becoming "sick" may be a way of coping with the conflicts as she moves toward further individuation. (McClure et al., 2002, pp. 24–25)

Take Action! Exercise: *Phillip's Case*

Phillip was always a healthy, happy child. Just before his 14th birthday he made the cut for his high-school football team, and began to work out regularly. His muscles became clearly defined; his family and his friends at school praised him for his newfound physique. Phillip was very proud of his accomplishments. But each day he wanted to exercise a little more and eat a little less. This had a dramatic effect: he lost a quarter of his body weight in four months and his behaviour changed. He grew distant from his friends, couldn't concentrate at school, and would get angry and aggressive if anyone challenged him about his weight or his diet. He gradually became superstitious; his days were filled with rituals. He grew severely emaciated, and his skin was dry and scaly. Phillip was diagnosed with AN, and was admitted to a residential adolescent unit. The treatment regime was very strict and extremely difficult for him to cope with. This fragile, emaciated 14-year-old had been thrust into a world of teenage girls with a wide array of behavioural issues ranging from AN to self-harm and attempted suicide. But Phillip complied with the treatment regime, and despite the odds that at times seem to be towering against him, he did get better.

Describe how Phillip's symptoms might be explained from each of the following paradigms: biological, psychodynamic, cognitive, and sociocultural. Re-examine the diathesis–stress framework presented in Figure 1.4 (see p. 35). Based on the factors highlighted there, what additional information about Phillip's history would you like to learn more about?

Source: Adapted from "Case study: Joe's story," n.d.

Families of youth with eating disorders tend to be concerned about food and appearance, and may thus role-model such concerns. If parents use food as a reward for children's compliant behaviour or as a symbol of nurturance, this, combined with other risk factors, including overt parental worrying about appearance and weight, may influence the development of issues with eating or produce eating disturbances for adolescents in the family (McClure et al., 2002).

HELPING CHILDREN AND ADOLESCENTS WITH EATING DISTURBANCES

Psychological Approaches to Treatment

Once diagnosed, treatment effectiveness is assessed by weight as well as behavioural change. The first line of response in the treatment of eating disorders is focused on restoring weight to a level that is not life-threatening (in the case of AN), as well as addressing associated medical concerns resulting from starvation, malnutrition, and compensatory strategies. Consequently, medical treatment and hospitalization should be among the first interventions explored. Interestingly, when weight is restored, improvements in mood, anxiety, and other psychological and emotional symptoms are also observed (Meehan et al., 2006). What is the best way to support a child or adolescent with AN, BN, or another eating disturbance? We've seen that psychological approaches to treatment for feeding and eating disturbances include those from the biological, psychodynamic, behavioural, cognitive, and sociocultural paradigms. In practice, of course, mental health professionals are likely to combine many strategies from each of these general approaches in their work to assist those diagnosed with eating disorders.

Before turning to a discussion of these treatments, it's important to recognize that no single intervention approach is consistently associated with positive outcomes in the literature (Gowers & Green, 2009). Adding to this complexity, high drop-out rates from treatment and lack of motivation to seek treatment have made it difficult for researchers to conduct large-scale randomized controlled studies in this area (Le Grange & Lock, 2005; Woodside et al., 2002). In addition, despite the rate at which children and youth are referred to specialists for treatment, a recent Canadian survey revealed that physicians and psychologists have low self-ratings of competence in treating eating disorders and identify various barriers to practice, including lack of skills, case complexity, and lack of resources (Lafrance Robinson, Boachie, & Lafrance, 2013). Clearly, continued research and training for all of those involved in working with youth diagnosed with eating disorders are required.

Jasmine's Case: *Revisited*

Jasmine has a background of sexual abuse perpetrated by her stepfather. Jasmine's mother didn't believe her allegations about the abuse, choosing instead to believe her husband's denials. Jasmine was subsequently removed from her mother's care. Prior to placement, it was known that she'd been experiencing serious difficulties in school; that she'd been running away and staying with a group of street youth; and that she'd been engaging in other risky behaviours, including using street drugs and having indiscriminate sexual relationships. It was therefore assessed that foster care wasn't the best option for Jasmine. She was placed in group care, where she's been stable for one year.

Biological Paradigm A biological approach to treatment for eating disorders has explored the effectiveness of altering levels of serotonin. Accordingly, antidepressants that increase activation of serotonin have been used in the treatment of both AN and BN. Considering that a comorbid mood disorder is not uncommon in the case of eating disorders, this seems logical. Research suggests that antidepressants (e.g., Prozac, Zoloft) can be effective in improving mood as well as in decreasing the frequency of binges (Fairburn & Harrison, 2003; Walsh et al., 2004). Their effectiveness, however, is more consistently observed for BN than AN (Walsh et al., 2006). In the case of BED, other medications (e.g., anticonvulsant medications, appetite suppressants) may be included in treatment approaches, and SSRIs in particular appear to reduce binge-eating episodes (Apopolinario et al., 2003). See Box 8.6 for a list of common medications used in the treatment of eating disorders.

Despite these encouraging results, medication alone isn't sufficient for eliminating the symptoms of AN or BN. In fact, some researchers and practitioners question the utility of medications in the treatment of eating disorders, suggesting that they should be used only when comorbid mood disorders are present. Regardless of where one stands on this issue, however, the use of psychotropic medications is not the predominant approach to treatment. As we've emphasized in earlier discussions, medications do not change behaviours. And in the case of some disorders (e.g., Rumination Disorder), medications haven't been found to be effective at all (Chial et al., 2003). Where do you stand with respect to the use of medications in the treatment of eating disorders?

Psychodynamic Paradigm Given that the psychodynamic approach views early family relationships as a predisposing factor in developing eating disorders, it's not surprising that family therapy is considered a particularly relevant treatment. Bringing emotional difficulties and conflicts to light in the context of the family is the recommended approach to intervention. In particular, issues of control, overprotection, self-identity, and independence are examined, as well as compassion, empathy, and care (Canetti et al., 2008).

Although this approach to therapy seems logical, a recent review comparing family therapy with other approaches in the treatment of AN found few controlled studies investigating its effectiveness with adolescents; in addition, those that were conducted had very small sample sizes (Gardner & Wilkinson, 2011). These researchers recommended that many more studies need to examine the effectiveness of family approaches in the treatment of AN, particularly for adolescents. More recent investigations suggest that a psychodynamic approach to treatment for eating disturbances may be beneficial

Box 8.6

Medications Used in the Treatment of Eating Disorders

Prozac	lithium	Xanax
Paxil	desipramine	naltrexone
Zoloft	imipramine	Zyprexa
Effexor	Wellbutrin	Luvox
Remeron		

when utilized in combination with behavioural techniques (e.g., Murphy, Russell, & Waller, 2005).

Behavioural Paradigm From a behavioural paradigm, eating disorders can be treated through the use of specific reinforcement and punishment techniques. For example, social praise or tangible reinforcers (e.g., money, tokens) can be provided following the desired behaviour (i.e., eating). *Negative reinforcement* (i.e., the removal of an unpleasant stimulus following the desired behaviour) can also been implemented in the treatment of eating disorders. For example, Hoch et al. (1994) held food to a child's lip (an aversive stimulus to the child), and after the child ate the food, the negative stimulus was removed. Exposure techniques that expose the individual to the feared stimulus in the absence of a painful outcome might also be used in the case of BED and ARFID.

A behavioural technique called *habit reversal* is frequently used in the treatment of Rumination Disorder. This strategy involves having the youth engage in deep breathing, which is a competing behaviour in that it can't occur at the same time as regurgitation. In other words, one behaviour (rumination/regurgitation) is replaced by another (deep breathing), and the former is decreased (Chial et al., 2003).

Although behavioural techniques are frequently used in the treatment of eating disorders, they're most often used together with cognitive strategies in the evidence-based treatment approach of *cognitive behavioural therapy*. We now turn to a discussion of these highly utilized interventions.

Cognitive Paradigm As we've seen in previous chapters, the goals of cognitive therapy include increasing awareness of personal cognitive biases and their negative emotions as well as challenging dysfunctional beliefs. *Cognitive behavioural therapy* (CBT), which uses both cognitive strategies and behavioural exercises, has been used in the treatment of both AN and BN (Vitousek, 2002). An abundance of research documents the effectiveness of CBT with BN (Fairburn & Harrison, 2003; Schmidt et al., 2007; Wilson, Grilo, & Vitousek, 2007), making it the treatment of choice for this diagnosis. Emphasis in this approach to treatment is on normalizing eating patterns (i.e., meal planning, nutritional education) and challenging the irrational beliefs that trigger binge-eating episodes in an effort to eliminate the binge–purge cycle. **Exposure with response-prevention techniques** (which has the adolescent eat "forbidden foods" and resist purging afterward) is also used to decrease inappropriate compensatory behaviours. It should be noted that although CBT is effective in decreasing the severity of bingeing and restrictive eating behaviours, concerns about weight and body image persist after treatment (Lundgren, Danoff-Burg, & Anderson, 2004).

While some studies have also demonstrated the effectiveness of CBT in the treatment of BED (e.g., Brownley, Berkman, & Seway, 2007), this treatment approach has been found to be less effective (and some argue ineffective) for those diagnosed with AN (Kaplan, 2002; Pike et al., 2003). Greater success has been demonstrated for a more behavioural approach to intervention, where rewards are provided for adhering to a prescribed diet (Johnson, Tsoh, & Varnado, 1996). For adolescents with AN, however, the preferred treatment is family therapy, which we'll consider below in our discussion of the sociocultural paradigm.

Before ending our discussion of the cognitive paradigm, it's worth revisiting the fact that a significant challenge in treating eating disorders (particularly AN) is the lack of motivation for change. Bewell and Carter (2008) found that a significant predictor of treatment success for AN was the client's *readiness for change*. As a result, researchers are currently evaluating the effectiveness of **motivational interviewing (MI)**, a cognitive-based strategy where therapist and client explore and attempt to resolve the client's mixed thoughts and feelings about treatment.

Sociocultural Paradigm   From a sociocultural standpoint, the treatment of eating disorders is best achieved by changing conditions in the social context. In addition to educating children and adolescents about the risks associated with unrealistic images presented in the media, school- and community-based programs encouraging healthy eating behaviours are recommended and are being implemented. Other researchers recommend future research that will help explain why some individuals internalize media images more readily and more extensively than others (Vander Wal, Gibbons, & Pilar Grazioso, 2008). Marketing campaigns that present realistic perceptions of beauty (e.g., Dove Campaign for Real Beauty) may also promote healthier attitudes toward body image and more positive feelings about self.

As we mentioned above, family therapy is currently the preferred treatment for adolescents diagnosed with AN (Le Grange & Lock, 2005; Loeb & Le Grange, 2009). Although its effectiveness varies from case to case, attempts to get parents working as a team to address family conflict have been found to result in long-term recovery for a significant number of adolescents (Le Grange & Lock, 2005). The effectiveness of such approaches in the treatment of BN is less clear. Few controlled studies have investigated the effectiveness of family therapy in treating BN (Le Grange et al., 2010), and those that have show that although some adolescents may benefit from family therapy, the effects are small (e.g., Le Grange et al., 2007). Other research suggests that family therapy for BN may be comparable to but no better than a cognitive-behavioural approach to treatment; however, adolescents are more likely to refuse family therapy than other interventions (Schmidt et al., 2007). Clearly, more controlled and long-term research is needed before firm conclusions can be drawn about the effectiveness of family therapy for adolescents diagnosed with BN.

CYC Approaches for Youth Struggling with Eating Disturbances

The experiences of eating disorders are specific to each individual and his or her family, and CYCPs' interventions must reflect such specificity. "A person-centered, recovery-oriented approach for eating disorders is . . . a sustained, long term approach that attends to all of the dimensions of the illness: physical, psychological, behavioural, social and practical. This approach must be maintained both during treatment and in the recovery process" (McGorry & Vickery, 2012, p. 29).

Strength-Based Relational CYC Practice   As with the other difficulties we address in this text, CYCPs must explore all aspects of the context of the young person's eating difficulties. This focus is in keeping with the ecological and relational framework of both assessment and intervention processes, regardless of the observed behaviours and how concerning these may be. It's particularly important to be strength-based, caring, supportive, and nonjudgmental when youth are struggling with an eating disturbance. As with all strength-based approaches, the emphasis is on identifying the young person's resilience, protective factors, assets, and strengths; communicating a sense of hope but establishing expectations for success within the young person's capacity; promoting empowerment and independence; and setting in motion the forces needed for improvement and success (Saleebey, 2006).

CYCPs need to assess the level of impact of disturbed eating symptoms on day-to-day functioning and know when to refer youth to collateral resources. They must respectfully consider what young people tell them about how they're feeling and explore any underlying issues with anxiety, substance misuse, mood difficulties, or other self-harming behaviours—and respond accordingly in the context of young people's strengths and the CYCP's relationship with them (e.g., CYCPs may sometimes need to assertively and pointedly challenge the dysfunctional beliefs underlying the eating difficulty). As always, the young person's cultural and family context will be important influences on the choice of treatment and support. Cultural influences in terms of food, eating behaviours, family structures and hierarchies, and ways of recognizing and addressing stress are the context in which young people must address and overcome their eating disorder (McGorry & Vickery, 2012).

Keep in mind that although those diagnosed with an eating disorder are typically adolescent girls, eating disorders also affect boys, as we saw in Phillip's case. Eating disorders among both gay youth and heterosexual young men are not as uncommon as in years past. And although once thought to be experienced only by young, white, affluent females, eating disorders are also increasing among youth of colour and Indigenous youth in Canada. It would appear that when young people from outside the dominant culture in Canada are exposed to more Westernized ideals of body weight and appearance, the rates of eating disorders among those populations increase significantly (McClure et al., 2002), as we saw in the Fiji study earlier.

Assessment

CYCPs need to know how to identify the signs and symptoms of eating disorders. Unfortunately, most affected youth are very successful in hiding the behaviour from families and friends, and, like Jasmine, from therapists and CYCPs.

Rating Scales. Clinicians (e.g., psychologists, psychiatric social workers) use a variety of measures to assess eating disorders; these include interview schedules; self-report forms for children, youth, and parents; and instruments designed to measure cognitive aspects and dysfunctional beliefs. Knowing the types of questions these measures employ will help guide CYCPs in their assessment. Most commonly used assessment measures for child and adolescent eating disorders have been adapted from instruments designed for use with adult populations. Specifically, the measures most widely used by clinicians include self-report questionnaires such as the Children's Eating Attitudes Test (ChEAT), the Children's Eating Disorders Inventory (EDI-C), and the Eating Disorder Examination Questionnaire (EDE-Q); semi-structured interviews such as the Children's Eating Disorder Examination (ChEDE); and online measures, including the Development and Well-Being Assessment (DAWBA) (Micali & House, 2011, p. 125).

If an eating disorder is suspected, CYCPs may consider the following questions to guide their day-to-day observations either before or in concert with a clinical consult or referral: Does she (or he) express an intense fear of being overweight in contrast to her (or his) real body weight? Does she worry constantly about being fat even though her weight is within normal range? How much weight has she lost and in what time frame? Has there been a disruption in her menstrual cycle? Does she severely restrict calories, or talk obsessively about food restriction and calories? Does she exercise excessively in order to lose weight? Describe any unusual food behaviours, including binge-eating, hoarding, concealment, and throwing food away. Does she go the bathroom immediately after eating? Listen for running water in the bathroom to hide sounds of self-induced vomiting. Observe for frequent use of laxatives. Is she preoccupied with her body image, constantly looking in the mirror and saying that she's too fat? Is she irritable or sad and withdrawn? Has there been a stressful event recently? Does she demonstrate any obsessive behaviours or a tendency to perfectionism in other aspects of life? Has there been a decrease of 10 pounds or more in a short amount of time? Does she express negative thoughts about herself? Is there a family history of an eating disorder? Does she engage in impulsive behaviours, including drug/alcohol use or sexual behaviours? (Micali & House, 2011).

If you're concerned about any of these behaviours, will she engage with you in a discussion about them? Does she realize that there's reason to be concerned? If yes, make your referral; if no, immediate help may be warranted (i.e., a medical appointment, a consult with a mobile crisis team, or, if necessary, a trip to emergency). Note that CYCPs must always first refer to a physical medical examination to rule out any physical cause for a concerning weight loss (Samuels & Sikorsky, 1998).

Specific questions should also be considered in the event that BN is suspected. For example, Does she appear to engage in binge eating frequently? How often? Describe the episodes in your log notes. Does the bingeing include consumption of high-calorie foods? Is there secretive eating? Does the eating episode stop due only to sleep, vomiting, interruption, or stomach pain? Is there use of purging behaviours, including self-induced vomiting or use of laxatives in order to avoid calories after bingeing? Does she engage in severe restriction of calories and/or excessive exercise? Is she preoccupied with her body image? Does she appear to be depressed following an eating episode? Does she use substances (e.g., alcohol, amphetamines)? Does she share with you her concern about feeling out of control? Does she appear to be having difficulties with her teeth? Do you often smell foul breath? (Samuels & Sikorsky, 1998). As above, if you're concerned about any of these behaviours, will she engage with you in a discussion about them? Does she realize that there's reason to be concerned? Follow the steps as outlined for AN.

Most major urban communities in Canada have specialized inpatient or outpatient hospital-based treatment programs for young people who may be struggling with eating disorders. A typical inpatient medical team includes a psychiatrist, a psychologist, a medical practitioner, nurses, and a dietitian or nutritionist. A complete medical assessment includes a cardiac examination and a measurement of nutrient levels in order to fully assess the physiological consequences of the disorder. An assessment and intake interview by a clinician includes discussions with the young person as well as with her caregivers. Clinical assessments begin with background questions about age, education, and living and family situation. In their assessment process, inpatient treatment programs will also conduct a mental status examination (MSE), which includes an assessment of attitudes about food, eating, and weight (for information about MSEs, see Chapter 9). Information from the family about

Table 8.3 Behavioural Indicators Checklist: Eating Disorders

✓ Anorexia Nervosa	✓ Bulimia Nervosa and Binge Eating Disorder
Restricted eating or fasting	Impaired control when eating (i.e., eating rapidly)
Excessive weighing or measuring of body	Eating until uncomfortably full
Repetitive checking of reflection in mirror	Eating large amounts of food when not hungry
Concerns about eating in public	Eating alone because of embarrassment
Perfectionism	Feeling disgust, guilt, or depression after overeating
Restrained emotional expression	
Decreased body weight, underweight	Average or above average weight

their perceptions of the youth's eating behaviours and weight loss as well as the parents' perception of their relationship with each other is also gathered, if possible. Generally, most youth struggling with AN or BN will resist being diagnosed and engaging in the therapeutic process; they may deny or withhold information, or provide misleading information. Therefore, "in interviewing individuals with eating disorders, acknowledging potential ambivalence about change early in the interview is central to establishing rapport" (B.C. Ministry of Health, 2010a, p. 24). CYCPs can assist in the referral and intake process and discussions by encouraging the youth, reassuring family, and providing answers to questions about the history of any other diagnosed disorders and any alcohol or drug misuse.

Indicators to Recognize We've noted that most eating disorders begin in adolescence or early adulthood. While young people suffering with AN often have severe and noticeable physical symptoms, those with BN frequently maintain a normal weight, which can make it very difficult to identify. As we've seen, however, most youth affected by these types of eating problems are very adept at hiding their behaviour from their families and friends; in other systems including schools, youth centres, and group care, they hide it from their teachers, counsellors, therapists, and CYCPs. Accordingly, CYCPs should be familiar with the DSM-5 criteria as summarized earlier in this chapter. Also see Table 8.3 for a summary of behavioural indicators associated with eating disorders. Which of these were apparent in the case of Jasmine that opened this chapter?

Intervention

With support and comprehensive treatment, most young people can learn to manage symptoms or control their eating difficulties. Treatment for eating disorders usually requires a multidisciplinary team approach, which includes individual and family therapy; working with a primary care physician and a dietitian or nutritionist; and often inpatient or outpatient medical treatment. CYCPs can provide an important adjunct to ongoing clinical treatment through their day-to-day supervision, support, and relational-focused interventions.

Since young people with eating disorders are usually reluctant to seek help, often denying the difficulty or concealing their behaviours, CYCPs can play a significant role in raising their awareness of the problem behaviours and supporting their recognition of the stages of recovery. As always when working one on one with young people who are struggling, CYCPs first establish a caring, trusting therapeutic relationship and then assess readiness for change using the *stages of change model*. CYCPs must remain nonjudgmental and supportive; *motivational interviewing techniques* ought to be used. (See Chapter 10 for a full discussion of the stages of change model and motivational interviewing. These models can be used in all therapeutic interventions with young people, and are particularly effective and warranted for use with addictive behaviours.) Young people will need support to learn new and more functional ways to cope with their feelings and to learn appropriate ways of relating to others. They'll also need support in recognizing their strengths and in appreciating themselves for who they are rather than trying to meet others' expectations (McClure et al., 2002). Empirical evidence suggests that the most successful types of interventions for young people with eating disturbances are CBT (individual and group), psychoeducation, and family therapy.

Behavioural and Cognitive-Behavioural Techniques for CYCPs CBT is the preferred treatment for eating disorders: extensive empirical research has shown it to be highly effective (particularly for BN, but for AN as well), and clinicians find that it works (Allen-Meares & Fraser, 2004). The practitioner works toward two treatment goals—problem solving and cognitive restructuring—while closely monitoring food intake as well as any dysfunctional thoughts, feelings, and emotions. CYCPs can support CBT treatment plans through adjunct one-on-one support—including helping young people with their food logs, teaching problem-solving skills and functional coping strategies, and identifying cues for binge-eating. They can also use CBT on their own by challenging young people's cognitive distortions and dysfunctional beliefs.

CBT is consistent with a CYC practice because it's solution-focused, helping young people identify specific problems and generate as many solutions as possible; each strategy is considered and the most feasible or realistic is selected. Specifically, CYCPs can help young people in *cognitive restructuring*, whereby the young person (1) records her thoughts and judgments about food and weight as well as her arguments and evidence for their validity; (2) records arguments and evidence doubting their validity as well as support for these counterarguments; (3) generates a realistic and appropriate interpretation; and (4) makes a reasoned conclusion for use in governing weight and weight-related behaviours (Halmi, 2012). CYCPs can help youth evaluate both the process and the results.

The Role of Medication Although studies have shown that CBT is the most successful treatment for eating disorders, medication is often used. Historically, clinicians used antipsychotics to treat AN in the belief that distorted thoughts about body shape and weight resembled psychotic delusions (Weisz, 2004). More recently, newer antipsychotics have been used, but with limited success. Antidepressants are used in the treatment of both AN and BN; however, studies have shown that SSRIs have been found to be largely unsuccessful in treating AN (Weisz, 2004).

Psychoeducation and Individual Counselling One of the main reasons why eating disordered behaviours are so difficult to treat is that they're highly reinforcing. It's theorized that they're reinforced in two primary ways: (1) as a coping mechanism for such difficult experiences as developmental transitions, fears of maturity and autonomy, distressing life events, feelings of ineffectiveness and helplessness, poor self-esteem, trauma, and disturbed relationships with family and friends; and (2) as an attempt to increase self-esteem and the feeling of control. Concerned family, friends, or other adults may also unknowingly reinforce the eating behaviours by making positive comments about lost weight or slim looks (Halmi, 2012).

In inpatient and outpatient programs, group work is always used as a treatment approach. CYCPs can co-facilitate psychoeducational groups (which provide information about eating disorders) and manage support groups (which focus on giving young people the opportunity to support and coach one another), whether in treatment or as an adjunct to treatment. Group work is highly recommended for those with BN, but is not always preferred for those struggling with AN until they're stabilized in their individual work. Clinicians and therapists have suggested that group therapy can be risky in inpatient treatment programs, given the members' likelihood of sharing weight-loss techniques and competing in losing weight (McFarren, 2005).

Family Support Interventions   With children and adolescents, it's essential that treatment providers use a family-based approach. By actively engaging and respecting the concerns of parents and/or caregivers throughout treatment, providers can foster trust and cooperation. Since family members are integral to positive treatment outcomes, the establishment of a respectful, collaborative, and informative relationship with the family is the cornerstone of effective treatment for eating disorders (B.C. Ministry of Health, 2010a).

Family therapy is almost always included in treatment programs for youth with eating disorders, and is purported to be the most effective treatment for adolescents with AN (Halmi, 2005). The approach most commonly used by family therapists is *structural family therapy*, which focuses on developing family cohesion, consistency, and communication skills and teaching conflict-resolution skills (Kearney, 2003). The overall goal is to support the family in disengaging the adolescent, allowing her to separate and establish autonomy (Austin & Sciarra, 2010). Structural family therapy has two main goals: (1) improving communication patterns, whereby families recognize how their adolescent's eating difficulties serve as a distraction from other family problems, such as alcoholism or anger issues; (2) helping the family recognize the adolescent's needs for autonomy (Weisz, 2004).

While young people are in treatment, their families need to support their treatment program. Families will themselves need education, and so family support groups are very important. CYC practice with families who are struggling with their adolescent's eating disturbance embraces the same guidelines as a good therapeutic relationship with young people: listen to their story; acknowledge the pain; look for strengths; ask questions about survival, support, positive times, interests, dreams, goals, and pride; point out strengths; link strengths to family members' goals and dreams; link families to resources to help them achieve these goals and dreams; and find opportunities for family members to be in support roles or teachers (Saleebey, 2006).

Additional techniques for intervention are summarized in Box 8.7.

Prevention: Advocacy, Community, and School-Based Strategies   The general areas in which to focus prevention efforts are as follows: (1) working to combat the strong negative influence of peer group pressure; (2) building on young people's developmental experiences to cultivate their overall sense of confidence, esteem, and individual effectiveness; (3) increasing physical activity; and (4) teaching participation and noncompetitiveness

Techniques for CYC Intervention

Use caring, supportive, nonjudgmental CYCP relationship-building techniques.

Gently challenge the dysfunctional attitudes and thoughts about eating, shape, body image, and weight.

Replace diet restrictions with healthy eating.

Carefully monitor food intake.

Teach youth to identify, journal, and record triggers, including any dysfunctional thoughts, feelings, and emotions.

Teach relaxation.

Identify and build on strengths.

Engage the family; teach communication skills and conflict-resolution skills.

Teach interpersonal communication skills and assertiveness.

Teach youth about how family relationships can contribute to healthy or unhealthy eating.

Teach about weight issues.

Develop a relapse prevention plan.

Have youth list assets, talents, and accomplishments, and review the list often.

Help youth focus on the positive aspects of life; teach them to stop criticizing themselves.

Help youth to stop thinking of food as "good" or "bad"; instead, encourage them to see food as "a good thing to eat frequently" or "a good thing to eat occasionally."

Help them develop mastery. Focus on strengths.

Help youth develop a more positive body image by appreciating their body's functional nature.

Source: From Box 8.7 in Self-Esteem Comes in All Sizes: How to Be Happy and Healthy at Your Natural Weight, 2E by Gary Foster, Carol A. Johnson M. A., pp. 152–154. Copyright © 2001 by Gurze Books. Reproduced by permission of the Gurze Books.

skills to influence participation of all young people, including those who refuse to participate in sports or other athletic activities if their performance can't be perfect (Halmi, 2012). According to research by Graber and Brooks-Gunn (1996), early-maturing girls are at particular risk for developing eating disorders, so it's important to begin preventative steps in the middle childhood or elementary-school years (Graber & Brooks-Gunn, 1996).

Only a few well-controlled research studies have been conducted on the effectiveness of eating disorders prevention, and most of these have insignificant or contradictory findings. Some researchers have suggested that this stems from the medical-model, or disease-specific, focus of most prevention programs, and that efforts should instead focus on influencing the social or political environments that first cause eating disorders to emerge and then allow them to be reinforced. As advocates, then, CYCPs can help girls develop their strengths and overcome media influences and peer pressure to be thin. In addition, CYCPs can be political advocates for change, focusing on systemic change efforts in their work (Graber & Brooks-Dunn, 1996).

CYCPs can also work to create a "body friendly" therapeutic environment. Assess the therapeutic milieu of your program: What images do you see on the walls of your school, treatment centre, or group home? How might you use teachable moments when viewing media portrayals of thinness? How do you manage nutrition education in your programs? How might mealtimes be improved? How can you include youth in menu planning? How can CYCPs model healthy relationships with food and their own bodies? How can you encourage sports and physical activities for all young people in your programs, meeting their needs for recreation activities regardless of fitness level, skill, or body size? How might you respond if a young person says to you, "I feel fat"? How will you cope with your own body image issues in a way that won't do harm to the youth in your care? (Lisa Naylor, personal communication, October 2009).

Alternative Healing   Although little research exists to support the use of the following interventions, CYCPs may find some of these approaches useful, particularly as adjuncts to more conventional treatments: dance therapy, art therapy, biofeedback, coaching, eye-movement desensitization, journalling, yoga, meditation, and relaxation training or mindfulness-based stress reduction (MBSR).

Relational CYC Practice   Food may represent many things for young people struggling with eating disorders: when their bodies and minds feel out of control with social and personal issues, developmental concerns, and hormonal changes, food becomes the one thing that can be *controlled*. As we've seen, control is a central feature of eating disorders. Young people who are seeking desperately to be loved and accepted often find that food meets both of these needs. Food can also meet unfulfilled needs for value and affirmation, given that young people are likely to believe what the media portrays: that being thin will bring admiration and acceptance from others (McClure et al., 2002). Food is symbolic of nurture, and thus many vulnerable youth have a very complicated relationship with it.

CYCPs can help create a healthy, "body friendly" therapeutic environment by including youth in menu planning and meal preparation.

Relational CYC practice builds on young people's resiliency by increasing their connectedness, establishing clear and consistent boundaries, teaching healthy eating and healthy coping skills, and setting high and realistic expectations about personal wellness in a caring, supportive environment. Every young person needs to be accepted, to feel as if she belongs and that she matters. If her needs for acceptance, love, and belonging are being met by engaging in unhealthy eating, we need to establish the caring relationships critical for developing her strengths by encouraging social competence and autonomy and instilling a sense of purpose (Dotterweich, n.d.).

In the context of a relational approach, then, CYCPs can use numerous strategies to support young people with eating disturbances. Refer to Box 8.8 for a summary of specific communication strategies that might be helpful.

WHERE DO YOU STAND?

Without question, CYCPs have a significant role in identifying indicators of eating disorders and in supporting recovery for those struggling with such difficulties. In concluding this chapter, we note that it's important to give youth the opportunity to hear from people who've recovered from an eating disorder. Speaking to those with lived experience who've successfully recovered can be very helpful in motivating young people to start or continue to engage with treatment. Revisit the case of Jasmine one last time in the *Viewpoint Challenge* exercise to evaluate your understanding of the appropriate psychological and CYC interventions for eating disturbances. Where do you stand with respect to interventions for eating disturbances?

Box 8.8

CYC Communication Strategies

Encourage regular, formalized eating (e.g., scheduled meals and snacks as per treatment regimen of clinician).

Minimize distractions during mealtimes (e.g., encourage youth not to eat in front of the TV or while reading).

Encourage a focus on the pattern of eating, not what is eaten.

Allow adolescents to choose the foods they eat during scheduled eating times.

Emphasize that regular, healthy eating decreases binges.

Encourage the use of time and the behaviour of others to guide when to eat, not feelings of hunger (in early treatment).

Encourage activities that are incompatible with eating between scheduled meals (e.g., listen to music, walk, visit friends).

Reframe the urge to eat as a temporary phenomenon to which one doesn't need to succumb.

Carefully teach about the harm associated with compensation strategies (i.e., vomiting, laxative use).

Challenge all cognitive distortions about body shape, weight, and food.

Include youth in meal planning.

Encourage physical activity: sports and games.

Teach nutrition and model healthy eating.

Source: Based on Fairburn, 2008.

Help youth understand that society is not always right about things.

Encourage personal style that announces to the world, "I like me!"

Help youth surround themselves with positive, supportive people.

Source: From Box 8.8 in Self-Esteem Comes in All Sizes: How to Be Happy and Healthy at Your Natural Weight, 2E by Gary Foster, Carol A. Johnson M.A., pp. 152–154. Copyright © 2001 by Gurze Books. Reproduced by permission of the Gurze Books.

Jasmine's Case: *Viewpoint Challenge Exercise*

Reread the excerpts of Jasmine's story that were presented in this chapter. If Jasmine were being treated by a psychologist for her disorder, what would her treatment likely involve? If you were working with Jasmine, what strategies might you use as a CYCP? Which strategies would you prefer and why?

CHAPTER SUMMARY

- Disordered eating is associated with specific behaviours (e.g., restricting food intake, bingeing, or ingesting large amounts of food in short time periods, skipping meals, eating to soothe emotional distress) and extreme concerns about body weight and shape resulting in preoccupation with food and eating.

- According the DSM-5, feeding and eating disorders are associated with disturbed eating behaviours, psychological features (e.g., distorted thoughts, feelings of distress), and harmful behavioural strategies or compensatory behaviours that put the youth at risk for a number of significant physical and/or social-emotional impairments.

- CYCPs need to recognize relevant indicators of eating disturbances and support treatment interventions for affected youth. An understanding of symptoms, explanations, and approaches to intervention for eating disorders will allow CYCPs to better support youth in their practice.

- Psychological explanations for eating disturbances include genetics, low levels of some neurotransmitters, illogical beliefs, including perfectionism, ideals about body image, and societal emphasis on the "ideal body type,"

- According to the CYC perspective, multiple risk factors affect the development of eating disturbances, including sociocultural, personality, and family factors.

- In a CYC assessment, specific questions can guide day-to-day observations either prior to or together with a clinical consult or referral if CYCPs are concerned about a youth struggling with an eating disorder.

- Psychological treatment approaches for eating disorders include antidepressants, exposure with response prevention, education strategies, and school- and community-based programs encouraging healthy eating behaviours.

- As advocates, CYCPs can focus on helping youth develop strengths and overcome media influences and peer pressure to obtain unrealistic standards of beauty. Other treatment approaches for youth with eating disturbances include referrals to treatment programs for individual therapy, family therapy, and group counselling.

Critical Thinking Questions

1. Are you surprised by the fact that purging occurs in both AN and BN? Explain.
2. Why do you think so many youth struggle with eating disorders in Canada today?
3. Identify ways in which CYCPs can act as advocates to effect change at the sociocultural level in order to prevent eating disorders and promote healthy body image for youth.
4. How can we use youths' peers in a protective way to prevent eating disorders?
5. Consider the various psychological approaches to treatment. What strategies or ideas from these approaches might be helpful to CYCPs, and why?
6. What questions would you feel most comfortable asking an adolescent in order to gain useful information about a possible eating disorder? What questions might you find difficult to ask and why?
7. What indicators of eating disturbances are you most likely to notice in your CYC practice? What indicators may be difficult to identify?
8. Identify ways in which CYCPs can create a "body image friendly" therapeutic milieu.

Key Terms

Anorexia Nervosa (AN), 316

Avoidant/Restrictive Food Intake Disorder (ARFID), 315

Binge Eating Disorder (BED), 318

binge-eating, 317

Bulimia Nervosa (BN), 317

compensatory behaviours, 314

direct self-harm, or self-inflicted violence (SIV), 330

exposure with response-prevention techniques, 335

familial over-enmeshment, 331

Supplemental Readings

Arnold, C. (2012). *Decoding anorexia: How breakthroughs in science offer hope for eating disorders.* New York: Routledge.

Costin, C. (2007). *The eating disorder sourcebook: A comprehensive guide to the causes, treatments, and prevention of eating disorders.* New York: McGraw-Hill.

Grilo, C., & Mitchell, J. E. (Eds). (2010). *The treatment of eating disorders: A clinical handbook.* New York: Guilford.

Johnson, C. A. (2001). *Self-esteem comes in all sizes.* Carlsbad, CA: Gurze Books.

Lask, B., & Bryant-Waugh, R. (Eds). (2007). *Eating disorders in childhood and adolescence* (3rd ed.). London: Routledge.

Mirror, Mirror . . . Kids and Body Image. (2000). *Reclaiming Children and Youth, 9*(3), www.cyc-net.org/Journals/rcy/rcy-9-3.html. (This volume of *Reclaiming Children and Youth* is dedicated to the issues of body image and eating issues.)

Murphy, S., Russell, L., & Waller, G. (2005). Integrated psychodynamic therapy for bulimia nervosa and binge eating disorder: Theory, practice, and preliminary findings. *European Eating Disorders Review, 13*(6), 383-391.

Online Resources

National Eating Disorder Information Centre, www.nedic.ca

The Body Positive, http://thebodypositive.org

Linda Bacon's Health at Every Size community, www.haescommunity.org

Body Image Health, http://bodyimagehealth.org/healthy-bodies-curriculum (Kathy Kater, author of *Healthy Body Image: Teaching Kids to Eat and Love Their Bodies Too!*, is a psychotherapist who has specialized in the treatment and prevention of body image, eating, fitness, and weight-related concerns. This comprehensive prevention curriculum has demonstrated significant, measurable improvement in weight-related attitudes among pubescent children, and was recommended by the U.S. Department of Health's Office of Women's Health in its BodyWise information packet for educators.)

U.S. National Institute of Mental Health, *Eating Disorders* booklet, www.nimh.nih.gov/health/publications/eating-disorders-new-trifold/index.shtml

Chapter 9
Psychosis and Schizophrenia

Sunshine Pics/Fotolia

Which one of these individuals has been diagnosed with Schizophrenia? The reality is that this psychotic disorder has many faces. You can't tell simply by looking at people who has been or might be diagnosed with this serious mental illness.

Case Example: *Rebecca*

Rebecca came into the care of Child and Family Services at age 4. When she was 14, after a series of foster families had complained about her being "too difficult," she was placed in a group home. Rebecca ran away repeatedly from her group home placement. While on the streets she began selling sex to survive; she was sexually exploited. She started using crack cocaine, and later injecting OxyContin in order to numb herself from the pain of the sexual exploitation. Soon she was addicted to these drugs.

At 17, Rebecca acquired HIV and later developed AIDS from the intravenous drug use. At 20, she was admitted to hospital with pneumonia. She was presenting with paranoia and incoherent speech, saying that people were out to "get her"; she described seeing ghosts on the ceiling who were telling her to kill those around her because they were plotting to kill her. As the days went by, Rebecca became increasingly paranoid and refused to speak to anyone. She was diagnosed with psychosis secondary to AIDS.

Learning Objectives

1. Define *psychosis* and outline its primary symptoms. Distinguish between hallucinations, delusions, and disordered thinking.

2. Summarize the DSM criteria for Brief Psychotic Disorder, Schizophrenia, and Substance/Medication-Induced Psychotic Disorder, distinguishing between negative and positive symptoms in your discussion.

3. Compare and contrast biological, psychodynamic, behavioural, cognitive, and socio-cultural explanations for psychotic disorders.

4. Summarize the diathesis–stress and traumagenic neurodevelopmental models of Schizophrenia.

5. Describe psychological treatment approaches used in treating psychotic disorders for each of the major psychological paradigms.

6. Describe specific indicators of psychosis and Schizophrenia.

7. Describe the multimodal treatment options used for adolescent Schizophrenia and psychosis.

8. Outline the role of CYCPs when working with youth with psychosis and/or Schizophrenia.

Chapter Overview

Psychosis represents a group of symptoms that can occur in the context of many different disorders. What symptoms are associated with psychosis? What conditions can result in the onset of psychotic symptoms? How does Rebecca's case illustrate psychotic symptoms? How are these different from and similar to Schizophrenia? This chapter will summarize the major characteristics of psychosis and associated disorders identified in the DSM-5. We will then examine explanations and approaches to intervention for psychotic symptoms from both a psychological and a CYC perspective. Compared with other disorders, the psychological and CYC perspectives are more similar in their accounts for these experiences and also demonstrate commonalities with respect to assisting children and youth with these disturbances.

From 1977 to 1997, one of the authors of this text was a front-line CYCP in a managed-care facility for youth. Although on occasion an adolescent would present with concerns that the team thought might be related to a psychotic disorder, this was relatively unusual. From time to time the team did have youth referred to the program who'd been diagnosed with psychosis or manic depression (as it was known in the 1980s). Such infrequency may have been related to fewer diagnoses, a lack of knowledge, or less accurate observations of psychosis by social workers, families, or out-of-home care providers. However, more recent anecdotal evidence from the CYC managed-care field in Manitoba suggests that the number of youth in care experiencing psychotic symptoms has increased over the past 10 years. Further, CYCPs working with homeless youth in Manitoba have also reported "skyrocketing" numbers of those presenting with psychosis and Schizophrenia (Kelly Holmes, personal communication, 2012). Depending on where CYCPs practise, what they need to know about the assessment and treatment of young people with psychosis and Schizophrenia will vary based on the primary system within which they work and the needs of the population they serve.

It's important to keep in mind that the CYCP's role is not to diagnose psychosis or Schizophrenia, nor to make any diagnostic assumptions based on observations. However, because CYCPs are often among the first to note potentially concerning behaviours and symptoms, they must be well informed not only about such signs but also about the relevant mental health referral resources in their jurisdiction. The foundational premise of this text is that mental health literacy is a basic competency required for the professional practice of CYC. This chapter outlines what CYCPs need to know in order to be effective in their practice with young people and families who may be struggling with these issues.

WHAT IS PSYCHOSIS?

The term *psychosis* refers to a group of symptoms associated with a loss of touch with reality. Specifically, *psychotic symptoms* (symptoms of psychosis) include three general types: *hallucinations*, *delusions*, and *disorganized thinking*. These symptoms can occur in the context of various psychological disorders (including bipolar disorder, major depressive disorder, and borderline personality disorder), as well as in relation to brain injury, medical conditions (e.g., seizures), and substance use/abuse.

Let's distinguish among these three types of symptoms. **Hallucinations** are disturbances in perception. For example, the individual may hear voices when no one is talking or see things that aren't really there. In the case of hearing voices, the individual may hear commands (e.g., "Go outside!") or simple conversations, although more often, critical and insulting statements are perceived (e.g., "You stink!"). **Delusions** are distortions in thought, including maintaining strong beliefs that aren't based in reality. For example, an adolescent may believe that other people can read his thoughts or can control his actions through the use of radio waves. Despite a lack of evidence to support the belief or even in the face of contradictory evidence, these beliefs persist. **Disorganized thinking** encompasses symptoms associated with confused thought. Often, this confusion is reflected in *disorganized speech*, which includes communications that fail to present a coherent idea. For example, the sentence "My face is a planet on which memories are based" seems complete, but the content is disorganized and meaningless (referred to as *incoherence*). As well, confusion can be reflected in frequent switching from one topic to another (referred to as *derailment*). Disorganized thinking can also be reflected in behaviour. For example, while in organized behaviour someone might walk up to a pay phone, insert coins, and then dial a number to speak with someone, in *disorganized behaviour* someone might walk up to a pay phone, insert coins, and then walk away. Disorganized behaviour may also be represented by inappropriate silliness, agitation, aggression, or even lack of self-care.

Before turning to a discussion of psychotic disorders, try to imagine what it would be like to experience psychotic symptoms by considering the *Think About It!* exercise.

WHAT IS A PSYCHOTIC DISORDER? THE PSYCHOLOGICAL PERSPECTIVE

From a psychological perspective, disorders primarily characterized by psychotic symptoms are referred to as *psychotic disorders*. Since psychotic symptoms can occur in the context of many mental and physical health issues, it's important to recognize that other explanations must be eliminated before a psychotic disorder diagnosis can be applied. According to the DSM-5, psychotic disorders are associated with abnormalities in at least one of the following five areas:

- *delusions* or irrational beliefs (e.g., believing that aliens are controlling your actions)
- *hallucinations* or perceptual disturbances (e.g., hearing voices)
- *disorganized thinking*, often reflected in disorganized speech (e.g., incoherent speech)
- *disorganized or abnormal motor behaviour* (e.g., silliness, rigid body posture)
- *negative symptoms* or diminished or absent thoughts, feelings, or behaviours (e.g., reduced expression of emotion; lack of speech).

Thus, the term **psychotic disorder** refers to disorders that are first and foremost associated with disturbances in one or more of these domains that interfere with daily functioning and the ability to achieve important goals. Note that the first four of these general areas are equivalent to our earlier discussion of psychotic symptoms. These are frequently referred to as **positive symptoms**, which represent excesses or alterations in expected functioning. The term *positive* doesn't mean that something is desirable but rather that it's *present* (think of the plus sign in addition). The domain of **negative symptoms** is distinct in that it represents symptoms associated with processes or functions that are diminished or reduced in comparison with expected functioning (think of minus sign in subtraction). For example, a *lack* of speech or *lack* of emotional expression is a negative symptom, referring to the absence of something usually present.

DSM-5 Categories

The DSM-5 groups those disorders primarily characterized by psychotic symptoms together in a single chapter entitled Schizophrenia Spectrum and Other Psychotic Disorders, to reflect their commonality with respect to psychosis as their major feature. Let's briefly overview this general category before considering specific symptoms of those diagnoses you're most likely to encounter in your CYC practice.

Schizophrenia Spectrum and Other Psychotic Disorders   The DSM-5 includes nine specific diagnoses in the general category of **Schizophrenia Spectrum and Other Psychotic Disorders**. Essentially, these disorders are differentiated from one another on the basis of the *number of domains affected* (e.g., delusions only versus hallucinations, delusions, and disordered thinking) as well as the *duration of symptoms* (e.g., one month versus at least six months). As we noted above, it's imperative that all other potential causes of psychotic symptoms (e.g., brain injury, tumour) are ruled out prior to applying the diagnosis of psychotic disorder. Refer to Box 9.1 for a list and brief description of these specific disorders.

Box 9.1

DSM-5 Schizophrenia Spectrum and Other Psychotic Disorders

Disorder	Core Features
Delusional Disorder	At least one month of non-bizarre delusions without other symptoms
Brief Psychotic Disorder	Psychotic symptoms last more than one day and end within one month
Schizophrenia	Lasts for at least six months, including at least one month of psychotic symptoms and a decline in functioning
Schizophreniform Disorder	Psychotic symptoms last for at least one month but less than six months, with no decline in functioning required
Schizoaffective Disorder	Psychotic symptoms occur together with a mood episode and were preceded or are followed by at least two weeks of delusions or hallucinations
Substance/Medication-Induced Psychotic Disorder	Psychotic symptoms are a direct consequence of a drug of abuse, a medication, or exposure to a toxin
Psychotic Disorder Due to General Medical Condition	Psychotic symptoms are a direct consequence of a general medical condition
Other Specified Schizophrenia Spectrum and Other Psychotic Disorder	Psychotic presentation that does not meet criteria for any of the above disorders, and the reason for not meeting criteria is specified
Unspecified Schizophrenia Spectrum and Other Psychotic Disorder	Psychotic presentation that does not meet criteria for any of the above disorders, but the reason for not meeting criteria is not specified

Source: Reprinted with permission from the Diagnostic and Statistical Manual of Mental Disorders, Fifth Edition, (Copyright ©2013). American Psychiatric Association. All Rights Reserved.

Schizophrenia Spectrum and Other Psychotic Disorders: Diagnoses and Criteria

We'll focus our discussion on three of the nine psychotic disorders discussed in the DSM-5: *Brief Psychotic Disorder*, *Schizophrenia*, and *Substance-Induced-Psychotic Disorder*—the conditions you're most likely to encounter in your CYC practice. We'll begin with a review of the specific diagnostic criteria for each and identify similarities and differences between these categories.

Brief Psychotic Disorder **Brief Psychotic Disorder** is characterized by two or more psychotic symptoms (i.e., delusions, hallucinations, disorganized speech, disorganized behaviour) that come on suddenly (within a two-week period), often without any warning. The symptoms last for at least one day but less than one month, after which the individual returns to his previous level of functioning.

It's worth noting that the DSM-5 requires consideration of the presence or absence of stressors prior to the onset of symptoms. *Brief Reactive Psychosis* refers to psychotic symptoms that occur following exposure to a significant stressful event that would be experienced similarly by almost anyone exposed to the event. As we'll see, compared with Schizophrenia, symptoms of Brief Psychotic Disorder are shorter in duration and are less likely to result in lasting impairments.

Hallucinations, or disturbances in perception, include hearing voices, a characteristic symptom of Schizophrenia. Covering one's ears can be a sign that one is hearing voices that are upsetting or creating distress.

Schizophrenia Owing to its symptoms' severe impact on functioning, **Schizophrenia** is considered to be one of the most serious psychological disorders. It's characterized by two or more psychotic symptoms (i.e., delusions, hallucinations, disorganized speech, disorganized behaviour) that persist for at least one month and are associated with a significant decline in functioning (e.g., work, self-care). At least one of the symptoms displayed must be hallucinations, delusions, or disorganized speech. We've seen that these are frequently referred to as *positive symptoms*, which represent excesses or alterations in expected functioning. These are generally considered to reflect the psychotic features of the disorder. In addition to positive symptoms, Schizophrenia is associated with *negative symptoms*, which refer to an absence or deficit of normally occurring behaviours. *Affective flattening*, for example, refers to a lack of emotional expression; *alogia* refers to brief verbal communications that convey very little information; and *avolition* refers to a failure to initiate or maintain goal-directed actions.

Historically, Schizophrenia has been associated with "madness" or "lunacy." Perhaps these conceptions arise in part from the fact that some of the symptoms associated with this disorder are more difficult to relate to than symptoms of other disorders. For example, although not everyone has experienced a mood episode, most people have experienced periods of sadness and thus can relate to the experience of a mood episode. Similarly, although not everyone meets the criteria for an anxiety disorder, most people can easily relate to feelings of anxiety (e.g., feeling anxious before a test or while making a presentation).

Monkey Business/Fotolia

In the case of Schizophrenia, however, it may be more difficult to relate to the experience of hearing voices or believing that others are intending to cause one personal harm to the point that daily functioning is disrupted. Although Schizophrenia is less common than some of the other disorders we discuss in this text, the diagnosis is of particular relevance to CYC practice because it often begins in adolescence. Consequently, being able to recognize possible symptoms of the disorder can be of outmost importance in the context of working with youth, given that early recognition and treatment is associated with better long-term outcomes.

Substance/Medication-Induced Psychotic Disorder   The DSM-5 specifies criteria for **Substance/Medication-Induced Psychotic Disorder**, which include prominent hallucinations or delusions that are a consequence of the direct physiological effects of a substance. The substance may be a medication, a toxin, or a drug of abuse. If the individual is aware that the hallucinations are substance-induced, the diagnosis would be *Substance Intoxication* or *Substance Withdrawal* rather than Substance/Medication-Induced Psychotic Disorder. In addition, other causes of the symptoms must be ruled out (e.g., Schizophrenia) before the diagnosis of Substance/Medication-Induced Psychotic Disorder is applied.

Conclusions about the cause of the symptoms must be based on history, physical examination, or laboratory findings. Substance/Medication-Induced Psychotic Disorder is associated with intoxication or withdrawal states but can last for weeks or as long as the substance use continues. Diagnosis is particularly challenging if the individual exhibited psychotic symptoms prior to exposure to a substance. Specifically, it can be difficult to determine whether the best diagnosis is Substance/Medication-Induced Psychotic Disorder or another psychotic disorder. Because substance use problems are often seen in those with Schizophrenia and other psychotic disorders, determining the cause of the symptoms may be complex. Refer to Table 9.1 for a list of substances associated with Substance-Induced Psychosis.

Before turning to a discussion of psychosis from a CYC perspective, test your understanding of the diagnostic categories we've looked at by trying the *Test Your Understanding* exercise. Can you identify the diagnosis that most closely matches the description of each case?

Table 9.1 Substances Associated with Substance-Induced Psychosis

Substance	Symptom
Alcohol	Auditory hallucinations, usually voices
Cocaine	Persecutory delusions, distorted body image, hallucinations of bugs crawling in or under skin (leads to scratching)
Amphetamines	Same as for cocaine
Cannabis	Persecutory delusions, anxiety
Antihistamines	Hallucinations, delusions
Fuel, paint	Hallucinations, delusions

Brad went to a party Saturday night, and at about 11 P.M. started to behave in a way that captured others' attention. He began laughing wildly for no reason; then suddenly he became fearful and started yelling violently at no one in particular. His friends called an ambulance, and told the emergency responders that just before behaving this way Brad had taken some kind of pill together with a beer.

Fifteen-year-old Gerry was sexually assaulted three months ago, and recently learned that she's pregnant from the attack. After she found out she began hearing voices and having difficulty focusing her thoughts. These symptoms have been present for two days now, and are frightening to both Gerry and those around her.

Carol's friends are concerned about her recent behaviour. Last year she was a sociable, fun-loving 17-year-old who enjoyed hanging out with her friends. But over the past several months she's been spending most of her time alone; she often whispers and talks to herself; she's been suspended for missing most of her classes, and she seems afraid of even her best friends.

A CYC APPROACH TO PSYCHOTIC DISORDERS: UNDERSTANDING PSYCHOSIS

Early in his career in the 1970s, Brock University Child and Youth Care professor Hans Skott-Myhre (2014) worked with a young man with psychosis in a community-based outpatient psychiatric facility. This young man experienced frequent episodes of catatonia (see Chapter 3, p. 133). After a particularly drastic episode that meant the young man would have to be hospitalized if he didn't improve, Skott-Myhre decided to stay with him in his bedroom overnight. The young man improved by morning, and thus avoided having to move to the hospital. Skott-Myhre was, however, reprimanded by his clinical supervisor for having violated patient–therapist boundaries. In his article about this experience, Skott-Myhre (2014) muses about the approaches of earlier psychiatrists such as Milton Erickson and R. D. Laing, who viewed "mentally ill" people as human beings first, not as psychiatric patients only. Indeed, relating to young people who are struggling with psychotic symptoms with caring kindness, respect, and as "persons first" is the foundation of the CYC perspective on psychosis and youth.

We've seen that Schizophrenia is a form of psychosis, a mental disorder that causes a distortion of, or loss of contact with, reality. Psychosis accompanies several psychiatric diagnoses, including Schizophrenia, Bipolar Affective Disorder, Depression, Schizophreniform Disorder, Delusional Disorder, and Schizoaffective Disorder, as well as some medical or neurological illnesses (Edwards & McGorry, 2002).

Psychosis has been referred to as "youth's greatest disabler." Psychosis and Schizophrenia are severe conditions that affect many aspects of cognitive and social functioning and will significantly interfere with the young person's ability to manage day-to-day in work, school, and relationships (Kearney, 2003). Although some adolescents who experience a psychotic episode may recover completely, for others, and especially those with Schizophrenia, a single episode may develop into a lifelong condition. Early intervention is key to decreasing the incidence and severity of symptoms: "There is some evidence to suggest that overall functioning deteriorates with each subsequent psychotic break. If that is the case, then early intervention can make the difference in many teenagers' lives" (McKenzie, 2008, p. 201). A Canadian study found that those experiencing psychosis for the first time sought help an average of 2.3 times, and that on average, their psychotic symptoms remained untreated for almost two years (Addington et al., 2003). It's critical to access treatment early, as there is ample clinical evidence that the longer the delay between the onset of psychosis and response with appropriate treatment, known as the *duration of untreated psychosis* (DUP), the poorer the treatment outcomes (Addington et al., 2003).

Historically, a variety of terms have been used to describe adolescent Schizophrenia: *childhood-onset*, *adolescent-onset*, and *early-onset* Schizophrenia are often used interchangeably. The term *adolescent Schizophrenia* usually refers to those cases whose onset occurs up to the age of 17. "The onset of schizophrenia before the age of 10 is exceedingly rare, and in fact the majority of cases referred to in the literature under the rubric of 'childhood-onset schizophrenia' have an onset of psychosis in early adolescence" (Hollis, 2000, p. 1).

The CYC approach considers the developmental stage of those experiencing an initial episode of psychosis. This is critical, since Schizophrenia presents differently in childhood and adolescence than it does in adulthood. In pre-adolescent children, it may be difficult to distinguish between psychotic symptoms and "normal" child behaviour.

> For example, delusions can be confused with normal childhood fantasies, and formal thought disorder may be impossible to distinguish from illogical thinking and loose associations seen in children with immature language development. Children may also find it hard to describe accurately the location of hallucinations. Hence, the limitations of normal cognitive development make it very difficult to identify psychotic symptoms reliably in children below the age of seven. (Hollis, 2000, p. 2)

The diagnostic features of adolescent Schizophrenia include poor premorbid functioning, below average IQ, insidious rather than acute (as with adults) onset; strong family history of psychosis/Schizophrenia, predominantly negative symptoms, and a severe and unremitting course (Hollis, 2000, p. 2). We've seen that psychosis and schizophrenic symptoms, particularly positive symptoms, can be brought on by drug-induced psychoses; however, young people who've experienced psychotic episodes often don't change their drug-use behaviour even after psychiatric hospitalization. We've also seen that each psychotic episode makes a full recovery less likely (Marty Chaulk, personal communication, 2011).

The risks related to suicide with this population are very high. Forty to 60 percent of young people with Schizophrenia attempt suicide, and the likelihood of people with this diagnosis dying by suicide is 15–20 times greater than that of the general population. In fact, the most common cause of death for people with Schizophrenia is suicide (Harkavy-Friedman & Nelson, 1997). Moreover, the cost of Schizophrenia to the Canadian economy has been estimated at $2.02 billion in direct and indirect costs; with an additional $4.83 billion for loss of productivity and loss due to suicide, the total is $6.85 billion (Goeree et al., 2005).

As we outline later in this chapter, the CYC approach is not to label these young people's experiences but rather to understand them, to instill hope for recovery, and to be accepting and caring despite the concerning behaviours we may see. CYCPs acknowledge that hearing voices might be an expected response to extreme stress, and thus teach young people ways to cope with the voices. CYCPs help youth engage in individual or group counselling or help them join a support group; they help them access housing and employment; they help by looking at dietary changes; and they teach various practices that will help improve young people's ability to handle stressful circumstances, such as mindfulness exercises, yoga, and physical exercise (Unger, 2014).

Consider the case of Rebecca, presented at the beginning of the chapter. Identify specific details from the case that might be associated with psychotic symptoms. If you were the street outreach CYCP, describe your strength-based CYC intervention for Rebecca based on the presenting evidence. What might you have done earlier for prevention? Advocacy? What do you think about the role of psychotropic medications for Rebecca?

A key part of recovery is often learning that one's brain does not have to work exactly like everyone else's in order to be healthy: for example many people find that they continue to hear voices, yet once they accept them and know how to cope, they can move on with their lives without hindrance or need to change that experience. (Unger, 2014, p. 1)

Before turning to a discussion of prevalence, development, and comorbidity, consider the details of the opening case in relation to the psychological and CYC views of mood disturbances in *Rebecca's Case: Revisited*.

HOW MANY YOUNG PEOPLE STRUGGLE WITH PSYCHOSIS?

Approximately 3 percent of people will experience a psychotic episode at some stage in their life, although a first episode usually occurs in adolescence or early adulthood. Psychosis occurs across all cultures and levels of socioeconomic status (BC Early Psychosis Intervention Program, 2015).

Schizophrenia begins most often in the 16–30 age group. The chance of a youth developing Schizophrenia if both parents have the disease is 50 percent, and youth who have a third-degree relative with Schizophrenia are twice as likely to develop it as those in the general population ("Preventing schizophrenia," 2014).

Psychosis is one of the most serious conditions that can affect a young person: there is a 10 percent lifetime risk of suicide, and 12 percent of those who suffer from psychosis are unemployed. However, with early intervention, suicide risk is halved and over 50 percent of successfully treated youth will go on to find employment ("Emerging psychosis," 2007). Schizophrenia is extremely rare in childhood and early adolescence. Among Canadian children aged 9 to 13, the estimated prevalence is only 0.1 percent, or 1 in 1000. This suggests that only 2100 people in Canada in this age range would meet the diagnostic criteria. However, the disorder becomes increasingly prevalent in later adolescence, eventually reaching the estimated Canadian prevalence of 1 percent, or 1 in 100, for the population as a whole. Furthermore, among individuals who are eventually diagnosed with Schizophrenia, nearly one-third will experience their first psychotic episode by age 19 ("Preventing schizophrenia," 2014). The 1 percent rates of Schizophrenia are similar from country to country; it ranks among the top 10 causes of disability worldwide ("Schizophrenia facts," 2015), and as we've seen, poses significant challenges for those affected and their families. According to the DSM-5, the sex ratio differs across samples and populations depending on the symptoms that are considered. For example, if negative symptoms are prominent, males tend to have higher incidence rates. In studies that include greater consideration of mood symptoms or if the symptoms are shorter in duration, the sex ratio is more equivalent. Sex differences also include the observation that males tend to be diagnosed earlier (around age 18) than females (around age 25). Biological and clinical similarities (Nicholson & Rapoport, 2000) suggest that childhood/adolescent-onset Schizophrenia is the same disorder as adult Schizophrenia, but a more severe form.

PSYCHOTIC DISORDERS AND DEVELOPMENT

Most of the literature examining psychotic disorders in childhood and adolescence focuses on Schizophrenia. The DSM-5 doesn't include specific consideration of childhood-onset Schizophrenia (COS) (usually referred to as onset prior to age 13); as we've seen, Schizophrenia is rarely observed prior to adolescence (American Psychiatric Association, 2013). Using adult criteria to study childhood Schizophrenia has been criticized (e.g., Dunn & McDougle, 2001). The DSM-5 acknowledges that diagnosing Schizophrenia in children may be particularly problematic because delusions and hallucinations may be less complex than those observed in adults and also because the experience of hallucinations and delusions are believed to be less distressing to children (due to their underdeveloped ability to distinguish reality from fantasy). Limitations in language skills and intelligence also may relate to symptoms presenting in different forms. Despite these challenges, Hollis (2000; 2002) argues that the diagnosis of youth with Schizophrenia is fairly reliable, although others suggest that diagnosis of Schizophrenia before age seven or eight is difficult (Gooding & Iacono, 1995). The study of COS is of particular importance, however, for both scientific and applied reasons.

The onset of Schizophrenia may be sudden (acute) or gradual. In general, earlier onset is associated with less favourable prognosis, as is gradual onset. During the initial stages of the disorder, the child or adolescent may exhibit difficulty concentrating, sleeping, and doing schoolwork, and may avoid friends. Later stages are associated with incoherent speech, delusions or hallucinations, and disorganized and/or paranoid thoughts. The observation of unpredictable, violent, or suicidal behaviour is most likely to be observed when experiencing the psychotic symptoms of the disorder, sometimes referred to as the *active phase* or more generally as a *psychotic episode*.

COMORBIDITY

In addition to psychotic symptoms, childhood Schizophrenia is associated with motor coordination problems, peculiar posture, and delay in achieving developmental milestones. Emotional and social disturbances in childhood-onset Schizophrenia are also observed; these include shyness, social isolation and withdrawal, and moodiness (Eggers, Bunk, & Krause, 2000). Recognition of these symptoms in adolescence is particularly challenging considering the normal developmental changes in adolescent behaviour associated with mood instability and social withdrawal.

Impaired language skills are also often observed; these are associated with an early view that Schizophrenia was similar to Autism Spectrum Disorder (ASD), a neurodevelopmental exceptionality discussed in Chapter 3. However, more recent research indicates many differences between ASD and Schizophrenia. For example, onset of symptoms is typically later in Schizophrenia than in ASD, and Schizophrenia is typically associated

Table 9.2 Differences Between Schizophrenia and Autism

Childhood Schizophrenia	Autism Spectrum Disorder
Late onset	Early onset (before 30 months)
Early normal development	Early abnormal development
Good language development	Language disturbances
Hallucinations, delusions	No hallucinations or delusions
Interacts socially	Social interaction deficits (social avoidance, poor eye contact)

Source: From Understanding Child Behaviour Disorders by Donna M. Gelfand, William R. Jenson, and Clifford J. Drew. Published by Wadsworth/Thompson Learning, © 1997.

with fewer intellectual impairments and less severe social and language deficits. See Table 9.2 for a summary of differences between the two disorders. Although they can occur in the same child, comorbidity is rare for these two disorders.

We've seen that substance-related disorders (discussed in Chapter 10) often co-occur with Schizophrenia, although this is more typically observed in adolescence and adulthood than in childhood. Other comorbid conditions include anxiety disorders (see Chapter 6), and some personality disorders (i.e., Schizotypal, Schizoid, or Paranoid Personality Disorder).

Before turning to a discussion of the explanations for psychotic disorders, read the statements in Box 9.2 to examine your own feelings about these behaviour patterns. How might your ideas about psychosis and related diagnoses impact your feelings about and behaviours toward those diagnosed with these disorders? How do your current beliefs about psychosis compare with the facts?

EXPLAINING PSYCHOTIC DISTURBANCES: PSYCHOLOGICAL PARADIGMS

What causes psychotic symptoms? Why do some develop Schizophrenia but not others? The answers to these questions vary according to the theoretical framework one adopts. From a psychological perspective, predominant explanations of psychotic disorders are those offered

Box 9.2

Common Myths About Psychosis and Schizophrenia

MYTH: *Schizophrenia is a rare condition.*

FACT: Schizophrenia is not rare; the lifetime risk of developing Schizophrenia is widely accepted to be around 1 in 100.

MYTH: *People with Schizophrenia are dangerous.*

FACT: Although the delusional thoughts and hallucinations of Schizophrenia sometimes lead to violent behaviour, most people with Schizophrenia are neither violent nor a danger to others.

MYTH: *People with Schizophrenia can't be helped.*

FACT: While long-term treatment may be required, the outlook for Schizophrenia is not hopeless. When treated properly, many people with Schizophrenia are able to enjoy life and function within their families and communities.

Source: From Understanding Schizophrenia: Symptoms, Types, Causes, and Early Warning Signs. Copyright © by HelpGuide.Org. Used by permission of HelpGuide.Org.

from the biological paradigm, so we'll focus primarily on that paradigm in our discussion of causal factors. And since environmental and cognitive factors also play a role in producing and sustaining symptoms of Schizophrenia, we'll examine models that consider these factors as well.

Biological Paradigm   The relationship between biological factors and psychotic symptoms has been investigated extensively. In fact, Schizophrenia is often referred to as a *medical* condition. Although most research in this area has focused on Schizophrenia and has been based on adult samples, the role of genetic, biochemical, and neurological factors in adult Schizophrenia and other psychotic disorders helps us better understand the origins of these disturbances.

Heredity and Genetics. Numerous studies have shown that individuals with greater degrees of genetic relatedness (e.g., identical versus fraternal twins, biological parents and children versus adoptive parents and children) have higher *concordance rates* (percentage sharing the disorder) for Schizophrenia (e.g., Braff, Schork, & Gottesman, 2007; Huttunen et al., 2008), supporting the notion that this disorder has a genetic component. However, even in the case of identical or monozygotic twins (having 100 percent of the same genetic material), not all twins in each identical twin pair will develop Schizophrenia. Therefore, other factors also contribute to the development of the disorder. It's generally assumed that multiple genes determine one's risk for Schizophrenia and may cause a subtle brain abnormality that, together with environmental factors, results in a heightened sensitivity to stress and consequently, the onset of the disorder (e.g., Hamilton, 2008a).

Brain Structures. Brain scans have shown abnormal activity in the frontal cortex, thalamus, and amygdala in those diagnosed with Schizophrenia (Ettinger et al., 2001). The thalamus (associated with processing sensory information) has been found to have decreased volume in those with Schizophrenia (Ettinger et al., 2001). Other researchers (e.g., Arnold, 2000) have observed abnormal distribution of cells in the hippocampus (associated with learning and memory). Some studies have found shrinkage in grey matter (i.e., loss of neurons) in the rear of the brain (associated with attention and perceptual processing) that later progresses to the frontal lobe (associated with planning, organization, and higher-level processing). The relationship of these changes to the onset of Schizophrenia is supported by deficits in motor, language, and cognitive and social functioning that are often observed before the presentation of psychotic symptoms (Gelfand & Drew, 2003). Research also suggests that those diagnosed with Schizophrenia are more likely to have larger fluid-filled spaces in the brain called *ventricles* (e.g., Harrison, 1995), which also reflects a loss of brain matter (or neurons). These structural differences are more likely to be seen in those with greater impairments, also supporting the role of brain abnormalities in the disorder. The enlarged ventricles (see Figure 9.1) observed in adults diagnosed with Schizophrenia have also been observed in adolescents with the disorder Gogtay et al., 2003). Other investigations found that adolescents diagnosed with Schizophrenia showed a progressive loss of brain tissue compared with healthy adolescents (Rapoport et al., 1999; 2005). This loss of brain tissue was observed in numerous areas, including the parietal area and later the temporal and frontal areas of the cortex. Generally, then, the loss of brain matter begins at the back of the brain and moves toward the front of the cortex. Clearly, numerous studies support the fact that there are differences in the brains of those diagnosed with Schizophrenia.

Neurotransmitters. From a biological approach, one explanation for the symptoms of Schizophrenia is an atypical level of certain neurotransmitters in the brain. As discussed in Chapter 1, neurotransmitters are chemicals in the nervous system that are responsible for communication between neurons. According to the **dopamine hypothesis**, which originated in the 1960s, high levels of dopamine might explain the disorder's positive symptoms while low levels of dopamine (particularly in the frontal lobes) explain its negative symptoms. If so, medications that increase the activation of dopamine should result in a decrease in positive symptoms but will not affect or may even increase negative symptoms.

This theory is consistent with the observation that changes in levels of neurotransmitters are associated with an increase or decrease in psychotic symptoms. For example, one of the first drugs used to treat Schizophrenia was *chlorpromazine*, which blocks dopamine receptors. This *decrease* in dopamine activation is associated with a decrease in hallucinations and delusions. By comparison, drugs that increase the availability of dopamine in the brain are associated with an *increase* in hallucinations and delusions. For example, L-DOPA is a drug used to treat the lack of motor coordination associated with Parkinson's disease, which is caused by low levels of dopamine in the basal ganglia. Psychotic symptoms are a complication associated with L-DOPA treatments. Interestingly, recreational drugs that increase levels of dopamine (e.g., amphetamines, cocaine) are also

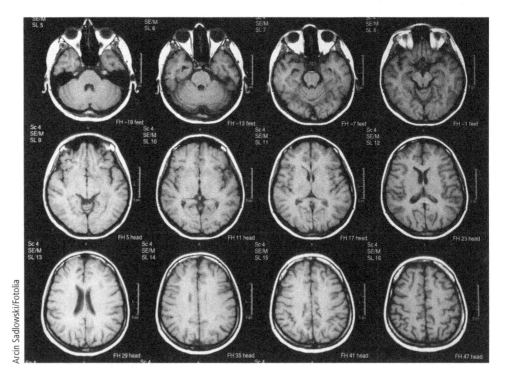

Arcin Sadlowski/Fotolia

Figure 9.1 Enlarged Ventricles

Individuals diagnosed with Schizophrenia often have larger ventricles (fluid-filled spaces that appear as dark spaces in the centre of the brain) compared with non-diagnosed individuals.

associated with Substance-Induced Psychotic Disorder, further supporting the role of neurotransmitters in psychosis.

While evidence clearly supports the role of dopamine in psychosis, other neurotransmitters have also been suspected to play a role in psychotic disorders. For example, low levels of activity of the neurotransmitter *glutamate* have been associated with both the positive and negative symptoms of Schizophrenia. This is consistent with the observation that PCP (angel dust), which blocks glutamate receptors (and therefore lowers activation of glutamate), results in both positive and negative symptoms very similar to those observed in Schizophrenia. In addition, when those diagnosed with Schizophrenia take PCP, their positive and negative symptoms become worse.

So, which neurotransmitter explains psychotic symptoms? Is it dopamine or glutamate? As it turns out, it seems the answer is both! One of the functions of dopamine is to control the release of glutamate. Correspondingly, if one has high levels of dopamine activation, glutamate may be overly suppressed, thus leading to the positive *and* negative symptoms of psychosis.

Psychodynamic Paradigm   Early psychodynamic explanations of psychosis (particularly Schizophrenia) viewed symptoms as developing in reaction to exposure to upsetting events. Freud (1924) suggested that Schizophrenia resulted when one is exposed to distressing event (e.g., harsh treatment by parents) and regresses to an earlier stage of ego development in an attempt to manage this experience. Recall from Chapter 1 that the ego develops in about the second year of life and is associated with the *reality principle*, and thus the pre-ego stage represents a time before the individual has a realistic awareness of the world. Accordingly, Freud viewed Schizophrenia as an "infantile state," with delusions reflecting the primitive nature of the condition and auditory hallucinations a sign of one's attempt to regain "ego-control." It's worth noting, however, that even Freud (1913/1949) acknowledged the role of heredity and genetics in the onset of Schizophrenia and that it was best left to biologists to study the condition.

With little evidence supporting Freud's (1924) early explanations of psychosis and Schizophrenia, later psychodynamic explanations focused on family dynamics as the primary factor. For example, Fromm-Reichmann (1948) argued that "schizophrenogenic mothers" (those who are rejecting, overprotective, and controlling) lay the foundation for Schizophrenia. Consistent with this idea, Rosen (1947) contended that "a schizophrenic is always one who is reared by a woman who suffers from a perversion of the maternal instinct" and uses harsh and cold treatment in interacting with her child. Although research findings don't support this theory, more recent research has found that family communication patterns (e.g., hostility and poor communication) are associated with the onset of Schizophrenia and other psychotic disorders (Norton, 1982; Tienari et al., 2004). However, it's difficult to determine whether these communication patterns are a cause or a result of the disorder (i.e., the parent's response to a child's symptoms of Schizophrenia). More recent theory and research associated with the role of family factors in Schizophrenia are reviewed later from a sociocultural approach.

Behavioural Paradigm   Although there is no comprehensive behavioural theory that attempts to explain the development of Schizophrenia or other psychotic disorders, behavioural mechanisms have been used to explain the persistence of specific symptoms. For example, engaging in bizarre behaviours may be more likely to occur in those circumstances in which they're reinforced (e.g., through the attention of others). More recent studies have investigated the relationship between neurological abnormalities in Schizophrenia and decreased ability to alter decisions and/or actions so as to increase positive reinforcements (Strauss et al., 2011). Such deficits seem to be particularly relevant in explaining negative symptoms (e.g., social withdrawal, lack of motivation).

Cognitive Paradigm   As with the behavioural paradigm, no specific theory from a cognitive perspective has been forwarded to explain the development of Schizophrenia or other psychotic disorders. However, more recent discussions of psychosis have explored the relevance of cognitive interpretation in the maintenance of specific symptoms. For example, Morrison (1998) emphasizes the importance of one's interpretation of hallucinations (e.g., "I'm crazy" or "I'll die if I don't follow the voices' instructions") in increasing physiological arousal (i.e., stress) and hence negative emotion. This stress can increase the likelihood of additional symptoms. Such misinterpretations of psychotic symptoms can also result in protective strategies (e.g., withdrawing from others) that in turn lead to avoiding situations that might disconfirm the belief. Thus, it's the *cognitive interpretation* of hallucinations and other psychotic symptoms rather than the symptoms themselves that results in significant distress and impairment.

Sociocultural Paradigm   Although genes seem to predispose some individuals to developing Schizophrenia, it's clear that other factors also play a role. Supporting this idea is the fact that not all identical/monozygotic twins are concordant for the disorder; in other words, in the case of two twins with the same genetic makeup, one may develop the disorder while the other does not. If only genes were responsible for the development of Schizophrenia, should one identical twin have the disorder, so should the other.

Accordingly, a *diathesis–stress model* of Schizophrenia (Zubin & Spring, 1977) suggests that the likelihood of developing the disorder is based on an interaction between a *diathesis* (a predisposition) and *stress* (environmental or psychosocial disturbances). The genetic diathesis increases one's sensitivity to stress, which increases the vulnerability of the individual to developing the disease. However, the person must be exposed to a certain amount of stress that, together with the diathesis, results in the onset of symptoms. Notice how this might explain why identical twins with the same genetic predisposition may not both develop the disorder: if one twin experiences significant stress but the other does not, only the former will develop Schizophrenia.

Substantial evidence has supported the diathesis–stress model. Both twin and adoptive studies demonstrate increased risk for those with biological relatives with the disorder, and the closer the genetic relationship, the greater the risk. For example, the concordance rate for identical twins has been found to be greater than twice the rate found between fraternal twins (e.g., Plomin, Owen, & McGuffin, 1994). Similarly, Tandon, Keshavan, and Nasrallah (2008) found greater concordance for the disorder between adopted children and their biological parents than between these children and their adoptive parents.

In addition to genes, other diatheses have been associated with a later diagnosis of Schizophrenia. For example, prenatal exposure to the influenza virus was found to be associated with a significantly higher risk of Schizophrenia later in life (Brown et al., 2004). Inadequate prenatal nutrition and complications during childbirth (e.g., oxygen deprivation) have also been identified as possible diatheses in some cases (Shenton et al., 2001; Walker et al., 2004). Even prenatal exposure to high levels of stress hormones has been considered a possible diathesis. Khashan et al. (2008), for example, found that children whose mothers had experienced a significantly stressful event during the first three months of pregnancy were more likely to have children later diagnosed with Schizophrenia. According to the diathesis–stress model, then, each of these factors can create a vulnerability to the disease by heightening the sensitivity of the nervous system to the effects of stress.

The stresses with which these predisposing factors interact have been traditionally defined in the literature as *environmental psychosocial events*. Examples of stresses include traumatic events (e.g., accidents, abuse), family conflict, loss, and disturbed family interactions. **Expressed emotion**, in which family members express significant hostility and criticism toward the individual diagnosed with Schizophrenia, is considered to be a particularly important stressor. Numerous studies have found that families scoring high in expressed emotion are less likely to be supportive and empathic toward the diagnosed individual, and that such dynamics predict future relapses for that individual (Kopelowicz, Liberman, & Zarate, 2006).

The fact that such psychosocial stressors have been found to exacerbate symptoms or result in relapse clearly supports the role of such events in the symptoms of Schizophrenia. Others have noted that the typical age of onset (i.e., adolescence or early adulthood) coincides with a time of development in which the individual is faced with the most significant stressors, also consistent with the diathesis–stress model. Economic difficulties, trauma, and abuse may also increase the likelihood that those with a genetic or other biological diathesis will develop the disorder. Comparatively, individuals who have access to supports and good parenting may be protected from developing the disorder.

Yet despite the general acceptance of the diathesis–stress model, the assumption it makes about the role of genetics as a primary predisposing factor has been questioned. Specifically, although it's possible that *psychological* or *psychosocial* diatheses contribute to Schizophrenia (e.g., personality characteristics, childhood experiences), Perry (2001) argues that current research based on the diathesis–stress model overemphasizes the role of *biological* diatheses (i.e., genetics, birth trauma) and largely ignores the role that *environmental* diatheses (i.e., abuse, neglect, and other traumas in childhood) may play in the onset of the disorder.

Perry (2001) proposes a **traumagenic neurodevelopmental (TN) model** of Schizophrenia whereby childhood psychosocial trauma affects the developing brain and results in the biological abnormalities that are characteristic of those diagnosed with Schizophrenia (e.g., dopamine abnormalities, enlarged ventricles, and other structural abnormalities). Thus, rather than merely acting as a factor in the *stress* part of the equation, these negative events could be considered possible *diatheses* and actually *result in* neural abnormalities that increase the likelihood of the individual developing Schizophrenia. According to Perry's (2001) view, then, genetics *or* psychosocial stressors can *cause* the neurobiological abnormalities and sensitivities that then predispose one to the disorder. One group of potential psychosocial stressors that may serve as a diathesis for Schizophrenia is childhood abuse and trauma. The TN model suggests that for some, childhood exposure to violence; sexual, physical, or emotional abuse; neglect; or family violence may create long-lasting neurobiological changes that cause the structural and biochemical abnormalities associated with adult Schizophrenia (Perry, 2001).

Various lines of evidence support the TN model of Schizophrenia. Studies have found that those diagnosed with Schizophrenia have a high level of child abuse; for example, Goff et al. (1991) found that abused psychiatric patients experienced positive symptoms of Schizophrenia more often than nonabused patients and exhibited these at a younger age (Goff et al., 1991). In fact, child abuse is related not only to Schizophrenia but to psychosis in general. Read (2001) found that hallucinations are more often seen in patients who had experienced childhood sexual or physical abuse than those who did not, and other research by Read and Argyle (1999) found that the content of the hallucinations was associated with earlier abuse experiences (e.g., hearing the voice of the perpetrator).

Other studies also demonstrate the relationship between early trauma and later psychotic disorder. For example, parental absence and childhood institutionalization were found to be associated with adolescent and adulthood Schizophrenia symptoms (Walker et al., 1981). Cannon et al. (2001) found that those diagnosed with adult Schizophrenia were 2.7 times more likely than undiagnosed individuals to have been in an institution or children's home. Tienari (1991) observed that children with biological parents diagnosed with Schizophrenia but raised in adoptive homes with high rates of rejection and conflict were significantly more likely to develop the disorder than other children with the same genetic predisposition but raised in adoptive families with low levels of dysfunction. Tienari (1991) concluded that family dysfunction and child maltreatment was a more significant predictor of Schizophrenia than genetic predisposition.

Perry (2001) argues that these early traumatic experiences result in neurobiological changes in the brain. This is consistent with the finding that there are similarities between the effects of traumatic events on the brain and the neurobiological abnormalities associated with Schizophrenia. For example, damage to the hippocampus (associated with learning and memory) is often seen in adults diagnosed with Schizophrenia (Chua & Murray, 1996). Research has demonstrated that child abuse is specifically associated with abnormalities in functioning of the limbic system, which includes the hippocampus (Teicher et al., 1996). Interestingly, recent research suggests that abnormalities in the hippocampus are associated with drug-seeking behaviour and may also explain the high prevalence of substance abuse (and consequently, drug-induced psychotic episodes) among those diagnosed with Schizophrenia (Brady et al., 2008).

Also consistent with the TN model, exposure to repeated stressors sensitizes the brain to other stressors. Specifically, exposure to psychosocial stressors increases the release of *cortisol*, a stress hormone that

Firma V/Shutterstock

According to the traumagenic neurodevelopmental model, early childhood abuse, neglect, and other trauma may act as a diathesis for Schizophrenia.

increases sympathetic nervous system activity. In a review by Walker and DiForio (1997), long-term exposure to cortisol may result in an increase in release of dopamine as well as an increase in dopamine receptors. This is consistent with the heightened activation of the dopamine system. Greater dopamine activation was observed in sexually abused girls compared with controls (De Bellis et al., 1994). This neural hypersensitivity is further supported by the observation that abused children and adults diagnosed with Schizophrenia have higher than normal resting heart rates (Perry, 1994; Zahn et al., 1997).

While Perry (2001) acknowledges that psychosocial trauma may not be a factor in the development of all cases of Schizophrenia, it may play more of a causal role in the disorder than the literature suggests. The TN model "recommends open-minded consideration and proper research investigation of whether severe adverse events in childhood might contribute, either independently or in interaction with the effects of genetic risk or perinatal factors . . . to the production of a neurodevelopmental diathesis for schizophrenia" (p. 322). Thus, oversensitivity to stressors may be partly due to traumatic psychosocial events rather than solely genetic or physical assaults. This will be more likely if the abuse is severe and persistent (Perry, 1994).

A CYC LENS ON THE PSYCHOLOGICAL PARADIGMS: A HOLISTIC CONCEPTUAL MODEL

Although it's not definitively known what causes Schizophrenia, we've seen that risk factors are embedded in the interplay between a genetic predisposition and the environment. For example, many young people with Schizophrenia have a history of abnormal fetal development and birth complications. The disruptions in brain development often found among those who eventually develop Schizophrenia include delayed achievement of developmental milestones, reduced cognitive functioning, limited social competence, and challenges in motor skills.

Vulnerability to developing psychosis is increased for those young people with what has been called a "fragile brain" (Marty Chaulk, personal communication, October 2012), meaning those who are predisposed to developing certain mental health issues as a result of genetic factors or having experienced toxicity or trauma in utero or in early childhood. We've seen that this genetic predisposition, combined with certain environmental stressors in child, adolescent, and early adult development, may lead to subtle alterations in the brain that makes a young person more susceptible to developing Schizophrenia ("A healthy family," 2010). No one, including CYCPs, can know whose brain is fragile and at risk for developing Schizophrenia, except through family history. Conversely, many environmental factors (external assets) can lessen the expression of genetic or neurodevelopmental defects and help to offset or decrease the risk of Schizophrenia developing. We've seen that Schizophrenia, along with almost all other mental illnesses, can be caused or prevented by a combination of biological, psychological, and social factors.

One family-based theory, developed in the 1950s and prevailing for decades thereafter, held that Schizophrenia is caused by dysfunctional communication patterns in families; in the 1970s, R. D. Laing, a prominent psychiatrist and leader of the antipsychiatry movement, opposed the labelling inherent in diagnosing mental illnesses but also suggested that familial patterns of communication played a role in the development of psychotic dysfunction. In fact, current literature refers to the 1970s as the era of "blaming the family" for Schizophrenia. However, as outlined earlier, more recent research has found some validity in the idea of the family operating as either a risk or a strength. That is, families with a child who develops Schizophrenia aren't necessarily less healthy (or more dysfunctional) than other families; instead, genetically at-risk children are much more sensitive to ongoing familial stress and dysfunctional communication. Nor will a healthier family environment eliminate the risk of developing Schizophrenia for all at-risk youth: in one study, a healthy family environment reduced the risk by about 86 percent; however, 5.8 percent of children developed the disorder (Tienari et al., 2004). Even in a healthy family environment, then, other environmental factors—including prenatal stress or toxin exposure, nutritional deficiencies, and social stress in peer groups, neighbour-hoods, or schools—may contribute to the risk or trigger Schizophrenia in those who are genetically at risk.

As with many mental health concerns affecting young people, substance abuse is common among those with Schizophrenia. Which comes first? Do youth who use sub-stances develop psychosis, or do youth with psychosis use substances to self-medicate? Young people often use multiple substances as a way of coping with the symptoms related to a mental health issue; such substances include alcohol, tobacco, marijuana, amphet-amines, crystal meth, cough medicines, antihistamines, and pain killers (Lumsden & Chaulk, personal communication, October 2011). For those youth with a fragile brain who are at risk of developing psychiatric disorders, even small amounts of alcohol, drugs, or other substances may produce severe psychiatric reactions. CYCPs must know how to respond to such situations, and where to refer for assessment and support. In addition, CYCPs working with young people who have a parent with psychosis and/or Schizo-phrenia must be able to help them make a fully informed choice about using marijuana and alcohol.

Facilitating early identification and early access to services is essential to successful treatment outcomes. CYCPs must be able to identify youth in need of help and to rec-ognize any concerning changes in a young person's behaviour or affect. Psychiatric reassessments should be undertaken periodically, particularly as the young person's needs and goals change. The focus of CYC treatment is to support youth experiencing psychosis in a therapeutic or healing environment and to recognize any potential comorbid disorders such as substance abuse. Young people should be encouraged to learn as much as possible about managing their own illness and its symptoms, a signifi-cant role for CYCPs working with youth who are affected by psychosis (B.C. Ministry of Health, 2010b).

WHERE DO YOU STAND?

Consider both the psychological and the CYC perspectives we've outlined. Clearly, even psychologists disagree about the relative contributions of genetics and experience to psy-chotic disorders like Schizophrenia. Where do you stand? Try the *Take Action!* exercise to evaluate your understanding of the psychological models of psychotic disorders.

Samantha is a 14-year-old Cree girl from Norway House First Nation in Manitoba. She was referred to a Winnipeg child and adolescent psychiatric hospital for an assessment after she'd experienced a severe six-week depression that had culminated in a suicide attempt by hanging. At her assessment, Samantha, whose first language is Cree, was initially noncommunicative with hospital staff. She was tearful and nonresponsive to all overtures. Samantha was accompanied by her grandmother, who also didn't speak English. But after the staff found an interpreter, they were finally able to communicate with Samantha and conduct an assessment. Samantha told the clinical staff that she'd been hearing voices telling her to kill herself. She'd also been having regular night terrors; she said she saw ghosts in her room and that this had forced her to stay awake. Eventually, Samantha shared with the staff that the onset of these symptoms occurred following a brutal sexual assault, which took place after a group of young people had been using solvents at a party. Samantha hadn't engaged in substance use before this. Samantha responded well to treatment, which included ongoing support from a cultural adviser and an Elder in the hospital. She eventually recovered fully and was able to return to her community.

Describe how Samantha's symptoms/diagnosis might be explained and treated from each of the following paradigms: biological, behavioural, cognitive, sociocultural, and holistic. For each paradigm, what additional information about Samantha's history would you need to know more about?

HELPING CHILDREN AND ADOLESCENTS WITH PSYCHOTIC DISTURBANCES

Psychological Approaches to Treatment

What is the best way to help a child or adolescent suffering from symptoms associated with a psychotic disorder? We'll review the predominant approaches to intervention from the biological, psychodynamic, behavioural, cognitive, and sociocultural paradigms. Although biological approaches are the foundation of treatment, interventions from other paradigms are also crucial in the management of symptoms and reduction of distress.

Biological Paradigm   Considering the role of neurotransmitters in psychosis, it's not surprising that one of the primary approaches to treatment for psychotic disorders (including both Schizophrenia and Substance-Induced Psychosis) is medication. Medications for psychosis (referred to as *antipsychotics*) affect various neurotransmitters, but of particular importance is the neurotransmitter *dopamine*. *First-generation antipsychotics* (sometimes called *neuroleptics* or *typical antipsychotics*) are generally believed to exert their effects through the blocking of dopamine receptors and work best for the positive symptoms of Schizophrenia.

Rebecca's Case: *Revisited*

Consider the case of Rebecca, presented in the beginning of the chapter. How might her symptoms be explained from a biological paradigm, the diathesis–stress approach, and the traumagenic neurodevelopmental model? Do you prefer one of these explanations over the others? Explain.

By comparison, *second-generation antipsychotics* (sometimes called *atypical antipsychotics*) are believed to exert their effects through altering the activation of a variety of neurotransmitters (not just dopamine); they appear to be effective in decreasing both positive and negative symptoms associated with Schizophrenia. For example, clozapine increases levels of serotonin, which decreases dopamine activity. These atypical antipsychotics are usually preferred, as they're generally associated with fewer side effects than typical antipsychotics.

As you might expect, the use of antipsychotic medication for the treatment of child and adolescent psychotic disorders is controversial. Of the numerous antipsychotics available, those most often used with children and adolescents include *quetipine*, *haloperidol*, and *risperidone*. It should be noted that these medications are also used to treat aggression, behavioural difficulties, and mood instability. Most controlled research has investigated the safety and efficacy of risperidone, and therefore, the use of other medications with children and adolescents is controversial. See Table 9.3 for an overview of common antipsychotics along with their mechanism of action, outcomes, and common side effects.

Psychodynamic Paradigm   We noted earlier that Freud (1914/1949) himself recommended that the study and treatment of Schizophrenia would be best left to those approaching these disturbances from a biological approach. Given that psychodynamic therapy is based on establishing a relationship between client and therapist, Freud and others believed that this wasn't possible given the "fantasy world" into which the individual with Schizophrenia has regressed. However, more recently, the utility of a psychodynamic approach in the treatment of psychosis has been reconsidered. Martindale (2007) reviewed the many ways psychodynamic theory can complement other approaches to the treatment of psychosis. Consider the following case:

> A woman, K., had longstanding insecurities as to whether she could make a stable relationship. She was heartbroken when someone she had fallen for did not reciprocate her feelings, and the experience exacerbated both her negative images of herself and her fears for her future, which she found very difficult to bear. After 2 weeks of

Table 9.3 Common Antipsychotic Medications

Drug	Mechanism of Action	Outcomes	Side Effects
First-Generation Antipsychotics/Neuroleptics Chlorpromazine (Largactil); Haloperidol (Haldol); Loxapine (Loxitane); Perphenazine (Trilafon); Thioridazine (Mellaril)	Block dopamine receptors	Work best for positive symptoms	Dry mouth, weight gain, dizziness, drowsiness, restlessness, involuntary movements (muscle spasms, shaking)
Second-Generation Antipsychotics Aripiprazole (Abilify); Clozapine (Clozaril); Olanzapine (Zyprexa); Quetiapine (Seroquel); Risperidone (Risperdal); Ziprasidone (Geodon);	Block a broader range of receptors including those for neurotransmitters other than dopamine	Decrease both positive and negative symptoms	Drowsiness/lethargy, weight gain, diabetes, high blood pressure, blood clots, low white blood cell count NOTE: fewer involuntary movement side effects

Source: Meltzer, 2002; Seida et al., 2012.

inconsolable misery, K. awoke with the persistent delusional belief that she was engaged to a young lord (who had recently been prominent in the newspapers). (Martindale, 2007, p. 26)

From a psychodynamic perspective, K.'s delusion represents an unconscious (i.e., out of her awareness) way of dealing with painful aspects of external reality. According to Martindale (2007), a psychodynamic approach to intervention encourages mental health professionals to consider the possibility that psychotic symptoms can reflect unconscious attempts to manage distressing events in the environment. Accordingly, rather than assuming that symptoms (e.g., delusions) are merely a function of biological processes, the psychodynamic approach can facilitate the identification of events/stressors that are associated with protective strategies, which can then be minimized in the future. Essentially, then, rather than simply eliminating the symptom, the psychodynamic approach encourages individuals to consider the meaning within the symptom.

Behavioural Paradigm   Behavioural approaches to the treatment of psychotic disorders include specific strategies aimed at decreasing symptoms that impair functioning as well as increasing adaptive behaviour. For example, **selective reinforcement** can be used to increase appropriate behaviour (e.g., by giving attention to desired communication and withdrawing attention following bizarre communications). **Social skills training** attempts to reduce the impact of negative symptoms (e.g., social withdrawal) by providing models of appropriate behaviour and social communication (e.g., conversational skills, assertiveness training); these are followed by opportunities to model and rehearse the desired behaviour in the context of a safe environment in which the therapist provides specific feedback. Studies have found social skills training to effectively improve social skills (Khalil, 2012) and result in the development of independent living skills and enhanced functioning in the community for those diagnosed with Schizophrenia (e.g., Liberman et al., 1998). Social skills training is thus an often important component in the overall treatment of this psychotic disorder.

Cognitive Paradigm   Although it might seem questionable to use cognitive approaches in the context of disorders that are characterized by irrational thought and lack of contact with reality, cognitive approaches (often together with behavioural strategies or CBT) have been used extensively in the treatment of psychotic disorders. Smith et al. (2003) argue that cognitive therapy is particularly relevant in the approach to managing psychosis for three reasons. First, medication alone doesn't entirely eliminate symptoms. Second, psychosis is often associated with impairing mood symptoms (e.g., depression, anxiety) that can be effectively managed through the use of cognitive interventions. Third, social impairments associated with psychotic disorders are not effectively treated with medication. Accordingly, cognitive approaches to managing psychosis tend to focus on specific symptoms (e.g., hallucinations, delusions) as well as the individual's thoughts about those symptoms and their connection to distress. The goals of cognitive treatment include increasing the individual's understanding of psychotic symptoms, reducing the distress associated with those symptoms, and reducing the preoccupation with delusional beliefs (Smith et al., 2003). For example, delusional beliefs might be identified, discussed in relation to specific evidence (i.e., challenged), and tested through behavioural "experiments." The use of such cognitive and behavioural elements in treatment has been found to be effective in reducing symptoms resistant to medical treatment (e.g., Kuipers et al., 1997; Sensky et al., 2000).

Sociocultural Paradigm   From a diathesis–stress approach, treatment for Schizophrenia involves biological, psychological, and psychosocial interventions. For most, the antipsychotics discussed earlier are an important component of treatment. Still, it's worth noting that even these biological interventions don't constitute a "cure" for Schizophrenia (Walker & Tessner, 2008). Rather, interventions seek to manage the disorder and limit the impairments that symptoms may create in daily life. For most, even if medication is continued, the return of significant symptoms is likely. As we've seen, early intervention is preferable, and is associated with decreased symptoms in the future (Hollis, 2002).

Helping individuals diagnosed with Schizophrenia better cope with stress and develop social skills, which in turn will help them deal with criticism and hostility from others, may serve to decrease the severity and reoccurrence of symptoms (Bustillo et al., 2001). *Social skills training* programs are also used to facilitate the development of desirable social skills (e.g., general conversation, assertiveness) that can increase functioning in daily living (Kurtz & Mueser, 2008). *Psychosocial rehabilitation* programs are used to support the development of cognitive skills (e.g., memory, attention) important in daily functioning (Penadés et al., 2006). *Family intervention* programs seek to educate family members of those diagnosed with Schizophrenia in order to improve communication, decrease expressed emotion, and decrease overall stressors. Such programs have been found to improve social functioning of the individual diagnosed with the disorder and may even reduce relapse rates (Patterson & Leeuwenkamp, 2008). When considering childhood/adolescent-onset Schizophrenia, facilitation of psychological and social development must also be emphasized, and consequently, the teaching of specific developmental skills is important.

Interventions based in a TN approach require that practitioners have a "clear understanding of how the brain and environment interact to produce thinking, feeling, and behaving" (Walker, 2009, p. 260). The **neurosequential model of therapeutics (NMT)** focuses on experiences that rewire the brain. Through the use of specific activities that target select brain areas that have been damaged and are consequently disorganized, NMT provides consistent, repetitive experiences that alter the functioning of relevant neural pathways. NMT isn't a specific technique or intervention but rather a general orientation to facilitating healing and development. This approach is directed toward children because the nervous system is more malleable and still developing at younger ages.

After the child's history and current functioning are assessed, activities for enriching the development of the nervous system are identified. Perry (2009) recommends beginning with the lowest brain structure and move upward through to higher structures associated with more complex functioning. For example, if the child demonstrates attentional deficits, intervention might begin with activities that alter *brainstem* activity (a lower brain structure associated with attentional capacities). Repetitive activities (including music, movement, controlled breathing, and drumming) that stimulate this area may serve to reorganize its processing and result in improvements in attention. Once progress in attentional capacities is demonstrated, deficits associated with higher brain structures (e.g., self-regulation is associated with the amygdala and hippocampus) may become the focus of intervention, and activities may include play therapy or role plays.

Some NMT approaches are consistent with more traditional therapeutic techniques, but the latter aren't typically repeated with the consistency and duration needed to reorganize the functioning of these brain structures. It's the patterned, repetitive activities of NMT that may enhance the development and reorganization of neural pathways, which can serve as a protective factor and decrease the occurrence and severity of psychotic symptoms. Interestingly, one area of emphasis is *relational interactions* (Perry, 2009): through building positive interactions with individuals who are safe, supportive, and familiar, children's neural responses to stress will be reorganized; consequently, they'll be better able to heal and later adjust their responses to future stressors. Thus, helpful, repetitive, patterned activities aren't only somatosensory in nature, but also include positive, reliable, psychosocial experiences—which are very much consistent with CYC practice.

Although NMT has been found to be effective in various settings and residential treatment centres (Barfield et al., 2011; Perry, 2006), additional studies investigating the effectiveness of this approach are needed. This model, however, is clearly consistent with findings that early and appropriate intervention in psychosis is associated with more favourable outcomes.

CYC Approaches for Youth Struggling with Psychotic Disturbances

For CYCPs, mental health literacy about psychosis means being able to recognize the symptoms, knowing how to seek appropriate help, and understanding the risk factors and possible causes. They also need to be able to assess the risk of lifestyle concerns that may increase the risk of psychosis. CYCPs must have substantial knowledge of these disturbances and the related interventions used in hospital settings or in community outpatient programs. Most importantly, CYCPs must embrace a nonjudgmental attitude that will promote these young people's own recognition and help-seeking.

Street outreach CYCPs are likely to work with young adults affected by psychosis.

1000 Words/Shutterstock

Given that a significant portion of the homeless youth population are affected by psychosis, the likelihood of street outreach CYCPs working with these young adults may be quite high. Moreover, many young people who've experienced psychotic episodes have survived sexual and physical abuse; some researchers have suggested a 50–80 percent prevalence rate of abuse in the histories of affected youth (Read et al., 2001). Psychotic disorders often involve responses to extreme stress and trauma, and the related behaviours often elicit responses from others that will exacerbate the already high level of stress.

Strength-Based Relational CYC Practice   For CYCPs, mental health literacy regarding psychosis involves the ability to recognize the symptoms, knowing how to seek appropriate help, and understanding the risk factors and possible causes. Most importantly, CYCPs must embrace a nonjudgmental attitude that will promote young people's recognition and help-seeking.

Assessment

We've seen that Schizophrenia typically involves deterioration from previous levels of functioning, difficulty in distinguishing what is real from what is unreal, withdrawal, and increasing isolation. Over time, symptoms may become more and more pronounced. The most significant changes in functioning occur in the areas of work and school, relating to others, and personal care and hygiene.

Clinicians use the mental status examination (MSE) to help them make a diagnosis. While CYCPs aren't qualified to use the MSE for diagnostic purposes, they should be familiar with the kinds of observations and questions this exam entails; it can serve as a helpful guide for their communication strategies. The purpose of an MSE is to assess whether the person is mentally impaired, and if so, the level of the impairment. The cognitive functions measured during the MSE include the person's sense of time, place, and personal identity; memory; speech; general intellectual level; mathematical ability; insight or judgment; and reasoning or problem-solving ability. The MSE is an important part of the diagnosis of all presenting psychiatric symptoms. It can also be used repeatedly to monitor or document changes in a person's functioning or mental condition ("Mental status examination," 2012).

In general, then, the MSE results in an overall statement of observations about how an individual looks, feels, and behaves at the time of the examination (Morrison, 2007). It begins with *orientation*; for example, does the individual know where he or she is, the date, the season? It then moves on to the following categories (Morrison, 2007):

1. *Appearance:* Various indicators associated with appearance are important to consider.

   a. *General appearance:* Is clothing tattered, dirty, or bizarre? Do you observe excessive thinness or any other concerns with appearance in general?

   b. *Level of attention:* How alert is the individual? Is he or she drowsy or inattentive? Hypervigilant? For example, is he or she looking around the room as though trying to locate a threat? Although hypervigilance is frequently associated with PTSD, it can also indicate psychosis.

   c. *Amount of activity:* Is there increased motor activity; for example, jiggling legs, hand wringing? Any abnormal body movements can indicate the use of a medication, including the older antipsychotic drugs. While excessive motion is the more common observation, little facial mobility, or a near-frozen expression, can indicate severe depression, although the "classic, near complete immobility of catatonia is now rare" (Morrison, 2007, p. 119).

2. **Mood/Affect:** The three qualities of mood to observe for are its type, lability, and appropriateness (Morrison, 2007). Although an individual's overall emotional state doesn't usually suggest much about mental health diagnoses, *mood lability* (the degree to which mood changes during any given time frame) will. For example, rapid changes from crying to laughing or bursts into raging fury cause concern. *Mood appropriateness* gauges its relationship to thought; for example, laughing when discussing the death of a loved one may suggest mania or Schizophrenia (Morrison, 2007). Depression is the mood symptom most often observed during the MSE (Morrison, 2007).

3. **Flow of speech:** Clinicians observe and listen for "loose associations" or evidence of "thought derailment." *Loose associations* refers to the breakdown of coherent thought, i.e., when one idea runs into another, unrelated idea (Morrison, 2007), resulting in illogical speech that no one besides the person speaking understands. Classic speech patterns related to psychosis and Schizophrenia include incoherence, perseveration (the repetition of words and statements over and over again), and echolalia (the mechanical repetition of words spoken by another person, which can occur in cases of brain damage, autism, and Schizophrenia).

4. **Content of thought:** "No matter how you frame them, delusions and hallucinations almost always mean psychosis" (Morrison, 2007, p. 121).

5. **Cognition and intellectual resources:** The abilities to reason, think abstractly, and do math are affected by serious mental health concerns. Sometimes people are also disoriented.

6. **Insight and judgment:** Poor insight into having a mental disorder may indicate psychosis. Lacking insight and judgment isn't unusual; however, in children and youth it may be consistent with their developmental capacities.

Although authors vary in how they title and organize the major areas of assessment for the mental status exam, a review of the literature reveals significant overlap and similarities with respect to key areas recommended in such an assessment. Knowledge of the general areas of observation can help guide CYCPs' own observations of children and youth. See Table 9.4 for an overview of the major areas of observation in the mental status exam according to Trzepacz and Baker (1993).

Young people with psychosis may exhibit many mood symptoms, including general demoralization and lack of insight. Depression is very common among youth who are developing Schizophrenia and among those who are living with it (Lumsden & Chaulk, personal communication, October 2011). As we noted earlier, CYCPs must carefully observe for suicidal ideation; understandably, the loss of hopes and dreams that is associated with the onset of Schizophrenia may contribute to this increased risk.

Indicators to Recognize   The loss of touch with reality that is the hallmark of psychoses can be recognized by observing one or more positive and negative symptoms. For psychosis, there must be at least one of these symptoms; for Schizophrenia, at least two.

Table 9.4 Areas of Observation for Mental Status Exam (MSE)

Area of Assessment	Sample Observations
Appearance	Age, weight, posture, state of grooming and hygiene, facial expressions
Behaviour	Repetitive or unusual motor movements; unusually slow motor movements, overactivity
Speech	Speed, volume, pitch, lack of speech, lack of meaningful content, slurred, mumbled
Mood	Irritable, elevated, anxious, fearful, depressed, angry
Thought content	Irrational beliefs and/or fears, reality-based beliefs, magical thinking, suicidal or homicidal thoughts
Thought processes	Logical, organized, repetitive, off-topic, irrelevant responses, attentive, memory (short- and long-term)
Perception	Hallucinations (auditory/visual, etc.), illusions; dissociation, derealization, depersonalization
Orientation	Accurate perception of time, place, self; confused
Insight/judgment	Awareness or denial of current difficulties

Let's first review the meaning of the terms *positive* and *negative* as they're used in this context. *Positive symptoms* are viewed as an excess or a distortion in normal, day-to-day functioning; they include hallucinations, delusions, and disorganized speech and behaviour. *Negative symptoms* reflect a decrease in or loss of normal functioning; they include social withdrawal, inappropriate or lack of emotional expression, and poverty of speech. These symptoms are often difficult to evaluate because they occur on the continuum with normalcy; moreover, they're nonspecific and may be related to a variety of other factors, including medication side effects and mood disorders.

CYCPs need to observe for both the positive and negative symptoms related to psychosis. Review the following common indicators so that they may help guide your observations and develop your mental health literacy. We begin with an overview of the positive symptoms of psychosis.

Hallucinations. These involve experiencing something through any of the five senses that doesn't actually exist or that others can't perceive (Kauffman & Landrum, 2013); for example, hearing voices when no one is speaking and seeing people and objects that aren't there. Hallucinations of smell, touch, and taste are far less common. If CYCPs observe a young person behaving as if he or she is experiencing a hallucination, they need to ask more questions. The film *A Beautiful Mind* portrays how real hallucinations can be for the individual (Morrison, 2007).

Igor Kovalchuk/Fotolia

One of the significant negative symptoms of Schizophrenia is social withdrawal.

Delusions. These involve holding a strong belief about something, someone, an event, or one's self with no evidence that it's true and even with evidence to the contrary (Kauffman & Landrum, 2013); the individual can't be persuaded otherwise. According to Lumsden and Chaulk (personal communication, 2012), the types of delusions include *persecutory delusions* (e.g., a belief that one is being followed, tormented, or ridiculed), *referential delusions* (e.g., a belief that certain gestures, comments, or songs are directed toward one), *religious delusions* (e.g., a belief that one is God or some other powerful person or deity), and *somatic delusions* (e.g., a belief that something unusual is happening in one's body despite clear medical evidence to the contrary).

Disorganized Speech. "Fragmented thinking is characteristic of Schizophrenia. Externally, it can be observed in the way a person speaks. People with Schizophrenia tend to have trouble concentrating and maintaining a train of thought" (Smith & Segal, 2015). The young person's speech or writing may be so impaired that you can't understand what he or she is saying. Often the individual will speak in rhymes or use puns that no one else understands (Morrison, 2007). This frequent incoherent "babbling" is also called *word salad*. There may be disjointed or rambling monologues in which an individual seems to talking to him- or herself or to other people or voices. Individuals may respond to queries with an unrelated answer, start sentences with one topic and end somewhere completely different, speak incoherently, or say illogical things.

According to the literature, the different types of disorganized speech involved in Schizophrenia include the following (Smith & Segal, 2015):

> **Loose associations:** Frequent and rapid movement from one topic to another with no connection between one thought and the next.

> **Tangentiality:** Ready digression from one discussion topic to another, arising through association (Lumsden & Chaulk, personal communication, October 2012), and a tendency to reply to questions in an oblique or irrelevant manner.

> **Incoherence:** Speech so disorganized that it can't be understood; it may include *neologisms*, made-up words or phrases that have meaning only to the individual.

> **Perseveration:** Repetition of words and statements; saying the same thing over and over.

> **Clang:** Meaningless use of rhyming words, as in "I said the bread and read the shed and fed Ned at the head."

Disorganized Behaviour. This is characterized by patterns of behaviour or actions that aren't directed toward a goal of any sort; examples include removing clothing in public, making the sign of the cross repeatedly, and maintaining unusual postures for extended periods (Morrison, 2007). Refer to Box 9.3 for a summary of the common types of disorganized behaviour to watch for.

There are numerous indicators that CYCPs might identify in their work with children and youth that can play a pivotal role in determining early intervention and assistance. See Table 9.5 for a summary of behavioural indicators of psychosis.

Negative Symptoms of Psychosis. Individuals with psychosis often have *blunted affect* or no affect, meaning restrictions in the range and intensity of emotional expression. Other negative symptoms include lack of fluency and productivity of thought and speech, limitations in the initiation of goal-directed behaviour, and limitations in physical movement (e.g., rigid walk with limited arm movement).

Intervention

Using observational assessment techniques to identify the indicators of psychosis is a fundamental precursor to providing appropriate interventions and treatment. Remember that the most common and significant barrier to young people's seeking help for symptoms is the stigma associated with psychosis and other mental illnesses. Moreover, the paranoia and suspicion that can mark psychosis can also prevent these young people from getting help. When they do access help, it's often precipitated by some sort of crisis, such as suicidal or violent behaviour.

Still, it's important to recognize that whereas Schizophrenia is treatable but not curable, psychosis is both treatable and curable. And for young people experiencing episodes of substance-induced psychosis, CYCPs have a role in ensuring they understand that each psychotic break becomes increasingly more difficult to treat.

A **psychotic episode** occurs in four distinct phases (Lumsden & Chaulk, personal communication, October 2011):

1. *Premormid:* This is the period of time prior to the onset of symptoms.

2. *Prodromal:* Early signs of psychosis may appear, but they're frequently vague and hardly noticeable to others. Individuals may be isolated, may be seen talking to themselves, and there may be changes in the way individuals describe their feelings and thoughts.

Table 9.5 Behavioural Indicators Checklist: Psychosis	
✓ **Positive Symptoms**	✓ **Negative Symptoms**
Covering ears	Social withdrawal
Movements directed at unseen targets	Limited or awkward movements
Humming or listening to headphones to block sounds of voices	Limited or disorganized speech
Agitation, looking apprehensively at others or around their environment	Lack of attention to hygiene, personal care

Features of the prodromal phase may include reduced concentration and attention, reduced drive and lack of energy, depressed mood, sleep disturbance, anxiety, social withdrawal, suspiciousness, irritability, and deterioration in everyday functioning. Since these symptoms may resemble those of social anxiety, CYCPs should make a referral to a mental health practitioner.

3. *Acute:* Psychotic symptoms include delusions and hallucinations.

4. *Residual or Recovery:* In this phase, young people may make a full recovery.

Knowledge of these phases can help CYCPs better recognize significant behaviours and indicators over time. As well, keep in mind that it's important to monitor symptoms in the context of relevant factors that surround their occurrence.

Mental health clinicians' assessment and treatment of adolescent Schizophrenia involves obtaining a detailed developmental history and other information from multiple informants; applying the DSM-5 diagnostic criteria, understanding that negative symptoms present early and have strong prognostic value; educating and supporting parents, being careful to avoid all suggestions of blame; carefully assessing cognitive and social deficits; and making plans for continued education. All physical causes must be ruled out. Once a diagnosis has been made, treatment almost always includes atypical antipsychotics as a first-line action (Hollis, 2000, p. 2).

Notwithstanding recent debate about the use of antipsychotic medications for youth in the prodromal stage of psychosis (Loewy & Rose, 2015), the preferred treatment is still antipsychotic medications. These are now offered within a *multimodal treatment package* that includes pharmacotherapy, family and individual counselling, psychoeducation, and an assessment of social and educational needs. It's important to note that although this multimodal approach represents current best practice, few, if any, nonpharmacological interventions have been systematically evaluated in adolescent Schizophrenia. According to one source, the parents of children and adolescents with Schizophrenia "express lower levels of criticism and hostility than parents of adult-onset patients, hence family interventions aiming to reduce high expressed emotion are likely to be misguided" (Hollis, 2000, p. 2).

Behavioural and Cognitive-Behavioural Techniques for CYCPs

CBT has been found to be an effective intervention with this population. The structure of the CBT approach, combined with a psychoeducational focus, helps young people dealing with psychosis not only to learn about their mental health concern but also to develop concrete strategies to deal with it (McKenzie, 2008). Tracking their automatic thoughts, their hearing of voices, or their seeing of images can help these young people recognize both the "dysfunctional and functional elements of their thinking" (McKenzie, 2008, p. 200).

In a variation of traditional CBT called *cognitive remediation therapy* (CRT), adolescents with Schizophrenia are taught problem-solving, attention, and social-perception skills. One study (Wykes et al., 2007) found that at a three-month follow-up, those who received CRT improved more on a test of memory and overall cognitive flexibility than did those who received basic care without CRT; that improvements in memory, social functioning and cognitive planning were all associated with decreases in psychiatric symptoms only among those who received CRT; and that CRT was found to have a moderating effect on other psychiatric outcomes (Wykes et al., 2007).

The Role of Medication Most psychotic disorders in youth can be managed very well with medication. Whether you agree or disagree with the use of psychotropic medications as an intervention, for many youth, medication is likely to have the most hope of providing symptom management for Schizophrenia. Risperdal is the most common antipsychotic medication used with adolescents.

However, there are barriers against young people taking their medication. The most significant of these is forgetting, which represents a problem for 40 percent of all individuals with any mental illness (Lumsden & Chalk, personal communication, October 2011). The second most significant is refusal, which includes getting adolescents to take it consistently (McKenzie, 2008); like many people, these adolescents often won't take their medication as soon as they start to feel better. Other reasons for refusal include loss of autonomy or freedom, the overall stigma associated with mental illness in general, and the negative side effects associated with the medication. The tremendous weight gain associated with the old psychotropic medications used to treat schizophrenia is a strong deterrent to most youth, especially young women. Finally, the cost of the medication may be prohibitive for many young people (Lumsden & Chaulk, personal communication, October 2011).

Accordingly, CYCPs should closely monitor the use of medications with young people with psychosis. Note too that abruptly ending the use of antipsychotic medications can be dangerous. CYCPs need to educate themselves and the young people they're working with about the effects of the medications; ongoing education should be a part of the treatment approach with adolescents suffering from Schizophrenia (McKenzie, 2008).

As described by Carey (2006), a U.S. study that compared the effects of various Schizophrenia drugs found that about 75 percent of people stopped taking their medications because they were dissatisfied with either the side effects or the lack of results. All antipsychotic drugs have significant side effects; the older medications can induce Parkinson's-like tremors and the movement disorder called *tardive dyskinesia*, and some of the newer drugs cause extreme weight gain and increase the risk of diabetes in youth (Marty Chaulk, personal communication, March 2013). Antipsychotic medications also create significant changes in brain function that are not yet well understood. The drugs numb the brain cell receptors to dopamine, the neural messenger that appears to circulate at high levels when people are having a psychotic episode. The body responds by making more dopamine receptors, which could make the brain more sensitive to future dopamine flooding (Carey, 2006).

Psychoeducation and Individual Counselling In addition to medication, ongoing counselling and support are important. Establishing a supportive therapeutic relationship with the young person is central to successful outcomes for psychosis, just as it is with all mental health concerns. Psychoeducation can focus on helping young people understand all aspects of psychosis. Psychotic experiences are very scary, and so explaining and reassuring is critical (Clark, 2001). Explaining the prognosis and possible effects on school, social relationships, and career plans is important, as is anticipating and talking about the related loss issues.

Insight-oriented approaches to individual counselling are contraindicated, given that probing into deeper emotional layers of the mind is likely to exacerbate the psychotic symptoms for adolescents (McKenzie, 2008). However, empathy and emotionally supportive interventions are critical.

Staying focused primarily on the surface level of thoughts, emotions, and behaviour can help adolescents with these difficulties learn to manage their lives more effectively, recognize the destructive quality of their symptoms, and ultimately lead more adaptive and functional lives. Adolescents suffering from schizophrenia need to remain focused on the tasks of daily living, reality checking, and symptom management. These are key factors for the person with schizophrenia. (McKenzie, 2008, p. 200)

Family Support Interventions The active engagement of families in the treatment plan is very important. A CYC family intervention approach focuses on providing information about the illness, including its effects and its treatment, and on reducing higher levels of hostile or critical expressed emotion within the family. There are also major bereavement and loss issues for parents around the young person's compromised adulthood, particularly if he or she is left with major residual disabilities or impairments. Clarifying what is appropriate parental concern and what is parental overprotection in these instances will likely need discussion and time. Family support also includes supporting siblings, who need understanding and information about the illness as well. Finally, CYCPs can assist families in accessing all needed support and psychoeducation services. Refer to Box 9.4 for a summary of guidelines for CYC interventions that might be considered in your practice.

Prevention: Advocacy, Community, and School-Based Strategies As noted in the *Program Policy Framework for Early Intervention in Psychosis* report (2004), although some adolescents who experience a psychotic episode may recover completely, for others, especially those with Schizophrenia, it may develop into a lifelong condition. We've seen that early intervention is the key to decreasing incidence and severity of symptoms; prevention and advocacy, then, are very important.

CYCPs can initiate early contact with the young person's school, and if necessary the special needs teacher; early involvement with the school can assist in a return to the mainstream school. If this isn't feasible, patient treatment programs have specialized school placements for youth with psychosis.

Box 9.4

Techniques for CYC Intervention

Use a mental status exam to guide your observations: record and refer.

Remain nonjudgmental and supportive.

Identify the strengths of the youth and family and incorporate these in your interventions.

Provide psychoeducation about the nature of psychosis to youth and family.

Use CBT methods of intervention.

Gently challenge delusions with an emphasis on the feelings associated with them.

Teach coping strategies for hallucinations.

Assess for depression and suicide ideation; refer when required.

Provide hope.

Use an advocacy model.

Ensure that cultural beliefs and values are respected and understood.

An advocacy approach for a CYC relational intervention fits with what's known as the *recovery model*. This model looks at the whole person from his or her own point of view, with a focus on strengths and hopes and a respect for the individual's way of coping with and managing difficulties (McDaid, 2013). Similarly, services for youth with psychosis are likely to be more motivating and appealing if they have a solution rather than a deficit focus, with an emphasis on competencies and achievements rather than on problems and concerns (O'Hanlon & Rowan, 1998).

Alternative Healing   If young people choose to stop using medication as a part of their recovery, it's important to provide them with education about, and ongoing support for, this decision. Dr. Peter Breggin, co-author of *Your Drug May Be Your Problem: How and Why to Stop Taking Psychiatric Drugs*, suggests the following: help youth gradually reduce doses, since gradually titrated withdrawal produces the most successful outcomes; educate youth about which withdrawal effects to look out for and how these effects are caused; assist with developing strategies to deal with the withdrawal states, which could include temporarily increasing the reduced dose or using temporary doses of benzodiazepines or other short-term medication; relaxation techniques; and alternative therapies (Breggin & Cohen, 1999).

According to one study (Baker, 2010), those at extremely high risk of developing a psychosis were found to be less likely to develop psychotic disorders after 12 weeks of taking fish oil capsules containing omega-3 fatty acids. The study's authors note that omega-3 supplementation may be effective because individuals with Schizophrenia have an underlying dysfunction in fatty acid metabolism (Baker, 2010). Homeopathy is also used in the natural treatment of psychosis.

Another interesting and relatively new approach to therapeutic interventions with those in acute psychiatric crises, called *open dialogue* (OD), has two important components: (1) a community-based, integrated treatment system that engages families and their social networks, and (2) a distinct and unique form of dialogue within the psychiatric sessions. This open dialogue seeks to level the power dynamics between professional and client whereby each participant in the treatment session feels heard and responded to. The process respects everyone's equally valid voice, or point of view, within the treatment meeting. In the context of a likely tense atmosphere due to the client's psychotic crisis, the process helps bring forth the voices of those "who are silent, less vocal, hesitant, bewildered, or difficult to understand" (Olson, Seikkula, & Ziedonis, 2014, p. 5). This approach has been found to be effective in reducing symptoms of psychosis, leading to fewer and shorter hospitalizations, reduced medication dosage, greater improvements in functioning, and improved likelihood of employment (Olson, Seikkula, & Ziedonis, 2014). The OD approach fits with a CYC perspective, and is currently being adopted in many countries around the world.

Relational CYC Practice   Any one of us can experience a psychotic episode. If an individual is under enough stress, grief, or trauma, it's possible to experience some or all of the symptoms of psychosis—paranoia, an inability to think straight, hallucinations, delusions, and a loss of contact with reality. When a young person experiences these symptoms without warning, it can be absolutely terrifying. "The remedy for all and every psychosis, therefore, is abating the terror," which is why an approach offering help based in gentle healing and kindness has proved so effective in the past, and will do so increasingly in the future (Johnson, 2009).

See Box 9.5 for a summary of specific communication strategies that might be helpful when working with those experiencing psychotic symptoms.

Box 9.5

CYC Communication Strategies

Avoiding discussing the specific content of delusions.

Focus on the emotional content of the youth's statements (e.g., "You feel frightened by these voices").

Identify and satisfy the needs of the child or adolescent (e.g., "What can I do to help you feel safe right now?").

Focus on assisting with the tasks of daily life and specific goals: "One day at a time."

Focus on the use of coping strategies (e.g., distraction, calming).

Use nonjudgmental language.

Build a therapeutic milieu or "reclaiming" environment based on kindness and caring.

Use a recovery model: instill hope and build social identity.

WHERE DO YOU STAND?

The symptoms of psychotic disturbances can be frightening and are associated with severe impairments in functioning. Given that adolescence is the time of development during which symptoms are often first demonstrated, it's imperative that CYCPs be able to identify early signs of long-term psychotic syndromes. Recognizing the symptoms of psychosis in relation to drug use and abuse can also facilitate effective intervention.

As we conclude our discussion of psychosis, revisit the cases of Rebecca and Samantha one last time in the *Viewpoint Challenge* exercise to evaluate your understanding of this chapter's core concepts. Where do you stand with respect to CYC interventions for those affected by psychotic symptoms?

Rebecca's and Samantha's Cases: *Viewpoint Challenge Exercise*

Reread the cases of Rebecca and Samantha discussed throughout this chapter. How would the psychological and the CYC perspectives differ in their approaches to understanding their symptoms? In their approaches to treatment? Can you identify any similarities between the two perspectives? What three intervention strategies discussed in this chapter would you most prefer to keep in mind in your work as a CYCP with youth? Explain your selection.

CHAPTER SUMMARY

- *Psychosis* refers to a group of symptoms associated with a loss of touch with reality and includes *hallucinations*, *delusions*, and *thought disorder*. Psychotic symptoms can occur in the context of various psychological disorders as well as in relation to brain injury, medical conditions, and substance use/abuse.

- The DSM-5 considers psychotic disorders in the general category of Schizophrenia Spectrum and Other Psychotic Disorders and differentiates various psychotic disorders on the basis of *number of domains affected* as well as the *duration of symptoms*.

- Although psychotic symptoms may be encountered less often in the field than other disturbances, the ability of CYCPs to identify specific indicators of such disorders and communicate these to mental health professionals is imperative for the early identification and intervention essential to successful treatment outcomes.

- Psychological explanations for Schizophrenia include genetic and biological explanations as well as the diathesis–stress model.

- CYCPs should be able to distinguish between the *positive symptoms* (including hallucinations, delusions, disorganized speech, and disorganized behaviour) and *negative symptoms* of Schizophrenia.

- Psychological approaches to treatment include *antipsychotic* medications, selective reinforcement, and social skills training.

- Literacy in the area of psychotic disorders will enable CYCPs to better assist children and youth experiencing psychotic symptoms or diagnosed with a specific psychotic disorder.

- Successful treatment approaches used in early intervention programs may include medication, psychoeducation, personal counselling, case management, CBT, substance treatment and supports, and crisis intervention.

Critical Thinking Questions

1. Examine your feelings about working with someone who is exhibiting psychotic symptoms. What role might this play in your CYC practice?
2. Discuss possible challenges in identifying the negative symptoms of Schizophrenia.
3. What is your view regarding the role of biological versus environmental factors in the development of Schizophrenia?
4. Does your opinion on the use of psychotropic medications as a symptom management tool for youth change when you think about its use to treat psychosis? Defend your opinion.
5. What implications might the traumagenic neurodevelopmental model have for CYCPs?
6. How will you differentiate between your observation of symptoms of depression and symptoms of psychosis with the young people you work with?
7. What are your views on the relationship between substance use/abuse and adolescent psychosis/Schizophrenia? How will this influence your CYC practice?
8. What is your opinion about the use of antipsychotic drugs with children and youth in the prodromal stage of psychosis?

Key Terms

Brief Psychotic Disorder, 352

delusions, 349

disorganized thinking, 349

dopamine hypothesis, 360

expressed emotion, 363

hallucinations, 349

negative symptoms, 351

neurosequential model of therapeutics (NMT), 370

positive symptoms, 350

Supplemental Readings

Edwards, G., & McGorry, P. D. (2002). *Implementing early intervention in psychosis: A guide to establishing early psychosis services*. London: Martin Dunn.

Findling, R. L., Schulz, S. C., Kashani, J. H., & Harlan, E. (2001). *Psychotic disorders in children and adolescents*. Thousand Oaks, CA: Sage Publications.

Harrop, C., & Trower, P. (2003). *Why does Schizophrenia develop at later adolescence? A cognitive-developmental approach to psychosis*. Chichester, Sussex: Wiley.

Online Resources

Canadian Mental Health Association, www.cmha.ca/bins/index.asp?lang=1

"New hope for youth with psychosis," http://madellen.hubpages.com/hub/psychosis

Early Psychosis and Prevention Intervention Centre, www.eppic.org.au/EPPIC

Worldwide Early Diagnosis and Treatment Centers for Psychosis and Schizophrenia, www.schizophrenia.com/earlypsychosis.htm

"Understanding schizophrenia," http://helpguide.org/mental/schizophrenia_symptom.htm#authors

Schizophrenia Society of Canada, "Cannabis and psychosis: Exploring the link," http://cannabisandpsychosis.ca/more-information/what-do-we-know

Harmful substance use that begins in adolescence may continue across the lifespan with potential serious negative consequences.

Case Example: *Teighan*

Teighan is a 15-year-old girl with a history of drug (cocaine, marijuana) and alcohol use. She was placed in a group home in Edmonton after Child and Family Services became involved with the family; Teighan's mother and stepfather said they "couldn't control" her any longer and demanded that CFS take her. In the group home, Teighan refused to engage with CYC staff and was unwilling to cooperate with any routines or group activities. She was disruptive during therapeutic group sessions and initially refused to say much during individual treatment meetings with the CYCP.

Teighan's school absences became more frequent. She would go downtown to hang out with the street youth, and after a short while on the street, her drug use increased. She began to stay out overnight with her boyfriend, who was dealing drugs. Soon after she met her boyfriend, she began to be sexually exploited by both him and his street gang members. Teighan used marijuana, crack, and alcohol to numb herself while she was being exploited.

Source: Adapted from "Raphael's story," National Child Traumatic Stress Network, n.d.

Learning Objectives

1. Distinguish between substance use, abuse, misuse, intoxication, tolerance, and withdrawal.

2. Distinguish between Substance Use and Substance-Induced Disorders as described in the DSM-5. Why is Gambling Disorder included in the category of Substance-Related and Addictive Disorders?

3. Define the major conceptual models for understanding substance abuse, including the harm-reduction approach.

4. Describe the extent of substance misuse among youth in Canada, with a focus on "out of the mainstream" youth.

5. Compare and contrast primary psychological explanations (biological, behavioural, cognitive, psychodynamic, and sociocultural) for substance use and substance-related disorders.

6. Summarize the risk and protective factors related to substance misuse in youth.

7. Compare and contrast the various psychological approaches to preventing and treating substance-related disturbances.

8. Outline various assessment and intervention strategies to use in CYC practice with youth who are misusing substances.

9. Describe universal approaches to prevention programs for youth substance use.

Chapter Overview

The use of substances to alter perception, thoughts, and emotions is a universal practice. As the following quote illustrates, substance use can become a way of managing distressing emotions and thoughts.

> If I don't do drugs, I feel like I'm going to go insane. Because I have all these thoughts and all this pain in my heart and I can't get rid of it, you know? Drugs are the only thing that takes that away. That's why I do drugs. Because it keeps me, not happy, but keeps me from being so sad that I want to die. (Gardner, 2002)

Although alterations of experiences using substances can be a common coping strategy, long-term and frequent use can significantly impair functioning and result in its own set of stressors, distress, and debilitating consequences. What distinguishes use from abuse? How much substance use is required before such use is defined as a disorder? Why are some youth more likely than others to develop substance-related disorders? From a psychological perspective, this chapter will outline the DSM-5 approach to considering substance-related disturbances and the major psychological paradigms' approaches to intervention.

From the CYC perspective, this chapter will examine substance use by vulnerable youth as a constantly evolving phenomenon, recognizing that mental health issues are almost always a factor in addictive behaviours. Today, street drugs and inexpensive synthetic drugs are more accessible than ever—and addiction can compromise a young person's life in many ways. Given that lifelong behaviour patterns are often established during adolescence and early adulthood, harmful substance use that begins in adolescence may continue across the lifespan, with potentially serious consequences. In this chapter we'll briefly review historical models used to explain substance use and addictions. We'll also introduce the levels-of-involvement assessment tool, the harm-reduction model, and other models of change suitable to CYC practice. As with all risky behaviours, understanding the reasons why youth use or misuse substances, and why they continue or discontinue use, is fundamental to developing effective supportive CYC interventions.

WHAT ARE SUBSTANCE USE, MISUSE, AND ABUSE?

The term **psychoactive substance** or *psychoactive drug* refers to either a chemical not normally found in the body or a normal body chemical used in a larger dose than is normally found in the body. Substances can be eaten, drunk, snorted, inhaled, and dissolved under the tongue, absorbed through the skin, injected, or inserted. The chemical is administered with the intent of producing a change in body functioning and a change in the central nervous system (CNS). "Psychoactive drugs are substances that alter brain functioning by decreasing (depressants), increasing (stimulants), or disrupting (hallucinogens) central nervous system activity" (Csiernik & Rowe, 2010, p. 11). Changes in the CNS produce changes in mood, perception, sensation, need, and behaviour. These physiological changes that follow substance use are referred to as **intoxication** (e.g., relaxed mood, decreased physiological arousal, impaired problem solving), and vary depending on the substance. All societies have psychoactive substances available, and most people in Canada have used some type of psychoactive substance or drug. Nicotine found in cigarettes is an example of such a substance. As you might imagine, psychoactive substances can be used for medical and non-medical purposes and can be licit (legal) or illicit (illegal).

Substance use refers to the use of *psychoactive substances*, including drugs, alcohol, plants, and chemicals, that cause observable or noticeable changes in an individual's CNS and thus in his or her mental functioning. Obviously, substance use varies significantly in terms of frequency, type, duration, and purpose. Not all substance use is harmful or problematic. In fact, some psychoactive substances can be considered beneficial, as in the case of using psychotropic prescription medications to treat psychosis, depression, and anxiety, or even in the enjoyment of a cup of coffee. **Substance misuse** is the occasional, *inappropriate* use of either a social or a prescription drug. What constitutes inappropriate use? From a psychological perspective and as outlined in the DSM-5, *inappropriate* use is defined in relation to the degree of impairment associated with substance use. By comparison, **substance abuse** is a general term used to define the use of any drug use that is disapproved of by members of the society in which it occurs (Csiernik, 2011; Csiernik & Rowe, 2010). *Substance abuse* often refers to the use of a drug to the point where it begins to interfere with the young person's economic or social functioning, or physical or psychological health. However, substance abuse can occur (and often does occur) without the youth ever developing dependence or an addiction to the drug.

Before turning to a discussion of substance-related disorders, examine your own experiences of substance use, misuse, and abuse in the *Think About It!* exercise.

WHAT IS A SUBSTANCE-RELATED DISORDER? THE PSYCHOLOGICAL PERSPECTIVE

When does substance use become a problem? From a psychological perspective, *substance abuse* is a pattern of use that leads to significant impairment or distress for an individual, manifested as one or more of the following:

■ **tolerance**, defined as the need for greater and greater amounts of the substance to achieve the desired effect, or noticeably reduced intoxication with continued use of the same amount of the substance

■ **withdrawal**, the negative physical reactions (which vary depending on the substance) experienced when the drug is no longer used; it also involves the continued use of the substance (or a closely related drug) to relieve or prevent withdrawal symptoms

Together, tolerance and withdrawal have been used to define **physical dependence**. For example, physical dependence on alcohol is associated with increased tolerance (i.e., with continued use, more alcohol is required in order to experience the same degree of intoxication) and withdrawal symptoms (i.e., sleep disturbance, nausea, anxiety) when the drug is no longer taken. Although physical dependence is often used to define *substance dependence*, **psychological dependence** encompasses the behavioural, emotional, and cognitive aspects of dependence, and can include the following:

■ repeated and continued use of the drug despite knowledge that it's causing or aggravating a persistent or recurrent physical or psychological problem

■ a persistent desire or need to use the substance, even in the absence of physical withdrawal symptoms

■ unsuccessful efforts to reduce or control substance use

■ spending a great deal of time in activities necessary to obtain or use the substance or to recover from its effects

■ giving up social, occupational, or recreational activities because of substance use

What is an *addiction*? An **addiction** can be defined as a chronic condition that is characterized by compulsive or habitual seeking and use of something, despite harmful consequences.

DSM-5 Categories

The DSM-5 groups psychological disturbances associated with substance use and addictions in one chapter entitled Substance-Related and Addictive Disorders. It's worth noting that, in order to be more neutral in its discussion of these disorders, the DSM-5 has removed the term *addiction* from its discussion of substance-related disturbances.

Substance-Related and Addictive Disorders   Within the general category of **Substance-Related and Addictive Disorders**, a distinction is made between *Substance Use Disorders*, associated with cognitive, behavioural, and physiological symptoms resulting from continued use of the substance, and *Substance-Induced Disorders*, including intoxication, withdrawal, and other psychological disorders (e.g., substance-induced depressive disorder) that result from the use of a psychoactive substance (APA, 2013). Other specific diagnoses presented in this chapter relate to the 10 specific classes of drugs identified in the DSM-5. This allows for inclusion of the specific features associated with the use of a particular substance (e.g., alcohol versus opioids).

The category of Substance-Related and Addictive Disorders also includes **Gambling Disorder**, associated with behavioural symptoms similar to those observed in the context of substance-related disorders but arising from repetitive gambling. Evidence that both addictive substance use and addictive gambling are maintained by similar reward systems supports the consideration of these seemingly very different behaviour patterns in the same diagnostic category (APA, 2013). Let's briefly review the two groups of substance-related disorders before considering specific symptoms of a couple of diagnoses you're likely to encounter in your CYC practice. Box 10.1 presents the specific diagnoses in this category.

Box 10.1

DSM-5 Substance-Related and Addictive Disorders

Substance-Related Disorders	Opioid-Related Disorders
Substance Use Disorders	Sedative-, Hypnotic-, or Anxiolytic-Related Disorders
Substance-Induced Disorders	Stimulant-Related Disorders
Alcohol-Related Disorders	Tobacco-Related Disorders
Caffeine-Related Disorders	Other (or Unknown) Substance-Related Disorders
Cannabis-Related Disorders	
Hallucinogen-Related Disorders	Non-Substance-Related Disorders
Inhalant-Related Disorders	Gambling Disorder

Substance-Related Disorders: Diagnoses and Criteria

As you can see, a long list of potential diagnoses is associated with the category of Substance-Related Disorders. Here, we consider the specific criteria for Substance Use and Substance-Induced Disorders to help capture the essence of this class of disorders. For each of these diagnoses, the diagnostic criteria for one particular substance (alcohol) are presented in order to illustrate the general framework of this DSM-5 category.

Substance Use Disorders   A **Substance Use Disorder** is characterized by continued use of a substance that is associated with cognitive, behavioural, and physiological symptoms. The use continues despite the negative consequences of this persistent use. The diagnosis of a Substance Use Disorder can be applied to any one of the 10 major classes of drugs identified in the DSM-5 (except caffeine). Although these drugs vary significantly in their effects on the nervous system, they do have something in common. As noted in the DSM-5, all of these drugs "that are taken in excess have in common direct activation of the brain reward system, which is involved in the reinforcement of behaviors and the production of memories" (APA, 2013, p. 481). This activation of the brain reward system, together with the effects of intoxication (e.g., feelings of pleasure), serves to perpetuate continued use of the substance, even if it means neglecting other activities and/or responsibilities that were previously pleasurable. Since gambling behaviours activate the same brain reward system, they can also involve the neglect of other activities and/or responsibilities that result in impaired functioning. Box 10.2 presents the major classes of drugs identified in the DSM-5.

Thus, a diagnosis of Substance Use Disorder can be applied to any of these major drug classes (except caffeine). For any one of the drug classes, the DSM organizes specific criteria for Substance Use Disorder in relation to four general areas: (1) impaired control with respect to substance use; (2) impaired social functioning; (3) risky use; and (4) tolerance and withdrawal.

Note that the criteria for any Substance Use Disorder are essentially the same as those for Alcohol Use Disorder. Thus, you can essentially take any other substance (e.g., cannabis) and replace every instance of the term *alcohol* in Box 10.3 below with *cannabis* and have the DSM-5 criteria for that particular substance. It's also important to note that the DSM-5 includes a consideration of the range of severity of substance use. Specifically, the terms *mild* (presence of two to three symptoms), *moderate* (presence of

---

Box 10.2

10 Drug Classes Identified in the DSM-5

Alcohol	Opioids (e.g., heroin)
Caffeine	Sedatives, hypnotics, and anxiolytics
Cannabis	Stimulants (e.g. cocaine, amphetamines)
Hallucinogens (phencyclidine and other hallucinogens)	Tobacco
Inhalants	Other (or unknown) substances

DSM-5 Criteria for Alcohol Use Disorder

A. A problematic pattern of alcohol use leading to clinically significant impairment or distress, as manifested by at least two of the following, occurring within a 12-month period:

1. Alcohol is often taken in larger amounts or over a longer period than was intended.

2. There is a persistent desire or unsuccessful efforts to cut down or control alcohol use.

3. A great deal of time is spent in activities necessary to obtain alcohol, use alcohol, or recover from its effects.

4. Craving, or a strong desire or urge to use alcohol.

5. Recurrent alcohol use resulting in a failure to fulfill major role obligations at work, school, or home.

6. Continued alcohol use despite having persistent or recurrent social or interpersonal problems caused or exacerbated by the effects of alcohol.

7. Important social, occupational, or recreational activities are given up or reduced because of alcohol use.

8. Recurrent alcohol use in situations in which it is physically hazardous.

9. Alcohol use is continued despite knowledge of having a persistent or recurrent physical or psychological problem that is likely to have been caused or exacerbated by alcohol.

10. Tolerance, as defined by either of the following:
    a. A need for markedly increased amounts of alcohol to achieve intoxication or desired effect.
    b. A markedly diminished effect with continued use of the same amount of alcohol.

11. Withdrawal, as manifested by either of the following:
    a. The characteristic withdrawal syndrome for alcohol. . . .
    b. Alcohol (or a closely related substance, such as a benzodiazepine) is taken to relieve or avoid withdrawal symptoms.

Source: Reprinted with permission from the Diagnostic and Statistical Manual of Mental Disorders, Fifth Edition, (Copyright ©2013). American Psychiatric Association. All Rights Reserved.

four to five symptoms), or *severe* (six ore more symptoms) are applied to any instance of Substance Use Disorder to indicate the severity of the disturbance.

Substance-Induced Disorders   We've seen that **Substance-Induced Disorders** include intoxication, withdrawal, and other psychological disorders (e.g., Substance-Induced Depressive Disorder) that result from the use of a psychoactive substance (APA, 2013). Accordingly, in addition to the criteria for Substance Use Disorders (a set of criteria for each substance class), the DSM specifies criteria for both *intoxication* and *withdrawal* symptoms for each particular substance. Unlike the criteria for Substance Use Disorder, the criteria for intoxication and withdrawal vary according to the particular substance because of its unique physiological effects. For example, symptoms of *alcohol intoxication* (e.g., slurred speech, unsteady gait, impairment in attention or memory) differ from symptoms of *cannabis intoxication* (e.g., increased appetite, dry mouth). Similarly, symptoms of *alcohol withdrawal* (e.g., hand tremor, insomnia, nausea/vomiting, anxiety) differ from symptoms of *cannabis withdrawal* (e.g., irritability, anger, nervousness, decreased appetite, depressed mood).

In addition to tolerance and withdrawal, **Other Substance-Induced Disorders** include those psychological disturbances described in other DSM-5 categories (e.g., bipolar and related disorders) that are brought about by substance use. For example, *Alcohol-Induced Bipolar Disorder* includes symptoms associated with Bipolar Disorder

Despite his repeated attempts to quit smoking, Carl can't stop thinking about smoking and usually gives in to his desires. Although he knows smoking makes his asthma symptoms worse, he continues to smoke.

After ingesting several glasses of beer, Caroline staggers to her bed, hitting her arm against the wall as she makes her way into her bedroom. When her roommate asks if she's all right, Caroline slurs, "Oh, ya, jus' fine."

Erica stops drinking alcohol, despite her previous heavy use, in order to improve her work performance. She notices that she's sweaty and shaky most of the time and that she can't sleep at night.

that develop in the context of alcohol use, intoxication, and/or withdrawal. Each alcohol-induced disorder is summarized in the specific diagnostic category that includes those key features of the presenting disorder. For example, the criteria for Alcohol-Induced Bipolar Disorder are presented in the chapter that summarizes *Bipolar and Related Disorders*.

Before turning to a discussion of incidence, development, and comorbidity, try the *Test Your Understanding* exercise to review your understanding of the core symptoms of substance-related disturbances. Can you identify the key concepts illustrated by each of these cases?

A CYC APPROACH TO SUBSTANCE MISUSE: UNDERSTANDING SUBSTANCE ABUSE AND ADDICTIONS

On any given day, many vulnerable youth in Canada will meet the APA diagnostic criteria for a Substance Use Disorder (SUD). Although the reasons adolescents give for beginning and continuing to use psychoactive substances are varied, and the risk and protective factors also vary, the signs and consequences of substance misuse and addictions are relatively consistent for all.

There are still no generally accepted guidelines for what constitutes problematic substance use or misuse, whether among youth in general or vulnerable youth in particular. Moreover, notwithstanding the problems inherent in the medical model, the DSM-5's diagnostic criteria may not be completely appropriate for use with adolescents. Young people's substance use may very well represent normative experimentation; that is, an expected feature of normal adolescent development. As Straus (2007) reminds us, young people have always been risk takers; neuroscience has shown us how risk taking stimulates the adolescent brain, and this is especially true of substance use. As well, substance experimentation can symbolize a rite of passage to adulthood. Some studies even indicate that some experimentation with drugs isn't inherently detrimental "and may, in fact have some benefit" (Straus, 2007, p. 269); thus, it's critical to distinguish between controlled experimentation and problematic use leading to harm. In their assessments, then, CYCPs should ask themselves, "Given the levels of involvement with the substance, does this young person's use reflect normative use, misuse, dependence, or an addiction?" (We'll discuss the "levels of involvement" later in this chapter.)

A key feature of Substance Use Disorders is the intense craving experienced in relation to the substance.

Kmiragaya/Fotolia

According to some reviewers, the DSM-5 criteria for diagnosing an SUD among adolescents include positive changes from the previous edition (Curley, 2010; Winters, 2011). For example, the DSM-5 has eliminated the disease categories for substance abuse and dependence. The new category includes a variety of Substance Use Disorders that are broken down by type of drug, such as Cannabis Use Disorder and Alcohol Use Disorder. The "drug craving" symptom has been added to these criteria, while the "problems with law enforcement" symptom has been eliminated. Substance use is defined as "maladaptive" in the DSM if use impairs day-to-day functioning in social relationships, school, or work; this makes it consistent with the other disorders.

Also new to the DSM-5 are diagnostic criteria for cannabis withdrawal, which the APA lists as being caused by "cessation of cannabis use that has been heavy and prolonged," results in "clinically significant distress or impairment in social, occupational, or other important areas of functioning," and is characterized by at least three of these symptoms: "irritability, anger or aggression; nervousness or anxiety; sleep difficulties (insomnia); decreased appetite or weight loss; restlessness; depressed mood; and or physical symptoms such as stomach pain, shakiness or tremors, sweating, fever, chills, and headache" (Curley, 2010).

We've seen that the DSM-5 includes pathological gambling among substance-related and addictive disorders, meaning that the term *addiction* is now officially applied. Video gaming and internet addiction had also been considered for inclusion in this category; however, APA work group members concluded that the research data were insufficient and instead recommended their inclusion in the manual's appendix, along with a statement that these are conditions for further study. This lack of inclusion has been the source of controversy, as it has serious implications for those needing to access treatment for problematic gaming through private insurance companies.

A variety of conceptual models have been used to explain addictive behaviours. We've discussed how conceptual models provide frameworks to help us understand mental health issues and to help in the planning of effective interventions (Csiernik, 2011). All conceptual models are based on, and reflect, morals and values. A CYC approach to understanding addictions is likewise based on our values of being caring, nonjudgmental, and compassionate; consequently, the CYC view of addictive behaviours is that they're a "bio-psycho-social" phenomenon (Csiernik, 2011, p. 30).

Here's a summary of the more predominant models of addiction, as outlined in Csiernik (2011).

The Moral Model. The **moral model** is based on the belief that using substances in any form is morally wrong and that if people choose to use a mind-altering substance they can also choose to stop using it, even if they've become addicted: "The moral model perceives dependence on a drug as a consequence of a weak moral character" (Csiernik, 2011, p. 31). This perspective underlies the major societal anti-drug campaigns, including the American "War on Drugs," anti-smoking lobbies, the criminalization of marijuana, and random drug testing in the workplace. Social class, race, and economic status all affect how the moral model is applied, although social drinking is approved by most proponents. Csiernik suggests that the moral model is the reason why some countries in the world still impose the death penalty for drug-related offences.

The moral model remains the predominant view of most people in Canada, and Canadian alcohol and drug policies are rooted in it. (And yet it's interesting to note, for example, that despite the Netherlands' well-known progressive drug-use policies, the number of addicts there is much lower than the rest of Europe; Straus, 2007, p. 272.) Most Canadians view drug and alcohol misuse and addictions as behaviours that can and should be managed by each person using appropriate choices and free will. That is, most of us continue to make a moral judgment about those with addictions; we tend to condemn the behaviour as well as the individual based on our values about the so-called "choice" to use or not use.

Biological Theories. These theories include the disease model, genetics, brain dysfunction, allergy theory, and biochemical theories. The disease model, with which most of us are familiar, is based on the premise that substance dependence is a chronic disease. Introduced in the 1930s as an alternative to the moral model, it proposes that those with addictions have a susceptibility to alcohol and drugs; although they're considered responsible for their problem in the first place, they're seen to need medical care and treatment. In the disease model, abstinence is the only "cure" for alcoholism (Csiernik, 2011, p. 36), and indeed it's the foundation of Alcoholics Anonymous (AA). Viewing alcoholism as a disease absolves anyone of guilt and disregards the related social factors.

The **genetic theory** views an addiction, primarily alcoholism, as an inherited risk. Research has shown that some may indeed have a greater predisposition for developing an issue with substance use. **Biochemical theories** propose that there are various chemical imbalances that exist in the body or are created by use and withdrawal. *Allergy theory* is supported by the doctor who treated the founding members of AA; he suggested that alcoholism was an allergy combined with an obsession. **Brain dysfunction theory** proposes that continued consumption of large amounts of alcohol or other substances leads to damage of brain cells that are responsible for willpower, making drug-dependent individuals biologically different. Evidence does exist that the brains of addicted individuals are in fact different from brains of those who are not addicted (Csiernik, 2011).

Harm-Reduction Model. The **harm-reduction model** is based on values related to public health, human rights, and social justice (Canadian Harm Reduction Network, n.d.). Harm reduction fits well with the CYC perspective on addictions in that the framework focuses not on the substance use itself but rather on reducing its risks and consequences. The harm-reduction model is underpinned by the knowledge that many drug-related problems are not the result of the drugs themselves; they are instead related to the unregulated manufacture

Consider the case of Teighan, presented in the beginning of the chapter. Identify any of the symptoms of an SUD from a psychological perspective using the DSM-5. What model would you choose to help you understand Teighan's substance use issue? Do you think she's self-medicating? If you were the CYCP working with Teighan, how might you involve her family? How might you work with her regarding her lifestyle choices and her partner? How will you keep her safe when she's on the street? What model might you use to explain Teighan's drug use?

and trade of drugs as well as government commitment to failed policies and inequitably applied laws. Finally, the idea of harm reduction is to ensure that people who use psychoactive substances are treated with respect and without stigma, and that substance-related problems and issues are addressed systemically (Canadian Harm Reduction Network, n.d.). Harm reduction accepts the fact that people use substances, and thus considers the drug-free society as an unrealistic goal. One of the major tenets of harm reduction is that it remains neutral on the topic of abstinence: use is neither condoned nor condemned. Thus, harm-reduction philosophy views abstinence as only one among a broad range of options that can reduce the health and social harms associated with substance misuse.

Harm reduction for youth in Canada is controversial, given that promoting harm-reduction approaches with underaged youth presents a difficult challenge for those who have a duty of care. The Criminal Code of Canada identifies young persons as a vulnerable subgroup of the population, and the law embeds abstinence as the response toward alcohol and other drug use for youth. In fact, regardless of age it's a criminal offence to possess, produce, or sell cannabis in Canada, and various provincial laws prohibit public intoxication, possession of alcohol by a minor, and sale of alcohol to a minor. As well, school administrators have a duty of care toward the student body and accountability to parents; formal school board policies support abstinence as a goal. Harm reduction as a universal intervention targeting underaged youth, then, should be informed by the legal and policy constraints placed on schools and school boards (Poulin, 2006). Moreover, the literature is inconclusive, with very little information about whether these interventions actually reduce substance-related harm or the risk of harm to youth (Poulin, 2006). The effectiveness of drug prevention education aimed toward youth, for example, has been repeatedly shown to be minimal (Poulin, 2006). We discuss harm reduction as a method of intervention for youth later in this chapter.

Before turning to a discussion of prevalence, development, and comorbidity, consider the details of the opening case in relation to the psychological and CYC views of Substance Use Disorders in *Teighan's Case: Revisited.*

HOW MANY YOUNG PEOPLE STRUGGLE WITH SUBSTANCE USE AND ABUSE?

The majority of mainstream youth in Canada don't have substance use or substance dependency problems. Indeed, fewer than one in five youth have ever tried any drugs other than alcohol and cannabis; around the same proportion use alcohol or cannabis regularly; and far fewer have used drugs such as heroin, ecstasy, cocaine, or crystal methamphetamine. Older adolescents are more likely to drink and experiment with drugs than younger ones, but those who start at younger ages are more likely to develop related personal and social issues, including clinically defined substance abuse or dependence disorders. There is a growing concern about the widespread use of synthetic drugs, also known as *designer drugs*, which are easily available to young people and have been responsible for a number of deaths in Canada.

Canadian surveys show that tobacco, alcohol, and cannabis remain the substances most frequently first used by mainstream youth. In fact, Canada ranks among the leading countries in prevalence and frequency rates of substance use among adolescents. Based on recent data (Winters, 2011), 7.6 percent of 12- to 17-year-olds in Canada met the criteria for at least one DSM-SUD, and an additional 17 percent, while not meeting an abuse diagnosis, still reported one or two substance-dependence criteria (Squeglia, Jacobus, & Tapert, 2009). In most jurisdictions in Canada, young people have access to public inpatient and outpatient assessment and treatment services for substance use, both voluntary and involuntary. Private residential and therapeutic treatment services are also available and usually require a medical diagnosis.

According to the Canadian Centre on Substance Abuse (CCSA), alcohol is by far the most common substance used; a recent national survey of students in grades 7–9 found that about two-thirds had already consumed alcohol. As well, data shows that 83 percent of youth aged 15–24 are alcohol drinkers ("Trends in drug use among youth," 2013). Male youth in Canada are likely to drink more, drink more often, and drink more on each occasion than female youth, and youth today are also starting to drink alcohol earlier than in previous generations ("Trends in drug use among youth," 2013).

Cannabis, reported to be the most widely used illicit drug in the world, is also the most common in Canada, used by one in seven adults and one in four youth (Health Canada, 2012). After alcohol, it's the first drug that many Canadian youth try. Lifetime cannabis use is reported by 17 percent of students in grades 7–9; 29 percent of 15- to 17-year-olds and almost half of 18- to 19-year-olds report past-year use; and Canadian boys report the highest rates of frequent use (more than 40 times in their lifetime) (Health Canada, 2012). It's important for CYCPs to know that cannabis use has been linked to low mood, depression and anxiety. Early marijuana use in adolescence has been shown to have significant long-term effects on later cognitive functioning, particularly self-management strategies. And in young people with pre-existing vulnerabilities, marijuana use can trigger or unmask psychiatric difficulties, including Schizophrenia, psychosis, and depression (Marty Chaulk, personal communication, 2011).

For youth at risk, tobacco use has been a controversial topic for CYCPs, who may consider tobacco to be the least harmful substance young people use when they have serious addictions or are using much more harmful substances. In 2008, among those aged 12–17, 8 percent reported that they were smokers (Statistics Canada, 2010). Canadians who smoke had their first cigarette as a preteen or teen, and indeed those aged 12–24, are most at risk for beginning to smoke. In 2011, the Canadian Tobacco Use Monitoring Survey (CTUMS) reported that among those aged 15–19, 6 percent reported smoking daily and 6 percent occasionally (Canadian Cancer Society, 2015).

SUBSTANCE-RELATED DISORDERS AND DEVELOPMENT

> The risk and severity of substance-related problems are magnified by lowered age of onset of regular use. . . . Those who begin drug use before age 15 are six times more likely than those who begin drug use after age 18 to develop adult symptoms of drug dependence. . . . Reduced age of drug exposure may become recognized as one of the most clinically and socially significant drug trends of the twentieth century. . . . Postponing . . . exposure to intoxicants to the latest point in the transition from childhood to young adulthood is a crucial strategy in the goal of reducing alcohol- and other drug-related problems. (White, Dennis, & Godley, 2002, p. 172)

The experimental or occasional use of substances, especially alcohol and marijuana, usually begins during adolescence. For most, substance use will remain purely experimental or somewhat occasional, but for a substantial minority of young people, especially many vulnerable youth, substance misuse may eventually cause harm to their life functioning, with major effects on their health and well-being in both the short and long term.

> Adolescent developmental tasks include challenges of identity, autonomy, sexuality, academic functioning, and peer relationships. For many, this period includes normative experimentation with perceived facets of adult life, such as experimentation with substances. Many adolescents who use substances also try out other risk-taking behaviors (RTBs) including antisocial behaviors, delinquency, and high-risk sexual behavior. Such behaviors raise concern due to their potentially adverse consequences. (Feldstein & Miller, 2006, p. 634)

During adolescence, the substantial developmental changes that occur in the brain contribute to increased risk-taking and sensation-seeking behaviours. And since the adolescent brain is still developing, alcohol and drug use have a great potential to disrupt normal brain development. The most affected brain regions include the hippocampus, related to learning and memory, and the prefrontal cortex, responsible for critical thinking, planning, impulse control, and emotional regulation. Adolescents engaged in heavy or hazardous drinking have been found to exhibit impaired memory, attention difficulties, and deficits in information processing. Those engaging in heavy substance use have also shown deficits in executive functioning, specifically in future planning, abstract reasoning strategies, and generation of new solutions to problems (Winters, 2008).

Refer to Figure 10.1 for a depiction of how substance use alters brain pathways.

When adolescents are feeling strong emotion or intense peer pressure, the still-maturing circuitry in the front part of brain is overwhelmed, or "hijacked," by the amygdala, which results in increased impulsivity and lack of good decision making. As well, increased hormonal production during adolescence (associated with novelty seeking and social competitiveness) may promote substance use, since for young people such use represents a novel experience ("Youth substance use prevention," 2015). Adolescents also show a diminished sensitivity to intoxication; their higher metabolic rates seem to allow them to consume larger amounts of alcohol.

It's important that CYCPs understand how substance use both affects and causes chemical changes in the brain, which, depending on substance type and frequency, make it difficult to stop using them. The inadvertent short- and long-term consequences of drug

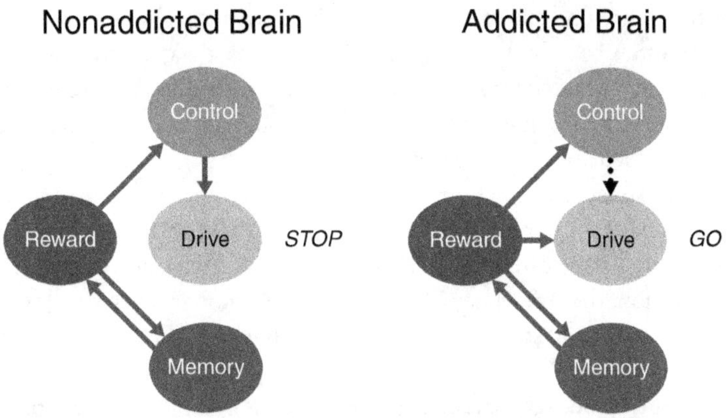

Nonaddicted Brain

Addicted Brain

STOP

GO

Figure 10.1 Brain Development and Substance Use

Substance use alters brain pathways, resulting in deficits in executive functioning, memory, and motivation each of which results in decreased likelihood of controlling substance use.

Source: Excerpt from Addiction: Pulling at the Neural Threads of Social Behaviors by Nora D. Volkow, Ruben D. Baler, Rita Z. Goldstein. Copyright © by Elsevier Ltd. Used by permission of Elsevier Ltd. via Rightslink Service of CCC.

use during adolescence can not only create harm in the brain but also cause ongoing vulnerability to future substance use. Indeed, long-term changes in the brain are likely at the root of most addictive behaviour that continues into adulthood ("Youth substance use prevention," 2015).

COMORBIDITY

> I have come to believe that trauma is the problem and substance use the solution . . .
> until the solution becomes the problem. (Talbot et al., 2011, p. 18)

Adolescent substance use can significantly overlap with both externalizing and internalizing behaviours. In the former, for example, ADHD will quite often coexist with substance misuse; in a sample of adolescents with ADHD, three times as many were found to have comorbid substance-use difficulties. Adolescents with CD also frequently struggle with substance-misuse behaviours. Externalizing disorders have been found to precede substance use difficulties (Leyton & Stewart, 2014). In relation to internalizing behaviours, youth and adults who abuse substances commonly experience mood and anxiety disorders. While the rates of depressive disorders in males and females are relatively equal in childhood, this changes dramatically when youth reach adolescence, with females becoming three times more likely to develop mood disorders. Generally, mood and anxiety problems precede the onset of substance abuse, suggesting that individuals self-medicate to diminish their anxiety.

Substance use is also intimately related to trauma. As we saw in Chapter 2, trauma is both an event and a response to an event; the related behaviours of complex trauma and PTSD, for example, both carry serious consequences. Trauma is all-pervasive and life changing, especially for those young people who've faced multiple traumatic events or repeated exposure to abuse. Young people accessing substance-use treatment and other mental health services commonly report experiences of trauma in their lives—and report that they use substances as a coping mechanism to deal with the overwhelming trauma-related stress. The out-of-mainstream youth population is at increased risk for substance misuse, often because they're using substances as a way to cope with toxic family environments and untreated trauma, as we saw with Teighan in the case example. Yet this seemingly adaptive coping mechanism can make young people even more vulnerable to substance use problems, and often to more traumas.

As we have stressed throughout, the role of the environment in shaping early and adolescent brain functioning includes many factors: the effects of maltreatment and trauma; prenatal exposure to drugs; family antisocial behaviour; a non-intact family; maternal depression; the influence of peers, especially among youth with low self-efficacy; and the cultural and social structures that so often channel young people toward drug and alcohol misuse (Poole, 2012).

The relationship between trauma and addiction is complex, and the pathways move in both directions. For example, consider the cycle of addiction so often experienced by sexually exploited youth. Youth who are exploited most often turn to substances to self-medicate symptoms of trauma related to sexual abuse, or they're introduced to substances by their street-involved peers. They become dependent on these substances and begin to sell sex for money to buy them; now they need the substances to numb themselves while they're being exploited. To meaningfully facilitate change and healing, CYCPs can help sexually exploited young people see the connections between their experience of trauma and their problematic substance use and any other mental health concerns.

However, there are many young people who've been trauma-exposed and who misuse or experiment extensively with substances who don't become adults with problems around substance misuse. As well, while youth who are heavy alcohol and cannabis users may develop drug or alcohol misuse problems as adults, 60 to 70 percent will not, or for that matter ever experience any other addictions in their lives.

In order to understand those at greatest risk for developing an addiction or problematic dependence, we also need to examine the biological basis of drug abuse and addiction (Leyton & Stewart, 2014), which we consider below.

Before turning to a discussion of the explanations for substance misuse, read the statements in Box 10.4 to explore some of the myths associated with substance use and abuse.

Box 10.4

Common Myths About Substance-Related Disorders

MYTH: *Overcoming substance-related disorders is a matter of willpower.*

FACT: Physiological changes associated with substance use, including the activation of the brain reward system, can make it very difficult to simply choose to quit.

MYTH: *It's less dangerous to use prescription medications to get a high than it is to use illegal substances.*

FACT: When used or misused outside of a doctor's recommendation, prescription medications can have deadly consequences.

MYTH: *People with drug dependence can return to occasional use.*

FACT: Physiological changes associated with substance dependence can lead to drug seeking and repetitive use despite risks to health and overall functioning.

EXPLAINING SUBSTANCE-RELATED DISORDERS: PSYCHOLOGICAL PARADIGMS

As is the case with any disorder, multiple explanations have been forwarded to explain how and why these disturbances arise. We consider some of the most common explanations for substance-related disorders from each of the major psychological paradigms.

Biological Paradigm   Historically, substance-related disorders were considered to be a matter of morality and weakness in character. More recently, however, biological factors have been found to be powerful influences in the development and maintenance of Substance Use Disorders. Genetics, biochemical processes, and neurobiological factors have all been found to be related to the development of substance-related disturbances.

Heredity and Genetics. A number of studies reveal the role of genetics in increasing one's risk for developing substance-related disorders. Specifically, twin, family, and adoption studies reveal a genetic predisposition for developing substance-related disorders for alcohol (Lowinson et al., 2005), nicotine (McCaffery et al., 2008), and cocaine and opiates (Matthews & Moylan, 2005). What is inherited? Although various genes appear to be involved in predisposing one to developing a substance-related disorder, those that are responsible for determining the sensitivity of the brain reward system have captured the attention of recent investigations (e.g., Epps & Wright, 2012).

Brain Structures. Activation of the **brain reward system** appears to be responsible for the persistent behaviours associated with devastating consequences in both substance and behavioural (i.e., gambling) addictive disorders. The brain reward system consists of specific brain pathways that, when activated, regulate our feelings of pleasure and reward. The *nucleus accumbens* (see Appendix 2) has been found to be one of the key structures associated with these pleasurable sensations. These positive sensations increase the likelihood that we'll repeat the actions that led to their activation. Eating and sexual activity are examples of activities that are associated with an activation of this brain reward system (Ray, 2012). It's easy to see, then, how these physiological pathways can serve to maintain substance use despite any negative consequences that might arise.

Neurotransmitters. Two important neurotransmitter pathways also play a role in maintaining substance use: one for dopamine, the other for serotonin. Activation of the dopamine pathway (including the nucleus accumbens) has been found to be associated with amphetamine and cocaine use (e.g., Koob et al., 2004; Wise, 2004). In fact, research has found that with continued cocaine and amphetamine use, these pathways show evidence of sensitization to the substance, resulting in greater and greater release of dopamine with continued use (Boileau et al., 2006). Activation of the serotonin pathway has been observed in alcohol use and is also associated with pleasurable experiences, including relaxation (and decreased anxiety) and rewarding effects (Lovinger, 1997). Clearly, these neural pathways are associated with pleasurable sensations that motivate the individual to repeat the behaviours (i.e., drug use) that lead to their experience, resulting in the *physical dependence* we've discussed.

Psychodynamic Paradigm   From a psychodynamic perspective, the basis of substance-related and addictive disorders is psychological, not biological. The

self-medication theory of addiction developed by Khantzian (1999, 2013), for example, explains Substance Use Disorders in relation to emotional suffering. According to this theory, some individuals experience *passive suffering*, feeling overwhelmed by negative emotions with no idea about how to explore these feelings. The motivation for drug use arises from their attempt to turn passive suffering into *active suffering* in which they have control over their painful emotions. Suffering with the consequences of addiction (e.g., social rejection, impaired daily functioning) is preferred over suffering the consequences of an internal emotional "storm" that they can't control. "True addicts don't use to escape life; rather, they use to find a place in life" (Zoja, 2000, p. 15).

Dodes (2002) also argues that the basis of substance use is psychological. Specifically, people use substances when they feel helpless and powerless in an area of their life. For example, individuals might feel powerless in relation to finances, a particular social relationship, or even their own emotional experience (e.g., feelings of depression or anxiety). These feelings of powerlessness create the sensation that they're "trapped," which creates feelings of intense rage. The use of substances creates the illusion that they're in control of their emotional experience, which serves to reduce feelings of helplessness.

Behavioural Paradigm   From a behavioural paradigm, operant conditioning processes provide explanations for continued drug use. For example, many substance-related disorders occur in relation to the pleasurable experience (a positive reinforcer) associated with psychoactive substance ingestion (Ray, 2012). It's worth noting that the more immediate the drug effect, the more powerful the reinforcing effect. Immediacy is an important factor in understanding the reinforcing properties of drug use; it can help explain why the negative consequences (i.e., painful withdrawal symptoms) that occur long afterward don't decrease substance use behaviour.

Negative reinforcement (where the removal of an aversive stimulus is associated with an increase in the behaviour) also plays a role in substance use. For example, if one is experiencing negative emotions (e.g., stress, anxiety) and alcohol use decreases these negative feelings, this behaviour will be further reinforced (likely to occur) because of this desirable consequence. Accordingly, repeated substance use can be conceptualized as a way of coping with painful emotions (Bailey & Baillie, 2012).

As well, classical conditioning processes have been found to maintain substance use. Neutral stimuli (e.g., sitting at a friend's house) that are paired with a meaningful stimulus (e.g., drinking alcohol) can become classically conditioned stimuli that trigger a desire or craving for the effects of the drug. Consequently, drug paraphernalia, people, situations, and other internal states (e.g., memories) can act as powerful triggers (i.e., conditioned stimuli) that trigger drug cravings and subsequent substance use (Lee et al., 2009; Westra & Stewart, 2002).

Cognitive Paradigm   From a cognitive perspective, substance-related disturbances are also influenced by how people think about substance use and the expectations they have about its effects. According to **expectancy outcome theory**, substance use is explained in relation to one's expectations of reinforcements or pleasurable outcomes that will result from engaging in drug use (White, Bates, & Johnson, 1990). Various socializing agents play a role in determining the development of such expectations (e.g., media, advertising, parental behaviour). In a recent study, Fulton, Krank, and Stewart (2012) found that Canadian students in grades 7 to 11 who expected positive consequences (e.g., feeling good) to be associated with alcohol and marijuana use were more likely to use and increase their use of these substances three years later.

Sociocultural Paradigm   From a sociocultural perspective, social and cultural factors play a significant role in determining one's risk for developing a substance-related disorder.

Culture. Cultural differences in the rates of substance-related disturbances suggest that aspects of culture are important determinants in substance use. For example, cultures with limited economic resources may have lower rates of substance-related disorders because of lack of availability (e.g., Jiloha, 2009). Within cultures, however, lower income groups have higher rates of drug use (e.g., tobacco, inhalants). Expectancies and cultural norms may explain these differences. Cross-cultural comparisons of alcohol use in various countries support this idea, suggesting that cultural norms regarding expectations of outcomes of use (e.g., positive or negative) are related to rates of use (e.g., Bennett et al., 1998). Similarly, other studies have found that migrants moving to a new country tend to adopt the substance-use norms of their new culture (e.g., Medina-Mora et al., 1988). These findings support the impact of the broader sociocultural context on substance use.

Family Influences. Various family factors, including family conflict, lack of support, and marital instability, have been related to adult substance use (Jacob & Johnson, 1997; NIDA, 1997). Specific dynamics within the family environment have been found to predict substance-related disorders. For example, early adolescent substance use was found to be associated with low levels of parent monitoring (Kerr, Stattin, & Burk, 2010). Similarly, specific discipline strategies (i.e., firm behavioural control) were found to be associated with decreased substance use in early adolescence (Galambos, Barker, & Almeida, 2003). Of all family factors, however, parental use appears to be one of the most significant factors in determining youth substance use. "The strongest social predictor of both drug and alcohol use has been shown to be use by parents and friends" (Velleman, Templeton, & Copello, 2005). Clearly, there is significant evidence that supports the role of immediate social factors in the occurrence of substance-related disturbances.

A CYC LENS ON THE PSYCHOLOGICAL PARADIGMS: A HOLISTIC CONCEPTUAL MODEL

Gabor Maté, who for years practised medicine in Vancouver's Eastside (known as North America's most concentrated urban centre of addictions), explains in his book *In the Realm of Hungry Ghosts* that there is really only one addictive process, whose core objective is self-soothing deep-seated sadness, fears, and discomfort (Maté, 2008). According to Maté, our addictive tendencies arise in the parts of our brains governing the most basic and life-sustaining functions, including our incentive and motivations, physical and emotional pain relief, the regulation of stress, and the capacity to feel and receive love. These crucial brain systems develop from our attachments and our nurturing environment in the early years; however, when attachments are lacking or maltreatment exists, they don't develop in the way nature intended. To meet the unmet needs for love and nurture, substances later replace attachment; the brain responds to these substances, triggering the pleasure receptors. Maté reminds us that the human brain continues to develop new circuitry well into adulthood and throughout the lifespan (Maté, 2008).

That last point ought to give CYCPs much hope for supporting young people who are struggling with addictions. And to effectively help these adolescents, we first need to understand why they use. Most adolescents say that peer pressure, curiosity, and experimentation are the main reasons for beginning substance use; notwithstanding Maté's explanation, very few cite the need to help them cope with difficulties. According to an American study (SAMHSA, 2008), corroborated by Canadian research, the reasons adolescents give for *continuing* to use are different: 29 percent said that it feels good; 23 percent said that it helps them cope with difficulties; 7 percent said they'd developed an addiction or habit; and 4 percent said that it enhanced their sense of self (e.g., more confidence, enhanced self-esteem). Among those who *stopped* using, 57 percent cited the negative effect that using had on their lives; 22 percent said they were tired of using; 21 percent were concerned about the effect drug use would have on their life path, and 14 percent were worried about the negative physical and psychological effects. Interestingly, pressure from others accounted for less than one-quarter of the reasons for quitting: 14 percent cited such external factors as jail or mandated treatment, 4 percent cited family and friends, and 3 percent cited avoiding getting into trouble (SAMHSA, 2008).

> "The reason I do drugs is so I don't feel the fucking feelings I feel when I don't do drugs," Nick, a forty-year-old heroin and crystal meth addict once told me, weeping as he spoke. "When I don't feel the drugs in me, I get depressed." His father drilled into his twin sons the notion that they were nothing but "pieces of shit." Nick's brother committed suicide as a teenager; Nick became a lifelong addict. (Maté, 2008, p. 14)

Young people's substance misuse behaviour is complex, and a wide range of risk factors are involved. As we've seen, stress, maltreatment, and trauma are among the most significant environmental risk factors that contribute to the development of mental health and/or substance use issues, and can increase their severity. According to an ecological conceptual model, the risk factors for youth substance misuse can be classified into five main categories, or domains: community, family, school, peers, and individual. Practitioners agree that it's the cumulative number of risk factors, rather than any one specific risk factor (which will be balanced by the individual's strengths and protective factors), that increases or decreases the likelihood of substance use, misuse, or addictions developing. As with all mental health issues, protective factors and strengths, such as family stability, supportive and nurturing relationships, and a strong community, can help prevent young people from developing difficulties with substance misuse in the first place.

Jessor and his colleagues (1998) developed a *problem-behaviour theory* to explain substance misuse and abuse; and although it's dated, it's still applicable today. This theory identifies risk and protective factors in interrelated domains (biology/genetics, social environment, perceived environment, personality, and behaviour) and across different social contexts (family, peer, neighbourhood, and school). The risk factors for substance use include a family history of substance use, poverty, persistent role models for deviant behaviour, low perceived life chances, and poor performance in school. The protective factors include high intelligence, quality schools, role models for conventional behaviour, value on achievement and health, and being part of a strong community and/or religious organization (Jessor, 1998).

Individual Risk Factors. The individual characteristics that have consistently been associated with a greater risk of use and abuse are as follows: (1) Age of onset is perhaps the strongest determinant of difficulties later in life; the younger a person begins use, the more likely he or she is to develop a substance use problem and to continue to experience difficulties with substances through adulthood ("Risk and protective factors," 2015). (2) In the past, gender was a strong predictor, with males more likely to use substances and to use heavily. However, the gender gap appears to be narrowing significantly. According to the literature, girls are now as or more likely than boys to drink alcohol, binge-drink, smoke tobacco, and use illegal drugs ("Girls and drugs," 2006). Other individual-level risk factors include (3) attitudes and beliefs about the risks of use, (4) impulsivity, and (5) sensitivity to sensation. As with all difficulties, CYCPs aim to identify and use young people's strengths in order to increase their protective factors, and use a harm-reduction approach to militate against the effects of using alcohol, tobacco, and other drugs ("Risk and protective factors," 2015).

Family Risk Factors. According to Jessor's theory, families can affect young people's substance use in a variety of ways. Poor parenting practices such as inadequate monitoring, a low degree of bonding between parent and child, child abuse, family conflict, family modelling of substance-using behaviours, and lax parental attitudes toward substance use have all been associated with young people's misuse (CCSA, 2007).

Peer Risk Factors. Among the strongest predictors of young people's substance use are associating with "deviant" peers and perceiving approval of drug-using behaviours among peers. Contrary to popular belief, the peer effect isn't entirely due to pressure from peers to use; rather, it often stems from choosing to hang out with friends who use substances and hold similar attitudes (CCSA, 2007).

School-Related Factors. Academic failure beginning early in the school career is related to substance use, as is lack of commitment to school and low bonding with students and teachers. Other school variables, such as a "drinking or using culture" within the student body or, conversely, disapproval of substance use, can also affect youth substance use (CCSA, 2007).

Community Risk Factors. Cultural and social environment significantly influences substance use and misuse. A substantial body of research on alcohol and tobacco shows that increased availability of substances—including ample supply and low price—increases the likelihood of its use, especially among young people. Media portrayals and social norms favourable to substance use also play influential roles.

While the risk and the severity of negative outcomes increase as risk factors multiply, it's important to note that risk factors for use are different from those for abuse (CCSA, 2007). Whereas the general onset of substance use by adolescents owes more to such social and environmental factors as peer use and drug availability, early use, heavy use, and abuse are generally associated with individual biological factors such as genetics and difficult temperament, and with psychological determinants such as childhood abuse and trauma (CCSA, 2007).

We've seen that while most adolescents don't have substance misuse problems, nonmainstream youth are more likely than their peers to experience heavy use, multi- or poly-drug use, social and economic problems due to use, and substance misuse or dependence difficulties. These are the youth with whom CYCPs most often engage.

Research indicates that young people who've experienced physical or sexual abuse/assault are three times more likely to report past or current substance misuse than those without a history of trauma. In fact, surveys of adolescents receiving treatment for substance abuse have shown that more than 70 percent had a history of trauma exposure. The link between trauma and substance abuse is even more striking among adolescents with PTSD: studies indicate that up to 59 percent of young people with PTSD subsequently develop substance abuse problems. Although recreational alcohol and drug use are more common in adults, studies have shown that youth who engage in drug and alcohol use are at greater risk for lifelong negative consequences, especially when they start using at a young age. Moreover, adolescent substance use is associated with higher rates of depression, aggression, violence, and suicide.

While representing only a small proportion of young people, out-of-the-mainstream youth are at the greatest risk of the most serious of harms associated with substance use and misuse. These youth include those who are street involved, homeless or mostly away from their family or group home, exploited in the sex trade, in the care of Child and Family Services or known to the justice system, and frequently absent from school. They're at higher risk overall of poly-drug use: extensive alcohol and marijuana use, the use of cocaine and opiates, and injection-drug use. Among the harms experienced by these young people (like Teighan) are blood-borne and sexually transmitted infectious diseases, including hepatitis and HIV, exploitation in the sex trade, pregnancy, victimization, physical abuse and assault, involvement in gangs, participation in criminal activity, drug overdose, and early death caused mainly by overdose and/or suicide (CCSA, 2007).

CYCPs are likely to work with young people who engage in heavy and/or multi-drug use and are experiencing negative consequences associated with such use.

Photographee.eu/Fotolia

WHERE DO YOU STAND?

Consider the psychological and CYC perspectives summarized above. Where do you stand? The issue of substance-related disorders is a controversial one, given the varying definitions and the role of value judgments in defining use, abuse, and addiction. Understanding the various perspectives on substance use and its related disturbances is essential to CYC mental health literacy.

Before turning to discussions of approaches to treatment, read the case of Laura and answer the related questions in order to actively explore your own position on these disorders.

It's been estimated that as many as 70–80 percent of all crimes committed by youth offenders occur while under the influence of substances. As well, substance abuse is second only to depression and other mood disorders as a risk factor for suicide; and suicide risk is at its highest when a young person already at risk is under the influence.

> Drug use by children on the streets is common as they look for means to numb the pain and deal with the hardships associated with street life. Studies have found that up to 90 percent of street children use psychoactive substances, including medicines, alcohol, cigarettes, heroin, cannabis, and readily available industrial products such as shoe glue. ("Street children," n.d.)

Take Action! Exercise: *Laura's Case*

Seventeen-year-old Laura has been living with her 18-year-old boyfriend for a few months. She's come by the youth resource centre where you work to get some information and advice. Laura tells you that she's a crack cocaine user. When she was 10 her father, whom she says was a heavy drinker, left her mother and the kids and never came back. At 14 Laura started drinking and smoking marijuana. At 15 she dropped out of high school, and at 17 she moved in her boyfriend, who introduced her to crack. In order to pay for the heroin and the rent on their apartment, she sells sex on the streets at night (her boyfriend doesn't work). Laura drinks four or five beers each night before going out. She and her boyfriend aren't having sex all that much anymore, and when they do, he never wears a condom. He says that's what makes him different from her johns. "Which is true," she says, "because I won't work without a condom." Lately Laura has noticed that her breasts have become swollen and tender; she hasn't had her period in the last 12 weeks. She's pretty sure she's pregnant, and knows that it's her boyfriend's baby. Still, she's not sure she can stop using crack, even though her boyfriend wants her to have the baby. She's really confused about the pregnancy, and is looking for some help to make some decisions.

1. What explanations for Laura's substance use might be offered from the psychological perspectives we've discussed?

2. What factors in her history might have contributed to the substance use?

3. What specific interventions might be recommended from a psychological approach?

4. Describe what you'd do, in the here and now, in this situation with Laura.

5. How will you work with her in the longer term?

6. How are your own morals and values influencing your responses to Laura's story? Your own experiences with substances?

7. Should you call CFS? Is Laura being exploited?

Source: Adapted from the Josiah Macy Foundation, http://www.cnsproductions.com/pdf/casestudies.pdf.

One night, Teighan was admitted to the ER after being sexually assaulted and beaten by her boyfriend's gang members. This proved to be the "crisis as opportunity" moment for Teighan. While in the hospital she detoxed, and after returning to the group home she began opening up to her key worker. She disclosed her difficult relationship with her mother as well as the physical and sexual abuse. She explained to the CYCP that she started using marijuana and alcohol at about age 12, and shared how both substances helped make her feel "better" and helped her "forget her bad feelings," which, she said, wouldn't go away any other way. It became clear that, for Teighan, drug and alcohol use were an effective method of self-medicating and numbing her emotional pain. As Teighan and her CYCP began to work through her trauma history, she started to develop better tools for coping with her intense feelings.

Source: Adapted from "Making the connection," 2008.

Of particular concern today are easily available street drugs, including methamphetamine, ecstasy, and crack. One especially dangerous street drug is the so-called *bath salts*, the street name for a family of drugs containing substituted cathinones, whose effects are similar to those of amphetamine and cocaine. (The white crystals often resemble Epsom salts or bath salts, hence the name.) CYCPs need to inform themselves as best they can about the latest available street drugs (and their potential consequences) that young people may be using.

HELPING CHILDREN AND ADOLESCENTS WITH SUBSTANCE MISUSE ISSUES

Psychological Approaches to Treatment

Considering the psychological explanations for substance use and disorders we've discussed, it's likely no surprise that there are various approaches to intervention. Let's consider some of these approaches from each of the major psychological paradigms.

Biological Paradigm A biological approach to treatment for substance-related disorders typically involves the use of medications that either increase or decrease the availability or activity of certain neurotransmitters. The effects of these medications vary; in some cases, the result is to prevent or reduce the intoxication associated with the substance, while in others, the result is to decrease the withdrawal symptoms associated with removal of the substance. For example, naltrexone is used to decrease alcohol and opioid use by *blocking* opioid receptor sites, which decreases the intoxication effect associated with these substances. By comparison, methadone is used to decrease withdrawal symptoms associated with opioid addiction by *activating* or stimulating opioid receptors in the brain. Different medications will affect different neurotransmitter systems. See Table 10.1 for an overview of some common medications used to treat substance-related disorders and their symptoms.

It should be noted that neither the effectiveness nor the safety of these medications has been ascertained in youth populations. Therefore, most of the effects noted in Table 10.1 are based on studies of adult populations. This presents a real concern, as there is little evidence to support the use of such medications in the treatment of children and adolescent substance-related disorders. Recent investigations, however, are attempting to address this lack of research with youth populations. For example, studies of adolescent

Table 10.1 Common Medications Used in Substance Disorder Treatment

Drug	Mechanism of Action	Intended Outcomes for Adults
Buprenorphine	Activates and blocks opioid receptors	Decreased withdrawal symptoms and reduced cravings for opioid addictions and nicotine addictions
Methadone	Activates opioid receptors in brain	Decreased withdrawal symptoms and reduced cravings for opioid addictions
Naltrexone	Blocks opioid receptors	Prevents/decreases the intoxication effects of opioids and alcohol
Acamprosate	Alters neural pathways involved in alcohol intoxication	Decreases withdrawal symptoms
Disulfiram	Inhibits enzyme responsible for breaking down alcohol	Results in negative physical reaction when alcohol is consumed; prevents intoxication
Varenicline	Stimulates the same receptors as nicotine	Reduces nicotine cravings

participants found that buprenorphine effectively reduced both withdrawal symptoms and cravings (Marsch et al., 2005; Woody et al., 2008). Future research will likely investigate the effectiveness of medications in youth.

Psychodynamic Paradigm Psychodynamic approaches to treatment for substance-related disorders emphasize a psychological (versus a biological) approach. Khantzian and Mack (1999), for example, suggest that providing genuine interest and an environment in which young people can explore their feelings, hurts, fears, and beliefs can help them rediscover a sense of personal worth, value, and self-interest. Through rediscovering these elements of self, new strategies of self-care evolve and replace substance use as the primary coping strategy.

Another approach to psychodynamic intervention involves exploring the user's feelings of helplessness and lack of control (Dodes, 2002). Substance use is first viewed as a way to cope with and manage these feelings. Such insights are followed by a realization that the illusion of control provided by substance use isn't the only way to deal with such feelings. Consequently, new adaptive strategies can be identified and replace substance use.

Behavioural Paradigm From a behavioural paradigm, various learning processes have been employed to decrease substance use. For example, in order to decrease classically conditioned substance-related responses, the process of extinction is used as the basis of "cue exposure" treatments. Treatment involves exposing individuals to a "trigger" (either through actual exposure or having the individual imagine the trigger) associated with their preferred substance. These triggers (real or imagined) prompt cravings, at which point individuals are asked to visualize resisting the craving. Although it's assumed that classically conditioned withdrawal and intoxication effects will be extinguished as a result of lack of reinforcement, there is mixed evidence supporting the efficacy of this approach (Health Canada, 1999).

One behavioural approach that has demonstrated greater success in reducing substance use is **contingency management**. Operant conditioning principles of reinforcement (e.g., providing reward such as money) and punishment (e.g., withholding money) are employed to increase adaptive behaviour (i.e., abstinence) and decrease maladaptive behaviour (i.e., substance use). See Figure 10.2 for an overview of primary contingency management principles.

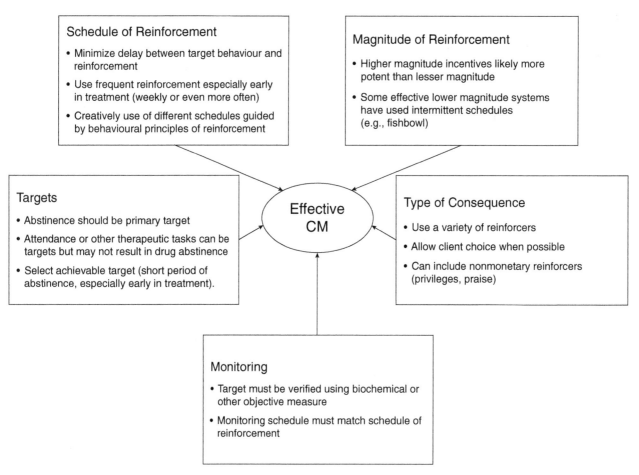

Figure 10.2 Key Principles in Contingency Management

Contingency management involves the use of operant conditioning principles to decrease substance use.

Source: Stanger & Budney, 2011.

Evidence supports the effectiveness of such approaches in enhancing abstinence from alcohol (Witkiewitz & Marlatt, 2008) and increased perceptions in the ability to abstain from substance use (Litt et al., 2009). Although most of the research has been conducted with adult populations, more recent investigations have determined that contingency management is also effective with adolescents in the treatment of tobacco use (Krishnan-Sarin et al., 2006), and researchers believe there is optimism that this model can be effectively applied to the treatment of other youth substance-related disorders (Stanger & Budney, 2011).

Cognitive Paradigm From a cognitive perspective, changing perceptions and interpretations (i.e., cognitive processes) of substance use and its consequences are the focus of treatment for Substance Use Disorders (Beck & Weishaar, 2005). Emphasis is placed on helping youth better identify triggers associated with drug use and developing coping strategies to help them avoid situations that might increase the likelihood of drug use.

These cognitive strategies, together with behavioural components (i.e., CBT), have been found to be effective in the treatment of various substance-related disorders, including those related to alcohol, marijuana, cocaine, and opiates (Magura et al., 2002; Maude-Griffin et al., 1998; Yen et al., 2004). Although much of the research has been conducted with the adult population, some studies do support its effectiveness with adolescents (Deas & Thomas, 2001; Kaminer, Burleson, & Goldberger, 2002).

Sociocultural Paradigm   Sociocultural interventions for substance-related disorders include a consideration of the cultural and family social environments when treating the child or adolescent.

Culture. What changes can be made at the broader cultural level to alter substance use? In Canada, the National Alcohol Strategy Working Group (2007) identifies four areas in which broader cultural change can result in decreased substance use. In the area of *health promotion, prevention, and education,* strategies that increase awareness of the consequences of substance use are aimed at altering expectancies and norms regarding substance use and subsequent behaviour. In the area of *health impacts and treatment,* the primary focus is on developing effective screening tools to better identify those at risk of substance-related disturbances and improving the availability of effective treatment programs. In the third area of *availability,* programs and policies that regulate the availability of substances are believed to be important in reducing substance use. In the fourth area of *safer communities,* the emphasis is on reducing harm associated with intoxication (e.g., drinking-and-driving prevention programs) as well as altering the cultural beliefs and values regarding substance use (e.g., moderation versus excess). Broader social change in each of these areas has been demonstrated to result in behaviour change at the individual level with respect to seatbelt use and smoking (National Alcohol Strategy Working Group, 2007), and so might be expected to evoke change in relation to substance use.

Family Influences. Various programs aimed at preventing or reducing substance use consider the role of family relationships and dynamics in their approach. Some research provides evidence that family-based interventions are more successful than individual approaches to prevention. Kumpfer and Alvarado (2003), for example, found that various family intervention components (e.g., family education, in-home family support, family therapy) were effective in reducing later substance use.

One broad-based approach to decreasing substance use aims to reduce the availability of substances for youth.

Highwaystarz/Fotolia

Multidimensional family therapy (MDFT) involves sessions not only with the affected youth but with parents as well. In these meetings, parents receive emotional support and explore such topics as parent–adolescent relationships and parenting skills (e.g., discipline and monitoring strategies). A recent investigation found that youth treated with MDFT compared with a comparison group receiving individual CBT showed lower rates of substance use and substance-related impairments even after 12 months following the intervention (Liddle et al., 2008; 2009).

CYC Approaches for Youth Struggling with Substance-Related Disturbances

We've seen that mental health issues, especially trauma, are almost always a factor in youth substance misuse. Many at-risk youth struggle with addictions; for example, homeless young people use drugs and alcohol at very high rates, with some estimates as high as 84 percent (Kelly Holmes, personal communication, 2013).

In one study (Stockburger et al., 2005), when 50 at-risk youth aged 18–24 were asked about their substance abuse, they said that it helped them improve their emotions or moods, relax, escape distressing thoughts, and find support from peers on the street, but that it also broke down their relationships with other people, made them easier targets for victimization, and sometimes even led to death. Importantly, these young people said that their substance abuse made them feel so isolated from others that even knowing its negative consequences wasn't enough to get them to quit (Stockburger et al., 2005). Another study showed that youth who used alcohol were more likely to want to change their behaviour if they were older, drank more frequently, or had a history of childhood sexual abuse. Unsurprisingly, those who'd experienced more negative consequences from using drugs were more likely to say they wanted to quit (Stockburger et al., 2005). Still, many of the factors that researchers thought might influence youth to stop using don't actually affect their desire to change—which means, researchers say, that we need to determine what *does* motivate youth to change, and that we need to help them in the ways they tell us will help. Strength-based practice, as always, is key.

Strength-Based Relational CYC Practice   Young people's voices matter. When the Centre of Excellence for Children and Adolescents with Special Needs (Stockburger et al., 2005) asked young people what they thought would constitute effective programming, their responses featured four critical characteristics: a friendly, welcoming, understanding environment; having staff with life experiences similar to their own; the opportunity to express their opinion about, and have an influence on, the program; and having youth work with them.

A number of participants in the youth voice study brought up the need for staff with relevant life experience, saying repeatedly that most helpers have the academic background but no actual experiences with substance abuse or a street lifestyle. These young people believed that staff didn't understand their situation, and consequently can't help them effectively.

> Youth facing substance (ab)use realities are interested in seeking services from people who can empathize as opposed to criticize, and while criticism may not be overt, youth nonetheless feel "judgment" is implicit by those who do not share a semblance of the

youth's realities or background. One participant noted that most social workers "are just coming out of college, thinking they are so hot . . . but they really don't give a shit." Another participant observed that because many social workers and other professionals "don't have any experience with drugs or . . . an abusive home," they are not much help for youth. (Stockburger et al., 2005, p. 30)

Programs aiming to effectively address issues of youth substance abuse, therefore, must move toward a nonjudgmental, youth-driven agenda. Programming and interventions need to be strength-based, supportive, and empowering of young people.

Assessment

The **levels of involvement (LOI) framework**, developed in 1997 by the Addictions Foundation of Manitoba (AFM) ("A biopsychosocial model," 2013), is a very effective assessment tool for CYCPs. In this framework, involvement in substance use exists on a continuum that ranges from noninvolvement to highly problematic involvement. The assessment gathers information from individuals, and then describes their level of involvement based on reported observable data from others and/or the individuals' reported experiences. The framework's focus is on identifying the consequences of involvement at different levels rather than descriptions of frequency of use or perceived reasons for use. This focus on consequences is congruent with a harm reduction approach.

According to AFM literature, the term *involvement* reflects the idea that drinking, using drugs, and gambling are activities individuals engage in actively rather than being passive recipients; the term also denotes the present tense, indicating that the level of involvement doesn't remain static and may change over time. And whereas commonly used descriptors—*alcoholic*, *addict*, *pathological gambler*—focus on the individual, LOI avoids labelling people and instead focuses on behaviour. The LOI framework also addresses an observation that front-line addictions counsellors have consistently made: that although most services are designed for individuals with addictions, many who come to an agency for help don't fit that description and yet are still experiencing significant problems related to their substance use or gambling behaviours. Moreover, accessing an "addictions" services agency carries a stigma. Most people believe that these work only with alcoholics or addicts and don't want to self-identify with those labels: it's as if people have to decide between having no concern about alcohol or being an alcoholic. As a result, many individuals who experience significant problems related to their substance use won't access services because they don't define themselves as addicts.

According to the AFM, the LOI framework helps people identify degrees of concern based on objective and descriptive criteria, without limiting them to either being addicted or having no problem at all. The framework is primarily intended to assist in the problem-naming process that occurs in the context of all helping relationships, whereby counsellors help people describe, identify, and name (or label) their experiences. There's an important distinction here: whereas in DSM diagnoses the meaning of the disorder is assigned by an expert, in problem naming the meaning of the behaviour is negotiated or co-created by individuals and counsellors working together. Therefore, it's empowering, strength-based, and congruent with a harm-reduction approach, thus reducing stigma and shame ("A biopsychosocial model," 2013).

The LOI Framework. The following levels make up the AFM's levels of involvement framework.

Non involvement: Never gambled, never used alcohol or other mood- or mind-altering drugs, or has chosen a non-use lifestyle following some involvement.

Irregular Involvement: Random, occasional, or infrequent involvement, usually confined to specific occasions or situations. Little or no evidence of any harmful or adverse consequences from use. This category includes experimental involvement, defined as trying a substance or a gambling activity once or even several times as an experiment or out of curiosity.

Regular Involvement: A regularly recurring involvement with the substance whereby patterns are evident; some evidence of adverse related consequences that are typically minor or isolated. This category is often characterized by young people who actively seek involvement, or whose involvement and use has become a regular feature of their lifestyle.

Harmful Involvement: Evidence of recurring adverse consequences; for example, recurring failure to fulfill major role obligations at home, school, or work and recurring financial or legal problems. Continuing involvement despite repeated or persistent problems, in one or more life areas, caused by or made worse as a result of the involvement.

Dependent Involvement: In addition to the preceding characteristics, involvement tends to be patterned and is characterized by consistent features. There is a physiological and/or psychological need for continued use, and the individual has experienced episodes of loss of control over the involvement. Amount of use frequently exceeds original intentions, and several unsuccessful efforts to cut down or otherwise control involvement have been made. The individual experiences a compelling need to continue involvement ("A biopsychosocial model," 2013).

A number of other tools are used to assess various aspects of substance use. For example, RAFFT is a five-item scale that covers alcohol as well as other drug use. The scale is marked by the following questions: Do you drink/drug to Relax, feel better about yourself, or fit in? Do you ever drink/drug while you're by yourself, Alone? Do any of your closest Friends drink/drug? Does a close Family member have a problem with drink/drugs? Have you ever gotten into Trouble from drinking/drugging? (Riggs & Alario, 1989). In addition, the Alcohol/Drug Acknowledgement Scale (ACK), the Alcohol/Drug Problem Proneness Scale (PRO), and the MacAndrew Alcoholism Scale–Revised (MAC-R) are all part of the Minnesota Multiphasic Personality Inventory–Adolescent (MMPI-A), and are also often used to assess aspects of drug use ("Screening for concurrent substance use," 2009).

CYCPs should also assess for mental health concerns (depression, anxiety, panic attacks, ADHD diagnosis, suicidal impulses, self-harm); determine level of risk; and assess for concurrent issues. Ask young people how their substance use fits in with their emotional health; for example, Do you use substances to cope? Does the substance increase or decrease your emotional health concerns? (Winters & Kaminer, 2008).

Indicators to Recognize According to the LOI framework's harmful and dependent-use categories, young people will display the following behavioural indicators:

Preoccupation: Spends increasing amounts of time, money, and energy on the activities related to maintaining involvement or recovering from use. The individual has given up or has significantly reduced involvement in other previously valued life activities.

Adverse Consequences: Continued use despite the knowledge that the persistent physical, mental, social, or financial problems experienced have likely been caused or made worse as a result of use. The individual attempts to cope with these losses through continued involvement.

Withdrawal Distress: Experiencing physical or mental distress as a result of abstaining from involvement.

Progression: Increased levels of involvement (frequency, quantity, or duration) are required over time to achieve or maintain the desired effects.

Transitional Abstinence: An individual with past involvement at harmful or dependent levels has chosen to abstain from alcohol, other drugs, or gambling but has yet to achieve a sense of comfort with, or confidence in, that decision. One of the characteristic features of dependent involvement is the occurrence of repeated unsuccessful attempts to abstain (relapse). Will typically occur in relation to the action stage of change, but could occur at other stages of change.

Stabilized Abstinence or Recovery: An individual with past experience at harmful or dependent levels has chosen to abstain from alcohol, drugs, or gambling, and has achieved a sense of comfort with the decision and/or a measure of confidence in the ability to maintain an abstinent lifestyle. Will occur in relation to the maintenance stage of change (Curley, 2010).

Table 10.2 provides a summary of behavioural indicators for substance use, misuse, and addiction.

Intervention

Given the relationship between trauma and youth substance misuse, it's critically important that CYCPs help young people both understand the common responses to trauma and make the connections between their own experience of trauma and any substance use. In this way, CYCPs can help these young people move forward in their healing.

According to the literature, trauma-informed services take into account an understanding of trauma in all aspects of service delivery and place priority on trauma survivors' safety, choice, and control. Working in a trauma-informed way doesn't necessarily require disclosure of trauma. Rather, services are provided in ways that recognize the need for physical and emotional safety as well as for choice and control in decisions affecting one's treatment. In trauma-informed services, CYC relational approaches are based on the creation of safety and

Table 10.2 Behavioural Indicators Checklist: Substance Use, Misuse, and Addictions

✓ Difficulties at home, school, or work

Recurring financial or legal problems related to use

Continuing or increasing regular use despite repeated or persistent problems, in one or more life areas, caused by or made worse as a result of the involvement

Physical or mental distress when trying to abstain from use

Inability to abstain despite continued efforts

Increased levels of involvement (frequency, quantity, or duration) required over time to achieve or maintain the desired effects

empowerment for the service user. Safety is created in every interaction, and confrontational approaches are always avoided. Substance use is always treated in a nonjudgmental way.

Advocates for trauma-informed approaches in the youth substance-use treatment field don't ask substance-use professionals to treat trauma, but rather to approach their work with an understanding of how common trauma is among those served and how it's manifested in young people's lives. It could be said that trauma-informed approaches are similar to harm-reduction approaches in that they focus on safety and engagement. In trauma-informed contexts, building trust and confidence paves the way for youth to consider taking further steps toward healing and recovery while not experiencing further traumatization (Poole, 2012).

The five key principles of trauma-informed practice (which have parallels with the principles underlying evidence-based practices in the youth substance-use field) are (1) trauma awareness; (2) emphasis on safety and trustworthiness; (3) opportunity for choice, collaboration, and connection; (4) strength-based skill building; (5) awareness that trauma can be experienced differently by newcomers, young people with developmental disabilities, males and females, members of the LGBTT community, Aboriginal peoples, and other populations. It's particularly important that CYCPs recognize the impact of historical, intergenerational trauma on Aboriginal peoples, and the implications this has for trauma-informed substance treatment of Aboriginal peoples as part of a broad approach to their treatment interventions (Poole, 2012).

Behavioural and Cognitive-Behavioural Techniques for CYCPs
Behavioural interventions for adolescents struggling with substance abuse are based on the principle that unwanted behaviour can be changed by consistently rewarding both the desired behaviour and all incremental steps toward achieving the desired behavioural goal. Therapeutic activities include implementing specific assignments, rehearsing the desired behaviours, and recording and reviewing progress, with praise and privileges given for every step. It's important to note that programs using a behavioural approach often include drug testing to regularly monitor use.

Most addiction programs usually use some form of behavioural therapy in their treatment regimen. According to the literature, these behavioural techniques and approaches aim to help young people gain control over their substance use. Youth learn such strategies as *stimulus control*, which helps avoid those situations that are associated with drug use and will thus trigger use; *urge control*, which assists in recognizing and changing the thoughts, feelings, and plans that lead to drug use; and *social control*, which involves friends and family members in helping the young person avoid drugs. According to some research, behavioural approaches may help some adolescents become drug free and stay drug free after treatment ends. There are indications that young people also show improvement in several other related areas, including work or school attendance and family relationships.

Relapse prevention, a type of cognitive-behavioural therapy, is based on the theory that learning processes play a critical role in the development of maladaptive behavioural patterns. Relapse prevention encompasses several cognitive-behavioural strategies that facilitate abstinence as well as provide help for those who experience relapse. The approach to treatment consists of strategies intended to enhance self-control. Specific techniques include exploring the positive and negative consequences of continued use, self-monitoring to recognize drug cravings early on and identify high-risk situations for use, and developing strategies for coping with and avoiding high-risk situations and the desire to use. A central element of this treatment, then, is anticipating the problems young people are likely to encounter and helping them develop effective coping strategies.

The Role of Medication   A number of medications have been used to treat addictions. Anti-alcohol drugs such as Antabuse and Temposil produce a strong aversive reaction to alcohol in the individual; neither of these drugs is currently being used. *Antagonists* are drugs that block the effects of abused drugs by occupying the same receptor sites in the brain. As discussed earlier in this chapter, there are antagonists for opioids and cocaine; naltrexone has been used to treat heroin addiction, and more recently alcoholism. However, naltrexone has been found to reduce relapse by 36 percent less than with counselling alone. Drug substitution is another approach, and includes methadone, valium, nicotine patches, and so on, which have been found to be very effective in supporting individuals through the initial stages of recovery (Csiernik, 2011).

Psychoeducation and Individual Counselling   In assessing for substance use, misuse, and abuse, CYCPs can educate young people about the risks and teach safe, moderate use of alcohol and drugs. For those whose substance use is designated at a harmful level of involvement or is putting them at risk for negative health or social outcomes, the following questions will provide an opportunity for referral to a specialized treatment program (Winters & Kaminer, 2008):

1. What types of substances have you used in the last month? In the last year? How often do you use the substance? How much of the substance do you typically use?
2. Which substances are you concerned about?
3. Is there anything you'd like to change about your substance use? How would you know if your substance use is getting out of control?
4. In a typical week, how many drinks do you have?
5. Do you drink to intoxication?
6. Do you tend to binge-drink?
7. Do you notice any difference in your mood when you use substances? Are there some feelings you express only when you're drinking or using?
8. Have any of your friends expressed concern about your use of substances?
9. Have you had any injuries while using substances (falling and hitting your head, fights, seizures, and other health concerns, including HIV, STDs, and hepatitis)?

Individual *supportive–expressive counselling* can be used along with other forms of therapeutic support. This type of counselling has two main components: (1) counsellors' nonjudgmental, supportive responses, which help young people freely share their substance-use experiences without fear of repercussion; (2) expressive techniques that help young people identify and work through any relationship issues related to the use or misuse. Expressive therapies or techniques involve the use of art, music, dance/movement, drama, poetry/creative writing, play, and sand tray within the context of psychotherapy and counselling (Malchiodi, 2005).

Addiction treatment programs usually use some form of small-group therapeutic process. Psychoeducational groups tend to be larger than counselling groups, and include lectures, videos, assigned readings, and discussions on specific substance-related topics. Many individuals have found the support of both counselling and psychoeducational groups to be very helpful (Csiernik, 2011).

As an individual counselling technique, psychoeducation is used to explore the role of substances in relation to all mutually identified problem feelings and behaviours; the counsellor helps the young person find ways to resolve problems without using substances. As well, psychoeducational approaches are used to educate youth about the harmful consequences of the substance of choice either in group or individually.

Motivational interviewing (MI), an important evidence-based technique in the addictions field, is consistent with trauma-informed practice. MI uses a collaborative, empowering approach to problem solving by eliciting the motivation to change from individuals themselves rather than having counsellors impose it; individuals are thus more likely to consider, initiate, and maintain specific changes to reduce their potentially harmful substance use behaviour. MI is founded on principles of motivational psychology, client-centred therapy, and the stages of change (discussed below) in recovery from addiction (Miller & Rollnick, 2002). Its approaches include empathy, developing discrepancy, rolling with resistance, and supporting self-efficacy. Based on Carl Rogers's work, *empathy* in MI involves the counsellors' ability to convey a sense of being present as well as an understanding of the client's words and emotions and their underlying meaning. MI practitioners help their clients understand the *discrepancy* between their current behaviour and their treatment goal by supporting the client's *self-efficacy* and inherent abilities and without being distracted by resistance (referred to as *rolling with resistance*) (Miller & Rollnick, 2002). By means of reflective, empathic listening, practitioners convey a sense of collaboration with their clients through acceptance, understanding of ambivalence, and ultimate support of their autonomy to change or not change (Feldstein & Ginsburg, 2006, p. 218).

MI also fits well with the *stages of change model* (Prochaska, Norcross, & DiClemente, 1992), which helps practitioners and their clients choose appropriate interventions. According to this model, people move through five primary stages as they seek to make changes in their lives: precontemplation, contemplation, preparation, action, and maintenance.

By identifying an adolescent's position in the change process, CYCPs can tailor this intervention using the strengths and skills the young person already has; in MI the focus is not to convince young people to change their behaviour but rather to help them move along the stages of change. Using this framework, the goal of MI is to shift from unrealistic expectations ("Get young people to stop using") to the realistic ("Engage them in a process to move to the next stage of change"). Refer to Figure 10.3 for an overview of the stages of change model.

> *Precontemplation Stage:* Young people aren't yet ready to seriously consider making any changes; they might lack motivation or be resistant to change. Through motivational interviewing, CYCPs focus on building rapport and trust, validating young people's perspective, and raising their awareness of other possible views. In this way CYCPs help prepare them to consider thinking about change.
>
> *Contemplation Stage:* Young people often have mixed feelings about making a change. CYCPs can use MI to help affirm their ambivalence, strengthen their motivation for change, and help them recognize that they can make the changes they see for themselves.
>
> *Preparation Stage:* Once young people have resolved their conflicting thoughts and are determined to change, CYCPs can help them outline the steps for change, identify the necessary supports and resources, resolve any inherent challenges, and implement the final plans. CYCPs can also use MI to give empathetic feedback and advice, strengthening young people's autonomy and reinforcing their motivation for change.

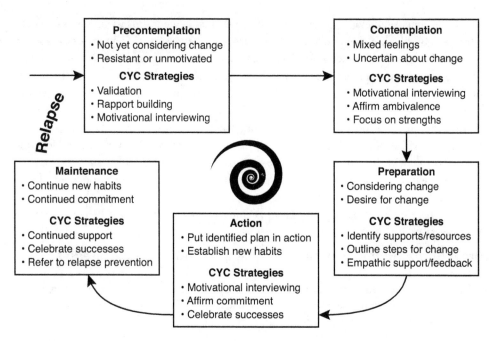

Figure 10.3 The Stages of Change Model

In this model, people move through five primary stages as they seek to make changes in their lives.

Action and Maintenance: Young people enact the plans or goals outlined in the preparation stage. Then, once these new habits have become established, they move into the maintenance stage. This final stage can last for an indefinite period of time, during which they may experience periodic relapses into pre-change behaviour. Although primarily designed to initiate change, MI can support young people in both the action and maintenance stages by continuing to affirm their commitment to change, celebrating successes along the way (Miller & Rollnick, 1991; Prochaska, DiClemente, & Norcross, 1992). Self-help groups like Alcoholics Anonymous, although not treatment modalities per se, are an excellent relapse prevention program for most people in recovery. AA appears to be very effective for a certain population, but it's not for everyone.

Family Support Interventions In youth addiction treatment programs, young people often receive services in isolation, with little or no involvement from their family. However, recognizing that substance misuse issues both influence and are influenced by family dynamics, these programs are increasingly including families in the treatment process.

Viewing the family as an organic whole, family support operates under the following premises: all families have difficulties, but substance misuse prevents resolution of problems and creates new ones; since no one can force another person to change, any change must come from taking responsibility for one's own behaviour; all family members are involved in the problem and all have responsibility in seeking its resolution; removal of the substances is a necessary first step in change and recovery (Csiernik, 2011). According to the literature, when family support or family therapy is included as an adjunct to other therapies, it significantly increases the level of improvement in post-treatment long- and short-term progress.

Multidimensional family therapy (MDFT) views adolescent drug use in terms of a network of individual, family, peer, and community influences; in this approach, reducing unwanted behaviour and increasing desirable behaviour occurs in multiple ways in different settings. Treatment includes individual and family sessions held in the clinic, in the home, or with family members at family court, school, or other community locations. During individual sessions, the therapist and adolescent work on developing such important developmental tasks as decision-making, negotiation, and problem-solving skills. Young people may acquire vocational skills as well as skills in communicating their thoughts and feelings to deal better with life stressors. Parallel sessions are held with family members; parents examine their particular parenting style, learning to distinguish influence from control and how to have a positive and developmentally appropriate influence on their child.

Box 10.5 summarizes guidelines for CYC interventions that might be considered in your practice.

Prevention: Advocacy, Community, and School-Based Strategies

> Education related to substance use was the main suggestion for the prevention of substance use among youth. One participant noted, "I wish I had had someone teaching me about not doing drugs." (Stockburger et al., 2005, p. 33)

Substance-use interventions for young people tend to be categorized as either *universal* (population-wide), *targeted* (e.g., early intervention for such at-risk groups as young offenders or children in care), or *specialist* (e.g., a planned, structured package of support for those who've already developed drug or alcohol misuse). Some suggest that universal prevention programs for youth don't adequately address the key issues for those at highest risk, and reach only the majority—who aren't likely to experience substantial harm from substance misuse in the first place. Harm reduction is increasingly being defined as a preventative intervention approach.

Box 10.5

Techniques for CYC Intervention

Use a "levels of involvement" framework in your assessment.

Help young people complete a self-assessment of their substance use.

Help youth explore and understand the role of trauma in their use, if appropriate.

Carefully examine with youth the potential effects of their drug of choice.

Use motivational interviewing techniques.

Use the ABC model (see Chapter 3, p. 137) to help young people identify and understand both the antecedents and consequences of use.

Teach coping, decision-making, negotiation, and problem-solving skills.

Refer to the appropriate addictions services in your jurisdiction.

Use a family-focused approach whenever possible.

Use a harm-reduction approach.

Help young people develop a relapse prevention plan.

Identify and support young people's strengths and resources, and use these in your interventions.

Use a psychoeducational approach both individually and in groups.

It's important for CYCPs to keep in mind that drug and alcohol treatments for youth need to offer significantly different approaches to treatment from those for adults, mostly because young people haven't used drugs long enough to develop serious, life-altering addictions or dependencies. Keep in mind that, since youth are much more likely to respond to psychosocial interventions than to forced abstinence programs, targeted programs should use a harm-reduction approach.

Harm-reduction strategies targeted at adults include methadone-maintenance and needle-exchange programs, approaches that are being increasingly advocated as population-based strategies for youth as well. Supporters of a universal harm-reduction approach for young people point out that high rates of substance use are found among all youth; that existing drug prevention programs are limited in their effectiveness; and that it's difficult to target programs at high-risk adolescents ("Generating and mobilizing knowledge," 2015). Nonetheless, harm-reduction strategies are best individualized according to the needs and wants of the individual or community, suggesting that a universal or one-size-fits-all program would be neither possible nor suitable for all. Appropriate goals can be tailored to meet the needs of individuals, whether they're oriented toward abstinence or not (Poulin, 2006). Programs that adopt the harm-reduction model must provide sufficient evidence for its effectiveness for reducing harm to both the substance abuser and the general public. Unfortunately, there are no practical means of measuring many of the harms associated with substance abuse (Weatherburn, 2008).

We've seen that since formal school board policies support abstinence as a goal, harm reduction as a universal intervention targeting underaged youth should be informed by the legal and policy constraints placed on schools and school boards (Poulin, 2006). What do you think? Should this be the same for treatment centres that provide services to underaged youth?

It's critically important that CYCPs be aware of all the resources and services in the addictions sector in their jurisdiction and be able to assist in referrals and appropriately matching services to the needs of the young people they support.

Alternative Healing   Alternative healing options that have been proposed in the literature include acupuncture, animal-assisted therapy, chiropractic, hypnosis, laser therapy, music therapy, subliminal audiotapes, and nutritional therapy. Holistic treatment approaches include MBSR, yoga, and tai-chi. These types of exercise and meditation are used to balance the body and put the mind at ease. Physical touch can also help those in recovery: massage helps relax the body and calm the mind, and acupuncture works to eliminate the imbalance in energy caused by substance abuse. Both of these can help a recovering addict by lessening withdrawal symptoms (Winkel, 2009).

Natural medicines can be controversial; for example, consider the case of ayahuasca. This medicine, which is legal in Brazil and Peru, is used for traditional spiritual purposes; the International Narcotics Control Board has ruled that it's not considered a controlled substance under the UN's drug-control treaties. Dr. Gabor Maté, to whom we referred earlier in this chapter, administered ayahuasca for the treatment of addicts in Eastside Vancouver. According to news reports, several of Maté's patients made significant progress while taking it. For example, one patient said that since her youth she'd battled addictions to cocaine, benzoates, marijuana, and alcohol. "Ayahuasca saved my life," she said. "It enabled me to look at all those dark things I buried long ago . . . to unleash them and the pain, so that I could move forward" (Posner, 2011). However, Health Canada instructed Maté to stop administering ayahuasca.

Relational CYC Practice   As Straus (2007) points out, all strength-based helpers work from the premise that young people have the resources that can help them overcome risk and adversity. The focus of CYCPs' work is helping these young people enhance the coping skills they already have and teaching, supporting, and encouraging the development of new ones. Harm reduction and motivational interviewing are strength-based approaches that go hand in hand. Thus, if we can work to provide opportunities to develop healthy problem-solving and coping strategies and give youth ample opportunities for developing belonging, mastery, generosity, and independence (Brendtro, Brokenleg, & Van Bockern, 2002), we'll be assisting young people struggling with substance use issues in a relational, CYC way (Straus, 2007, p. 276). Refer to Box 10.6 for an overview of specific communication strategies that can be used in your CYC practice.

Box 10.6

CYC Communication Strategies

Be strength-based and nonjudgmental in your language and messages.

Use motivational interviewing techniques, including the following:

  Paraphrase young people's words and reflect their emotions.

Express empathy.

Challenge discrepancies between youth's current behaviour and the treatment goal.

Support self-efficacy and inherent abilities; "roll with the resistance."

Use teachable moments.

WHERE DO YOU STAND?

Consider the approaches to treatment and intervention summarized above. Where do you stand? What treatment approaches would you be most likely to consider in your CYC practice? Before leaving the topic of substance-related disorders, revisit the cases of Teighan and Laura. How would you describe your preferred approach to working with those affected by substance-related disturbances?

Teighan's and Laura's Cases: *Viewpoint Challenge Exercise*

Reread the cases of Teighan and Laura presented throughout this chapter. Which psychological approach to explanation and treatment would you be most likely to consider in relation to each of these cases? Which CYC approach to explanation and treatment would you be most likely to consider in relation to each of these cases? How might your personal views of substance use impact your choices of explanation and approach to treatment? What are the most important factors to consider from a CYC approach? Explain your answer.

CHAPTER SUMMARY

■ *Substance use* refers to using psychoactive substances; *substance misuse* refers to the occasional, inappropriate use of either a social or a prescription drug; and *substance abuse* is a general term used to define the use of any drug that is disapproved of by the members of the society in which it occurs.

■ Psychological disturbances associated with substance use and addictions are included together in one chapter in the DSM-5, Substance-Related and Addictive Disorders, and include Substance Use Disorders and Substance-Induced Disorders.

■ From a CYC approach, there are still no generally accepted definitive guidelines for deciding what constitutes problematic substance use or misuse among youth.

■ Psychological explanations of substance-related disturbances include theories related to the brain reward system, the self-medication theory of addiction, and expectancy outcome theory, as well as the role of social and cultural norms and values.

■ A harm-reduction model is congruent with a CYC perspective on addictions because it focuses on reducing the risks and consequences of substance use rather than focusing on the use itself.

■ Psychological approaches to treatment include the use of medications, exploring the user's feelings of helplessness and lack of control, and contingency management, as well as broader strategies that seek to alter cultural norms and values associated with psychoactive substances.

■ A CYC ecological conceptual model acknowledges that it's the cumulative number of risk factors combined, rather than any one specific risk factor, that increases or decreases the likelihood of substance use, misuse, or addictions developing.

■ CYCPs use motivational interviewing as their primary treatment approach in addiction counselling; MI is consistent with trauma-informed CYC practice.

Critical Thinking Questions

1. Do you think there's a difference between psychological and physical dependence? How would you recognize either of these in a youth population?

2. Some researchers and clinicians suggest that the DSM is not a useful tool for categorizing or defining adolescent substance use. What do you think? Explain your position.

3. Should CYCPs give a youth a cigarette when they're struggling with intense emotional issues or feeling suicidal? Would doing so be considered a harm-reduction method? Is it unethical because it's illegal?

4. Should marijuana be legalized in Canada? Why or why not? What groups would be most affected by such a change?

5. The death penalty is imposed in 34 countries for drug-related offences, including trafficking, cultivation, and, in some situations, possession. What do you think about these consequences? Which conceptual models or paradigms would agree with these harsh consequences? Which would disagree?

6. Do you believe adolescents are capable of making informed choices about drug use? Should they be permitted to make their own decisions about use?

7. Which of the psychological approaches to treatment fit best with your views of substance-related disorders? Explain your choice.

8. Should CYCPs focus entirely on using a harm-reduction approach in their work with at-risk youth struggling with addictions?

9. Can you think of any situations in which abstinence may be the preferred approach?

Key Terms

Supplemental Readings

Hester, A., & Miller, W. R. (Eds.). (2003). *The handbook of alcoholism treatment approaches: Effective alternatives* (3rd ed.). Boston: Allyn & Bacon.

Hester, R. K. (2002). The drinker's check-up: A brief motivational intervention for problem drinkers. *Smart Recovery News and Views, 8*(4), 8–9.

Csiernik, R., & Rowe, W. (2010). *Responding to the oppression of addiction* (2nd ed.). Toronto: Canadian Scholars' Press.

Maté, G. (2008). *In the realm of hungry ghosts*. Toronto: Random House.

Miller, W. R., & Rollnoick, S. (2002). *Motivational interviewing* (2nd ed.). New York: Guilford Press.

Csiernik, R. (2011). *Substance use and abuse: Everything matters*. Toronto: Canadian Scholars' Press.

Online Resources

"Young Canadians see marijuana as a harmless herb," *Globe and Mail*, http://fw.to/I6t13EY

A selection of resources for youth, http://adai.uw.edu/pubs/infobriefs/ADAI-IB-2012-02.pdf

Open minds, healthy minds: Ontario's comprehensive mental health and addiction strategy, www.health.gov.on.ca/en/common/ministry/publications/reports/mental_health2011/mentalhealth_rep2011.pdf

Youth harm reduction programs in Ontario, www.theresearchshop.ca/sites/default/files/LaMarre_Andrea_Youth%20Harm%20Reduction%20Report_RevisedSeptember2012.pdf

U.S. National Institute on Drug Abuse, www.drugabuse.gov

UK's National Treatment Agency for Substance Abuse, *Assessing young people for substance abuse* report, www.emcdda.europa.eu/attachements.cfm/att_101826_EN_8.%20UK08_young%20drug%20users.pdf

Appendix 1
Understanding Suicide

Suicidal thoughts can occur in the context of any psychological disorder or in the face of challenging events.

Carballo/Shutterstock

Case Example: *Jessica*

Jessica is a 16-year-old Métis girl living with her birth parents in a small town in rural Manitoba. She's recently been experiencing online bullying by a group of girls in her school. Although Jessica is a smart, attractive young woman, she often struggles with depression and low self-esteem. She's also exploring her sexual identity, and was recently involved in a romantic relationship with another girl—which is what gave rise to the most recent gossip on social media. Lately Jessica has seemed particularly distraught, and the classroom support CYCP has identified some concerning symptoms. Jessica has been withdrawn, and the other girls are openly shunning her. She's been isolating herself at home as well, increasing her use of marijuana to the point that the CYCP can see that she's high almost every day. Jessica used to take pride in her appearance; her edgy, fashionable style was important to her. But now she's coming to school in sweats, her hair isn't styled, and her hoodie is always up in front of her face.

The CYCP has decided to ask Jessica about her suicide ideation. She will do a preliminary lethality assessment and ask for a psychiatric consultation (with either a crisis team or the hospital). If it's determined that Jessica is in fact thinking about suicide, the CYCP will complete a safety plan with her.

Learning Objectives

1. Summarize the psychological and CYC perspectives of youth suicide.

2. List the risk factors and the signs and symptoms of suicide.

3. Explain how to complete a risk or lethality assessment and a safety plan.

4. List when, where, and how to refer youth who are suicidal in your jurisdiction.

Appendix Overview

Suicide is one of the leading causes of death for adolescents (Centers for Disease Control and Prevention, 2010b). Although suicidal behaviours have been observed in every time period and in every culture in the history of humankind, attempts to prevent and better understand suicide continue. Why do some people take their lives while others do not? Can we predict those most at risk for suicide? From a psychological perspective, we'll examine the risk factors, causal explanations, and approaches to treatment and intervention.

From the CYC perspective, we'll introduce the risk factors for suicidal behaviours in youth and review risk-assessment procedures, theories of risk, behavioural indicators, lethality assessment, and safety planning. We'll examine the rates of youth suicide in Canada, with a particular focus on the current suicide crisis in many Aboriginal communities. Note that we provide only a general introduction to the issue of youth suicide in this appendix. All CYCPs need to ensure that they access specific suicide intervention training; they must be aware of assessment services, crisis mobilization services, suicide crisis lines, crisis programs, and longer-term treatment options in their jurisdictions.

WHAT IS SUICIDE?

Suicide, defined as the act of one intentionally ending one's own life, is one of the leading causes of death for people of all ages worldwide (Pinto, 2009). The general term **suicidal behaviour** is used to refer to ideas, thoughts, and acts associated with intentionally taking one's own life.

SUICIDE: THE PSYCHOLOGICAL PERSPECTIVE

In the psychological literature, the ideas, thoughts, and acts associated with *suicidal behaviour* are distinguished more specifically from one another as follows:

- **suicidal ideation** refers to thoughts and ideas associated with suicide
- **suicidal attempt** refers to an unsuccessful attempt to take one's own life
- **completed suicide** refers to a successful attempt (often referred to as *committing* suicide).

Thus, *suicidal behaviour* as a general term can refer to any or all of these ideas, thoughts, and behaviours.

DSM-5 Categories

Suicidal behaviour can occur in the context of many disorders and situations, and in the DSM-5, it's considered in a general grouping titled Conditions for Further Study. Although the conditions identified in this section of the DSM aren't currently used by mental health practitioners to make diagnoses, the proposed criteria for the disorders in this chapter are meant to provide a common language for professionals *studying* these conditions.

Suicidal Behaviour Disorder: Proposed Criteria   Suicidal Behaviour Disorder is characterized by self-initiated behaviour intended to lead to one's own death. This diagnostic category hasn't yet been verified by current research, but it's included in the DSM-5 with the hope that providing some guidelines on the behaviour pattern will help researchers study the condition in a more consistent way. With future research findings, it's possible that later versions of the DSM will include formal criteria for suicidal behaviour. The proposed diagnostic criteria for Suicidal Behaviour Disorder are presented in Box A1.1 for your consideration (remember, these haven't yet been verified by scientific research). What are your thoughts and reactions to these criteria?

As noted in the DSM-5, suicidal behaviour is often categorized on the basis of (1) violence of the method (ranging from *non-violent* drug overdose to *violent* gunshot wound), (2) medical consequences of the act (ranging from *low-lethality acts*, meaning a low likelihood of death, to *high-lethality acts*, with a high likelihood of death and requiring medical attention), and (3) degree of impulsivity associated with the behaviour (i.e., a planned or an impulsive act).

Box A1.1

DSM-5 Proposed Criteria for Suicidal Behaviour Disorder

A. Within the last 24 months, the individual has made a suicide attempt.

NOTE: A suicide attempt is a self-initiated sequence of behaviors by an individual who, at the time of initiation, expected that the set of actions would lead to his or her own death. The "time of initiation" is the time when a behavior took place that involved applying the method.

B. The act does not meet criteria for nonsuicidal self-injury— that is, it does not involve self-injury directed to the surface of the body undertaken to induce relief from a negative feeling/cognitive state or to achieve a positive mood state.

C. The diagnosis is not applied to suicidal ideation or to preparatory acts.

D. The act was not initiated during a state of delirium or confusion.

E. The act was not undertaken solely for a political or religious objective.

Specify if:

Current: Not more than 12 months since the last attempt.

In early remission: 12–24 months since the last attempt.

A CYC APPROACH TO UNDERSTANDING YOUTH SUICIDE

When articulating an approach to understanding youth suicidal behaviours, it's very important to first identify how we conceptualize the issue overall (White, 2014). This approach is critical in providing the foundation for a CYC approach to understanding youth suicide.

> When suicide is viewed exclusively as a private, individual problem that is directly linked to psychopathology or mental disorders, there is very little opportunity to see its relational, social, historical, cultural or political dimensions. Such a narrow conceptualization often invites responses or professional interventions that target the individual person for change, while neglecting many of the sociopolitical processes and structural forces that confer risks for suicide, including for example social inequity, racism, heteronormativity, or colonization. Contemporary ideas about mental health, distress, and healing are culture-bound notions, which have arisen within specific traditions and may not be appropriate for all individuals in every context. (White, 2014, p. 5)

We've stressed throughout this text that social, cultural, and economic factors play a major role in mental health and well-being, and are particularly significant risk factors that impact marginalized groups in society. The determinants of positive mental health and well-being identified by the Canadian Mental Health Association (n.d.) include social inclusion, freedom from discrimination and violence, and access to economic resources. If marginalized youth and families don't feel included, are threatened by discrimination or violence, and/or have little access to financial or other resources, they're at increased risk for mental health issues, including a potentially greater risk of suicidal behaviours.

We've also identified the fact that the stigma associated with mental health concerns often prevents people, particularly youth, from seeking and accessing help. And while numerous public awareness campaigns in Canada over the past few years have been attempting to address this, particularly in relation to depression and suicide, more needs to be done. Distressed young people usually remain silent, often reaching a point of hopelessness and desperation as a result. And even when mental health services are available and accessible in their communities, they're perceived as not helpful, or as simply too public for self-conscious youth to access (Canadian Institute for Health Information, 2004).

Highlighting the economic and sociopolitical aspects of suicide is the fact that it occurs roughly five to six times more often among First Nations youth than non-Aboriginal youth in Canada (Royal Commission on Aboriginal Peoples, 2010). Suicide was rare among First Nations people before the arrival of the Europeans (Canadian Mental Health Association, 2003). Although rates vary enormously across First Nations communities in Canada, for First Nations men aged 15–24 the rate is 126 per 100 000 (compared with 24 per 100 000 for non-Aboriginal Canadian men of the same age group); for young women, the rate is 35 per 100 000 (compared with only 5 per 100 000 for non-Aboriginal Canadian women). And the suicide rate for Inuit peoples living in northern Canada is staggering, ranging between 60 and 75 per 100 000 people (Health Canada, 2013).

It's important for CYCPs to recognize the specific, unique risk factors affecting youth suicide rates in First Nations communities in Canada: these include the history of colonization, economic marginalization, rapid culture change, cultural discontinuity, forced assimilation and forced relocation, the residential school experience, denigration of culture, exposure to violence and abuse, and the clustering effects due to the close ties and identification among youth in small communities. In addition, the frequency with which youth suicide occurs in some First Nations may lead to its normalization in the community, which in itself can become an additional risk factor.

Another group at high risk for suicide in Canada owing to its sociopolitical context is LGBTT youth (lesbian, gay, bisexual, transgendered, two-spirited). In general, LGBTT youth face higher rates of depression, anxiety, Obsessive-Compulsive and Phobic Disorders, PTSD, suicidality, self-harm, and substance use. At the same time, they also experience multiple forms of marginalization or disadvantage. LGBTT youth have approximately 14 times the risk of suicide and substance abuse of their heterosexual peers; 77 percent of transgendered respondents in an Ontario-based survey had seriously considered suicide, and 45 percent had attempted it (Health Canada, 2013).

HOW MANY YOUNG PEOPLE ARE AT RISK FOR SUICIDE?

Suicide is a tragic phenomenon. In the year 2000, 815 000 people in the world lost their lives to suicide, a figure that at that time was more than double the number of people who died as a direct result of armed conflict in the world. The World Health Organization reports that someone in the world completes suicide every 40 seconds.

Canada's suicide rate—15 per 100 000 people—is ranked thirteenth in the world, with Quebec having the highest suicide rate in the country (World Health Organization, 2002). In 2009, suicide was the ninth leading cause of death in Canada. Even more people have been hospitalized due to attempted suicide: there were 23 000 hospitalizations in Canada for suicide attempts in 2001, with 73 percent of these involving people between the ages of 15 and 44. Worldwide, for those aged 15 to 44, suicide is the fourth leading cause of death and the sixth leading cause of disability and infirmity (Canadian Institute for Health Information, 2004).

In the North American population as a whole, 4.6 percent have made at least one suicide attempt in their lives. Suicide rates for males are three times higher than the rate for females, because males tend to use more lethal methods: whereas three times as many females as males attempt suicide, males are three times more successful in their suicide attempts (McWhirter et al., 2007). Men show highest risk of suicide activity between 15 and 49 years old, while females are more at risk between the ages of 15 and 34. However, children as young as 8 to 11 have been reported to attempt and complete suicide (Navaneelan, 2012).

It is especially distressing for all involved when young people take their own lives. In Canada, suicide accounts for 24 percent of all deaths among 15- to 24-year-olds, and is the *second leading cause of death* for young Canadians between the ages of 10 and 24 (Canadian Mental Health Association, 2015). Young people's inability to deal with developmental stresses or overall life stresses, real or perceived, make them more likely to attempt suicide. Adolescent suicides have common precipitating stressors, such as family conflict, bullying, relationship breakups, and school and legal trouble, which we identify below. Combined with other risk factors, such as mental health difficulties, many youth are at increased risk. In 2003, the Centers for Disease Control and Prevention in the United States conducted mass surveys targeting high-school students. Twenty-nine percent of these students reported feelings of sadness and hopelessness almost every day for at least two consecutive weeks. Approximately 17 percent said they were thinking about attempting suicide, while 9 percent had actually attempted it (Centers for Disease Control and Prevention, 2015b).

We've seen that mental health issues are the most significant risk factor for suicide, with more than 90 percent of people who've attempted or completed suicide having had a mental or addictive disorder. Depression is the most common of these mental health concerns; however, among those who die from suicide, there is usually no single mental health issue, including depression, that is enough on its own to cause someone to attempt or complete suicide. Suicide results from the interaction of many risk factors, which we'll discuss below (Centers for Disease Control and Prevention, 2015c).

From 1950 to 1990, youth suicide increased an average of 300 percent; however, from 1990 to 2003, it showed a decline of 35 percent. Suicide rates in Canada are even higher among specific groups. We saw earlier that Aboriginal and LGBTT youth are at highest risk for suicide in Canada, with the elderly, inmates in correctional facilities, and individuals who have previously attempted suicide also at greater risk.

SUICIDE AND DEVELOPMENT

Suicide rates in Canada rise dramatically between the childhood and teen years. With girls, it rises from 1.5 per 100 000 of those aged 10 to 14 to 5.0 per 100 000 of those aged 15 to 19. With boys, the rate rises from 1.7 per 100 000 of the younger group to 11.4 per 100 000 of the 15–19 age group (Statistics Canada, 2007). These numbers are exclusive of suicide attempts and ideations.

Youth suicide relates, in part, to events associated with adolescence as a developmental life stage (White, 2014). The challenges involved in healthy youth development—including forming an identity and gaining acceptance and approval from families and peers—can make adolescence a stressful time. Such factors as the loss of a valued relationship, interpersonal conflict with family and friends, and the perceived pressure for high scholastic achievement can be overwhelming. For those who are already vulnerable to suicide because of other risk factors, these developmental stressors can create a serious crisis for which suicide may seem to be the only solution. The impulsiveness of youth and their lack of experience in dealing with stressful issues also contribute to the higher risk of suicide (Government of Canada, 2006).

The fact that suicide rates tend to increase with age in adolescence is partly due to the fact that risk factors for suicide, including Major Depressive Disorder, also increase during adolescence. Certain social stressors exacerbate suicide risk when they co-occur with other vulnerabilities, and these stressors (e.g. relationships, educational challenges, and other pressures) tend to increase during adolescence as well.

Though rare, suicide does occur among pre-pubertal children, and appears to be increasing in frequency. It's important not to underestimate children's understanding of the meaning of suicide, nor to discount the possibility of children engaging in suicidal behaviour. By age nine, children usually have an understanding of suicide, although they may not fully understand the finality of death. Suicide among young children is often associated with parent–child conflict (White, 2014).

COMORBIDITY

Among adolescents who complete suicide, a high level of comorbidity has been observed with mood, anxiety, and substance abuse disorders. As cited earlier, research has found that 90 percent of those who have attempted or completed suicide have a history of one or more psychiatric or addictive disorders. Mood disorders and Substance Use Disorders are the key disorders related to suicide. Although studies of the general population of Canada and the U.S. suggest that depression is the strongest mental health issue correlated with suicidality, we've seen that, among youth who die from suicide, no single mental health issue (including depression) is usually enough. Other issues exacerbate the risk; for example, alcohol and drug use clouds judgment, lowers inhibition, and worsens depression. Such use is associated with 50–67 percent of adolescent suicides, and can be seen as the top of the risk assessment pyramid. It's important to keep in mind that suicidal behaviour results from the interaction of many variables and risk factors, which are discussed below (Navaneelan, 2012).

Before moving on to a discussion of explanations for suicidal behaviour, review some common myths of suicide presented in Box A1.2.

Box A1.2

Common Myths About Suicide

MYTH: *Young people who talk about suicide are just trying to get attention or manipulate others, and they usually don't actually try to kill themselves.*

FACT: Youth who talk about wanting to die by suicide often do kill themselves, and they usually talk about it first. They're in pain, and will often reach out for help because they don't know what to do and have lost hope. Always treat talk about suicide seriously.

MYTH: *Suicide always occurs without any warning signs.*

FACT: There are almost always warning signs.

MYTH: *You should never ask people who are suicidal if they're thinking about suicide or if they've thought about a method, since just talking about it will give them the idea.*

FACT: Asking people if they're thinking about suicide doesn't give them the idea for suicide. It's important to talk about suicide with people who are suicidal: you'll learn more about their mindset and intentions, and allow them to diffuse some of the tension that's causing their suicidal feelings.

Source: Adapted from "Myths about suicide," 2011.

EXPLAINING SUICIDE: PSYCHOLOGICAL PARADIGMS

Why do some youth engage in suicidal behaviour while others do not? Attempts to explain suicide have been proposed throughout history. Emile Durkheim (1951) distinguished between various types; for example, *formalized suicide* referred to those that were socially approved of (e.g., killing oneself to regain a family's honour), and *egoistic suicide* referred to taking one's own life in the face of recent loss of social supports. Indeed, it's been recognized that the explanation for suicide varies significantly for each individual and his or her unique circumstances.

> It is tempting when looking at the life of anyone who has completed suicide to read into the decision to die a vastly complex web of reasons; and, of course, such complexity is warranted. No one illness or event causes suicide; and certainly no one knows all, or perhaps even most, of the motivations behind the killing of the self. But psychopathology is almost always there, and its deadliness is fierce. Love, success, and friendship are not always enough to counter the pain and destructiveness of severe mental illness. (Jamison, 1999)

Thus, while the psychological paradigms reviewed below offer various explanations for suicidal behaviour, note that one or more of these explanations might be differentially relevant for any one particular case.

Biological Paradigm   It might seem difficult to imagine that biological factors can play a role in suicidal behaviour. However, research results support the role of genetics as well as neurobiological factors in the risk of suicide.

Heredity and Genetics.   Studies show that suicide risk increases if a family member has committed suicide (Hantouche, Angst, & Azorin, 2010). Nock et al. (2011) found a greater degree of similarity in suicide risk between biological relatives of adopted individuals who had committed suicide compared with a group of adopted individuals who had not committed suicide. Similarly, Brent and Mann (2005) found that suicidal behaviour in adopted individuals was best predicted by the suicidal behaviour of their biological relatives. What could be inherited that might increase one's risk of suicidal behaviour? As discussed in previous chapters, genetics wires the nervous system in particular ways, which may create certain conditions and characteristics that increase the likelihood of suicidal thoughts and behaviours.

Brain Structures.   Recent neurobiological studies suggest that abnormalities in specific brain areas are associated with suicidal behaviour. Van Heeringen (2010), for example, found that suicidal behaviour is correlated with changes in areas of the prefrontal cortex (see Appendix 2 to locate this area in the brain). Given that these areas are associated with problem solving and decision making, van Heeringen (2010) concluded that suicidal behaviour results in part from impaired problem solving and impulsivity. Van Heeringen et al. (2010) also found changes in prefrontal activity associated with increased mental pain, hopelessness, and suicidal ideation. Pan et al. (2013) studied adolescents who had attempted suicide (and were diagnosed with Major Depressive Disorder) and found that areas of their frontal lobes were more responsive to pictures of angry faces than in other adolescents. The researchers concluded that the frontal lobes of adolescent attempters may be particularly sensitive to negative emotional processing, increasing the risk for suicidal behaviour.

Neurotransmitters. A number of studies suggest that low levels of serotonin are associated with suicidal behaviour (Pompili et al., 2010; van Heeringen, 2010). In particular, abnormalities in levels of serotonin are related to completed suicide, suicide attempts, and non-suicidal self-injury in adults (Mann, Brent, & Arango, 2001). Although few studies have been conducted with adolescents (Mann, 2003), Crowell et al. (2008) found that low levels of serotonin were associated with increased risk of suicidal behaviour in those living in family environments that were emotionally negative and filled with conflict. These researchers concluded that while biological factors play a role in suicidal risk, it is the interaction of biology with environmental factors that ultimately determines suicidal behaviour.

Psychodynamic Paradigm Psychodynamic explanations of suicidal behaviour have included self-directed aggression, grief resulting from significant object loss, and impaired relationships. For example, early views of suicide explained it in relation to "anger turned inward," whereby suicidal behaviour was a consequence of directing anger felt toward another person (e.g., a lost relationship) toward oneself. Thus, rather than representing a desire to harm oneself, suicidal behaviour is actually a way to release the intense anger experienced toward a lost love object. Recent theories of suicidal behaviour are still related to these early views. Kaslow et al. (1998), for example, found that adults who had attempted suicide were more likely to have a negative view of their relationships and be less invested in them than were a group of non-attempters. This study also found that attempters were significantly more likely to have a history of loss in childhood together with significant loss in adulthood.

Behavioural Paradigm From a behavioural paradigm, suicidal behaviour might be considered in relation to its consequences. For example, youth suicide ideation and attempts are often viewed as an attempt to escape feelings of pain and suffering (De Wilde, Kienhorst, & Diekstra, 2001). In the absence of perceiving other options, suicide represents a way out. Other desirable consequences (e.g., attention and support from others) might also serve to reinforce suicidal thoughts and attempts, possibly making future attempts more likely (and more lethal). This doesn't imply that those contemplating suicide are simply seeking attention. Rather, the behavioural approach emphasizes the reinforcing consequences that might

Tracy Whiteside/Fotolia

Psychodynamic explanations of suicidal behaviour include the importance of loss in both youth and adulthood.

be associated with this behaviour in order to increase understanding of the motivation of youth contemplating suicide. Any suicidal behaviour (including thoughts, ideas) should be treated seriously.

Observational learning might also be considered in an explanation of suicidal behaviour. For example, media coverage of suicidal behaviour is associated with an increased rate of suicide (Sisask & Värnik, 2012). Some argue that such media coverage not only romanticizes such behaviour but also provides a how-to guide for those who might be considering this course of action (Gould, 1990). It's been estimated that as many as 5 percent of all teenage suicides are the result of such imitation (Gould et al., 2003).

Cognitive Paradigm   From a cognitive approach, suicidal behaviour is associated with thought processes. For example, suicide attempters are more likely to pay greater attention to stimuli associated with suicide (e.g., Cha et al., 2010). This "attentional bias" predicts future suicide attempts even better than the presence of a mood disorder.

Pessimistic thinking, defined as the absence of positive thoughts of the future, has also been found to predict suicidal behaviour (MacLeod et al., 1997). Other thought patterns found to predict various forms of suicidal behaviour include perceptions of few reasons for living and concerns for the future (Chatterjee & Basu, 2010), thoughts of defeat (O'Connor, 2011), and feelings of being trapped (O'Connor et al., 2013).

Sociocultural Paradigm   Attitudes toward suicide have varied historically; today, they still differ from society to society and from culture to culture. Criminals in ancient Greece were permitted to take their own lives, and the Japanese practice of *seppuku* allows Samurai warriors to use suicide as a way of maintaining honour and demonstrating loyalty. In the twentieth century, members of certain religious movements performed mass suicides; during World War II Japan used Kamikaze suicide bombers. Buddhist monks and nuns throughout history have performed sacrificial suicide by self-immolation as a form of social protest. However, the act of suicide is condemned by most religions worldwide, including Islam, Judaism, and Christianity, and there is considerable controversy in North American society today regarding physician-assisted suicide for the terminally ill. Within Canada, prevailing views have transitioned from suicide being considered in the realm of criminal activity to being viewed as a mental

Pessimistic thinking, the absence of positive thoughts of the future, has been found to predict suicidal behaviour.

Mitarart/Fotolia

health concern (Spiwak et al., 2012). Accordingly, since the 1950s, suicide-prevention programs and community-based strategies (including telephone crisis lines) have been established in most cities and communities in North America to assist those at risk of suicide, and efforts to develop a national suicide-prevention strategy continue (Spiwak et al., 2012).

Consistent with these variations in ways of thinking about suicide, sociocultural explanations of suicidal behaviour emphasize the context in which they occur. Both the broader societal context (i.e., culture) and the immediate social context (e.g., family) are considered relevant in attempts to understand suicidal behaviour in youth.

Stressful Life Events.   Stressful life events (particularly those viewed as being humiliating) are significant risk factors for suicidal behaviour. Examples include failure at work or school, social rejection, and victimization by peers (Joiner & Rudd, 2000; Kaminski & Fang, 2009). The fact that rates of suicide vary by ethnicity and gender supports the idea that social variables play a role in suicidal behaviour (Amitai & Apter, 2012). For example, higher suicide rates in males have been related not only to the use of more violent methods, but also to greater vulnerability to stressors as well as decreased likelihood of expressing distress and asking others for support (Levi et al., 2008). For girls, social isolation from peers is associated with increased risk for suicidal ideation (Bearman & Moody, 2004).

Family Influences.   Research supports the idea that family environment is a predictor of suicidal behaviour in youth. Specific family-related risk factors include loss of a parent, poor quality of parent–child relationships, maltreatment, parental psychopathology, and family conflict (Bridge, Goldstein, & Brent, 2006). The nature of communication and bonds within the family system are particularly relevant, with high levels of criticism, hostility, and emotional overinvolvement found to be associated with both suicide and self-harm (Wedig & Nock, 2007). By comparison, strong, supportive emotional bonds among family members appear to serve as a protective factor in adolescent suicide (Brent et al., 2009).

A CYC LENS ON THE PSYCHOLOGICAL PARADIGMS: A HOLISTIC CONCEPTUAL MODEL

A CYC holistic conceptual model for understanding youth suicide could incorporate the following strength-based practice approaches, which were presented in a report on youth suicide prepared by Jennifer White for the British Columbia government (White, 2014).

1. *Build a therapeutic relationship:* Ensure that you develop a strong therapeutic alliance; attend to diversity needs; engage with the community in respectful ways.

2. *Assess risk:* Use a comprehensive, culturally sensitive approach to risk assessment; adopt a collaborative stance with youth and families; be able to estimate level of risk.

3. *Plan for safety:* Actively involve young people and their parents/caregivers, significant others, and community members in the safety plan; individualize the plan, tailoring treatment to the strengths (always build on identified strengths and enhance resilience) and needs of the young person.

4. *Treat and monitor suicidal behaviour:* Reduce any existing threats to well-being; work to prevent future suicidal behaviours.

5. *Assess for and address co-occurring problems:* Ensure that you're aware of co-occurring problems.

6. *Explore cultural contexts:* Provide culturally responsive care; ensure that you're aware of the unique needs of Indigenous youth and families, sexual minority youth, and all cultural minorities.

7. *Engage parents:* Respect their knowledge and what they have to offer; collaborate with parents in treatment planning, safety planning, and monitoring wherever possible and appropriate.

8. *Engage hard-to-reach young people and families:* Use collaborative, flexible models of care and outreach; work with informal and formal partners.

9. *Document:* Document as soon as possible; record treatment and safety plans that correspond with the risk formulation; regularly update changes in suicide risk.

10. *Strengthen professional expertise and organizational capacity:* Link emergency departments and mental health services to address broad social determinants (White, 2014).

As with all program development, implementation, and evaluation, it's important that CYCPs solicit youth voice when designing and delivering suicide prevention and intervention programs. At a minimum, the opportunity to have their voices heard is empowering for young people; but more than this, they have a right to define the issues that most affect them.

Suicide intervention and prevention in general involves finding ways to reduce risk factors and promote strengths and protective (preventive) factors, which may be understood in terms of individual and collective resilience—the ability to spring back from negative conditions. Research has identified a wide range of these factors in the general population; to understand risk and vulnerability in youth suicide, it's important to be aware of the predisposing factors, precipitating events, contributing factors, and protective factors (McWhirter et al., 2007; Public Health Agency of Canada, 2002).

Predisposing factors are historical in nature (situations that occurred in the past) and can set the stage for an individual's vulnerability to suicide. At the *self or individual (intrapersonal) level*, these factors include a history of previous attempts and a diagnosis of depression or mental health issues; at the *family level* they include abuse, parental mental health issues, early loss, attachment issues, and family history of suicide; and at the *peer, school, community, culture, and societal level* they include long-term difficulties with peers, a history of antisocial behaviours and isolation, a history of school problems, frequent moves, and societal change and pressure (McWhirter et al., 2007; Public Health Agency of Canada, 2002).

Precipitating events, or *trigger events*, are sudden in onset; at the *self level* they include health crisis, pregnancy, developmental crisis, and sudden loss in esteem; at the *family level* they include conflict with family members, death or divorce of parents, and perceived rejection by family; at the *school, community, and societal level* they include failure, expulsion from school, transition to and from school, pressure to succeed, conflict with the law, legal problems, sudden loss of status within the cultural group, alienation from religion, and financial difficulties (McWhirter et al., 2007).

Contributing factors can exacerbate the risk caused by the predisposing or precipitating factors and can be either sudden or historical in nature. At the *self level* these include

Consider both the CYC and psychological perspectives of suicidal behaviour described above. Where do you stand? As with the other behaviour patterns discussed in this text, most theorists and professional today agree that a complex combination of various factors contributes to an increased risk of suicidal behaviour. What do you think? Do you believe any particular factors are more relevant to suicide risk than others?

substance abuse, risk taking or other destructive behaviours, attitudes about the acceptability of suicide, illness, impulsivity, sexual identity issues, learning disability or cognitive defect, loss that leads to depression or repeated loss, and complex trauma combined with poor coping skills; at the *family level* they include family members' abuse of alcohol or drugs, unstable relationships, and dysfunctional communication; at the *school, peer, community, and societal level* they include having a friend die, unreasonable emphasis on academic success, social isolation, media influences, increased violence, access to firearms and other lethal methods, and the rapid rate of technological advances (McWhirter et al., 2007; Public Health Agency of Canada, 2002).

Protective factors (or *resiliency factors*) act to lessen the risk for suicide and include availability of one significant adult who can provide warmth, care, and understanding; perceived parent and family connectedness; emotional well-being (especially for females); availability of support and involvement of extended family; problem solving and coping skills; healthy peer modelling; peer friendship, acceptance willingness to seek help; good physical and mental health; experience/feelings of success; and strong spiritual and cultural identity (McWhirter et al., 2007; Public Health Agency of Canada, 2002).

HELPING CHILDREN AND ADOLESCENTS AT RISK FOR SUICIDAL BEHAVIOUR

Jessica's Case: *Revisited*

The CYCP conducted a suicide risk assessment with Jessica. After establishing a rapport, she asked her the following questions:

1. What has happened lately to upset you?
2. Are you thinking about killing yourself?
3. How long have you been thinking about suicide?
4. How often (*frequency*) do you have thoughts of suicide?
5. How strong (*intensity*) are your thoughts?
6. How long (*duration*) do your thoughts last?
7. Do you have a plan to use to end your life? What is the plan? Please describe it in detail to me.
8. Do you have the means (everything you need) to carry out the plan?
9. Do you know anyone who's committed suicide?
10. Have you attempted suicide in the past? How long ago?
11. Have you been feeling depressed or sad lately?
12. Do you use drugs or alcohol?
13. Have you experienced losses recently?
14. Any concerns about your sexuality?
15. What do you think about yourself and your future?
16. What do you visualize? Is there anyone to stop you?

Psychological Approaches to Treatment

It's been estimated that approximately 60 percent of those struggling with suicidal thoughts and related distressing emotions don't receive treatment (Bruffaerts et al., 2011). Equally concerning is the fact that there are few well-established evidence-based treatments for suicidal behaviour (O'Connor & Nock, 2014). From a psychological approach, cognitive-behavioural interventions aimed at decreasing suicidal thoughts and behaviour have shown some promise (e.g., Brown et al., 2005), but these studies are in need of replication. Given that the most common approaches to intervention are similar to those proposed by a CYC approach, we forgo the usual review of psychological approaches to treatment and move directly to a discussion of those intervention approaches considered appropriate from a CYC perspective.

CYC Approaches for Youth Suicide

As we've highlighted throughout this text, healing occurs through many different modalities—and suicide is no exception. Early identification and treatment programs address suicide's predisposing factors; crisis intervention addresses its precipitating factors; treatment programs address its contributing factors; and mental health promotion programs can help build on the individual's protective factors. CYCPs will be involved at all levels of suicide prevention and intervention with young people.

When other mental health issues exist—and as we've seen, in 90 percent of cases they do—longer-term professional intervention is needed. When working with suicide victims and those at risk, it's critical that the full circle of activities (primary prevention, intervention, and post-intervention) offer treatment and support.

CYCPs engage with young people in their life space 24 hours a day, and are thus well placed to observe any changes in behaviour that may signal distress, depression, or suicidal thinking—just as the CYCP was able to do with Jessica. Keep in mind, too, that self-awareness is critically important in understanding and intervening with youth suicide: CYCPs must first explore their own attitudes about the issue of youth suicide, since particular attitudes can definitely affect, whether positively or negatively, their intervention.

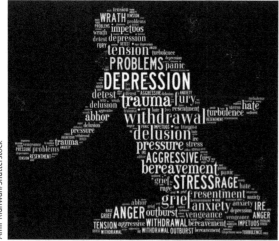

It's important that CYCPs explore their own thoughts and feelings about the issue of youth suicide, since these can help or hinder an effective response.

As well, recall our discussion in Chapter 2 regarding the difference between *self-harm* and *suicide*. While these terms are often used interchangeably, the behaviours differ at both a conceptual and treatment level. While suicide is an intentional, self-inflicted act that results in death, self-harm is an intentional, usually repetitive behaviour that involves the infliction of harm to the body (excluding that which is socially condoned, like piercing) but without suicidal intent. Since both are self-directed and dangerous, it may be very difficult to distinguish between the two, and in fact most CYCPs engage with young people who are both self-harming and suicidal. The greatest difficulty in differentiating between suicidal behaviours and intentional self-harm is in determining the young person's motivation, or the intent—a critical distinction, since the intervention approaches will be different. What need is being met? Was the intent to end unbearable pain or the young person's life, or was it a desperate call for help and a means of soothing the pain in a temporary escape? The majority of those who engage in self-harm don't wish to die; rather, they're using self-harm as a coping mechanism to provide temporary relief from great psychological distress. Thus, we can interpret self-harming behaviours as an "effective," albeit harmful, form of coping for some youth. (We discussed the ways to intervene with self-harming behaviour in Chapter 2.) And although most of these young people know when to stop a session of self-harm (i.e., when their need is satisfied), accidental death can sometimes result. Such cases of self-harm may be mistakenly labelled as suicide attempts.

The thinking patterns common in suicidal youth are almost always distorted, and these same faulty thinking patterns and irrational beliefs are also found in those who struggle with depression and low self-esteem. Often, the distorted thinking patterns become pervasive and lead the young person to isolate. The common motivations for young people considering suicide are wanting to escape from intolerable situation, to join someone who's died, to attract attention from family and friends, to manipulate someone to get revenge, to avoid punishment, to be punished, to control when and how death occurs, to end a conflict that seems unresolvable, and to punish survivors.

A child whose behavior pushes you away is a child who needs connection before anything else.

-Kelly Bartlett
Encouraging Words for Kids

www.kellybartlett.net

Strength-based and supportive responses from CYCPs for youth who may be suicidal include a willingness to initiate dialogue without fear or hesitation, a nonjudgmental approach, and a sense of optimism about helping.

Strength-Based Relational CYC Practice   The basic requirements for strength-based, supportive responses from CYCPs and other caregivers engaged with youth who may be suicidal include the following: a willingness to initiate dialogue with a potentially suicidal adolescent with genuine concern but without fear or hesitation, a nonjudgmental approach, and a sense of optimism about helping. CYCPs also need basic suicide crisis intervention skills (like ASIST) for determining the level of risk and providing a rapid, safe, and effective response. Other intervention skills include how to initiate a suicide intervention, how to estimate the level of suicide risk, how to develop a safety plan, how to respond to an acute suicide crisis event, and how to communicate with collaterals and parents.

Assessment

Suicide risk assessment is a multifaceted process for learning about a youth's motivation for suicide; recognizing and addressing the risks, needs, and stressors; and working with the youth to mobilize strengths and supports. Suicide assessment is commonly based on identifying and appraising the suicide warning signs as well as identifying the individual's risk and protective factors. In order to accurately assess the degree of risk and keep these young people safe, CYCPs need to gather information about their history, experience with suicide, present plans, current ideation, and available support networks.

Other critical areas to explore in a suicide assessment include mental health issues, such as mood disorders; prior suicide attempts; self-harm; medical diagnoses; family history of suicide attempts; family history of mental illness; individual strengths/vulnerabilities; coping skills; personality traits; past responses to stress; religious beliefs; past and present suicidal ideation, plans, behaviours, intent, and methods; presence of overt suicidal and/or self-destructive behaviour; hopelessness; anxiety symptoms; and reasons for living (Centers for Disease Control and Prevention, 2010).

We've seen that although CYCPs don't rely on rating scales, these can be used to support the risk-assessment process rather than guiding it. Suicide risk assessment is a complex process involving the consideration of a multitude of factors; the use of tools in the risk-assessment process must remain person-focused and be incorporated into the clinical interview.

The *Beck Hopelessness Scale* (1988) was designed to measure negative attitudes about one's future and perceived inability to avert negative life occurrences.

The *Beck Scale for Suicide Ideation* (1979) measures the current and immediate intensity of attitudes, behaviours, and plans for suicide-related behaviour with the intent to end life among psychiatric patients.

The *Columbia Suicide Severity Rating Scale* assesses a full range of suicide-related ideation and behaviour as well as the intensity of the ideation. Training is required to administer the C-SSRS.

The *Reasons for Living Inventory* assesses potential protective factors among those who report suicide ideation. It may be used to explore differences in the reasons for living among individuals who engage in suicide-related behaviour and those who do not (e.g., "I believe that I can cope with anything life has to offer").

The *SAD PERSONS Scale* (Centers for Disease Control and Prevention, 2010) isn't a validated rating scale, but it can help us assess risk. Each letter in the acronym stands for a suicide risk factor; the more areas into which an individual fits, the higher the risk.

S Sex: Females are more likely to attempt suicide, but males are more likely to choose a more deadly means; males are at higher risk.

A Age: 15- to 24-year-olds, along with men aged 75 and older, are high-risk groups.

D Depression

P Previous attempts

E Ethanol (alcohol) and other drug use

R Rational thinking loss

S Social support lacking

O Organized plan: The more specific, detailed, and realistic the plan, the greater the risk.

N No spouse/partner

S Sickness

Indicators to Recognize   We've seen that pain-based behaviours are expressed differently by individual youth depending on age and stage of development. Thus, in their assessment and intervention planning, CYCPs must consider some important distinctions. Although similar DSM criteria may be used with adults and youth, some features are more common in children and adolescents than in adults. Moreover, as discussed in Chapter 7, children can exhibit very different depressive symptoms from those of adolescents. "Children commonly display irritable mood rather than depressed mood, somatic complaints and social withdrawal; depressed adolescents typically display psychomotor retardation and hypersomnia" (McWhirter et al., 2007, p. 107).

The relationship between mood disturbances and expected emotions is a key point for CYCPs to consider. Expected responses to overwhelming life circumstances, including expressions of extreme sadness, grief, and loss, are common among the young people CYCPs work with. Central to our observations are the factors described earlier: that the sadness is *overwhelming*, *persistent* over time and on a day-to-day basis, and *significantly affecting the youth's ability to function* on a day-to-day basis and interfering with his or her ability to experience success or joy in daily living. When watching for these potential signs and symptoms of mood disorders, it's important to note that they should represent an observable or noticeable *change* in usual behaviour; for example, a "loss of interest or pleasure in daily activities consistently for at least a two-week period" must represent a *change in the pattern* of the young person's usual mood. If there are concerns and CYCPs are uncertain about the nature of the behaviours, a referral to a physician or other clinician for assessment is warranted. Remember that coping with depression can be a risk factor for suicide ideation. See Table A1.1 for a summary of behavioural indicators of suicide.

Table A1.1 Behavioural Indicators Checklist: Suicide

✓ Behaviour that is out of character, reckless, and high risk in someone who's usually careful

Expressions of hopelessness, apathy, desperation, or feelings of being a burden

Signs of depression, sleeplessness, social withdrawal, loss of appetite, loss of interest in usual activities

A sudden and unexpected change from sadness to a cheerful attitude

Change of eating and sleeping habits

Giving away personal possessions to family and friends

Making remarks related to death and dying, or an expressed intent to commit suicide

Neglect of personal appearance

Constant fatigue, unexplained illness, aches, pains

Decreased school activity, isolation from peers, drop in achievement and interest in school

Unexplained use of drugs or alcohol

Source: Adapted from Jacobs, 1995.

✓ Mnemonic for the warning signs of suicide: IS PATH WARM?

I Ideation

S Substance abuse

P Purposelessness

A Anxiety

T Trapped

H Hopelessness

W Withdrawal

A Anger

R Recklessness

M Mood change

Source: Canadian Mental Health Association, 2010.

Intervention

A comprehensive intervention program for youth suicide includes the following strategies (Centers for Disease Control and Prevention, 2010):

- Increase public awareness and decrease the stigma associated with suicidal behaviour.
- Implement prevention programs for youth, for individuals at high risk for suicidal behaviour, and for family members post-suicide.
- Provide and ensure equitable access to coordinated, integrated services, including crisis phone counselling and treatment of mental illnesses.
- Reduce access to lethal means of suicide, particularly firearms and lethal doses of prescription drugs.
- Train service providers in the early identification of predisposing factors and crisis management.

In an individual intervention plan, family members, caregivers, significant others, and friends will need to be educated about suicide risk through a comprehensive discussion about what to look for and how to recognize more subtle risk behaviours (Centers for Disease Control and Prevention, 2010).

A safety plan also needs to be developed. Here's a sample safety contract (Therapist Aid, 2012) that you and a young person could use to develop your own. The young person agrees to follow this contract and to keep him- or herself safe. Ensure that you have an agreement that is timelined (i.e., an agreement to stay safe for a certain number of hours).

1: KNOW WHEN TO ACCESS HELP: What are my warning signs when I begin thinking of suicide or when I feel very distressed? These include thoughts, moods, images, or behaviours.

2: COPING SKILLS: What can I do by myself to take my mind off the problem? What obstacles might there be to using these coping skills?

3: SOCIALIZING WITH FRIENDS AND FAMILY: If I'm unable to deal with my depressed mood alone, who will I contact? Trusted family members or friends?

My list: Name _____ Phone Number _____

4: CONTACT PROFESSIONALS AND AGENCIES: I agree to contact _____ or emergency services if I continue to have suicidal thoughts or serious distress.

Local emergency number _____

Refer to Box A1.3 for a summary of guidelines for CYC interventions that ought to be considered in your practice.

Prevention: Advocacy, Community, and School-Based Strategies Suicide prevention strategies can be seen as circular, involving three interconnected stages. **Primary prevention** aims to reduce suicide risk by improving the physical, mental, emotional, and spiritual health or well-being of a population. **Secondary prevention** (early intervention) aims to help with potentially suicidal youth either before they attempt or during a suicidal crisis. **Tertiary prevention** (or postvention) focuses on youth and others who've been affected by suicidal behaviour: suicide attempters, who are at high risk for a recurrence, and bereaved friends and family members, who are also at risk for increased

Techniques for CYC Intervention

Recognize the warning signs.

Use crisis management techniques.

Contact relevant professionals.

Assess risk and lethality.

Develop a safety plan to decrease sense of crisis (see above for steps in safety planning).

distress, psychiatric morbidity, and the development of suicidal thoughts and behaviours (Kirmayer et al., 2007).

Primary prevention (risk reduction) programs usually focus on public education, life skills, and parenting skills; they may also involve training professionals in suicide assessment and prevention, providing support to families, operating crisis hotlines, and reducing access to lethal means, particularly guns and substances. Intervention programs include crisis counselling, close supervision, and treatment of individuals who have expressed suicidal thoughts. Postvention efforts include counselling and other supports for individuals or groups close to a suicide victim, who may be at risk as a result of trauma.

As we cited earlier, research has provided evidence of a strong inverse relationship between Aboriginal youth suicide and the idea of self-government or community control, known as *cultural continuity:* First Nations communities with some measure of self-government are found to have the lowest rates of youth suicide. Cultural programming and enhancement has also been shown to help suicidal young people; a study of 25 Aboriginal youth from British Columbia found that connecting with culture and tradition was one of the most successful healing strategies (Kirmayer et al., 2007). Participants said that connecting to culture and traditions had led to empowerment, pride, purpose, and meaning, and had strongly contributed to their healing from suicidal ideation. Another study from British Columbia found that Aboriginal communities that have taken active steps to preserve and renew their own cultures are those in which youth suicide rates are lowest, and that the opposite holds true in those communities that have not done so (Kirmayer et al., 2007).

In 1995, the Royal Commission on Aboriginal Peoples recommended that, in order to help prevent Aboriginal youth suicide, First Nations communities should work on enhancing cultural knowledge and identity and on instilling pride in young people's roots and heritage, as this has been empirically shown to have positive effects on Indigenous youth at risk for suicidal behaviours in all aspects of their mental health and well-being.

Alternative Healing   Alternative healing methods for helping young people with mood disturbances (see Chapter 7) can also help those struggling with thoughts of suicide. Note, however, that these approaches are not a substitute for suicide intervention. They include increasing enjoyable activities and levels of physical activity and encouraging consistent sleep and healthy eating. CYCPs can help young people with daily problem solving, goal setting, and sustaining concentration; they can provide social supports; and they can help explore cultural beliefs and traditional healing alternatives. CYCPs can also teach relaxation and MBSR techniques as well as CBT techniques to help young people challenge their cognitive distortions. Finally, they can help young people make

CYC Communication Strategies

Be willing to initiate dialogue with a potentially suicidal adolescent.

Adopt a nonjudgmental approach and encourage self-disclosure.

Be open to seeking consultation.

Remain calm and supportive.

Acknowledge the reality of suicide as a choice, but don't normalize it.

Don't attempt any in-depth counselling.

Listen actively, and reinforce the positives.

Assess lethality.

informed choices about using drugs and alcohol during a time of stress. Box A1.4 lists specific communication strategies that can be used in CYCPs' work with those at risk for suicidal behaviour.

WHERE DO YOU STAND?

Without question, youth suicide is a complex issue. There is no one typical suicidal young person; the motivations for such behaviour are varied and determined by multiple factors. From a CYC perspective, awareness of the various explanations of suicidal behaviour will enhance your work with youth struggling with extreme circumstances and events that might make suicide an appealing option. Revisit the case of Jessica one final time in the *Viewpoint Challenge* exercise to assist you in this process.

Jessica's Case: *Viewpoint Challenge Exercise*

Reread the case of Jessica. How would the psychological and CYC perspectives differ in their approach to explaining Jessica's suicidal ideation? Are there similarities between the two perspectives? Which CYC intervention approach might you try with Jessica? Why? Develop a plan for Jessica based on the CYC interventions outlined above.

Critical Thinking Questions

1. Why do you think so many young people in North America today attempt or complete suicide?
2. What do you think is the relationship between suicide attempts and self-harming behaviour? What is the main difference?
3. Why is it so important to know the motivations of youth engaged in self-harming behaviours?
4. How do interventions for self-harming behaviours differ from those for suicidal behaviour?
5. What is the difference between euthanasia and other forms of suicide? Do you agree or disagree with physician-assisted suicide? Do you think terminally ill people have a right to die? Why or why not?

Key Terms

Supplemental Readings

Centre for Addiction and Mental Health. (2011). *Suicide prevention and assessment handbook*. Retrieved from www.camh.ca/en/hospital/health_information/a_z_mental_health_and_addiction_information/suicide/Documents/sp_handbook_final_feb_2011.pdf

McWhirter, J. J., McWhirter, B. T., McWhirter, E., H., & McWhirter, R. J. (2007). Youth suicide. In *At risk youth: A comprehensive response for counselors, teachers, psychologists and human services professionals*. (4th ed., pp. 210–230). Belmont, CA: Brooks/Cole.

Royal Commission on Aboriginal Peoples. (1994). *Choosing life: Special report on suicide among Aboriginal people*. Ottawa: Royal Commission on Aboriginal Peoples.

Online Resources

A helpful resource about suicide, www.suicideinfo.ca/Library/AboutSuicide/FAQ.aspx

Suicide-Related Research in Canada: A Descriptive Overview, www.phac-aspc.gc.ca/publicat/mh-sm/suicide-research/app-x2d-eng.php

Practice Guidelines for Working with Children and Youth at Risk for Suicide in Community Mental Health Settings, www.mcf.gov.bc.ca/suicide_prevention/pdf/practice_guidelines.pdf

Self-injury myths, www.lifesigns.org.uk/what/self-injury-myths

Suicide prevention resources in Canada, www.ctvnews.ca/suicide-prevention-resources-where-to-get-help-across-canada-1.704877

Centre for Suicide Prevention, www.suicideinfo.ca/Library/Links.aspx

Turtle Island Native Network: Healing and Wellness, www.turtleisland.org/healing/healing-suicide.htm

Canadian Association for Suicide Prevention, http://suicideprevention.ca

Richard Cardinal: Cry from a Diary of a Métis Child documentary, www.nfb.ca/film/richard_cardinal (Richard Cardinal was a Métis adolescent who committed suicide in 1984. Taken from his home by CFS at the age of four, he was moved in and out of 28 foster homes, group homes, and shelters in Alberta. As relevant today as it was in 1984.)

Patrick's Story video, www3.nfb.ca/sg/69025.pdf (A powerful, moving film that presents the major contributors to youth suicide but also highlights strengths, illustrating how finding a caring person and culture can create hope.)

Brain Structures

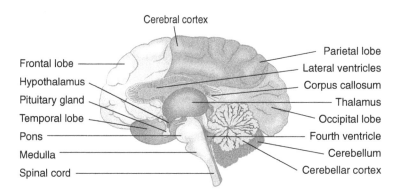

Figure A2.1 Cerebral Cortex

The cerebral cortex is divided into four general areas: the frontal lobe (executive functioning, inhibition, decision making), parietal lobe (somatosensory information/touch processing), occipital lobe (visual processing), and temporal lobe (language processing, hearing, memory).

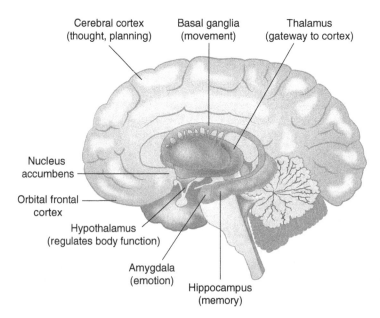

Figure A2.2 Inner Structures of the Brain

Various brain structures beneath the cerebral cortex are directly associated with emotion, cognitive processing, motivation, and behaviour regulation.

Source: "Figure 6.4", from Psychological Science: Mind, Brain, and Behavior 2E by Michael S. Gazzaniga and Todd F. Heatherton. Copyright © 2006, 2003 by W.W. Norton & Company, Inc. Used by permission of W.W. Norton & Company, Inc.

References

Abela, J. R. Z., & Hankin, B. L. (2008). Cognitive vulnerability to depression in children and adolescents: A developmental psychopathology perspective. In J. R. Z. Abela & B. L. Hankin (Eds.), *Handbook of depression in children and adolescents* (pp. 35–78). New York: Guilford.

About attachment. (n.d.). The International Association for the Study of Attachment (IASA). Retrieved from http://www.iasa-dmm.org/index.php/about-attachment

About SPD. (2015). Sensory Processing Disorder Foundation. Retrieved from http://www.spdfoundation.net/about-sensory-processing-disorder.html

Abraham, C. (2010, October 18). Are we medicating a disorder or treating boyhood as a disease? *The Globe and Mail*. Retrieved from http://www.theglobeandmail.com/news/national/time-to-lead/part-3-are-we-medicating-a-disorder-or-treating-boyhood-as-a-disease/article4330080/?page=all

Abramowitz, J. S. (2006). The psychological treatment of Obsessive-Compulsive Disorder. *Canadian Journal of Psychiatry, 51*(7), 407–416.

Acosta, M. T., Castellanos, F. X., Bolton, K. L., Balog, J. Z., Eagen, P., Nee, L., . . . Muenke, M. (2008). Latent class subtyping of Attention-Deficit/Hyperactivity Disorder and comorbid conditions. *Journal of the American Academy of Child and Adolescent Psychiatry, 47*, 797–807.

Addictions Foundation of Manitoba. (1997). *Levels of Involvement Framework*. Retrieved from http://www.afm.mb.ca/Learn%20More/Levels%20Invol.pdf

Addington, A. M., & Rapoport, J. L. (2012). Annual research review: Impact of advances in genetics in understanding developmental psychopathology. *Journal of Child Psychology and Psychiatry, 53*, 510–518.

Addington, J., Coldham, E. L., Jones, B., Ko, T., & Addington, D. (2003). The first episode of psychosis: The experience of relatives. *Acta Psychiatrica Scandinavica 108*(4), 285–290. Retrieved from http://www.health.gov.on.ca/english/public/pub/ministry_reports/mentalhealth/psychosis.pdf

Addressing myths about autism. (2014). Retrieved from http://www.community.advanceweb.com/blogs/sp_12/archive/2014/04/21/addressing-myths-about-autism.aspx

ADHD and coexisting disorders. (2009). National Resource Center on ADHD. Retrieved from http://www.help4adhd.org/en/treatment/coexisting/wwk5

ADHD medications: Mayo Clinic study contradicts MTA study. (2008). Retrieved from http://www.playattention.com/adhd-medications-mayo-clinic-study-contradicts-mta-study

Agency for Healthcare Research and Quality. (2010). Screening, assessment and treatment for people with eating disorders. National Institute of Mental Health. Retrieved from http://www.psychceu.com/eating_disorders/eating_disorder_index.asp

Ages and developmental stages: Symptoms of exposure. (n.d.). The National Child Traumatic Stress Network. Copyright © by the National Child Traumatic Stress Network. Used by permission of the National Child Traumatic Stress Network. Retrieved from http://www.nctsnet.org/content/ages-and-developmental-stages-symptoms-exposure

Aichhorn, A. (1935). *Wayward youth*. New York: Viking Press.

Alfano, M. S., Joiner, T. E., & Perry, M. (1994). Attributional style: A mediator of the shyness–depression relationship? *Journal of Research in Personality, 28*(3), 287–300.

Allen-Meares, P., & Fraser, M. W. (2004). *Intervention with children and adolescents: An interdisciplinary perspective*. Boston: Pearson Education.

Alloy, L. B., Abramson, L. Y., Keyser, J., Gerstein, R. K., & Sylvia, L. G. (2008). Negative cognitive style. In K. S. Dobston & D. J. A. Dozois (Eds.), *Risk factors in depression* (pp. 237–262). Oxford: Elsevier/Academic Press.

Alloy, L. B., Abramson, L. Y., Whitehouse, W. G., Hogan, M. E., Panzarella, C., & Rose, D. T. (2006). Prospective incidence of first onsets and recurrences of depression in individuals at high and low cognitive risk for depression. *Journal of Abnormal Psychology, 115*, 145–156.

American Academy of Child and Adolescent Psychiatry (AACAP). (2007). Practice parameters for the assessment and treatment of children, adolescents, and adults with Attention-Deficit/Hyperactivity Disorder. *Journal of American Academy of Child and Adolescent Psychiatry, 46*(7), 894–921.

American Academy of Child and Adolescent Psychiatry (AACAP). (2012, April). Complementary and integrative medicine. Retrieved from http://www.aacap.org/App_Themes/AACAP/docs/facts_for_families/101_complementary_and_integrative_medicine.pdf

American Psychiatric Association. (2000). *Diagnostic and statistical manual of mental disorders* (4th ed., text revision). Washington, DC: Author.

American Psychiatric Association. (2013). *Diagnostic and statistical manual of mental disorders* (5th ed.). Washington, DC: Author. Reprinted with permission from the Diagnostic and Statistical Manual of Mental Disorders, Fifth Edition, (Copyright © 2013). American Psychiatric Association. All Rights Reserved.

American Psychiatric Association. (2014). Recent updates to proposed revisions for DSM-5. Retrieved from http://www.dsm5.org/Pages/RecentUpdates.aspx

American Psychological Association. (2004). *Rethinking the DSM: Psychological perspective*. L. Beutler & M. Malik, (Ed.). Washington, DC: Author.

American Psychological Association Presidential Task Force on Evidence-Based Practice. (2006). Evidence-based practice in psychology. *American Psychologist, 61*(4), 271–285.

Amitai, M., & Apter, A. (2012). Social aspects of suicidal behavior and prevention in early life: A review. *International Journal of Environmental Research and Public Health, 9*(3), 985–994.

Anastopoulos, A. D., & Farley, S. E. (2003). A cognitive behavioral training program for parents of children with Attention-Deficit/Hyperactivity Disorder. In A. E. Kazdin & J. R. Weisz (Eds.), *Evidence-based psychotherapies for children and adolescents* (pp. 187–203). New York: Guilford.

Anastopoulos, A. D., Guevremont, D. C., Shelton, T. L., & DuPaul, G. J. (1992). Parenting stress among families of children with Attention Deficit Hyperactivity Disorder. *Journal of Abnormal Child Psychology, 20*, 503–520.

Anastopoulos, A. D., Klinger, E. E., & Temple, E. P. (2001). Treating children and adolescents with Attention Deficit/Hyperactivity Disorder. In J. N. Hughes, A. M. La Greca, & J. C. Conoley (Eds.), *Handbook of psychological services for children and adolescents* (pp. 245–265). New York: Oxford University Press.

Anastopoulos, A. D., Klinger, E. E., & Temple, E. P. (2015). The key components of a comprehensive assessment of ADHD. Retrieved from http://www.chadd.org/Understanding-ADHD/Parents-Caregivers-of-Children-with-ADHD/Evaluation-and-Treatment/Comprehensive-Assessment-of-ADHD-in-Children.aspx

Anda, R. F., Felitti, V. J., Bremner, J. D., Walker, J. D., Whitfield, C., Perry, B. D., et al. (2006). The enduring effects of abuse and related adverse experiences in childhood: A convergence of evidence from neurobiology and epidemiology. *European Archives of Psychiatry and Clinical Neuroscience, 256*(3), 174–186.

Anderson, C. A., Berkowitz, L., Donnerstein, E., Huesmann, L. R., Johnson, J., Linz, D., et al. (2003). The influence of media violence on youth. *Psychological Science in the Public Interest, 4,* 81–110.

Anglin, J. (2002). *Pain, normality, and the struggle for congruence.* New York: Haworth Press.

Antony, M. M., & Barlow, D. H. (Eds.). (2002). *Handbook of assessment and treatment planning for psychological disorders.* New York: Guilford.

Anxiety. (2007). Retrieved from http://www.holisticonline.com/Remedies/Anxiety/anx_exercise.htm

Anxiety and depression in children and youth: Diagnosis and treatment. (2010, January). B.C. Guidelines. Copyright © 2010 by Province of British Columbia. All rights reserved. Reproduced with permission of the Province of British Columbia. Retrieved from http://www.guideline.gov/content.aspx?id=38904

Anxiety: Risk and protective factors. (n.d). National Assembly on School Based Health Care. Retrieved from http://ww2.nasbhc.org/RoadMap/Public/MH_list_risk_factors.pdf

Apopolinario, J. C., Bacaltchuk, J., Sichieri, R., Claudino, A. M., Godoy-Matos, A., Morgan, C., et al. (2003). A randomized, double-blind, placebo-controlled study of sibutramine in the treatment of Binge-Eating Disorder. *Archives of General Psychiatry, 60,* 1109–1116.

Apter, A., Bernhout, E., & Tyano, S. (1984). Severe Obsessive Compulsive Disorder in adolescence: A report of cases. *Journal of Adolescence, 7*(4), 349–358.

Archer, J. (1991). The influence of testosterone on human aggression. *British Journal of Psychology, 82,* 1–28.

Areas of care: Youth. (n.d.). The Royal. Retrieved from http://www.theroyal.ca/mental-health-centre/mental-health-programs/areas-of-care/youth

Are too many kids taking antipsychotic drugs? (2013, December). *Consumer Reports.* Retrieved from http://www.consumerreports.org/cro/2013/12/are-too-many-kids-taking-antipsychotic-drugs/index.htm

Arehart-Treichel, J. (2014). Prevalence rates of autism continues steady rise. *Psychiatric News, 49*(9), 1. Retrieved from http://psychnews.psychiatryonline.org/doi/full/10.1176%2Fappi.pn.2013.1b11

Arnold, L. E., Elliott, M., Sachs, L., Bird, H., Kraemer, H., Wells, K. C., et al. (2003). Effects of ethnicity on treatment attendance, stimulant response, dose, and 14-month outcome in ADHD. *Journal of Consulting and Clinical Psychology, 71,* 713–727.

Arnold, S. E. (2000). Cellular and molecular neuropathology of the parahippocampal region in Schizophrenia. *Annals of the New York Academy of Sciences, 911*(4), 275–292.

Artz, S. (2000). *When G. I. Joe meets Barbie: Youth violence in the twenty-first century.* Conference Presentation, School of Child and Youth Care, University of Victoria.

Artz, S., Nicholson, D., Helsall, E., Larke, S., & Boya, S. (2004). Need and risk and how to tell the difference. *Journal of Child and Youth Care Work, 19,* 109–117.

Asperger syndrome. (2015). Retrieved from http://www.autism-society.org/about-autism/aspergers-syndrome

Assessment of complex trauma. (n.d.). Retrieved from http://www.nctsn.org/trauma-types/complex-trauma/assessment

Attwood, T. (1999). *Asperger's syndrome: A guide for parents and professionals.* London Jessica Kingsley.

Austin, V. L., & Sciarra, D. T. (2010). *Children and adolescents with emotional and behavioral disorders.* Boston: Merrill. Merrill, NJ: Pearson (2010).

Autism Canada Foundation. (2011). Screening tools. Retrieved from http://www.autismcanada.org/aboutautism/screeningtools.html

Autism: Making sense of a confusing world. (2009). Retrieved from http://www.cbc.ca/news/technology/autism-making-sense-of-a-confusing-world-1.785671

Bailey, R. C., & Baillie, A. J. (2012). The relationship between placebo alcohol and affect: Motives for drinking. *Drug and Alcohol Review, 32*(2). doi:10.1111/j.1465-3362.2012.00500.x

Baker, S. L. (2010). Mental illness breakthrough: Fish oil prevents psychotic disorders. Retrieved from http://www.naturalnews.com/028193_fish_oils_mental_illness

Bandura, A., Ross, D., & Ross, S. A. (1961). Transmission of aggression through imitation of aggressive models. *Journal of Abnormal and Social Psychology, 63,* 575–582.

Barfield, S., Gaskill, R., Dobson, C., & Perry, B. D. (2011). Neurosequential Model of Therapeutics© in a therapeutic preschool: Implications for work with children with complex neuropsychiatric problems. *International Journal of Play Therapy Online First Publication,* October 31, 2011. doi:10.1037/a0025955

Barkley, R. A. (1988). *Attention-Deficit Hyperactivity Disorder: A handbook for diagnosis and treatment.* New York: Guilford.

Barkley, R. A. (2003). Attention Deficit/Hyperactivity Disorder. In E. Mash & R. Barkley (Eds.), *Child psychopathology* (pp. 75–143). New York: Guilford.

Barkley, R. A. (2006). *Attention Deficit Hyperactivity Disorder: A handbook for diagnosis and treatment* (3rd ed.). New York: Guilford.

Barkley, R. A. (2008). Classroom accommodations for children with ADHD. Retrieved from http://www.russellbarkley.org/factsheets/ADHD_School_Accommodations.pdf

Barkley, R. A. (2013). *Oppositional Defiant Disorder: The Four Factor Model for assessment and management.* Retrieved from http://www.continuingedcourses.net/active/courses/course079.phpt

Barlow, D. H. (2000). Unraveling the mysteries of anxiety and its disorders from the perspective of emotion theory. *American Psychologist, 55,* 1247–1263.

Barlow, D. H., & Durand, V. M. (2005). *Abnormal psychology: An integrative approach.* Belmont, CA: Thomson Wadsworth. Copyright © by Cengage Learning. Used by permission of Cengage Learning via CCC.

Baron-Cohen, S., Leslie, A. M., & Frith, U. (1985). Does the autistic child have a "theory of mind"? *Cognition, 21,* 37–46.

Barrett, P., Healy-Farrell, L., & March, J. S. (2004). Cognitive behavioral family treatment of childhood Obsessive-Compulsive Disorder: A controlled trial. *Journal of the American Academy of Child and Adolescent Psychiatry, 43,* 46–62.

Barrett, P., & Shortt, A. (2003). Parental involvement in the treatment of anxious children. In A. Kazdin & J. Weisz (Eds.), *Evidence-based psychotherapies for children and adolescents* (pp. 101–119). New York: Guilford.

Barrett, P. M., Dadds, M. R., & Rapee, R. M. (1996). Family treatment of childhood anxiety: A controlled trial. *Journal of Consulting and Clinical Psychology, 64,* 333–342.

Barrios, B. A., & Hartmann, D. P. (1997). Fears and anxieties. In E. J. Mash & L. G. Terdal (Eds.), *Behavioral assessment of childhood disorders* (3rd ed., pp. 230–327). New York: Guilford Press.

Barth, F. D. (2008). Hidden eating disorders: Attachment and affect regulation in the therapeutic relationship. *Clinical Social Work Journal, 36,* 355–365.

Barth, J. M., Dunlap, S. T., Dane, H., Lochman, J. E., & Wells, K. C. (2004). Classroom environment influences on aggression, peer relations, and academic focus. *Journal of School Psychology, 42,* 115–133.

Bates, J. E., Bayles, K., Bennett, D. S., Ridge, B., & Brown, M. M. (1991). Origins of externalizing behavior problems at eight years of age. In D. J. Pepler & K. H. Rubin (Eds.), *The development and treatment of childhood aggression.* Hillsdale, NJ: Erlbaum.

Bath, H. (2008). The three pillars of trauma-informed care. *Reclaiming Children and Youth, 17*(3), 17–21.

Baughman, F. (2006). *The ADHD fraud: How psychiatry makes "patients" of normal children.* Oxford: Trafford, © 2006.

Baxter, M. G., Parker, A., Lindner, C. C., Izquierdo, A. D., & Murray, E. A. (2000). Control of response selection by reinforcer value requires interaction of amygdala and orbital prefrontal cortex. *Journal of Neuroscience, 20,* 4311–4319.

Baydala, L., Sherman, J., Rasmussen, C., Wikman, E., & Janzen, H. (2006). ADHD characteristics in Canadian Aboriginal children. *Journal of Attention Disorders, 9*(4), 642–647.

B.C. Early Psychosis Intervention Program. (2015). Who gets psychosis? Retrieved from http://www.earlypsychosis.ca/pages/curious/who-gets-psychosis

B.C. Ministry of Health. (2010a). Clinical practice guidelines for the BC eating disorders continuum of services. Retrieved from http://www.bcmhsus.ca/global-resources

B.C. Ministry of Health. (2010b). Standards and guidelines for early psychosis intervention programs (EPI). Retrieved from http://www.health.gov.bc.ca/library/publications/year/2010/BC_EPI_Standards_Guidelines.pdf

Bearman, P., & Moody, J. (2004). Suicide and friendships among American adolescents. *American Journal of Public Health, 94,* 89–95.

Beaver, K. M., Wright, J. P., Delisi, M., Daigle, L. E., Swatt, M. L., & Gibson, C. L. (2007). Evidence of a gene x environment interaction in the creation of victimization: Results from a longitudinal sample of adolescents. *International Journal of Offender Therapy and Comparative Criminology, 51*(6), 620–645.

Beck, A. T. (1967). *Depression: Clinical, experimental, and theoretical aspects.* New York: Hoeber.

Beck, A. T. (1976). *Cognitive therapy and the emotional disorders.* New York: International Universities Press.

Beck, A. T. (1979). *Beck Scale for Suicide Ideation (BSI).* Retrieved from http://www.med.upenn.edu/suicide/beck/scales.html

Beck, A. T. (1983). Cognitive therapy of depression: New perspectives. In P. J. Clayton & J. E. Barrett (Eds.), *Treatment of depression: Old controversies and new approaches* (pp. 265–290). New York: Raven Press.

Beck, A. T., Emery, G., & Greenberg, R. L. (1985). *Anxiety disorders and phobias: A cognitive perspective.* New York: Basic Books.

Beck, A. T., & Weishaar, M. E. (2005). Cognitive therapy. In R. J. Corsini & D. Wedding (Eds.), *Current psychotherapies* (pp. 238–268). Belmont, CA: Brooks/Cole Thomson Learning.

Becker, A. E., Burwell, R. A., Gilman, S. E., Herzog, D. E., & Hamburg, P. (2002). Eating behaviors and attitudes following prolonged exposure to television among ethnic Fidjian adolescent girls. *British Journal of Psychiatry, 180,* 509–514.

Beesdo, K., Knappe, S., & Pine, D. S. (2009). Anxiety and anxiety disorders in children and adolescents: Developmental issues and implications for DSM-V. *Psychiatric Clinics of North America, 32,* 483–524.

Behavior support strategies. (2006). Teach ADHD. Retrieved from http://www.teachadhd.ca/teaching-children-with-adhd/Pages/Behavior-Support-Strategies.aspx

Bellefeuille, G., & Jamieson, D. (2008). Relational-centred planning: A turn toward creative potential and possibilities. In G. Bellefeuille & F. Ricks (Eds.), *Standing on the precipice: Inquiry into the creative potential of child and youth care practice* (pp. 35–72). Edmonton: MacEwan Press.

Bellefeuille, G., & Ricks, F. (Eds.). (2008). *Standing on the precipice: Inquiry into the creative potential of child and youth care practice.* Edmonton: MacEwan Press.

Bennett, L. A., Campillo, C., Chandrashekar, C. R., & Gureje, O. (1998). Alcohol beverage consumption in India, Mexico, and Nigeria: A cross-cultural comparison. *Alcohol Health and Research World, 22*(4), 243–252.

Bentley, S. (2005, March/April). A short history of PTSD: From Thermopylae to Hue, soldiers have always had a disturbing reaction to war. *The VVA Veteran.* Copyright © by Vietnam Veterans Of America. Retrieved from http://www.vva.org/archive/TheVeteran/2005_03/feature_HistoryPTSD.htm

Bergen, A. W., van den Bree, M. B., Yeager, M., Welch, R., Ganjei, J. K., Haque, K., . . . Kaye, W. H. (2003). Candidate genes for Anorexia Nervosa in the 1p33–36 linkage region: Serotonin 1D and delta opioid receptor loci exhibit significant association to Anorexia Nervosa. *Molecular Psychiatry, 8,* 397–406.

Berkowitz, S. J., Smith Stover, C., & Marans, S. R. (2011). The child and family traumatic stress intervention: Secondary prevention for youth at risk of developing PTSD. *Journal of Child Psychology and Psychiatry, 52*(6), 676–685.

Bernstein, G. A. (2010). Advances in child and adolescent anxiety disorder research. Retrieved from http://aacap.org/cs/root/development/advances_in_child_and_adolescent_anxiety_disorder_research

Bernstein, G. A., Borchardt, C. M., & Perwien, A. R. (1996). Anxiety disorders in children and adolescents: A review of the past 10 years. *Journal of the American Academy of Child and Adolescent Psychiatry, 35,* 1110–1119.

Bewell, C. V., & Carter, J. C. (2008). Readiness to change mediates the impact of eating disorder symptomatology on treatment outcome in Anorexia Nervosa. *International Journal of Eating Disorders, 41,* 368–371.

Biederman, J. (2005). Attention-Deficit/Hyperactivity Disorder: A selective overview. *Biological Psychiatry, 57,* 1215–1220.

Biederman, J., & Faraone, S. V. (2005). Attention-Deficit Hyperactivity Disorder. *Lancet, 366,* 237–248.

Biederman, J., Rosenbaum, J. F., Bolduc-Murphy, E. A., Faraone, S. V., Chaloff, J., Hirshfeld, D. R., & Kagan, J. (1993). A 3-year follow-up of children with and without behavioral inhibition. *Journal of the American Academy of Child and Adolescent Psychiatry, 32,* 814–821.

Binford, R. B., & le Grange, D. (2005). Adolescents with Bulimia Nervosa and eating disorder not otherwise specified–purging only. *International Journal of Eating Disorders, 38*(2), 157–161.

Binford, R. B., Mussell, M. P., Rogers, L., Johnson-Lind, J. L., & Miller, K. B. (2003). Eating disorders: Prevention and intervention strategies with children and adolescents. In P. Allen-Meares & M. W. Fraser (Eds.), *Intervention with children and adolescents: An interdisciplinary perspective.* Boston, MA: Allyn & Bacon.

A biopsychosocial model of addiction. (2013). Addictions Foundation of Manitoba. Retrieved from http://www.afm.mb.ca/wp-content/uploads/2013/03/BPS-FINAL.pdf

Bird, H. R., Davies, M., Duarte, C. S., Shen, S., Loeber, R., & Canino, G. J. (2006). A study of disruptive behavior disorders in Puerto Rican youth: II. Baseline prevalence, comorbidity, and correlates in two sites. *Journal of American Academic Child and Adolescent Psychiatry, 45*(9), 1042–1053.

Birmaher, B., & Brent, D. A. (2003). Antidepressants: II. Tricyclic agents. In A. Martin, L. Scahill, D. S. Chaney, & J. F. Leckman (Eds.), *Pediatric psychopharmacology: Principles and practice* (pp. 466–483). New York: Oxford University Press.

Birmaher, B., Ryan, N. D., Williamson, D. E., Brent, D. A., Kaufman, J., Dahl, R. E., Perel, J., & Nelson, B. (1996). Childhood and adolescent depression: A review of the past 10 years: Part I. *Journal of the American Academy of Child and Adolescent Psychiatry, 35,* 1427–1439.

Blagys, M. D., & Hilsenroth, M. J. (2002). Distinctive activities of cognitive-behavioral therapy: A review of the comparative psychotherapy process literature. *Clinical Psychology Review, 22,* 671–706.

Bloomquist, M. L. (2006). *Skills training for children with behavior problems.* New York: Guilford.

Bloomquist, M. L., & Schnell, S. V. (2002). *Helping children with aggression and conduct problems.* New York: Guilford.

Boesky, L. (2002). *Juvenile offenders with mental health disorders: Who are they and what do we do with them?* Lanham, MD: American Correctional Association.

Bögels, S. M., & Brechman-Toussaint, M. L. (2006). Family issues in child anxiety: Attachment, family functioning, parental rearing and beliefs. *Clinical Psychology Review, 26,* 834–856.

Boileau, I., Dagher, A., Leyton, M., Gunn, R. N., Baker, G. B., Diksic, M., & Benkelfat, C. (2006). Modeling sensitization to stimulants in humans: An [11C] raclopride/PET study in healthy volunteers. *Archives of General Psychiatry, 63,* 1386–1395.

Bombay, A., Matheson, K., & Anisman, H. (2009). Intergenerational trauma: Convergence of multiple processes among First Nations peoples in Canada. *Journal of Aboriginal Health, 5*(3), 6–46. Retrieved from http://www.naho.ca/jah/english/jah05_03/V5_I3_Intergenerational_01.pdf

Bond, L., Toumbourou, J. W., Thomas, L., Catalano, R. F., & Patton, G. (2005). Individual, family, school, and community risk and protective factors for depressive symptoms in adolescents: A comparison of risk profiles for substance use and depressive symptoms. *Prevention Science, 6*(2), 73–88.

Boney-McCoy, S., & Finkelhor, D. (1995). Psychological sequelae of violent victimization in a national youth sample. *Journal of Consulting and Clinical Psychology, 70,* 726–736.

Bostic, J. Q., Prince, J., Frazier, J., DeJong, S., & Wilens, T. E. (2003). Pediatric psychopharmacology update. *Psychiatric Times, 20,* 9.

Bouchard, L. L. (2004). An instrument for the measure of Dabrowskian overexcitabilities to identify gifted elementary students. *The Gifted Child Quarterly, 48*(4), 339–349. Retrieved from http://dx.doi.org/10.1177/001698620404800407

Boulware, C. (2006). What is EMDR? Retrieved from http://www.psychotherapist.net/emdr.html

Bowlby, J. (1969). *Attachment and loss, Vol. 1: Attachment.* New York: Basic Books.

Boyd-Webb, N. (2006). *Working with traumatized youth in child welfare.* New York: Guilford.

Brady, A. M., McCallum, S. E., Glick, S. D., & O'Donnell, P. (2008). Enhanced methamphetamine self-administration in a neurodevelopmental rat model of Schizophrenia. *Psychopharmacology (Berlin), 200,* 205–215.

Braff, D., Schork, N. J., & Gottesman, I. I. (2007). Endophenotyping Schizophrenia. *American Journal of Psychiatry, 164,* 705–707.

Brault, M. (2012). Prevalence of prescribed Attention-Deficit Hyperactivity Disorder medications and diagnosis among Canadian preschoolers and school-age children: 1994–2007. *Canadian Journal of Psychiatry, 57*(2), 93–101.

Brave Heart, M. Y. H. (2005). From intergenerational trauma to intergenerational healing. A keynote talk by Dr. Maria Yellow Horse Brave Heart (Hunkpapa Oglala-Lakota) given at the Fifth Annual White Bison Wellbriety Conference in Denver, Colorado. Retrieved from https://www.whitebison.org/magazine/2005/volume6/wellbriety!vol6no6.pdf

Breggin, P. R., & Cohen, D. (1999). *Your drug may be your problem: How and why to stop taking psychiatric drugs.* Reading, MA: Perseus Books.

Bremner, J. D. (2005). Effects of traumatic stress on brain structure and function: Relevance to early responses to trauma. *Journal of Trauma and Dissociation, 6*(2), 51–68.

Brendtro, L. (1988). Problems as opportunity: Developing positive theories about troubled youth. *Journal of Child and Youth Care, 3*(6), 15–24. Published by CYC-NET Journals, © 1988.

Brendtro, L. K. (2006). The vision of Urie Bronfenbrenner: Adults who are crazy about kids. *Reclaiming Children and Youth, 15*(3), 162–166. Retrieved from http://www.cyc-net.org/cyc-online/cyconline-nov2010-brendtro.html

Brendtro, L. (2010). The vision of Urie Bronfenbrenner: Adults who are crazy about kids. *Cyc-on-line, 141.* Retrieved from http://www.cyc-net

Brendtro, L. L., Brokenleg, M., & Van Bockern, S. (2002). *Reclaiming youth at risk: Our hope for the future* (2nd ed.). Bloomington, IN: National Education Service.

Brendtro, L. L., Brokenleg, M., & Van Bockern, S. (2005). The circle of courage and positive psychology. [Editorial]. *Reclaiming children and youth. 14*(3), 130–137. Retrieved from http://www.cyc-net.org/journals/rcy-14-3html#ed

Brendtro, L., & Shabazian, M. (2004). *Troubled children and youth: Turning problems into opportunities.* Champaign, IL: Research Press, © 2004.

Brenner, I. (2001). *Dissociation of Trauma: Theory, Phenomenology, and Technique.* Madison, CT: International Universities Press.

Brent, D. A., Greenhill, L. L., Compton, S., Emslie, G., Wells, K., Walkup, J. T., . . . Turner, J. B. (2009). The Treatment of Adolescent Suicide Attempters Study (TASA): Predictors of suicidal events in an open treatment trial. *Journal of the American Academy* of Child and Adolescent Psychiatry, 48(10), 987–996. doi: 10.1097/CHI.0b013e3181b5dbe4

Brent, D. A., & Mann, J. J. (2005). Family genetic studies, suicide, and suicidal behavior. American Journal of Medical Genetics, Part C: Seminars in Medical Genetics, 133C, 13–24.

Breslau, N., Davis, G. C., Andreski, P., & Peterson, E. (1991). Traumatic events and Posttraumatic Stress Disorder in an urban population of young adults. Archives of General Psychiatry, 48, 216–222.

Brewin, C. R., Andrews, B., & Valentine, J. D. (2000). Meta-analysis of risk factors for Posttraumatic Stress Disorder in trauma-exposed adults. Journal of Consulting and Clinical Psychology, 68, 748–766.

Bridge, J. A., Goldstein, T. R., & Brent, D. A. (2006). Adolescent suicide and suicidal behavior. Journal of Child Psychology and Psychiatry, 47, 372–394.

Bridge, J. A., Iyengar, S., Salary, C. B., Barbe, R. P., Birmaher, B., Pincus, H. A., . . . Brent, D. A. (2007). Clinical response and risk for reported suicidal ideation and suicide attempts in pediatric antidepressant treatment: A meta-analysis of randomized controlled trials. Journal of the American Medical Association, 297(15), 1683–1696.

Brief Mental Status Exam (MSE) Form. (n.d.). Retrieved from http://www.ehcounseling.com/materials/brief_mental_status_exam.pdf

Brinkmeyer, M., & Eyberg, S. M. (2003). Parent–child interaction therapy for oppositional children. In A. E. Kazdin & J. R. Weisz (Eds.), Evidence-based psychotherapies for children and adolescents (pp. 204–223). New York: Guilford.

British Columbia. Provincial Health Officer. (2008). An ounce of prevention revisited: A review of health promotion and selected outcomes for children and youth in BC schools. Provincial Health Officer's Annual Report 2006. Victoria, BC: Ministry of Health. Retrieved from http://www.health.gov.bc.ca/pho/pdf/phoannual2006.pdf

Brown, A. S., Begg, M. D., Gravenstein, S., Schaefer, C. A., Wyatt, R. J., et al. (2004). Serologic evidence of prenatal influenza in the etiology of Schizophrenia. Archives of General Psychiatry, 61, 774–780.

Brown, G. K., Have, T. T., Henriques, G. R., Xie, S. X., Hollander, J. E., & Beck, A. T. (2005). Cognitive therapy for the prevention of suicide attempts: A randomized controlled trial. Journal of the American Medical Association, 294, 563–570.

Brown, J. D. (1993). Self-esteem and self-evaluation: Feeling is believing. In J. Suls (Ed.), Psychological perspectives on the self (Vol. 4, pp. 27–58). Hillsdale, NJ: Erlbaum.

Brown, K. M. O., Bujac, S. R., Mann, E. T., Campbell, D. A., Stubbins, M. J., & Blundell, J. E. (2007). Further evidence of association of OPRD1 & HTR1D polymorphisms with susceptibility to Anorexia Nervosa. Biological Psychiatry, 61(3), 367–373.

Brown, T. E. (2005). 10 myths and facts about Attention Deficit Disorder. Attention Deficit Disorder: The Unfocused Mind in Children and Adults. New Haven, CT: Copyright © 2005 by Yale University Press. Used by permission of Yale University Press. Retrieved from http://www.drthomasebrown.com/pdfs/myths_and_facts.pdf

Brownley, K. A., Berkman, N. D., & Seway, J. A. (2007). Binge Eating Disorder treatment: A systematic review of randomized controlled trials. International Journal of Eating Disorders, 40, 337–348.

Bruch, H. (1962). Perceptual and conceptual disturbances in Anorexia Nervosa. Psychosomatic Medicine, 24, 187–194.

Bruch, H. (1973). Eating disorders. New York: Basic Books.

Bruch, H. (1974). Eating disorders: Obesity, Anorexia, and the person within. New York: Basic Books.

Bruffaerts, R., Demyttenaere, K., Borges, G., Haro, J. M., Chiu, W. T., Hwang, I., . . . Nock, M. K. (2010). Childhood adversities as risk factors for onset and persistence of suicidal behavior. British Journal of Psychiatry, 197(1), 20–27.

Bruffaerts, R., Demyttenaere, K., Hwang, I., Chiu, W. T., Sampson, N., Kessler, R. C., . . . de Graaf, R. (2011). Treatment of suicidal people around the world. British Journal of Psychiatry, 199, 64–70.

Bryant-Waugh, R., & Lask, B. (2002). Childhood-onset eating disorders. In C. G. Fairburn & K. D. Brownell (Eds.), Eating disorders and obesity: A comprehensive handbook (2nd ed., pp. 210–214). New York: Guilford.

Bryson, S. E., Rogers, S. J., & Fombonne, E. (2003). Autism spectrum disorders: Early detection, intervention, education, and psychopharmacological management. Canadian Journal of Psychiatry, 48(8), 506–516.

Building a better school environment for youth with mental health and addiction issues. (2013). Youth Action Committee. Children's Mental Health Ontario. © 2013 Children's Mental Health Ontario. Reprinted by permission of Youth Action Committee of Children's Mental Health Ontario. Retrieved from http://www.kidsmentalhealth.ca/documents/res-building-a-better-school-environment-for-youth-with-mental-health-and-addiction-issuesv2.pdf

Bulik, C., & Tozzi, F. (2004). Genetics in eating disorders: State of the science. CNS Spectrums, 9, 511–515.

Bulik, C. M., Devlin, B., Bacanu, S. A., Thornton, L., Klump, K. L., Fichter, M. M., . . . Kaye, W. H. (2003). Significant linkage on chromosome 10p in families with Bulimia Nervosa. American Journal of Human Genetics, 72, 200–207.

Bustillo, J. R., Lauriello, J., Horan, W. P., & Keith, S. J. (2001). The psychosocial treatment of Schizophrenia: An update. American Journal of Psychiatry, 158, 163–175.

Cahill, M. (1996). Handbook of diseases. Springhouse, PA: Springhouse Corporation, © 1996.

Canadian Attention Deficit Hyperactivity Disorder Resource Alliance (CADDRA). (2007). Canadian ADHD practice guidelines 2007–2008. Toronto: Author.

Canadian Cancer Society. (2015). Smoking rates in Canada. Retrieved from http://www.cancer.ca/en/cancer-information/cancer-101/what-is-a-risk-factor/tobacco/youth-andtobacco-use

Canadian Centre on Substance Abuse (CCSA). (2007). Substance abuse in Canada: Youth in focus. Ottawa: Author.

Canadian Mental Health Association. (n.d.). Lesbian, gay, bisexual and trans people and mental health. Retrieved from http://ontario.cmha.ca/mental-health/lesbian-gay-bisexual-trans-people-and-mental-health

Canadian Harm Reduction Network. (n.d.). What is harm reduction? Retrieved from http://canadianharmreduction.com

Canadian Institute for Health Information (CIHI). (2004). National Trauma Registry Analytic Bulletin: Hospitalizations Due to Suicide Attempts and Self-Inflicted Injury in Canada, 2001-2002. Toronto ON: CIHI.

Canadian Mental Health Association. (2010). CAMH suicide prevention and assessment handbook. Retrieved from http://www.mcf.gov.bc.ca/suicide_prevention/pdf/practice_guidelines.pdf

Canadian Mental Health Association. (2015). Suicide statistics. Retrieved from http://toronto.cmha.ca/mental_health/suicide-statistics

Canetti, L., Kanyas, K., Lerer, B., Latzer, Y., & Bachar, E. (2008). Anorexia Nervosa and parental bonding: The contribution of parent–grandparent relationships to eating disorder psychopathology. *Journal of Clinical Psychology, 64*, 703–716.

Canino, G., & Alegria, M. (2008). Psychiatric diagnosis: Is it universal or relative to culture? *Journal of Child Psychology and Psychiatry, 49*(3), 237–250.

Canino, G., Shrout, P. E., Rubio-Stipec, M., Bird, H. R., Bravo, M., Ramirez, R., . . . Martinez-Taboas, A. (2004). The DSM-IV rates of child and adolescent disorders in Puerto Rico: Prevalence, correlates, service use, and the effects of impairment. *Archives of General Psychiatry, 61*, 85–93.

Cannon, M., Walsh, E., Hollis, C., Maresc, K., Taylor, E., Murray, R., & Jones, P. (2001). Predictors of later Schizophrenia and affective psychoses among attendees at a child psychiatry department. *British Journal of Psychiatry, 178*, 420–426.

Capaldi, D., DeGarmo, D., Patterson, G. R., & Forgatch, M. (2002). Contextual risk across the early life span and association with antisocial behavior. In J. B. Reid, G. R. Patterson, & J. Snyder (Eds.), *Antisocial behavior in children and adolescents* (pp. 123–145). Washington, DC: American Psychological Association.

Capaldi, G. (n.d.). Triad of impairments. [Image File]. Retrieved from http://www.nawra.org.uk/Documents/Rotherham_Dec_08/Autism_Spectrum_Disorders_Gill_Capaldi.ppt

Cappadocia, M. C., Desrocher, M., Peplar, D., & Schroeder, J. H. (2009). Contextualizing the neurobiology of Conduct Disorder in an emotion dysregulation framework. *Clinical Psychology Review, 29*(6), 506–518. Copyright © 2009 by Elsevier Ltd. Used by permission of Elsevier Ltd. via Copyright Clearance Center.

Carey, B. (2006, March 21). Revisiting Schizophrenia: Are drugs always needed? *New York Times.* Retrieved from http://www.freedom-center.org/pdf/NYT3-21-06AreSchizophreniaDrugsAlwaysNeeded.pdf

Carlson, G. A. (1994). Adolescent Bipolar Disorder: Phenomenology and treatment implications. In W. M. Reynolds & H. F. Johnston (Eds.), *Handbook of depression in children and adolescents* (pp. 41–60). New York: Plenum.

Carr, A. (2004). Interventions for Post-Traumatic Stress Disorder in children and adolescents. *Pediatric Rehabilitation, 7*(4), 231–244.

Carvalho, J. P., & Hopko, D. R. (2011). Behavioral theory of depression: Reinforcement as a mediating variable between avoidance and depression. *Journal of Behavior Therapy and Experimental Psychiatry, 42*, 154–162.

Case study: Joe's story. (n.d.). Retrieved from http://www.boyanorexia.com/case-study-joes-story

Casey, B. J. (2001). Disruption of inhibitory control in developmental disorders: A mechanistic model of implicated frontostriatal circuitry. In J. L. McClelland & R. S. Siegler (Eds.), *Mechanisms of cognitive development: Behavioral and neural perspectives* (Vol. 14, pp. 327–349). Mahwah, NJ: Erlbaum.

Casey, L. M., Oei, T. P. S., & Newcombe, P. A. (2004). An integrated cognitive model of Panic Disorder: The role of positive and negative emotions. *Clinical Psychology Review, 24*, 529–555.

Caspi, A., Moffitt, T. E., Newman, D. I., & Silva, P. A. (1996). Behavioral observations at age 3 years predict adult psychiatric disorders. *Archives of General Psychiatry, 53*, 1033–1039.

Caspi, A., & Shiner, R. L. (2006). Personality development. In W. Damon & R. Lerner (Series Eds.) & N. Eisenberg (Vol. Ed.), *Handbook of child psychology: Vol. 3. Social, emotional, and personality development* (6th ed., pp. 300–365). New York: Wiley.

Castellanos, F. X. (2001). Neural substrates of Attention-Deficit Hyperactivity Disorder. *Advances in Neurology, 85*, 197–206.

Centers for Disease Control and Prevention. (2010). Fatal injury data. Retrieved from http://www.cdc.gov/injury/wisqars/fatal.html

Centers for Disease Control and Prevention. (2015a). Autism Spectrum Disorder: Signs and symptoms. Retrieved from http://www.cdc.gov/ncbddd/autism/signs.html

Centers for Disease Control and Prevention. (2015b). Suicide in children. Retrieved from http://www.cdc.gov/ncipc/wisqars

Centers for Disease Control and Prevention. (2015c). Suicide prevention. Retrieved from http://www.cdc.gov/violenceprevention/pub/youth_suicide.html

Centre for Addiction and Mental Health (CAMH). (2010). *Suicide prevention and assessment handbook.* Retrieved from http://www.mcf.gov.bc.ca/suicide_prevention/pdf/practice_guidelines.pdf

Cha, C. B., Najmi, S., Park, J. M., Finn, C. T., & Nock, M. K. (2010). Attentional bias toward suicide-related stimuli predicts suicidal behavior. *Journal of Abnormal Psychology, 119*(3), 616–622.

Chabrol, H., & Fouraste, R. (1996). Father–child hospitalization in a severe case of Separation Anxiety Disorder with panic attacks. *Clinical Psychology and Psychotherapy, 3*(4), 288–290. Copyright © 1996 by John Wiley & Sons, Inc. Used by permission of John Wiley & Sons, Inc. via Copyright Clearance Center (CCC).

Chansky, T. E., & Kendall, P. C. (1997). Social expectancies and self-perceptions in anxiety-disordered children. *Journal of Anxiety Disorders, 11*, 347–363.

Charach, A., Dashti, B., Carson, P., Booker, L., Lim, S. G., Lillie, E., . . . Schachar, R. (2011). Attention Deficit Hyperactivity Disorder: Effectiveness of treatment in at-risk preschoolers; long-term effectiveness in all ages; and variability in prevalence, diagnosis, and treatment. *Comparative Effectiveness Review, 44.* Retrieved from http://www.ncbi.nlm.nih.gov/pubmedhealth/PMH0054664

Chatterjee, I., & Basu, J. (2010). Perceived causes of suicide, reasons for living and suicidal ideation among students. *Journal of the Indian Academy of Applied Psychology, 36*(2), 311–316.

Cheng, M., & Boggett-Carsjens, J. (2005). Consider sensory processing disorders in the explosive child: Case report and review. *The Canadian Child and Adolescent Psychiatry Review, 14*(2), 44–48.

Chial, H. J., Camilleri, M., Williams, D. E., Litzinger, K., & Perrault, J. (2003). Rumination syndrome in children and adolescents: Diagnosis, treatment, and prognosis. *Pediatrics, 111*(1), 158–162.

Children's Mental Health Initiative (CMHI). (2012). Promoting recovery and resilience for children and youth involved in juvenile justice and child welfare systems. Retrieved from http://gucchdtacenter.georgetown.edu/resources/SAMHSA_ShortReport_2012.pdf

Children with Fetal Alcohol Spectrum Disorders (FASD) have more severe behavioral problems than children with Attention Deficit Hyperactivity Disorder (ADHD). (2009, July 20). *Science Daily.* Alcoholism: Clinical & Experimental Research, 33(10), pp: 1647–1846. Published by John Wiley & Sons, Inc. Retrieved from www.sciencedaily.com/releases/2009/07/090716164335.htm

Child Welfare Information Gateway. (2012). Trauma-focused cognitive behavioral therapy for children affected by sexual abuse or trauma. U.S. Department of Health and Human Services, Children's Bureau. Retrieved from https://www.childwelfare.gov/pubs/trauma

Chovil, N. (2009). Engaging families in child and youth mental health: A review of best, emerging, and promising practices. The F.O.R.C.E. Society for Kids' Mental Health. Retrieved from http://www.forcesociety.com/sites/default/files/Engaging%20

Families%20in%20Child%20%26%20Youth%20Mental%20
Health.pdf

Chua, S., & Murray, R. (1996). The neurodevelopmental theory of Schizophrenia: Evidence concerning structure and neuropsychology. *Annals of Medicine, 28*, 547–551.

Clark, A. (2001). Proposed treatment for adolescent psychosis: Schizophrenia and Schizophrenia-like psychoses. *Journal of Continuing Professional Development, 7*, 16–23.

Clark, D. A., Beck A. T., & Alford, B. A. (1999). *Scientific foundations of cognitive theory and therapy of depression.* New York: Wiley.

Clarke, I. (2009). Coping mechanisms: Strategies and outcomes: Coping with crisis and overwhelming affect: Employing coping mechanisms in the acute inpatient context. Unpublished paper.

Coelho, C. M., Waters, M. A., Hine, T. J., & Wallis, G. (2009). The use of virtual reality in acrophobia research and treatment. *Journal of Anxiety Disorders, 23*, 563–574.

Cohen, J. A. (1998). American Academy of Child and Adolescent Psychiatry, Work Group on Quality Issues: Practice parameters for the assessment and treatment of Posttraumatic Stress Disorder. *Journal of the American Academy of Child and Adolescent Psychiatry, 37*(Supp.), 4S–26S.

Cohen, J. A., Berliner, L., & Mannarino, A. (2010). Trauma focused CBT for children with co-occuring trauma and behavior problems. *Child Abuse and Neglect, 34*, 215–224.

Cohen, J. A., Mannarino, A. P., & Rogal, S. S. (2001). Treatment practices for childhood Posttraumatic Stress Disorder. *Child Abuse and Neglect, 25*, 123–136.

Cohen, P., Cohen, J., & Brook, J. S. (1993). An epidemiological study of disorders in late childhood and adolescence: II. Persistence of disorders. *Journal of Child Psychology and Psychiatry, 34*, 869–877.

Compas, B. E., Connor-Smith, J. K., Saltzman, H., Thomsen, A. H., & Wadsworth, M. E. (2001). Coping during childhood and adolescence: Problems, progress, and potential. *Psychological Bulletin, 127*, 87–127.

Compton, S. N., March, J. S., Brent, D., Albano, A. M., Weersing, V. R., & Curry, J. (2004). Cognitive-behavioral psychotherapy for anxiety and depressive disorders in children and adolescents: An evidence-based medicine review. *Journal of the American Academy of Child and Adolescent Psychiatry, 43*, 930–959.

Conduct Disorders: An overview. (n.d.). Retrieved from http://rcpsych.ac.uk/files/samplechapter/80_3.pdf

Conners, C. K., March, J. S., Frances, A., Wells, K. C., & Ross, R. (2001). Treatment of Attention Deficit Hyperactivity Disorder: Expert consensus guidelines. *Journal of Attention Disorders, 4*, 7–128.

Connor, D. F. (2002). Preschool Attention Deficit Hyperactivity Disorder: A review of prevalence, diagnosis, neurobiology, and stimulant treatment. *Journal of Developmental and Behavioral Pediatrics, 23*(1Supp), S1–S9.

Connor, D. F. (2007). Psychostimulants in Attention Deficit Hyperactivity Disorder: Theoretical and practical issues for the community practitioner. In D. Gozal & D. L. Molfese (Eds.), *Attention Deficit Hyperactivity Disorder: From genes to patients* (pp. 487–528). Totowa, NJ: Humana Press.

Connors, M. E. (2001). Integrative treatment of symptomatic disorders. *Psychoanalytic Psychology, 18*(1), 74–91.

Connor-Smith, J. K., & Compas, B. E. (2002). Vulnerability to social stress: Coping as a mediator or moderator of sociotropy and symptoms of anxiety and depression. *Cognitive Therapy and Research, 26*, 39–55.

Cook, A., Spinazzola, J., Ford, J., Lanktree, C., Blaustein, M., Cloitre, M., . . . van der Kolk, B. (2007). Complex trauma in children and adolescents. *Focal Point, Winter 2007 21*(1). Copyright © 2007 by Portland State University. Used by permission of Portland State University.

Cool Kids. (2015). California Evidence-Based Clearinghouse for Child Welfare. Retrieved from http://www.cebc4cw.org/program/cool-kids/detailed

Cooper, S.-A., & Smiley, E. (2012). Prevalence of intellectual disabilities and epidemiology of mental ill-health in adults with intellectual disabilities. In M. G. Gelder, N. C. Andreasen, J. J. Lopez-Ibor, & J. R. Geddes (Eds.), *New Oxford textbook of psychiatry* (2nd ed., Vol. 2, pp. 1825–1829). New York: Oxford University Press.

Cope, N., Eicher, J. D., Meng, H., Gibson, C. J., Hager, K., Lacadie, C., & Gruen, J. R. (2012). Variants in the DYX2 locus are associated with altered brain activation in reading-related brain regions in subjects with reading disability. *NeuroImage, 63*(1), 148–156.

Copeland, W. E., Keeler, G., Angold, A., & Costello, E. J. (2007). Traumatic events and posttraumatic stress in childhood. *Archives of General Psychiatry, 64*, 577–584.

Cortesi, F., Giannotti, F., Sebastiani, T., Vagnoni, C., & Marioni, P. (2008). Cosleeping versus solitary sleeping in children with bedtime problems: Child emotional problems and parental distress. *Behavioral Sleep Medicine, 6*, 89–105.

Costello, E. J., Mustillo, S., Erkanli, A., Keeler, G., & Angold, A. (2003). Prevalence and development of psychiatric disorders in childhood and adolescence. *Archives of General Psychiatry, 60*, 837–844.

Costello, J., & Angold, A. (1994). Bad behavior: A historical perspective on disorders of conduct. In R. Ketterlinus & M. Lamb (Eds.), *Adolescent problem behaviors: Issues and research* (pp. 1–31). Hillsdale, NJ: Lawrence Erlbaum Associates.

Côté, S. M., Boivin, M., Liu, X., Nagin, D. S., Zoccolillo, M., & Tremblay, R. E. (2009). Depression and anxiety symptoms: Onset, developmental course and risk factors during early childhood. *Journal of Child Psychology and Psychiatry, 50*(10), 1201–1208.

Cottrell, D. (2003). Outcome studies of family therapy in child and adolescent depression. *Journal of Family Therapy, 25*(4), 406–416.

Coyne, J. C. (1976). Toward an interactional description of depression. *Psychiatry, 39*, 28–40.

Craighead, W. E., Miklowitz, D. J., Frank, E., & Vajk, F. C. (2002). Psychosocial treatments for Bipolar Disorder. In P. E. Nathan & J. M. Gorman (Eds.), *A guide to treatments that work* (2nd ed., pp. 263–275). New York: Oxford University Press.

Craske, M. G. (2003). *Origins of phobias and anxiety disorders: Why more women than men?* Oxford: Elsevier.

Crisp, A. H. (1997). Anorexia Nervosa as a flight from growth: Assessment and treatment based on the model. In D. M. Garner & P. E. Garfinkel (Eds.), *Handbook for eating disorders* (pp. 248–277). New York: Guilford.

Crits-Christoph, P. (2002). Psychodynamic-interpersonal treatment of Generalized Anxiety Disorder. *Clinical Psychology: Science and Practice, 9*, 81–84. Published by American Psychological Association (APA), © 2002.

Crittenden, P. (2004). A dynamic-maturational model of attachment. *Australian and New Zealand Journal of Family Therapy, 27*(2), 105–115.

Crittenden, P. (2005). *Attachment theory, psychopathology, and psychotherapy: The dynamic-maturational approach* (Teoria dell'attaccamento, psicopatologia e psicoterapia: L'approccio dinamico maturativo). *Psicoterapia, 30*, 171–182. Published by Family Relations Institute, Inc. © 2005. Retrieved from http://www.iasa-dmm.org/index.php/about-attachment

Crittenden, P. (2006). A dynamic-maturational model of attachment. *Australian and New Zealand Journal of Family Therapy, 27*, 105–115.

Crittenden, P., & Kulbotten, G. R. (2007). Familial contributions to ADHD: An attachment perspective. *Tidsskrift for Norsk Psykologforening, 44*(10), 1220–1229.

Crowell, S. E., Beauchaine, T. P., McCauley, E., Smith, C. J., Vasilev, C. A., & Stevens, A. L. (2008). Parent–child interactions, peripheral serotonin, and self-inflicted injury in adolescents. *Journal of Consulting and Clinical Psychology, 76*, 15–21.

Crowther, J. H., Kichler, J. C, Sherwood, N. E., & Kuhnert, M. E. (2002). The role of familial factors in the etiology of Bulimia Nervosa. *Eating Disorders: The Journal of Treatment and Prevention, 10*, 141–151.

Csiernik, R. (2011). *Substance use and abuse: Everything matters.* Toronto: Canadian Scholars' Press.

Csiernik, R., & Rowe, W. S. (2010). *Responding to the oppression of addiction: Canadian social work perspectives* (2nd ed.). Toronto: Canadian Scholars' Press.

Culture and depression. (2008). Centre for Addiction and Mental Health. Retrieved from http://www.sciencedaily.com/releases/2008/07/080715071401.htm

Cummings, E. M., & Davies, P. T. (1994). Maternal depression and child development. *Journal of Child Psychology and Psychiatry, 35*, 73–112.

Curley, B. (2010). DSM-V: Major changes to addictive disease classifications. Retrieved from http://www.recoverytoday.net/articles/143-dsm-v-major-changes-to-addictive-disease-classifications

Currie, C. L., Wild, T. C., Schopflocher, D. P., Laing, L., Veugelers, P., & Parlee, B. (2012). Racial discrimination, post traumatic stress, and gambling problems among urban Aboriginal adults in Canada. *Journal of Gambling Studies, 29*(3). doi:10.1007/s10899-012-9323-z

Curry, D., Lawler, M. J., Schneider-Munoz, A. J., & Fox, L. (2011). A child and youth care approach to professional development and training. *Relational Child and Youth Care Practice, 24*(1–2), 1–25. Published by CYC-Net Journals, © 2011.

Curtis, N. M., Ronan, K. R., & Borduin, C. M. (2004). Multisystemic treatment: A meta-analysis of outcome studies. *Journal of Family Psychology, 18*, 411–419.

Dabbs, J. M., Frank, J., Bernieri, R. K., Strong, R., Campo, R., & Milun, R. (2001). Going on stage: Testosterone in greetings and meetings. *Journal of Research in Personality, 35*, 27–40.

Dadds, M. R. (2002). Learning and intimacy in the families of anxious children. In R. J. McMahon & R. D. Peters (Eds.), *The effects of parental dysfunction on children* (pp. 87–104). New York: Kluwer Academic/Plenum.

Davidson, R. J., Jackson, D. C., & Kalin, N. H. (2000). Emotion, plasticity, context and regulation: Perspectives from affective neuroscience. *Psychological Bulletin, 126*, 890–909.

Davila, J., Ramsay, M., Stroud, K. B., & Steinberg, S. J. (2005). Attachment. In B. Hankin & J. Abela (Eds.), *Development of psychopathology: A vulnerability-stress perspective* (pp. 215–242). Thousand Oaks, CA: Sage.

Davis, L. & Siegel, L. (2000). Posttraumatic Stress Disorder in children and adolescents: A review and analysis. *Clinical Child and Family Psychology Review, 3*(3), 135–154.

Davis, M. (2002). Neural circuitry of anxiety and stress disorders. In K. L. Davis, D. Charney, J. T. Coyle, & C. Nemeroff (Eds.), *Neuropsychopharmacology: The fifth generation of progress* (pp. 931–951). Philadelphia, PA: Lippincott Williams & Wilkins.

Deacon, B. J., & Abramowitz, J. S. (2004). Cognitive and behavioral treatments for anxiety disorders: A review of meta-analytic findings. *Journal of Clinical Psychology, 60*, 429–441.

Deas, D., & Thomas, S. E. (2001). An overview of controlled studies of adolescent substance abuse treatment. *American Journal of Addiction, 10*, 178–189.

De Bellis, M. D. (2001). Developmental traumatology: The psychobiological development of maltreated children and its implications for research, treatment, and policy. *Development and Psychopathology, 13*, 539–564.

De Bellis, M. D. (2005). The psychobiology of neglect. *Child Maltreatment, 10*, 150–172.

De Bellis, M. D., Lefter, L., Trickett, P. K., & Putnam, F. W. (1994). Urinary catecholamine excretion in sexually abused girls. *Journal of the American Academy of Child and Adolescent Psychiatry, 33*, 320–327.

Degnan, K. A., Henderson, H. A., Fox, N. A., & Rubin, K. H. (2008). Predicting social wariness in middle childhood: The moderating roles of childcare history, maternal personality and maternal behavior. *Social Development, 17*, 471–487. doi:10.1111/j.1467-9507.2007.00437.x

Delaney, R. (1998). *Fostering changes: Treating attachment-disordered foster children.* Oklahoma City, OK: Wood 'N' Barnes Publishing.

DeName, K. A. (2012). Neurofeedback therapy: An effective, non-drug treatment for ADHD. World of Psychology. Retrieved from http://psychcentral.com/blog/archives/2013/06/10/neurofeedback-therapy-an-effective-non-drug-treatment-for-adhd

De Panfilis, C., Rabbaglio, P., Rossi, C., Zita, G., & Maggini, C. (2003). Body image disturbance, parental bonding and alexithymia in patients with eating disorders. *Psychopathology, 36*, 239–246.

Depression. (2013). Canadian Mental Health Association. B.C. Division. Retrieved from http://www.cmha.bc.ca/get-informed/mental-health-information/depression

Depression and suicide. (2015). The Homeless Hub: Research Matters. Retrieved from http://www.homelesshub.ca/about-homelessness/mental-health/depression-and-suicide

Depression in children and adolescents: Treament considerations. (n.d.). Canadian Centre for Mood and Anxiety Treatments. Retrieved from http://www.canmat.org/cme-depression-depression-in-children-and-adolescents-treatment-considerations.php

Depression, suicide risk and autism. (2015). Retrieved from http://www.autism-help.org/family-suicide-depression-autism.htm

Desmeules, G. (2007). A sacred family circle: A family group conferencing model. Ch. 8 in I. Brown, F. Chaze, D. Fuchs, J. Lafrance, S. McKay, & S. Thomas Prokop (Eds.), *Putting a human face on child welfare: Voices from the prairie* (pp. 161–188). Prairie Child Welfare Consortium/Centre of Excellence for Child Welfare. Published by University of Regina Press, © 2007. Retrieved from http://www.cecw-cepb.ca/publications/1017

De Wilde, E. J., Kienhorst, C. W. M., & Diekstra, R. F. (2001). Suicidal behavior in adolescents. In I. M. Goodyer (Ed.), *The depressed child and adolescent* (pp. 267–291). Cambridge, UK: Cambridge University Press.

Dickson, R. A., Maki, E., Gibbins, C., Gutkin, S. W., Turgay, A., & Weiss, M. D. (2011). Time courses of improvement and symptom remission in children treated with atomoxetine for Attention-Deficit/Hyperactivity Disorder: Analysis of Canadian open-label studies. *Child and Adolescent Psychiatry Mental Health, 5*, 14.

DIR and the DIR Floortime approach. (2015). Retrieved from http://www.icdl.com/dir

Diseth, T. (2005). Dissociation in children and adolescents as reaction to trauma: An overview of conceptual issues and neurobiological factors. *Nordic Journal of Psychiatry, 59*, 79–91.

Dispelling the myths about Post-Traumatic Stress Disorder (PTSD). (n.d.). Defense Centers of Excellence for Psychological Health and Brain Injury. Retrieved from http://bhin.usmc-mccs.org/uploads/PTSD_Myths_and_Misconceptions_Factsheet.pdf

Disruptive Behavior Disorders. (2015). Behavioral Neurotherapy Clinic. Retrieved from http://www.adhd.com.au/conduct.htmnic

Dissociation FAQ's. (2014). International Society for the Study of Trauma and Dissociation. Retrieved from http://www.isst-d.org/?contentID=76

Dodes, L. M. (2002). *The heart of addiction: A new approach to understanding and managing alcoholism and other addictive behaviors.* New York: HarperCollins.

Dopheide, J. A. (2005). Therapeutic position statement on ADHD. American Society of Health System Pharmacists. *American Journal of Health-System Pharmacology, 62*, 2–18.

Dotterweich, J. (n.d). *Positive youth development resource manual.* Retrieved from https://ecommons.library.cornell.edu/bitstream/1813/21946/2/PYD_ResourceManual.pdf

Douzgou, S., Breen, C., Crow, Y. J., Chandler, K., Metcalfe, K., Jones, E., & Clayton-Smith, J. (2012). Diagnosing fetal alcohol syndrome: New insights from newer genetic technologies. *Archives of Disease in Childhood, 97*(9), 812–817.

Dozois, D. J. A., & Beck, A. T. (2008). Cognitive schemas, beliefs and assumptions. In K. S. Dobson & D. J. A. Dozois (Eds.), *Risk factors in depression* (pp. 121–143). New York: Academic Press.

Drevets, W. C. (2001). Neuroimaging and neuropathological studies of depression: Implications for the cognitive-emotional features of mood disorders. *Current Opinion in Neurobiology, 11*, 240–249.

Dubner, A. E., & Motta, R. W. (1999). Sexually and physically abused foster care children and Posttraumatic Stress Disorder. *American Psychological Association, 7*(3), 367–373.

Dumas, J. E. (2001). From unpublished manual by Dumas, J. E. (2001) cited in J. E. Dumas & W. J. Nilsen (2003), *Abnormal child and adolescent psychology* (p. 232). New York: Allyn & Bacon.

Dunn, D. W., & McDougle, C. J. (2001). *Childhood-onset Schizophrenia.* Philadelphia: Lippincott, Williams, & Wilkins.

Dunnachie, B. (2007). *Evidence-based age-appropriate interventions: A guide for Child and Adolescent Mental Health Services (CAMHS).* Auckland, New Zealand: The Werry Centre for Child and Adolescent Mental Health Workforce Development.

Duran, B., Malcoe, L. H., Sanders, M., Waitzkin, H., Skipper, B., & Yager, J. (2004). Child maltreatment prevalence and mental disorders outcomes among American Indian women in primary care. *Child Abuse and Neglect, 28*, 131–145.

Durkheim, E. (1897/1951). *Suicide.* New York: Free Press.

Durrant, M. (1993). *Residential treatment: A cooperative, competency-based approach to therapy and program design.* New York: W. W. Norton, © 1993.

Eaves, L. J., Silberg, J. L., & Maes, H. H. (2005). Revisiting the children of twins: Can they be used to resolve the environmental effects of dyadic parental treatment on child behavior? *Twin Research in Human Genetics, 8*, 283–290. doi:10.1375/twin.8.4.283

Edwards, G., & McGorry, P. D. (2002). *Implementing early intervention in psychosis: A guide to establishing early psychosis services.* London: Martin Dunitz.

Eggers, C., Bunk, D., & Krause, D. (2000). Schizophrenia with onset before the age of eleven: Clinical characteristics of onset and course. *Journal of Autism and Developmental Disorders, 30*, 29–38.

Ehrensaft, M. K., Cohen, P., Brown, J., Smailes, E., Chen, H., & Johnson, J. G. (2003). Intergenerational transmission of partner violence: A 20-year prospective study. *Journal of Consulting and Clinical Psychology, 71*, 741–753.

11 myths about autism. (2015). Retrieved from http://blog.autismspeaks.org/2011/11/21/11-myths-about-autism

Eley, T. C. (1999). Behavioral genetics as a tool for developmental psychology: Anxiety and depression in children and adolescents. *Clinical Child and Family Psychology Review, 2*, 21–36.

Eley, T. C., Bolton, D., O'Connor, T. G., Perrin, S., Smith, P., & Plomin, R. (2003). A twin study of anxiety-related behaviors in pre-school children. *Journal of Child Psychology and Psychiatry, 44*, 945–960.

Eley, T. C., & Gregory, A. M. (2004). Behavioral genetics. In T. L. Morris & J. S. March (Eds.), *Anxiety disorders in children and adolescents* (2nd ed., pp. 71–97). New York: Guilford.

Eley, T. C., Lichtenstein, P., & Moffitt, T. E. (2003). A longitudinal behavioral genetic analysis of the etiology of aggressive and non aggressive antisocial behavior. *Developmental Psychopathology, 15*, 383–402. doi:10.1017/S0954 57940300021X

Eley, T. C., & Stevenson, J. (2000). Specific life events and chronic experiences differentially associated with depression and anxiety in young twins. *Journal of Abnormal Child Psychology, 28*, 383–394.

Elimination disorders. (2015). *The encyclopedia of mental disorders.* Retrieved from http://www.minddisorders.com/Del-Fi/Elimination-disorders.html#ixzz3bihy5bk0

Elkovitch, N., Latzman, R. D., Hansen, D. J., & Flood, M. F. (2009). Understanding child sexual behavior problems: A developmental psychopathology framework. *Clinical Psychology Review, 29*(7), 586–598.

Ellis, A. (1962). *Reason and emotion in psychotherapy.* New York: Lyle Stuart.

Ellis, A., & Bernard, M. E. (2006). *Rational emotive behavioral approaches to childhood disorders: Theory, practice and research.* New York: Springer.

Ellis, A., & Harper, R. A. (1997). *A new guide to rational living* (3rd ed.). North Hollywood, CA: Wilshire.

Elsass, P. (2001). Individual and collective study of traumatic memories: A qualitative study of Post-Traumatic Stress Disorder symptoms in two Latin American countries. *Transcultural Psychiatry, 38*(3), 306–316.

Emerging psychosis in young people: New guidance launched. (2007). Retrieved from http://www.cyc-net.org/otherjournals/oj-november2007.html

Emslie, G. J., Rush, J. A., Weinberg, W. A., Kowatch, R. A., Hughes, C. W., Carmody, T., et al. (1997). A double-blind, randomized, placebo-controlled trial of fluoxetine in children and adolescents with depression. *Archives of General Psychiatry, 54*, 1031–1037.

Engelhard, I., van den Hout, M. A., & Kindt, M. (2003). The relationship between neuroticism, pre-traumatic stress, and post-traumatic stress. *Personality and Individual Differences, 35*, 381–388.

Epps, C., & Wright, E. L. (2012). The genetic basis of addiction. In C. Epps & E. L. Wright (Eds.), *Perioperative addiction* (pp. 35–50). New York: Springer.

Etkin, A., Prater, K. E., Schatzberg, A. F., Menon, V., & Greicius, M. D. (2009). Disrupted amygdalar subregion functional connectivity and evidence of a compensatory network in Generalized Anxiety Disorder. *Archives of General Psychiatry 66*, 1361–1372.

Ettinger, U., Chitnis, X., Kumari, V., Fannon, D. G., Sumich, A. L., O'Ceallaigh, S., . . . Sharma, T. (2001). Magnetic resonance imaging of the thalamus in first episode psychosis. *American Journal of Psychiatry, 158*, 116–118.

Evans, J. (2010). The challenge of treating Conduct Disorder in low-resourced settings: Rap music to the rescue. *Journal of Child and Adolescent Mental Health, 22*(2), 145–152. Published by Taylor & Francis, © 2010.

Evans, S. W., Pelham, W. E., & Grudberg, M. V. (1995). The efficacy of notetaking to improve behavior and comprehension with ADHD adolescents. *Exceptionality, 5*, 1–17.

Evans, S. W., Schultz, B. K., DeMars, C. E., & Davis, H. (2011). Effectiveness of the challenging horizons after-school program for young adolescents with ADHD. *Behavior Therapy, 42*, 462–474.

Evans, S. W., Timmins, B., Sibley, M., White, L. C., Serpell, Z., & Schultz, B. K. (2006). Developing coordinated multimodal school-based treatment for young adolescents with ADHD. *Education and Treatment of Children, 29*, 1–20.

The evidence: Family psychoeducation. (2009). Center for Mental Health Services Substance Abuse and Mental Health Services Administration. Retrieved from http://store.samhsa.gov/shin/content/SMA09-4423/TheEvidence-FP.pdf

Eyberg, S. M., Nelson, M. M., & Boggs, S. R. (2008). Evidence-based treatments for child and adolescent disruptive behavior. *Journal of Clinical Child and Adolescent Psychology, 37*, 213–235.

Fabiano, G. A, Chacko, A., Pelham, Jr., W. E., Robb, J., Walker, K. S., Wymbs, F., . . . Pirvics, L. (2009). A comparison of behavioral parent training programes for fathers of children with Attention-Deficit/Hyperactivity Disorder. *Behavior Therapy, 40*(2), 190–204.

Fairburn, C. G. (2008). *Cognitive behavior therapy and eating disorders.* New York: Guilford.

Fairburn, C. G., & Harrison, P. J. (2003). Eating disorders. *Lancet, 361*, 407–416.

Fairburn, C. G., Welch, S. L., Dol, H. A., Davies, B. A., & O'Connor, M. E. (1997). Risk factors for Bulimia Nervosa: A community-based case-control study. *Archives of General Psychiatry, 54*, 509–517.

Fallon, B., & Shlonsky, A. (2011). Risk, resilience and outcomes: Special Issue. *International Journal of Mental Health and Addiction, 9*(5), 435–440.

Farrell, L. J., & Barrett, P. M. (2007). Prevention of childhood emotional disorders: Reducing the burden of suffering associated with anxiety and depression. *Child and Adolescent Mental Health, 12*(2), 58–65.

Farrington, D. P. (1987). Epidemiology. In H. C. Quay (Ed.), *Handbook of juvenile delinquency* (pp. 33–61). New York: Wiley.

Fast facts about mental illness. (2015). Retrieved from http://www.cmha.ca/media/fast-facts-about-mental-illness

Feldstein, S., & Ginsburg, J. (2006). Motivational interviewing with dually diagnosed adolescents in juvenile justice. *Brief Treatment and Crisis Intervention, 6*(3), 218–233.

Feldstein, W. W., & Miller, W. R. (2006). Substance use and risk-taking among adolescents. *Journal of Mental Health, 15*(6), 633–643. Published by Routledge, © 2006.

Fellitti, V., Anda, R., Nirdenberg, D., Williamson, D., Spiitz, A., Edward V., Koss, M., & Marks, J. (1998). Relationship of childhood abuse and household dysfunction to many of the leading causes of death in adults. *The Adverse Childhood Experiences (ACE) Study, 14*(4), 245–258.

Feng, X., Shaw, D. S., & Silk, J. S. (2008). Developmental trajectories of anxiety symptoms among boys across early and middle childhood. *Journal of Abnormal Psychology, 117*, 32–47. doi:10.1037/0021-843X.117.1.32

Ferster, C. B. (1961). Positive reinforcement and behavioral deficits of autistic children. *Child Development, 32*, 437–456.

Fewster, G. (2002). The DSM IV you but not IV me. *Child and Youth Care Forum, 31*(6), 365–380.

Fewster, G. (2004). If you meet the pill fairy on the road, kill it. [Editorial]. *Relational Child and Youth Care Practice, 17*(1), 3–10.

Fewster, G. (2012). cyc-net Discussion. Retrieved from http://www.cyc-net.org/discussion

Fidler, J. A. (2015). Strengths and weaknesses of children with ADHD. Retrieved from http://everydaylife.globalpost.com/strengths-weaknesses-children-adhd-11411.html

Flament, M. F., & Cohen, D. (2000). Child and adolescent Obsessive-Compulsive Disorder: A review. In M. Maj, N. Sartorius, A. Okasha, & J. Zohar (Eds.), *Obsessive-Compulsive Disorder* (pp. 145–183). Chichester, UK: Wiley.

Fletcher, K. E. (2003). Childhood Posttraumatic Stress Disorder. In E. J. Mash & R. A. Barkley (Eds.), *Child psychopathology* (2nd ed., pp. 330–371). New York: Guilford.

Flick, G. (1998). *ADD/ADHD behavior-change resource kit: Ready-to-use strategies and activities for helping children with Attention Deficit Disorder.* San Francisco, CA: Jossey-Bass.

Flisher, A. J., Sorsdahl, K., Hatherill, S., & Chehil, S. (2010). Packages of care for Attention-Deficit Hyperactivity Disorder in low- and middle-income countries. *PLoS Med, 7*(2): e1000235. doi:10.1371/journal.pmed.1000235

Foa, E. B., & Kozak, M. J. (1986). Emotional processing of fear: Exposure to corrective information. *Psychological Bulletin, 99*, 20–35.

Foa, E. B., & Riggs, D. S. (1994). Posttraumatic Stress Disorder and rape. In R. S. Pynoos (Ed.), *Posttraumatic Stress Disorder: A clinical review* (pp. 133–163). Baltimore, MD: The Sidran Press.

Foa, E., Rothbaum, B., & Molnar, C. (1995). Cognitive-behavioral treatment of Post-Traumatic Stress Disorder. In M. Friedman, D. S. Charney, & A. Y. Deutch (Eds.), *Neurobiological and clinical consequences of stress: From normal adaptation to Post-Traumatic Stress Disorder* (pp. 483–494). New York: Raven Press.

Foltz, R. (2006). Balancing the Imbalance: Integrating a Strength-Based Approach with a Medical Model. *Reclaiming Children And Youth* 15(02). Copyright © 2006 by Reclaiming Children and Youth Journal. Used by permission of Reclaiming Children and Youth Journal.

Foltz, R. (2008a). Behind the veil of Conduct Disorder: Challenging current assumptions in search of strengths. *Reclaiming Children and Youth 16*(4), 5–9. © 2008.

Foltz, R. (2008b). Medicating relational trauma in youth. [Editorial]. *Reclaiming Children and Youth, 17*(3), 3–8.

Foltz, R. (2010a). Medicating our youth: Who determines rules of evidence? *Reclaimimg Children and Youth, 19*(2), 10–15. Used by permission of Reclaiming Children and Youth, © 2010.

Foltz, R. (2010b). Searching for strengths: Rethinking disorders. *Reclaiming Children and Youth, 18*(4), 26–28.

Fonagy, P., Target, M., Cottrell, D., Phillips, J., & Kurtz, Z. (2002). *What works for whom: A critical review of treatments for children and adolescents.* Published by Guilford Press, © 2002.

Fowles, D. C. (2001). Biological variables in psychopathology: A psychobiological perspective. In P. B. Sutker & H. E. Adams (Eds.),

Comprehensive handbook of psychopathology (3rd ed., pp. 85–104). New York: Kluwer/Plenum.

Fox, N. A., Henderson, H. A., Marshall, P. J., Nichols, K. E., & Ghera, M. M. (2005). Behavioral inhibition: Linking biology and behavior within a developmental framework. *Annual Review of Psychology, 56*, 235–262.

Fox, T. L., Barrett, P. M., & Shortt, A. L. (2002). Sibling relationships of anxious children: A preliminary investigation. *Journal of Clinical Child and Adolescent Psychology, 31*(3), 375–383. doi:10.1207/S15374424JCCP3103_09

Foxman, P. (2004). *The worried child: Recognizing anxiety in children and helping them heal.* Copyright © 2004 by Turner Publishing. Used by permission of Turner Publishing.

Foxman, P. (2010). Anxiety disorders in children and adolescents: Recognizing and treating the emerging epidemic; A presentation. Winnipeg, MB. Retrieved from http://jkseminars.com/handouts/F1107.pdf

Foxman, P. (2011). *The worried child: Recognizing anxiety in children and helping them heal.* Published by Turner Publishing, © 2011.

Frances, A. (2012). DSM5 in distress: The DSM's impact on mental health practice and research. *Psychology Today.* Used by permission. Retrieved from http://www.psychologytoday.com/blog/dsm5-in-distress/201212/dsm-5-is-guide-not-bible-ignore-its-ten-worst-changes

Frank, E. (2005). *Treating Bipolar Disorder: A clinician's guide to interpersonal and social rhythm therapy.* New York: Guilford.

Franklin, M. E., Edson, A. L., & Freeman, J. B. (2010). Behavior therapy for pediatric Trichotillomania: Exploring the effects of age on treatment outcome. *Child and Adolescent Psychiatry and Mental Health, 4*, 18.

Freud, A. (1965). *Normality and pathology in childhood: Assessments of development.* New York: International Universities Press.

Freud, S. (1913/1949). *Totem and taboo: Resemblances between the mental lives of savages and neurotics.* London: Beacon Press.

Freud, S. (1914/1949). Predisposition to obsessional neurosis. *Sigmund Freud, Collected Papers* (Vol. 2). Hogarth Press. (Original work published in 1914).

Freud, S. (1924). Neurosis and psychosis. Reprinted (1953–1974) in the *Standard Edition of the Complete Psychological Works of Sigmund Freud* (Vol. 19, p. 151). (J. Strachey, Ed. and Trans.). Hogarth Press.

Freud, S. (1933/1964). *New introductory lectures on psychoanalysis.* (J. Strachey, Ed. and Trans.). New York: Norton. (Original work published 1933).

Freud, S. (1946). *The ego and the mechanisms of defense* (American Ed.). New York: International Universities Press.

Frick, P. J. (2004). Developmental pathways to Conduct Disorder: Implications for serving youth who show severe aggressive and anti social behavior. *Psychology in the Schools, 41*(8), 823–834. Copyright © 2004 by John Wiley & Sons. Used by permission of John Wiley & Sons via CCC.

Frick, P. J., Cornell, A. H., Bodin, S. D., Dane, H. E., Barry, C. T. & Loney, B. R. (2003). Callous-unemotional traits and developmental pathways to severe Conduct Disorder. *Developmental Psychology, 39*, 246–260.

Frick, P. J., O'Brien, B. S., Wootton, J. M., & McBurnett, K. (1994). Psychopathy and conduct problems in children. *Journal of Abnormal Psychology, 103*, 700–707.

FRIENDS Program. (2012). Intervention summary. SAMHSA's National Registry of Evidence-Based Programs and Practices. Retrieved from http://www.nrepp.samhsa.gov/ViewIntervention.aspx?id=334

Fromm-Reichmann, F. (1948). Notes on the development of treatment of Schizophrenia by psychoanalytic psychotherapy. *Psychiatry, 11*, 263–273.

Fulcher, L. (2001). *Cultural safety: Lessons from Maori wisdom 10*(3). Copyright © 2001 by CYC-NET Journals. Used by permission of CYC-NET Journals. Retrieved from http://www.cyc-net.org/CYR101C/culturalsafety.htm

Fulton, H. G., Krank, M., & Stewart, S. H. (2012). Outcome expectancy liking: A self-generated, self-coded measure predicts adolescent substance use trajectories. *Psychology of Addictive Behaviors, 26*(4), 870–879.

Gagnon, E. (2001). Power Cards: Using Special Interests to Motivate Children and Youth with Asperger Syndrome and Autism. Published by Autism Asperger Publishing Company, © 2001.

Galambos, N. L., Barker, E. T., & Almeida, D. M. (2003). Parents do matter: Trajectories of change in externalizing and internalizing problems in early adolescence. *Child Development, 74*, 578–594.

Garbarino, J., & Kostelny, K. (1996). The effects of political violence on Palestinian children's behavior problems: A risk accumulation model. *Child Development, 67*, 33–45.

Garber, J., Keiley, M. K., & Martin, N. C. (2002). Developmental trajectories of adolescents' depressive symptoms: Predictors of change. *Journal of Consulting and Clinical Psychology, 70*, 79–95.

Garber, J., & Weersing, V. R. (2010). Comorbidity of anxiety and depression in youth: Implications for treatment and prevention. *Clinical Psychology: Science and Practice, 17*, 293–306.

Gardner, D. (2002). Understanding the links between adolescent trauma and substance abuse. The National Child Trauma Stess Network. *Skid Row High.* Published by The Ottawa Citizen, © 2002. Retrieved from http://www.nctsn.org/sites/default/files/assets/pdfs/satoolkit_providerguide.pdf

Gardner, J., & Wilkinson, P. (2011). Is family therapy the most effective treatment for Anorexia Nervosa? *Psychiatria Danubina, 23*(Suppl. 1), S175–S177.

Garfat, T. (1987). Remembering Fritz Redl. From a presentation at Today's Child—Tomorrow's Adult, National Conference of the National Association of Child Care Workers, Johannesburg, South Africa.

Garfat, T. (1998). The effective child and youth care intervention: A phenomenological inquiry. *Journal of Child and Youth Care, 12*(1–2), 1–168.

Garfat, T. (2003, March). Four parts magic: The anatomy of a child and youth care intervention. *The International Child and Youth Care Network, 50.*

Garfat, T., & Charles, G. (2010). *A guide to developing effective child and youth care practice with families.* Cape Town: Pretext. Copyright © by CYC-Net Journals. Used by permission of CYC-Net Journals.

Garfat, T., & McElwee, N. (2007). *Reflective relational practice in social care/child and youth care: An EirCan perspective.* Cape Town: Pretext.

Garland, J. E. (2001). Sleep disturbances in anxious children. In G. Stores & L. Wiggs (Eds.), *Sleep disturbance in children and adolescents with disorders of development: Its significance and management* (pp. 155–160). London: Mac Keith Press.

Garner, D., & Garfinkel, R. (Eds.). (1997). *Handbook of treatment for eating disorders* (2nd ed.). New York: Guilford.

Gelfand, D. M., & Drew, C. J. (2003). *Understanding child behavior disorders.* Belmont, CA: Thompson Wadsworth Learning, © 2003.

Gelhorn, H., Stallings, M., Young, S., Corley, R., Rhee, S. H., Christian, H., & Hewitt, J. (2006). Common and specific gene influences on aggressive and non aggressive Conduct Disorder domains. *Journal of the American Academy of Child and Adolescent Psychiatry, 45*, 570–577.

Geller, D. A., Biederman, J., Stewart, S. E., Mullin, B., Martin, A., Spencer, T., & Faraone, S. V. (2003). Which SSRI? A meta-analysis of pharmacotherapy trials in pediatric Obsessive Compulsive Disorder. *American Journal of Psychiatry, 160*, 1919–1928.

Generalized Anxiety Disorders. (n.d.). *Encyclopedia of mental disorders.* Retrieved from http://www.minddisorders.com/Flu-Inv/Generalized-anxiety-disorder.html

Generalized Anxiety Disorders. (2012). Centre for Addiction and Mental Health. Retrieved from http://www.camh.ca/en/hospital/health_information/a_z_mental_health_and_addiction_information/GeneralizedAnxietyDisorder/Pages/default.aspx

Generating and mobilizing knowledge: Matters of substance. [Blog]. (2015). Retrieved from http://www.ccsa.ca/2006%20CCSA%20Documents/ccsa-11340-2006.pdf

Gentle teaching. (2014). Retrieved from http://www.gentleteaching.nl/gentle/index.php/en

Gershon, E. S. (1990). Genetics. In F. K.Goodwin & K. R. Jamison (Eds.), *Manic-depressive illness* (pp. 373–401). New York: Oxford University Press.

Gharabaghi, K. (2010). Expansion to what end? *Online Journal of the International Child and Youth Care Network (CYC-Net), 139.* Retrieved from http://www.cyc-net.org/cyc-online/cyconline-sep2010-gharabaghi.html

Gibbs, J. C. (1991). Socio-moral developmental delay and cognitive distortion: Implications for the treatment of antisocial youth. In W. M. Kurtines & J. L. Gewirt (Eds.), *Handbook of moral behavior and development: Vol. 3. Application* (pp. 95–110). Hillsdale, NJ: Lawrence Erlbaum Associates.

Gibbs, J. C., Potter, C., & Goldstein, A. P. (1995). *The EQUIP Program: Teaching youth to think and act responsibly through a peer-helping approach.* Champaign, IL: Research Press.

Gilbert, P. (2010). *The compassionate mind: A new approach to life's challenges—compassion focused therapy.* London: Routledge.

Gillham, J. E., Reivich, K. J., Jaycox, L. H., & Seligman, M. E. P. (1995). Prevention of depressive symptoms in schoolchildren: Two-year follow-up. *Psychological Science, 6*, 343–351.

Girls and drugs: A new analysis: Recent trends, risk factors and consequences. (2006). Office of National Drug Control Policy Executive Office of the President. Washington, D.C. Retrieved from http://www.qdref.org/downloads/girls_and_drugs.pdf

Glancy, G., & Saini, M.A. (2005). An evidenced-based review of psychological treatments of anger and aggression. *Brief Treatment and Crisis Intervention, 5*, 229–248.

Glaser, D. (2000). Child abuse and neglect and the brain: A review. *Journal of Child Psychology and Psychiatry, 41*(1), 97–116.

Goddard, L., Dritschel, B., & Burton, A. (1996). Role of autobiographical memory in social problem solving and depression. *Journal of Abnormal Psychology, 105*, 609–616.

Goelitz, A. (2013). *From trauma to healing: A social worker's guide to working with survivors.* Published by Routledge, © 2013.

Goeree, R., Farahati, F., Burke, N., Blackhouse, G., O'Reilly, D., Pyne, J., & Tarride, J.-E. (2005). Economic burden of Schizophrenia in Canada in 2004. *Current Medical Research and Opinion, 21*(12), 2017–2028.

Goff, D., Brotman, A., Kindlon, D., Waites, M., & Amico, E. (1991). Self-reports of childhood abuse in chronically psychotic patients. *Psychiatry Research, 37*, 73–80.

Gogtay, N., Sporn, A., Clasen, L. S., Greenstein, D., Giedd, J. N., Lenane, M., Gochman, P. A., . . . Rapoport, J. L. (2003). Structural brain MRI abnormalities in healthy siblings of patients with childhood-onset Schizophrenia. *American Journal of Psychiatry, 160*(3), 569–571.

Goldstein, H. (2002). Communication intervention for children with autism: A review of treatment efficacy. *Journal of Autism and Developmental Disorders, 32*(5), 373–396.

Gonzalez, J. E., Nelson, J. R., Gutkin, T. B., Saunders, A., Galloway, A., & Shwery, C. S. (2004). Rational emotive therapy with children and adolescents: A meta-analysis. *Journal of Emotional and Behavioral Disorders, 12*, 222–235.

Gooding, D. C., & Iacono, W. G. (1995). Schizophrenia through the lens of a developmental psychopathology perspective. In D. Cicchetti & D. J. Cohen (Eds.), *Manual of developmental psychopathology: Risk, disorder, and adaptation, Vol. II* (pp. 535–580). New York: Wiley.

Goodman, S. (2002). Depression and early adverse experiences. In I. Gotlib & C. Hammen (Eds.), *Handbook of depression* (pp. 245–267). New York: Guilford.

Goodyer, I. M., Herbert, J., Secher, S., & Pearson, J. (1997). Short-term outcome of major depression, I: Comorbidity and severity at presentation as predictors of persistent disorder. *Journal of American Academy of Child and Adolescent Psychiatry, 36*, 179–187.

Gould, M. S. (1990). Suicide clusters and media exposure. In S. J. Blumenthal & D. G. Kupfer (Eds.), *Suicide over the life cycle: Risk factors, assessment and treatment of suicidal patients* (pp. 517–532). Washington, DC: American Psychiatric Press.

Gould, M. S., Greenberg, T., Velting, D. M., & Shaffer, D. (2003). Youth suicide risk and preventive interventions: A review of the past 10 years. *Journal of the American Academy of Child and Adolescent Psychiatry, 42*(4), 386–405.

Government of Canada. (2006). *The human face of mental health and mental illness in Canada.* Ottawa: Author.

Gowers, S., & Bryant-Waugh, R. (2004). Management of child and adolescent eating disorders: The current evidence base and future directions. *Journal of Child Psychology and Psychiatry, 45*, 63–83.

Gowers, S. G., & Green, L. (2009). *Eating disorders: Cognitive behavior therapy with children and younger people.* London: Routledge.

Graber, J. A., & Brooks-Gunn, J. (1996). Growing up female: Navigating body image, eating and depression. *Reclaiming Children and Youth, 5*(2), 76–80.

Grandin, T. (1984). My experiences as an autistic child. *Journal of Orthomolecular Psychiatry, 13*, 144–174.

Grandin, T. (2010). The world needs all kinds of minds. Retrieved from http://www.ted.com/talks/temple_grandin_the_world_needs_all_kinds_of_minds?language=en

Grandin, T. (2014). Temple Grandin to parents: Don't delay, work with your kids early. Retrieved from https://www.autismspeaks.org/news/news-item/temple-grandin-parents-don039t-delay-work-your-kids-early

Grant, K. E., Compas, B. E., Thurm, A. E., McMahon, S. D., & Gipson, P. Y. (2004). Stressors and child and adolescent psychopathology: Measurement issues and prospective effects. *Journal of Clinical Child and Adolescent Psychology, 33*, 412–425.

Grant, R., Riguel-Lynch, L., Redlener, E., & Redlener, I. (n.d.). Crisis counselling following 9/11: Implications for policy preparedness.

The Children's Health Fund. Retrieved from http://www.childrenshealthfund.org/sites/default/files/publications/Preparedness.pdf

Gray, J. A. (1987). *The psychology of fear and stress* (2nd ed.). London: Cambridge University Press.

Gray, P. (2010). The decline of play and rise in children's mental disorders. Retrieved from https://www.psychologytoday.com/blog/freedom-learn/201001

Gray, P. (2012). Free to Learn: Why Unleashing the Instinct to Play Will Make Our Children Happier, More Self-Reliant, and Better Students for Life. Published by Basic Books. © 2012.

Greenspan, S. I., & Wieder, S. (2005). Can children with autism master the core deficits and become empathetic, creative and reflective? A ten to fifteen year follow-up of a subgroup of children with autism spectrum disorders (ASD) who received a comprehensive developmental, individual-difference, relationship-based (DIR) approach. *The Journal of Developmental and Learning Disorders, 9,* 1–29.

Gregg, N. (2009). *Adolescents and adults with learning disabilities and ADHD: Assessment and accommodation.* New York: Guilford.

Gross-Tsur, V., Manor, O., & Shalev, R. S. (1996). Developmental dyscalculia: Prevalence and demographic features. *Developmental Medicine and Child Neurology, 38*(1), 25–33.

Gualterie, C. T., & Johnson, L. G. (2005). ADHD: Is objective diagnosis possible? *Psychiatry (Edgmont), 2*(11), 44–53.

Guerra, N. G., Huesmann, L. R., & Spindler, A. (2003). Community violence exposure, social cognition, and aggression among urban elementary school children. *Child Development, 74,* 1561–1576.

Guetzloe, E. (1994). Risk, resilience, and protection. *Reclaiming Children and Youth, 3*(2), 2–6. Published by CYC-Net Journals, © 1994. Retrieved from http://www.cyc-net.org/journals/rcy-3-2.html

Habib, M., & Labruna, V. (2006). *The Trauma History Checklist and Interview (THC).* Retrieved from http://www.nctsn.org/content/standardized-measures-assess-complex-trauma

Hackney, L., & MacMillan, K. (2008). Relational-based interventions: The medium is the message. *Journal of Child and Youth Care Work, 21,* 57–68.

Halmi, K. A. (2005). The multimodal treatment of eating disorders. *World Psychiatry, 4*(2), 69–73. Retrieved from http://www.ncbi.nlm.nih.gov/pmc/articles/PMC1414734/?report=reader

Halmi, K. (2012). Seminal issues in the treatment of eating disorders: An interview with Dr. Katherine Hamli. The Child Study Centre. Retrieved from http://www.aboutourkids.org/articles/seminal_issues_in_treatment_eating_disorders

Halverson, J. L. (2014). Cognitive behavioral therapy for depression technique. Retrieved from http://emedicine.medscape.com/article/2094696-technique

Hamilton, J. M. (2008). Culture-bound: Anxiety Disorder in adolescence: A case study. *Journal of Child and Adolescent Psychiatric Nursing, 21*(3), 186–190.

Hamilton, S. (2008a). Schizophrenia candidate genes: Are we really coming up blank? *American Journal of Psychiatry, 165,* 420–423.

Hamilton, S. S., & Armando, J. (2008). Oppositional Defiant Disorder. *American Family Physician, 78*(7), 861–866. Copyright © 2008 by the American Academy of Family Physicians. Used by permission of the American Academy of Family Physicians. Retrieved from http://www.aafp.org/afp/2008/1001/p861.html

Hammen, C., & Rudolph, K. (2003). Childhood depression. In E. J. Mash & R. A. Barkley, *Child Psychopathology* (2nd ed., pp. 233–278). New York: Guilford.

Hane, A. A., Fox, N. A., Henderson, H. A., & Marshall, P. J. (2008). Behavioral reactivity and approach withdrawal bias in infancy. *Developmental Psychology, 44,* 1491–1496.

Hantouche, E., Angst, J., & Azorin, J.-M. (2010). Explained factors of suicide attempts in major depression. *Journal of Affective Disorders, 127,* 305–308.

Harchik, A. (2014). Including children with special needs in regular classrooms: Pros and cons. Retrieved from http://www.newsforparents.org/experts_inclusion_pros_cons.html

Harrison, P. (1995). On the neuropathology of Schizophrenia and its dementia: Neurodevelopmental, neurodegenerative, or both? *Neurodegeneration, 4,* 1–12.

Hart, M. (2002). *Seeking mino-pimatisiwin: An Aboriginal approach to helping.* Halifax, NS: Fernwood.

Hartman, K., & Bush, M. (1975). Action-oriented family therapy. *The American Journal of Nursing, 75*(7), 1184–1187.

Harkavy-Friedman, J. M., & Nelson, E. (1997). Management of suicidal patients with schizophrenia. *Psychiatric Clinics of North America, 20*(3), 625–640.

Hassija, C. M., & Gray, M. J. (2010). Are cognitive techniques and interventions necessary? A case for the utility of cognitive approaches in the treatment of PTSD. *Clinical Psychology: Science and Practice, 17,* 112–127.

Hastings, P. D., & De, I. (2008). Parasympathetic regulation and parental socialization of emotion: Biopsychosocial processes of adjustment in preschoolers. *Social Development 17,* 211–238.

Hazell, P. (2010). Review of Attention-Deficit/Hyperactivity Disorder comorbid with Oppositional Defiant Disorder. *Australas Psychiatry, 18*(6), 556–559.

Hazell, P., O'Connell, D., Heathcote, D., Robertson, J., & Henry, D. (1995). Efficacy of tricyclic drugs in treating child and adolescent depression: A meta-analysis. *British Medical Journal, 310*(6984), 897–901.

Hazell, P. L., & Stuart, J. E. (2003). A randomized controlled trial of clonodine added to psychostimulant medication for hyperactive and aggressive children. *Journal American Academy of Child and Adolescent Psychiatry, 42*(8), 886–894.

Health Canada. (1999). Best practices—substance abuse treatment and rehabilitation. Prepared for Office of Alcohol, Drugs and Dependency Issues, Health Canada. Minister of Public Works and Government Services. Cat. No. H39-438/1998E. Ottawa: Author.

Health Canada. (2002). A report on mental illnesses in Canada. Ottawa: Author.

Health Canada. (2003a). *Canadian Community Health Survey.* Ottawa: Statistics Canada.

Health Canada. (2003b, March). Closing the gaps in Aboriginal health. *Health Policy Research Bulletin, 5.* Retrieved from http://hc-sc.gc.ca/sr-sr/alt_formats/iacb-dgiac/pdf/pubs/hpr-rps/bull/2003-5-aborignalautochtone/2003-5-aborignal-autochtone_e.pdf

Health Canada. (2012). Drug and alcohol use statistics. Retrieved from http://www.hc-sc.gc.ca/hc-ps/drugsdrogues/stat/index-eng.php

Health Canada. (2013). Acting on what we know: Preventing youth suicide in First Nations. Retrieved from http://www.hc-sc.gc.ca/fniah-spnia/pubs/promotion/_suicide/prev_youth-jeunes/index-eng.php#s2121

Health Canada and FDA Advisories for Antidepressants. (2013). Health Link B.C. Retrieved from http://www.healthlinkbc.ca/healthtopics/content.asp?hwid=zu1129

A healthy family social environment may reduce Schizophrenia risk by 86% for high genetic risk groups. (2010). Retrieved from http://www.schizophrenia.com/familyenv1.htm

Healy, J. M. (2004). *Your child's growing mind: Brain development and learning from birth to adolescence*. New York: Broadway Books.

Healy, W. (1915). *The individual delinquent*. Boston: Little, Brown.

Hechtman, L., & Greenfield, B. (2003). Long-term use of stimulants in children with Attention Deficit Hyperactivity Disorder: Safety, efficacy, and long-term outcome. *Paediatric Drugs, 5*(12), 787–794.

Heckenlaible-Gotto, M. J. (2006). From problems to strengths. *The International Child and Youth Care Network, 15*(3). Retrieved from http://cyc-net.org/Journals/rcy/rcy-15-3.html#Editorial

Hehir, T. (2007). Confronting ableism. *Educational Leadership, 64*(5), 8–14.

Heide, K., & Solomon, E. (2006). Biology, childhood trauma, and murder: Rethinking justice. *International Journal of Law and Psychiatry, 29*, 220–233.

Hendrickson, C. (2009). Trauma and co-occurring disorders among youth. Retrieved from http://www.aodpolicy.org/Docs/Trauma_and_COD_Among_Youth.pdf

Herzberg, D. S., Hammen, C., Burge, D., Daley, S. E., Davila, J., & Lindbert, N. (1998). Social competence as a predictor of chronic interpersonal stress. *Personal Relationships, 5*, 207–218.

Hess, E. B. (2013). DIR®/Floortime™: Evidence based practice towards the treatment of autism and sensory processing disorder in children and adolescents. *International Journal of Child Health and Human Development, 6*(3), 263–264.

Hettema, J. M., Neale, M. C., & Kendler, K. S. (2001). A review and meta-analysis of the genetic epidemiology of anxiety disorders. *American Journal of Psychiatry, 158*, 1568–1578.

Highlights of changes from DSM-IV-T-R to DSM-5. (2013). American Psychiatric Association. Reprinted with permission from the Diagnostic and Statistical Manual of Mental Disorders, Fifth Edition. (Copyright © 2013). American Psychiatric Association. All Rights Reserved. Retrieved from http://www.dsm5.org/Documents/changes%20from%20dsm-iv-tr%20to%20dsm-5.pdf

Hirschowitz, J., Kolevzon, A., & Garakani, A. (2010). The pharmacological treatment of Bipolar Disorder: The question of modern advances. *Harvard Review of Psychiatry 18*(5), 266–278.

Hirshfeld-Becker, D., Micco, J., Henin, A., Bloomfield, A., Biederman, J., & Rosenbaum, J. (2008). Behavioral inhibition. *Depression and Anxiety, 25*, 357–367.

Hirshfeld-Becker, D. R., Biederman, J., & Rosenbaum, J. F. (2004). Behavioral inhibition. In T. L. Morris & J. S. March (Eds.), *Anxiety disorders in children and adolescents* (2nd ed., pp. 27–58). New York: Guilford.

Hitti, M. (2006). Eating disorders may run in families. Retrieved from http://psychologytoday.webmd.com/content/article/119/113373?src=rss_psychtoday

Hoarding food. (n.d.). cyc-net discussion thread. Retrieved from http://www.cyc-net.org/threads/choice.html

Hobfoll, S. E., Tracy, M., & Galea, S. (2006). The impact of resource loss and traumatic growth on probable PTSD and depression following terrorist attacks. *Journal of Traumatic Stress, 19*, 867–878.

Hoch, T., Babbitt, R., Coe, D., Krell, D., & Hackbert, L. (1994). Contingency contacting: Combining positive reinforcement and escape extinction procedures to treat persistent food refusal. *Behavior Modification, 18*(1), 106–128.

Hoek, H. W. (2007). Incidence, prevalence and mortality of Anorexia and other eating disorders. *Current Opinion in Psychiatry, 19*(4), 389–394.

Hofmann, S. G. (2008). Common misconceptions about cognitive mediation of treatment change: A commentary to Longmore and Worrell (2007). *Clinical Psychology Review, 28*, 67–70.

Holahan, C. J., Holahan, C. K., Moos, R. H., Brennan, P. L., & Schutte, K. K. (2005). Stress generation, avoidance coping, and depressive symptoms: A 10-year model. *Journal of Consulting and Clinical Psychology, 73*(4), 658–666.

Holden, M. (2009). *Children and residential experiences: Creating the conditions for change*. Washington, DC: Child Welfare League of America. Published by Residential Child Care Project, Cornell University, © 2009.

Holding therapy and autism. (2014). Retrieved from http://www.researchautism.net/autism-interventions/our-evaluations-interventions/71/holding-therapy-and-autism/Introduction

Hollis, C. (2000). Adolescent Schizophrenia: Advances in psychiatric treatment. *Journal of Continuing Professional Development, 6*, 83–92. Published by Columbia International Publishing, © 2000.

Hollis, C. (2002). Schizophrenia and allied disorders. In M. Rutter & E. Taylor (Eds.), *Child and adolescent psychiatry* (pp. 612–635). Oxford: Blackwell.

Hollon, S. D., Stewart, M. O., & Strunk, D. (2006). Enduring effects of cognitive behavior therapy in the treatment of depression and anxiety. *Annual Review of Psychology, 57*, 285–315.

Hollon, S. D., Thase, M. E., & Markowitz, J. C. (2002). Treatment and prevention of depression. *Psychological Science in the Public Interest, 3*, 39–77.

Honos-Webb, L. (2011). *The ADHD workbook for teens: Activities to help you gain motivation and confidence*. Oakland, CA: New Harbinger Publishing.

Hopko, D. R., Armento, M. E., Cantu, M. S., Chambers, L. L., & Lejuez, C. W. (2003). The use of daily diaries to assess the relations among mood state, overt behavior, and reward value of activities. *Behavior Research and Therapy, 41*(10), 1137–1148.

Hopko, D. R., & Mullane, C. M. (2008). Exploring the relation of depression and overt behavior with daily diaries. *Behavior Research and Therapy, 46*(9), 1085–1089.

Horney, K. (1950). *Neurosis and human growth: The struggle toward self-realization*. New York: Norton.

Horney, K. (1967/1973). *Feminine psychology*. New York: Norton.

Horowitz, M. J. (1997). *Stress response syndromes* (3rd ed.). Northvale, NJ: Jason Aronson.

Hoza, B., Kaiser, N. M., & Hurt, E. (2008). Evidence-based treatments for Attention Deficit/Hyperactivity Disorder (ADHD). In M. Roberts, D. Elkin, & R. Steele (Eds.), *Handbook of evidence-based therapies for children and adolescents* (pp. 189–211). New York: Springer.

Hudson, J. I., Hiripi, E., Pope, H. G., & Kessler, R. C. (2007). The prevalence and correlates of eating disorders in the National Comorbidity Survey Replication. *Biological Psychiatry, 61*(3), 348–358.

Hudson, J. L., & Rapee, R. M. (2001). Parent–child interactions and anxiety disorders: An observational study. *Behavior Research and Therapy, 39*, 1411–1427.

Huemer, J., Erhart, F., & Steiner H. (2010). Posttraumatic Stress Disorder in children and adolescents: A review of psychopharmacological treatment. *Child Psychiatry and Human Development, 41*(6), 624–640.

Humphries, T., Kinsbourne, M., & Swanson, J. (1978). Stimulant effects on cooperation and social interaction between hyperactive children and their mothers. *Journal of Child Psychology and Psychiatry, 19*, 13–22.

Huttunen, J., Heinimaa, M., Svirskis, T., Nyman, M., Kajander, J., Forsback, S., . . . Hietala, J. (2008). Striatal dopamine synthesis in first-degree relatives of patients with Schizophrenia. *Biological Psychiatry, 63*, 114–117.

Ialongo, N., Edelsohn, G., Werthamer-Larsson, L., Crockett, L., & Kellam, S. (1995). The significance of self-reported anxious symptoms in first grade children: Prediction to anxious symptoms and adaptive functioning in fifth grade. *Journal of Child Psychology and Psychiatry, 36*, 427–437.

Ingram, R. E., Nelson, T., Steidtmann, D. K., & Bistricky, S. L. (2007). Comparative data on child and adolescent cognitive measures associated with depression. *Journal of Consulting and Clinical Psychology, 75*(3), 390–403.

An introduction to family group conference, An. (n.d.). NetCare Consultancy and Training. Retrieved from http://www.netcare-ni.com/media/uploads/Practice%20and%20theory.pdf

Jack, S., Munn, C., Cheng, C., & MacMillan, H. (2006). *Child maltreatment in Canada: National clearinghouse on family violence*. Ottawa: Public Health Agency of Canada.

Jackowski, A. P., Douglas-Palumberi, H., Jackowski, M., Win, L., Schultz, R. T., Staib, L. W., Krystal, J. H., & Kaufman, J. (2008). Corpus callosum in maltreated children with Posttraumatic Stress Disorder: A diffusion tensor imaging study. *Psychiatry Research, 162*, 256–261.

Jacob, T., & Johnson, S. (1997). Parenting influences on the development of alcohol abuse and dependence. *Alcohol Health and Research World, 21*(3), 204–209.

Jacobi, C., Hayward, C., de Zwaan, M., Kraemer, H. C., & Agras, W. S. (2004). Coming to terms with risk factors for eating disorders: Application of risk terminology and suggestions for a general taxonomy. *Psychological Bulletin, 130*(1), 19–65.

Jacobs, D. G. (1995). National Depression Screening Day: Educating the public, reaching those in need of treatment, and broadening professional understanding. *Harvard Review of Psychiatry, 3*(3), 156–159.

Jacobson, N. S., & Gortner, E. T. (2000). Can depression be de-medicalized in the 21st century? Scientific revolutions, counter-revolutions and the magnetic field of normal science. *Behavior Research and Therapy, 38*, 103–117.

James, A., & Javaloyes, A. (2001). The treatment of Bipolar Disorder in children and adolescents. *Journal of Child Psychology and Psychiatry, 42*, 439–449.

James, N. M., & Chapman, C. J. (1975). A genetic study of Bipolar Affective Disorder. *British Journal of Psychiatry, 126*, 449–456.

Jamison, K. R. (1999). *Night falls fast: Understanding suicide*. New York: Alfred A. Knopf. Published by Random House.

Jaycox, L. H., Reivich, K. J., Gillham, J., & Seligman, M. E. P. (1994). Prevention of depressive symptoms in school children. *Behavior Research Therapy, 32*, 801–816.

Jensen, P. S. (2000). Current concepts and controversies in the diagnosis and treatment of Attention Deficit Hyperactivity Disorder. *Current Psychiatry Reports, 2*(2), 102–109.

Jensen, P. S. (2004). *Making the system work for your child with ADHD*. New York: Guilford.

Jersild, A. T., & Holmes, F. B. (1935). Some factors in the development of children's fears. *Journal of Experimental Education, 4*, 133–141.

Jessor, R. (Ed.). 1998. *New perspectives on adolescent risk behavior*. New York: Cambridge University Press.

Jiloha, R. C. (2009). Social and cultural aspects of drug abuse in adolescents. *Delhi Psychiatry Journal, 12*(2), 167–175.

Johnson, B. (2009). The cause and cure for psychosis. Retrieved from http://www.truthtrustconsent.com/public_html/psychiatry/the-cause-and-cure-of-psychosis

Johnson, C. A. (2001). *Self-esteem comes in all sizes: How to be happy and healthy at your natural weight*. Carlsbad, CA: Gurze Books. Copyright © 2001 by Gurze Books. Reproduced by permission of the Gurze Books.

Johnson, J. G., Cohen, P., Kasen, S., & Brook, J. (2002). Childhood adversities associated with risk for eating disorders or weight problems during adolescence or early adulthood. *American Journal of Psychiatry, 159*, 394–400.

Johnson, W. G., Tsoh, J. Y., & Varnado, P. J. (1996). Eating disorders: Efficacy of pharmacological and psychological interventions. *Clinical Psychology Review, 16*, 457–478.

Johnston, C., & Mash, E. J. (2001). Families of children with Attention-Deficit/Hyperactivity Disorder: Review and recommendations for future research. *Clinical Child and Family Psychology Review, 4*, 183–206.

Joiner, T. R., & Rudd, M. (2000). Intensity and duration of suicidal crisis vary as a function of previous suicide attempts and negative life events. *Journal of Consulting and Clinical Psychology, 68*, 909–916.

Jones, L. (2007). Articulating a Child and Youth Care approach to family work. Retrieved from http://www.cyc-net.org/cyc-online/cycol-0709-jones.html

Jongsma, A. E., Peterson, L. M., & McInnis, W. P. (1999). *The child and adolescent treatment planner*. New York: Wiley.

Jonstang, I. C. (2009). The effect of body dissatisfaction on eating disorder symptomatology: Mediating effects of depression and low self-esteem: A partial test of the Dual-Pathway Model. Unpublished dissertation. University of Oslo.

Jordan, R. (2006). *Overcoming attention deficit disorders in children, adolescents, and adults*. (4th ed.). Austin, TX: Pro-Ed.

Jorm, A. F., Korten, A. E., Patricia, A., Jacomb, P. A., Christensen, H., Rodgers, B., & Pollitt, P. (1997). Mental health literacy: A survey of the public's ability to recognise mental disorders and their beliefs about the effectiveness of treatment. *Medical Journal of Australia, 166*(4), 182.

Jun, A. (2009). Attention-Deficit/Hyperactivity Disorder: The road travelled and the road ahead. [Editorial]. *American Journal of Health-Systems Pharmacology, 66*, 2003.

Kabat-Zinn, J. (2003). Mindfulness-based interventions in context: Past, present, and future. *Clinical Psychology: Science and Practice, 10*(2), 144–156.

Kagan, J. (1994). *Galen's prophecy: Temperament in human nature*. New York: Basic Books.

Kagan, J., Reznick, J. S., & Snidman, N. (1988). Biological bases of childhood shyness. *Science, 240*, 167–171.

Kaminer, Y., Burleson, J. A., & Goldberger, R. (2002). Cognitive behavioral coping skills and psychoeducation therapies for adolescent substance abuse. *The Journal of Nervous and Mental Disease, 190,* 737–745.

Kaminski, J. W., & Fang, X. (2009). Victimization by peers and adolescent suicide in three US samples. *Journal of Pediatrics, 155*(5), 683–688.

Kaplan, A. S. (2002). Psychological treatments for Anorexia Nervosa: A review of published studies and promising new directions. *Canadian Journal of Psychiatry, 47*(3), 235–242.

Kariholu, P. L., Jakareddy, R., HemanthKumar, M., Paramesh, K. N., & Pavankumar, N. P. (2008). Pica—a case of acuphagia or hyalophagia? *Indian Journal of Surgery, 70,* 144–146.

Karnik, N., & Steiner, H. (2007). Evidence for interventions for young offenders. *Child and Adolescent Mental Health, 12*(4), 154–159.

Karp, D. A., & Sisson, G. E. (2010). *Voices from the inside: Readings on the experiences of mental illness.* New York: Oxford University Press.

Kaski, M. (2012). Aetiology of intellectual disability: General issues and prevention. In M. G. Gelder, N. C. Andreasen, J. J. Lopez-Ibor, & J. R. Geddes (Eds.), *New Oxford textbook of psychiatry* (2nd ed., Vol. 2, pp. 1830–1837). New York: Oxford University Press.

Kaslow, N. J., Deering, C. G., & Racusin, G. R. (1994). Depressed children and their families. *Clinical Psychology Review, 14,* 39–59.

Kaslow, N. J., Reviere, S. L., Chance, S. E., Rogers, J. H., Hatcher, C. A., Wasserman, F., . . . Seelig, B. (1998). An empirical study of the psychodynamics of suicide. *Journal of the American Psychoanalytic Association, 46,* 777–796.

Katie, B. (2015). Do the work. The Work of Byron Katie. Retrieved from https://thework.com/do-work

Kauffman, J. M. (2001). *Characteristics of emotional and behavioral disorders of children and youth* (7th ed.). Upper Saddle River, NJ: Merrill Prentice-Hall.

Kauffman, J. M., & Landrum, T. J. (2013). *Characteristics of emotional and behavioral disorders of children and youth* (10th ed.). Toronto: Pearson.

Kaye, W. H., Frank, G. K., Meltzer, C. C., Price, J. C., McConaha, C. W., Crossan, P. J., Klump, K. L., & Rhodes, L. (2001). Altered serotonin 2A receptor activity in women who have recovered from Bulimia Nervosa. *American Journal of Psychiatry, 158,* 1152–1155.

Kaye, W. H., Greeno, C. G., Moss, H., Fernstrom, J., Fernstrom, M., . . . Mann, J. J. (1998). Alterations in serotonin activity and psychiatric symptomatology after recovery from Bulimia Nervosa. *Archives of General Psychiatry, 55,* 927–935.

Kazdin, A. E. (1996). Problem solving and parent management in treating aggressive and antisocial behavior. In E. D. Hibbs & P. S. Jensen (Eds.), *Psychosocial treatments for child and adolescent disorders: Empirically based strategies for clinical practice* (pp. 377–408). Washington, DC: American Psychological Association.

Kazdin, A. E. (2003). *Research design in clinical psychology* (4th ed.). Boston: Allyn & Bacon.

Kazdin, A. E., & Wassell, G. (2000a). Predictors of barriers to treatment and therapeutic change in outpatient therapy for antisocial children and their families. *Mental Health Services Research, 2,* 27–40.

Kazdin, A. E., & Wassell, G. (2000b). Therapeutic changes in children, parents, and families resulting from treatment of children with conduct problems. *Journal of the American Academy of Child and Adolescent Psychiatry, 39,* 414–420.

Keane, T. M., Zimering, R. T., & Caddell, J. M. (1985). A behavioral formulation of Posttraumatic Stress Disorder in Vietnam veterans. *Behavior Therapist, 8,* 9–12.

Kearney, C. A. (2003). *Casebook in child behavior disorders.* Belmont, CA: Wadsworth/Thomson Learning, © 2003.

Kemper, K. J., Gardiner, P., & Birdee, G. S. (2013). Use of complementary and alternative medical therapies among youth with mental health concerns. *Academic Pediatrics, 13*(6), 540–545.

Kendall, P. C., & Braswell, L. (1993). *Cognitive-behavioral therapy for impulsive children* (2nd ed.). New York: Guilford.

Kendall, P. C., & Comer, J. S. (2000). *Childhood disorders.* New York: Psychology Press, © 2000.

Kendall, P. C., & Comer, J. S. (2010). *Childhood disorders* (2nd ed.). New York: Psychology Press.

Kendall, P. C., & Pimentel, S. S. (2003). On the physiological symptom constellation in youth with Generalized Anxiety Disorder (GAD). *Journal of Anxiety Disorders, 17,* 211–221.

Kendler, K. S., Kuhn, J. W., Vittum, J., Prescott, C. A., & Riley, B. (2005). The interaction of stressful life events and a serotonin transporter polymorphism in the prediction of episodes of major depression. *Archives of General Psychiatry, 62,* 529–535.

Kendler, K. S., Maclean, C., Neale, M., Kessler, R., Heath, A., & Eaves, L. (1991). The genetic epidemiology of Bulimia Nervosa. *American Journal of Psychiatry, 148,* 1627–1637.

Kennedy, D., Banks, R., & Grandin, T. (2002). *The ADHD–autism connection: A step toward more accurate diagnoses and effective treatments.* Colorado Springs, CO: Waterbrook Press.

Kent, G. (1997). Dental phobias. In G. C. L. Davey (Ed.), *Phobias: A handbook of theory, research and treatment.* New York: Wiley.

Kerr, M., Stattin, H., & Burk, W. J. (2010). A reinterpretation of parental monitoring in longitudinal perspective. *Journal of Research on Adolescence, 20*(1), 39–64.

Kessler, R. C., Berglund, P., Demler, O., Jin, R., Merikangas, K. R., & Walters, E. E. (2005). Lifetime prevalence and age-of-onset distributions of DSM-IV disorders in the National Comorbidity Survey Replication. *Archives of General Psychiatry, 62,* 593–602.

Kessler, R. C., Turner, J. B., & House, J. S. (1988). The effects of unemployment on health in a community survey: Main, modifying, and mediating effects. *Journal of Social Issues, 44*(4), 69–86.

Kessler, Z. (2015). The horse who read my mind. ADDitude: Strategies and Support for ADHD and LD. Retrieved from http://www.additudemag.com/adhd/article/9309.html

Khalil, A. I. (2012). A community based treatment: Impact of social skills training program on improving social skills among schizophrenic patients. *World Applied Sciences Journal, 18*(3), 370–378.

Khantzian, E. J. (1999). *Treating addiction as a human process: A plea for a measure of marginality.* New York: Jason Aronson.

Khantzian, E. J. (2013). Addiction as a self-regulation disorder and the role of self-medication. *Addiction, 108*(4), 668–669.

Khantzian, E. J., & Mack, J. E. (1999). Alcoholics Anonymous and contemporary psychodynamic theory. In Khantzian, E. J. (Ed.), *Treating addiction as a human process* (pp. 399–429). Northvale, NJ: Aronson.

Khashan, A., Abel, K., McNamee, R., Pedersen, M., Webb, R., Baker, P., Kenny, L., & Mortensen, P. (2008). Higher risk of offspring Schizophrenia following neonatal maternal exposure to severe life events. *Archive of General Psychology, 65*(2), 146–152.

Kidd, G. E. (1946). Trepanation among the early Indians of British Columbia. *Canadian Medical Association Journal, 55,* 513–516.

Kilpatrick, D. G., Ruggiero, K. J., Acierno, R., Saunders, B. E., Resnick, H. S., & Best, C. L. (2003). Violence and risk of PTSD, major depression, substance abuse/dependence, and comorbidity: Results from the national survey of adolescents. *Journal of Consulting and Clinical Psychology, 71*, 692–700.

King, J. (2013). Nutrition, herbs and vitamins for Oppositional Defiance Disorder. Retrieved from http://www.livestrong.com/article/493854-oppositional-defiance-disorder-nutrition-herbs-and-vitamins

Kirmayer, L. J., Brass, G. M., Holton, T. L., Paul, K., Simpson, C., & Tait, C. L. (2007). *Suicide among Aboriginal Peoples in Canada.* Ottawa: Aboriginal Healing Foundation. Published by Aboriginal Healing Foundation, © 2007.

Kiro, C. (2009). Children, parenting and education: Addressing the causes of offending. *Policy Quarterly, 5*(2). Retrieved from http://ips.ac.nz/publications/files/1c07d49b1ef.pdf

Kliewer, W., Cunningham, J. N., Diehl, R., Parrish, K. A., Walker, J. M., Atiyeh, C., . . . Mejia, R. (2004). Violence exposure and adjustment in inner-city youth: Child and caregiver emotion regulation skill, caregiver–child relationship quality, and neighborhood cohesion as protective factor. *Journal of Clinical Child and Adolescent Psychology, 33*(3), 477–487.

Kobak, R., Ferenz-Gillies, R. (1995). Emotion regulation and depressive symptoms during adolescence: A functionalist perspective. *Development & Psychopathology, 7*, 183–192.

Kolko, D. J., Hurlburt, M. S., Jinjin, Z., Barth, R. P., Leslie, L. K., & Burns, B. J. (2010). Posttraumatic Stress symptoms in children and adolescents referred for child welfare investigation. *Child Maltreatment, 15*(1), 48–63.

Koob, G. F., Ahmed, S. H., Boutrel, B., Chen, S. A., Kenny, P. J., Markou, A., . . . Sanna, P. P. (2004). Neurobiological mechanisms in the transition from drug use to drug dependence. *Neuroscience and Biobehavioral Reviews, 27*, 739–749.

Kopelowicz, A., Liberman, R. P., & Zarate, R. (2006). Recent advances in social skills training for Schizophrenia. *Schizophrenia Bulletin, 32*(Suppl. 1), S12–S23.

Koroll, M. (2006). What's going on with children today? *Relational Child and Youth Care Practice, 19*(4), 54–55. Copyright © 2006 by CYC-Net Journals. Used by permission of CYC-Net Journals. Retrieved from http://www.cyc-net.org/quote3/quote-1592.htmlI

Kotler, J. S., & McMahon, R. J. (2005). Child psychopathy: Theories, measurement, and relations with the development and persistence of conduct problems. *Clinical Child and Family Psychology Review, 8*, 291–325.

Kousha, M., & Tehrani, S. M. (2013). Normative life events and PTSD in children: How easy stress can affect children's brain. *Acta Medica Iranica, 51*(1), 47–51.

Kovacs, M. (1997). Depressive disorders in childhood: An impressionistic landscape. *Journal of Child Psychology and Psychiatry and Allied Disciplines, 38*, 287–298.

Kowalik, J., Weller, J., Venter, J., & Drachman, D. (2011). Cognitive behavioral therapy for the treatment of pediatric Posttramatic Stress Disorder: A review and meta-analysis. *Journal of Behavior Therapy and Experimental Psychiatry, 42*, 405–413.

Kozioff, M., LaNunziata, L., Cowardin, J., & Bessellieu, F. (2000, December). Direct instruction: Its contribution to high school achievement. *The High School Journal, 84*(2), 54–71. Retrieved from PsycINFO database.

Krain, A. L., & Kendall, P. C. (2000). The role of parental emotional distress in parent report of child anxiety. *Journal of Clinical Child Psychology, 29*, 328–335.

Krenichyn, K., Saegert, S., & Evans, G. W. (2001). Parents as moderators of psychological and physiological correlates of inner-city children's exposure to violence. *Applied Developmental Psychology, 22*, 581–602.

Krishnan-Sarin, S., Duhig, A., McKee, S., McMahon, T. J., Liss, T., McFetridge, A., & Cavallo, D. A. (2006). Contingency management for smoking cessation in adolescent smokers. *Experimental and Clinical Psychopharmacology, 14*(3), 306–310.

Kronmüller, K-T., Postelnicu, I., Hartmann, M., Stefini, A., Geiser-Elze, A., Gerhold, M., Horn, H., & Winkelmann, K. (2005). Zur Wirksam-keit psychodynamischer Kurzzeitpsychotherapie bei Kindern und Jugendlichen mit angststörungen. *Praxis der Kinderpsychologie Kinderpsychiatrie, 54*, 559–577.

Krueger, M. A. (2000). Central themes in child and youth care. Issue 12 January 2000. Copyright © 2000 by CYC-NET Journals. Used by permission of CYC-NET Journals. Retrieved from http://www.cyc-net.org/LZ/a-8-3.html

Krupnick, J. L. (2002). Brief psychodynamic theory and PTSD. *Journal of Clinical Psychology, 58*(8), 919–932.

Kuch, K. (1997). Accident phobia. In G. C. L. Davey (Ed.), *Phobias: A handbook of theory, research and treatment* (pp. 153–162). New York: Wiley.

Kuczynski, L., & Kochanska, G. (1995). Function and content of maternal demands: Developmental significance of early demands for competent action. *Child Development, 66*, 616–628.

Kuhn, T. (1996). *The structure of scientific revolutions* (3rd ed.). Chicago: University of Chicago Press.

Kuipers, E., Garety, P., Fowler, D., Dunn, G., Bebbington, P., Freeman, D., & Hadley, C. (1997). The London–East Anglia randomised controlled trial of cognitive-behavioral therapy for psychosis. I. Effects of the treatment phase. *British Journal of Psychiatry, 171*, 319–327.

Kumpfer, K. L., & Alvarado, R. (2003). Family interventions for the prevention of drug abuse. *American Psychologist, 58*(6/7), 457–465.

Kumpfer, K. L., Molgaard, V., & Spoth, R. (1996). Family interventions for the prevention of delinquency and drug use in special populations. In R. V. De Peters & R. McMahon (Eds.), *Preventing childhood disorders, substance abuse, and delinquency.* Thousand Oaks, CA: Sage.

Kuntzi, J., & Stevenson, J. (2000). Hyperactivity in children: A focus on genetic research and psychological theories. *Clinical Child and Family Psychology Review, 3*, 1–23.

Kurtz, M. M., & Mueser, K. T. (2008). A meta-analysis of controlled research on social skills training for Schizophrenia. *Journal of Consulting and Clinical Psychology, 76*, 491–504.

Kutscher, M. (2005). *Kids in the Syndrome Mix of ADHD, LD, Asperger's, Tourette's, Bipolar and More!: The One Stop Guide for Parents, Teachers and Other Professionals* by Martin L. Kutscher. Published by Jessica Kingsley Publishers, Inc © 2008.

Ladouceur, C. D., Dahl, R. E., Williamson, D. E., Birmaher, B., Ryan, N. D., & Casey, B. J. (2005). Altered emotional processing in pediatric anxiety, depression, and comorbid anxiety-depression. *Journal of Abnormal Child Psychology, 33*, 165–177.

Lafrance Robinson, A., Boachie, A., & Lafrance, G. (2013). "I want help!": Psychologists' and physicians' competence, barriers, and needs in the management of eating disorders in children and adolescents in Canada. *Canadian Psychology, 54*, 160–165.

La Greca, A. M., Silverman, W. K., Vernberg, E. M., & Prinstein, M. J. (1996). Symptoms of posttraumatic stress in children after Hurricane Andrew: A prospective study. *Journal of Consulting and Clinical Psychology, 64*(4), 712–723.

Lahey, B. B., & Waldman, I. D. (2003). A developmental propensity model of the origins of conduct problems during childhood and adolescence. In B. B. Lahey, T. E. Moffitt, & A. Caspi (Eds.), *Causes of Conduct Disorder and juvenile delinquency* (pp. 76–117). New York: Guilford.

Lam, D. H., Watkins, E. R., Hayward, P., Bright, J., Wright, K., Kerr, N., Parr-Davis, G., & Sham, P. (2003). A randomized controlled study of cognitive therapy for relapse prevention for Bipolar Affective Disorder: Outcome of the first year. *Archives of General Psychiatry, 60,* 145–152.

Lambe, Y., & McLellan, R. (2009). *Drugs in our system: An exploratory study on the chemical management of Canadian systems youth.* Published by Youth in Care Canada, © 2009. Retrieved from http://www.youthincare.ca

Lang, P. J., Davis, M., & Öhman, A. (2000). Fear and anxiety: Animal models and human cognitive psychophysiology. *Journal of Affective Disorders, 61,* 137–159.

Lanza, M., Anderson, J., Bosvert, C., LeBlanc, A., Fardy, M., & Steel, B. (2002). Assaultive behavior intervention in the Veterans Administration: Psychodynamic group psychotherapy compared to cognitive behavior therapy. *Perspectives in Psychiatric Care, 38,* 89–97.

Larsson, B., Fossum, S., Clifford, G., Drugli, M. B., Handegård, B. H., & Mørch, W. T. (2009). Treatment of oppositional defiant and conduct problems in young Norwegian children: Results of a randomized controlled replication trial. *European Child and Adolescent Psychiatry, 18,* 42–52.

Last, C. G., Perrin, S., Hersen, M., & Kazdin, A. E. (1996). A prospective study of childhood anxiety disorders. *Journal of the American Academy of Child and Adolescent Psychiatry, 35,* 1502–1510.

Laursen, E. K., & Yazdgerdi, S. (2012). Autism and belonging. *Reclaiming Children and Youth, 21*(2), 44–47.

Lavin, P., & Park, C. (1999). *Despair turned into rage.* Washington, DC: Child Welfare League of America.

Lawton, K., & Kasari, C. (2012). Teacher-implemented joint attention intervention: Pilot randomized controlled study for preschoolers with autism. *Journal of Consulting and Clinical Psychology, 80*(4), 687.

LeDoux, J. E. (2002). *Synaptic self: How our brains become who we are.* New York: Viking.

Lee, H., Rhee, P. L., Park, E. H., Kim, J. H., Son, H. J., Kim, J. J., & Rhee, J. C. (2007). Clinical outcome of rumination syndrome in adults without psychiatric illness: A prospective study. *Journal of Gastroenterology and Hepatology, 22*(11), 1741–1747.

Lee, S. H., Han, D. H., Oh, S., Lyoo, I. K., Lee, Y. S., Renshaw, P. F., & Lukas, S. (2009). Quantitative electroencephalographic (qEEG) correlates of craving during virtual reality therapy in alcohol-dependent patients. *Pharmacology Biochemistry and Behavior, 91*(3), 393–397.

Legerstee, J. S., Huizink, A. C., van Gastel, W., Liber, J. M., Treffers, P. D., & Verhulst, F. C. (2008). Maternal anxiety predicts favourable treatment outcomes in anxiety-disordered adolescents. *Acta Psychiatrica Scandinavica, 117*(4), 289–298. doi:10.1111/j.1600-0447.2008.01161.x

Le Grange, D., Crosby, R., Rathouz, P., & Leventhal, B. (2007). A randomized controlled comparison of family-based treatment and supportive psychotherapy for adolescent Bulimia Nervosa. *Archives of General Psychiatry, 64,* 1049–1056.

Le Grange, D., & Lock, J. (2005). The dearth of psychological treatment studies for Anorexia Nervosa. *International Journal of Eating Disorders, 37,* 79–81.

Le Grange, D., Lock, J., Loeb, K., & Nicholls, D. (2010). Academy for eating disorders position paper: The role of the family in eating disorders. *International Journal of Eating Disorders, 43,* 1–5.

Leichsenring, F. (2005). Are psychodynamic and psychoanalytic therapies effective? A review of empirical data. *International Journal of Psychoanalysis, 86,* 1–26.

Leichsenring, F., Rabung, S., & Leibing, E. (2004). The efficacy of short-term psychodynamic psychotherapy in specific psychiatric disorders: A meta-analysis. *Archives of General Psychiatry, 61,* 1208–1216.

Lenze, E. J., & Wetherell, J. L. (2011). A lifespan view of anxiety disorders. *Dialogues in Clinical Neuroscience, 13*(4), 381–399.

Lerner, R. M., & Benson, P. L. (Eds.). (2003). *Developmental assets and asset-building communities: Implications for research, policy, and practice.* New York: Kluwer Academic/Plenum.

Leschied, A. W. (2008). *The roots of violence: Evidence from the literature with emphasis on child and youth mental health disorder.* Ottawa: The Centre of Excellence in Children's Mental Health, Children's Hospital of Eastern Ontario, © 2008.

Levels of involvement. (1998). Addictions Foundation of Manitoba. Retrieved from http://www.afm.mb.ca/Learn%20More/Levels%20Invol.pdf

Levenkron, S. (1998). *Cutting: Understanding and overcoming self-mutilation.* Published by W. W. Norton & Company, Inc., © 1998.

Levi, Y., Horesh, N., Fischel, T., Treves, I., Or, E., & Apter, A. (2008). Mental pain and its communication in medically serious suicide attempts: An "impossible situation." *Journal of Affective Disorders, 111,* 244–250.

Lewinsohn, P. M. (1974). A behavioral approach to depression. In R. J. Friedman & M. M. Katz (Eds.), *The psychology of depression: Contemporary theory and research* (pp. 157–178). New York: Wiley.

Lewinsohn, P. M., Hops, H., Roberts, R. E., Seeley, J. R., & Andrews, J. A. (1993). Adolescent psychopathology: Prevalence and incidence of depression and other DSM-III-R disorders in high school students. *Journal of Abnormal Psychology, 102,* 133–44.

Lewinsohn, P. M., Rohde, P., Seeley, J. R., Klein, D. N., & Gotlib, I. (2003). Psychosocial functioning of young adults who have experienced and recovered from Major Depressive Disorder during adolescence. *Journal of Abnormal Psychology, 112,* 353–363.

Leyton, M., & Stewart, S. (Eds.). (2014). *Substance abuse in Canada: Childhood and adolescent pathways to substance use disorders.* Ottawa: Canadian Centre on Substance Abuse. Retrieved from http://www.ccsa.ca/Resource%20Library/CCSA-Child-Adolescent-Substance-Use-Disorders-Report-2014-en.pdf

Liberman, R. P., Wallace, C. J., Blackwell, G., Mintz, J., & Kopelowicz, A. (1998). Skills training vs. psychosocial occupational therapy for persons with persistent Schizophrenia. *American Journal of Psychiatry, 155,* 1087–1091.

Liddle, H. A., Dakof, G. A., Turner, R. M., Henderson, C. E. & Greenbaum, P. E. (2008). Treating adolescent drug abuse: A randomized trial comparing multidimensional family therapy and cognitive behavior therapy. *Addiction, 103*(10), 1660–1670.

Liddle, H. A., Rowe, C. L., Dakof, G. A., Henderson, C. E., & Greenbaum, P. E. (2009). Multidimensional family therapy for young adolescent substance abuse: Twelve-month outcomes of a randomized controlled trial. *Journal of Consulting and Clinical Psychology, 77*(1), 12–25.

Lilenfeld, L., Wonderlich, S., Riso, L. P., Crosby, R., & Mitchell, J. (2006). Eating disorders and personality: A methodological and empirical review. *Clinical Psychology Review, 26,* 299–320.

Lindgren, S., & Doobay, A. (2011). Evidence-based interventions for Autism Spectrum Disorders. Published by Development of the University of Iowa Children's Hospital, © 2011. Retrieved from http://www.uihealthcare.org/uploadedFiles/UIHealthcare/Content/Services/Center_for_Disabilities_and_Development/UCEDD/DHS%20Autism%20Interventions%206-10-11.pdf

Lindhout, I. E., Markus, M. T., Hoogendijk, T. H., & Boer, F. (2009). Temperament and parental child-rearing style: Unique contributions to clinical anxiety disorders in childhood. *European Child and Adolescent Psychiatry, 18*, 439–446.

Litt, M. D., Kadden, R. M., Kabela-Cormier, E., & Petry, N. M. (2009). Changing network support for drinking: Network Support Project two-year follow-up. *Journal of Consulting and Clinical Psychology, 77*(2), 229–242.

Littell, J. H., Popa, M., & Forsythe, B. (2005). Multisystemic therapy for social, emotional, and behavioral problems in youth aged 10–17. *Cochrane Library, Issue 3*. Chichester, UK: Wiley.

Loeb, K. L., & Le Grange, D. (2009). Family-based treatment for adolescent eating disorders: Current status, new applications and future directions. *International Journal of Child Adolescent Health, 2*, 243–254.

Loeber, R. (1990). Development and risk factors of juvenile antisocial behavior and delinquency. *Clinical Psychology Review, 10*, 1–41.

Loeber, R., Burke, J. D., & Pardini, D. A. (2009). Oppositional Defiant Disorder, Conduct Disorder and psychopathy. *Journal of Child Psychology and Psychiatry, 50*, 133–140.

Loeber, R., & Farrington, D. P. (2000). Young children who commit crime: Epidemiology, developmental origins, risk factors, early interventions, and policy implications. *Development and Psychopathology, 12*, 737–762.

Loewy, R., & Rose, D. (2015). The psychosis prodrome. *The Carlat Psychiatry Report*. Retrieved from http://www.thecarlatreport.com/free_articles/psychosis-prodrome-free-article

Logsdon, A. (2015). Focus on the person first is good etiquette. Retrieved from http://learningdisabilities.about.com/od/assessmentandtesting/qt/personfirst.htm

Lombardo, M. V., Chakrabarti, B., & Baron-Cohen, S. (2009). The amygdala in autism: Not adapting to faces? *American Journal of Psychiatry, 166*(4), 395–397.

Long, R. (2009). *Rob Long's intervention toolbox for social, emotional, and behavioral difficulties*. Thousand Oaks, CA: Sage, © 2009.

Lonsdorf, T. B., Weike, A. I., Nikamo, P., Schalling, M., Hamm, A. O., and Öhman, A. (2009). Genetic gating of human fear learning and extinction: Possible implications for gene–environment interaction in Anxiety Disorder. *Psychological Science, 20*, 198–206.

Lovaas, O. I. (1977). *The autistic child: Language development through behavioral modification*. New York: Irvington.

Lovinger, D. M. (1997). Serotonin's role in alcohol's effects on the brain. *Alcohol Health and Research World, 21*, 2, 114–120.

Lowinson, J., Marion, I., Joseph, H., et al. (2005). Methadone maintenance. In J. Lowinson, P. Ruiz, R. Millman, & J. Langrod (Eds.), *Substance abuse: A comprehensive textbook* (4th ed., pp. 616–633). Philadelphia: Lippincott Williams and Wilkins.

Luby, J., Heffelfinger, A., Mrakotsky, C., Hessler, M., Brown, K., & Hildebrand, T. (2002). Preschool Major Depressive Disorder: Preliminary validation for developmentally modified DSM-IV criteria. *Journal of the American Academy of Child and Adolescent Psychiatry, 41*, 928–937.

Luman, M., Oosterlaan, J., & Sergeant, J. A. (2005). The impact of reinforcement contingencies on AD/HD: A review and theoretical appraisal. *Clinical Psychology Review, 25*, 183–213.

Lundgren, J. D., Danoff-Burg, S., & Anderson, D. A. (2004). Cognitive-behavioral therapy for Bulimia Nervosa: An empirical analysis of clinical significance. *International Journal of Eating Disorders, 35*(3), 262–274.

Lynch, W. C., Heil, D. P., Wagner, E., & Havens, M. D. (2008). Body dissatisfaction mediates the association between body mass index and risky weight control behaviors among White and Native American adolescent girls. *Appetite, 51*, 210–213.

Lyons, J., Kiser, K., Beck, V., Connors, K., Gardner, S., & Strieder, F. (2009). *Family Assessment of Needs and Strengths: Trauma Exposure and Adaptations* (FANS-TEA). Retrieved from https://www.fans.umaryland.edu

Lyons, J. A. (1987). Posttraumatic Stress Disorder in children and adolescents: A review of the literature. *Journal of Developmental and Behavioral Pediatrics, 8*, 349–356.

Maag, J. W. (1993). Cognitive-behavioral strategies for depressed students. *Reclaiming Children and Youth, 2*(2), 48–53.

Macfarlane, J. W., Allen, L., & Honzik, M. P. (1954). *A developmental study of the behavior problems of normal children between twenty-one months and fourteen years*. Berkeley, CA: University of California Press.

Mack, K. (2004). Explanations for Conduct Disorder. *Child and Youth Care Forum, 33*(2), 95–113. Published by Springer, © 2004.

MacLeod, A. K., Pankhania, B., Lee, M., & Mitchell, D. (1997). Parasuicide, depression and anticipation of positive and negative future experiences. *Psychological Medicine, 27*, 973–977.

MacLeod, C., Campbell, E., Rutherford, L., & Wilson, E. (2004). The causal status of anxiety-linked attentional and interpretive bias. In J. Yiend (Ed.), *Cognition, emotion and psychopathology: Theoretical, empirical and clinical directions* (pp. 172–189). New York: Cambridge University Press. doi:10.1017/CBO9780511521263.010

Magnusson, D. (1988). *Individual development from an interactional perspective*. Hillsdale, NJ: Lawrence Erlbaum Associates.

Magura, S., Rosenblum, A., Fong, C., Villano, C., & Richman, B. (2002). Treating cocaine-using methadone patients: Predictors of outcomes in a psychosocial clinical trial. *Substance Use and Misuse, 37*, 1927–1955.

Making the connection: Trauma and substance abuse. (2008). The National Child Traumatic Stress Network (NCTN). Retrieved from http://www.nctsn.org/sites/default/files/assets/pdfs/SAToolkit_1.pdf

Malchiodi, C. (2005). *Expressive techniques*. New York: Guilford.

Malchiodi, C. (2008). *Creative interventions with traumatized children*. New York: Guilford.

Mancini, C., Van Ameringen, M., Szatmari, P., Fugere, C., & Boyle, M. (1996). A high-risk pilot study of the children of adults with social phobia. *Journal of the American Academy of Child and Adolescent Psychiatry, 35*, 1511–1517.

Mandal, A. (2014). Autism history. Retrieved from http://www.news-medical.net/health/Autism-History.aspx

Mann, J. J. (2003). Neurobiology of suicidal behavior. *Nature Reviews: Neuroscience, 4*, 819–828.

Mann, J. J., Brent, D. A., & Arango, V. (2001). The neurobiology and genetics of suicide and attempted suicide: A focus on the serotonergic system. *Neuropsychopharmacology, 24*, 467–477.

Manos, R. C., Kanter, J. W., & Busch, A. M. (2010). A critical review of assessment strategies to measure the behavioral activation model of depression. *Clinical Psychology Review, 30*, 547–561.

Margolin, G. (1998). Effects of domestic violence on children. In P. K. Trickett & C. J. Schellenbach (Eds.), *Violence against children in the family and the community*. Washington, DC: American Psychological Association.

Marsch, L. A., Bickel, W. K., Badger, G. J., Stothart, M. E., Quesnel, K. J., Stanger, C., & Brooklyn, J. (2005). Comparison of pharmacological treatments for opioid-dependent adolescents: A randomized controlled trial. *Archives of General Psychiatry, 62*(10), 1157–1164.

Marsella, A. J. (2010). Ethnocultural aspects of PTSD: An overview of concepts, issues, and treatments. *Traumatology, 16*(4), 17–26. Published by American Psychological Association (APA), © 2010.

Marshall, J. K., & Mirenda, P. (2002). Parent–professional collaboration for positive behavior support in the home. *Focus on Autism and Other Developmental Disabilities, 17*(4), 216–228.

Martell, C. R., Addis, M. E., & Jacobson, N. S. (2001). *Depression in context: Strategies for guided action*. New York: W. W. Norton.

Martin, B. (2013). Additional treatments for ADHD. Psych Central. Retrieved from http://psychcentral.com/lib/additional-treatments-for-adhd

Martindale, B. V. (2007). Psychodynamic contributions to early intervention in psychosis. *Advances in Psychiatric Treatment, 13*, 34–42. Published by The Royal College of Psychiatrists, © 2007.

Massachusetts Advocates for Children. (2005). Helping traumatized children learn. Retrieved from http://traumasensitiveschools. org/tlpi-publications/download-a-free-copy-of-helping-traumatized-children-learn

Masten, A. S., & Powell, J. L. (2003). A resilience framework for research, policy, and practice. In S. S. Luthar (Ed.), *Resilience and vulnerability: Adaptation in the context of childhood adversities* (pp. 1–25). New York: Cambridge University Press.

Maté, G. (1999). *Scattered Minds: How Attention Deficit Disorder Originates And What You Can Do About It*. Published by Penguin USA, © 1999

Maté, G. (2000). *Scattered Minds: How Attention Deficit Disorder Originates And What You Can Do About It*. Published by Penguin USA, © 2000

Maté, G. (2004). *When the body says no: The hidden cost of stress*. Toronto: Vintage Canada.

Maté, G. (2008). *In the realm of hungry ghosts: Close encounters with addictions*. Toronto: Vintage Canada.

Matthews, J., & Moylan, A. (2005). Substance-related disorders: Cocaine and narcotics. In A. Stern & J. Herman (Eds.), *Massachusetts General Hospital Psychiatry and Board Preparation* (pp. 85–96). New York: McGraw-Hill.

Mattingly, M., Stuart, C., & VanderVen, K. (2002). North American Certification Project Competencies for professional child and youth work practitioners. *Journal of Child and Youth Care Work, 17*, 16–49.

Maude-Griffin, P. M., Hohenstein, J. M., Humfleet, G. L., Reilly, P. M., Tusel, D. J., & Hall, S. M. (1998). Superior efficacy of cognitive-behavioral therapy for urban crack cocaine abusers: main and matching effects. *Journal of Consulting and Clinical Psychology, 66*(5), 832–837.

McBurnett, K., & Lahey, B. B. (1994). Psychophysiological and neuroendocrine correlates of Conduct Disorder and antisocial behavior in children and adolescents. In D. C. Fowles, P. Sutker, & S. H. Goodman (Eds.), *Progress in experimental personality and psychopathology research* (pp. 199–231). New York: Springer.

McCaffery, J. M., Papandonatos, G. D., Stanton, C., Lloyd-Richardson, E. E., & Niaura, R. (2008). Depressive symptoms and cigarette smoking in twins from the National Longitudinal Study of Adolescent Health. *Health Psychology, 27*, S207–S215.

McClellan, J. M., & Werry, J. S. (2003). Evidence-based treatments in child and adolescent psychiatry: An inventory. *Journal of the American Academy of Child and Adolescent Psychiatry, 42*, 1388–1400.

McCloskey, L. A., & Walker, M. (2000). Posttraumatic stress in children exposed to family violence and single-event trauma. *Journal of the American Academy of Child and Adolescent Psychiatry, 39*, 108–115.

McClure, F. H., & Teyber, E. (2002). *Casebook in child and adolescent treatment: Cultural and familial contexts (Children & Adolescents)*. Published by Brooks/Cole, a division of Cengage Learning, © 2002.

McDaid, S. (2013). Recovery: What you should expect from a good quality mental health service. Retrieved from http://www.mentalhealthreform.ie/wp-content/uploads/2013/03/MHR-Recovery-paper-final-April-2013.pdf

McEachin, J. J., Smith, T., & Lovaas, O. I. (1993). Long-term outcome for children with autism who received early intensive behavioral treatment. *American Journal on Mental Retardation, 97*, 359–372.

McFarlane, A. C. (1988). The longitudinal course of posttraumatic morbidity: The range of outcomes and their predictors. *Journal of Nervous and Mental Disease, 176*, 30–39.

McFerran, K. (2005). Dangerous liaisons: Group work for adolescent girls who have Anorexia Nervosa. *Voices: A World Forum for Music Therapy, 5*(1). Retrieved from https://voices.no/index.php/voices/article/view/215/159

McGeady, M. R. (1999). The girl in the hood (and how we drew her out). *Reaching Today's Youth, 4*(1), 14–16.

McGorry, P., & Vickery, C. (2012). An integrated response to complexity: National Eating Disorders Framework. The Commonwealth Department of Health and Ageing. Published by Butterfly Foundation of Eating Disorders, a unit of the Commonwealth of Canada. Retrieved from http://www.nedc.com.au/files/pdfs/National%20Framework%20An%20integrated%20Response%20to%20Complexity%202012%20-%20Final.pdf

McKay, D., & Storch, E. A. (Eds). (2009). *Cognitive behavior therapy for children: Treating complex and refractory cases*. New York: Springer.

McKay, M. M., & Bannon, W. M. J. (2004). Engaging families in child mental health services. *Child and Adolescent Psychiatric Clinics of North America, 13*(4), 905–921. Published by Elselvier. © 2004.

McKenzie, F. R. (2008). *Theory and practice with adolescents: An applied approach*. Chicago: Lyceum Books Inc., © 2008.

McLeod, B. D., Wood, J. J., & Weisz, J. R. (2007). Examining the association between parenting and childhood anxiety: A meta-analysis. *Clinical Psychology Review, 27*(2), 155–172.

McLoone, J., Hudson, J. L., & Rapee, R. M. (2006). Treating anxiety disorders in a school setting. *Education and Treatment of Children, 29*, 219–242.

McMahon, R. J., & Kotler, J. S. (2008). Evidence-based therapies for oppositional behaviors in young children. In R. G. Steele, T. D.

Elkin, & M. C. Roberts (Eds.), *Handbook of evidence-based therapies for children and adolescents*. New York: Springer.

McMains, B., Maynard, A., & Conlan, L. (2003). Conduct disorder: Treatment recommendations for Vermont youth from the State Interagency team. Fall 2003. Published by Vermont Federation of Families for Children's Mental Health, © 2003. Retrieved from http://mentalhealth.vermont.gov/sites/dmh/files/publications/DMH-CAFU_Conduct_Disorder_Treatment.pdf

McNally, R. J. (2000). Information-processing abnormalities in Obsessive-Compulsive Disorder. In W. K. Goodman, M. V. Rudorfer, & J. D. Maser (Eds.), *Obsessive-Compulsive Disorder: Contemporary issues in treatment* (pp. 105–116). Mahwah, NJ: Erlbaum.

McWhirter, J. J., McWhirter, B. T., McWhirter, E. H., & McWhirter, R. J. (2007). *At risk youth*. Belmont, CA: Brooks/Cole.

McWhirter, J. J., McWhirter, B. T., McWhirter, E. H., & McWhirter, R. J. (2013). *At risk youth* (4th ed.). Belmont, CA: Brooks/Cole.

McWilliams, N. (1994). *Psychoanalytic diagnosis: Understanding personality structure in the clinical process*. New York: Guilford Press.

Medina-Mora, M. E., Rascon, M. L., Otero, B. R., & Gutierrez, E. (1988). Patrones de consumo. In M. J. Gilbert (Ed.), *Alcohol consumption among Mexicans and Mexican Americans: A binational perspective* (pp. 27–52). Los Angeles: Spanish Speaking Mental Health Research Center, University of California.

Meehan, K. G., Loeb, K., Roberto, C., & Attia, E. (2006). Mood change during weight restoration. *International Journal of Eating Disorders*, 39, 587–589.

Meichenbaum, D. (n.d.). Understanding resilience in children and adults: Implications for prevention and interventions. Published by The Melissa Institute For Violence Prevention and Treatment. Retrieved from http://www.melissainstitute.org/documents/resilienceinchildren.pdf

Mellin, L. M., Irwin, C. E., Jr., & Scully, S. (1992). Prevalence of disordered eating in girls: A survey of middle-class children. *Journal of the American Dietetic Association*, 92, 851–853.

Melrose, R. (2006). Why Students Underachieve: What Educators and Parents Can Do About It. Published by Rowman & Littlefield Education. © 2006.

Melrose, R. (2009). Not ADHD, not bipolar, not learning disabilities: Trauma. Retrieved from http://ezinearticles.com/?Not-ADHD,-Not-Bipolar,-Not-Learning-Disabilities—Trauma&id=1862616

Meltzer, H. Y. (2002). Mechanism of action of atypical antipsychotic drugs. In K. L. Davis, D. Charney, J. T. Coyle, & C. Nemeroff (Eds.), *Neuropsychopharmacology: The fifth generation of progress*. Brentwood, TN: American College of Neuropsychopharmacology.

Mental health: Myths and facts. (n.d.). Retrieved from http://www.mentalhealth.gov/basics/myths-facts

Mental Health Commission of Canada. (2012). *Changing directions, changing lives: The mental health strategy for Canada*. Calgary: Author.

Mental Health Commission of Canada. (2013). *School-based mental health in Canada: A final report*. Retrieved from http://www.mentalhealthcommission.ca/English/system/files/private/document/ChildYouth_School_Based_Mental_Health_Canada_Final_Report_ENG.pdf

Mental status examination. (2012). Retrieved from http://medical-dictionary.thefreedictionary.com/Mental+status+examination

Micali, N., & House, J. (2011). Assessment measures for child and adolescent eating disorders: A review. *Child and Adolescent Mental Health*, 16, 122–127.

Michelson, D., Allen, J., Busner, J., Casat, C., Dunn, D., Kratochvil, C., . . . Harder, D. (2002). Once-daily atomoxetine treatment for children and adolescents with Attention Deficit/Hyperactivity Disorder: A randomized, placebo-controlled study. *American Journal of Psychiatry*, 159, 1896–1901.

Midgley, N., and Kennedy, E. (2011). Psychodynamic psychotherapy for children and adolescents: A critical review of the evidence base. *Journal of Child Psychotherapy*, 37(3), 1–29.

Miles, D. R., & Carey, G. (1997). Genetic and environmental architecture of human aggression. *Journal of Personality and Social Psychology*, 72, 207–217.

Miles, J. (2011). Autism spectrum disorders—A genetics review. *Genetics in Medicine*, 13, 278–294. Retrieved from http://www.nature.com/gim/journal/v13/n4/full/gim9201151a.html

Miller, J. (2012). Cyc-net ODD discussion thread.

Miller, L. D. (2008). Facing fears: The feasibility of anxiety universal prevention efforts with children and adolescents. *Cognitive and Behavioral Practice*, 15, 28–35.

Miller, M., & Hinshaw, S. P. (2012). Hyperactivity. Encyclopedia on Early Childhood Development. Retrieved from http://www.child-encyclopedia.com/Pages/PDF/hyperactivity.pdf

Miller, W. R., & Rollnick, S. (1991). *Motivational interviewing: Preparing people to change addictive behavior*. New York: Guilford.

Miller, W. R., & Rollnick, S. (2002). *Motivational interviewing: Preparing people for change* (2nd ed.). New York: Guilford.

Milrod, B., Leon, A. C., Busch, F., Rudden, M., Schwalberg, M., Clarkin, J., . . . Shear, M. K. (2007). A randomized controlled clinical trial of psychoanalytic psychotherapy for Panic Disorder. *American Journal of Psychiatry*, 164, 265–272.

Mineka, S., & Zinbarg, R. (2006). A contemporary learning theory perspective on the etiology of anxiety disorders: It's not what you thought it was. *American Psychologist*, 61, 10–26.

Minuchin, S., Rosman, B. L., & Baker, B. L. (1978). *Psychosomatic families: Anorexia Nervosa in context*. Cambridge, MA: Harvard University Press.

Mitchell, R. (2003). Ideological reflections on the DSM-IV-R (or pay no attention to that man behind the curtain, Dorothy!). *Child and Youth Care Forum*, 32(5), 281–298. Published by Human Sciences Press, © 2003.

Mitchell, T. L., & Maracle, D. T. (2005, March). Healing the generations: Post-traumatic stress and the health status of Aboriginal populations. *Journal of Aboriginal Health*, 2(1), 14–24. Published by National Aboriginal Health Organization, © 2005.

Modestin, J., Matutat, B., & Würmle, O. (2001). Antecedents of opioid dependence and personality disorder: Attention–Deficit/Hyperactivity Disorder and Conduct Disorder. *European Archives of Psychiatry and Clinical Neuroscience*, 251(1), 42–47.

Moffitt, T. E. (1993). "Life-course persistent" and "adolescent-limited" anti-social behavior: A developmental taxonomy. *Psychological Review*, 100, 674–701.

Moffitt, T. E., & Lynam, D. R. (1994). The neuropsychology of Conduct Disorder and delinquency: Implications for understanding antisocial behavior. In D. Fowles, P. Sutker, and S. Goodman (Eds.), *Psychopathy and antisocial personality: A developmental perspective* (pp. 233–262). Vol. 18 in the series Progress in Experimental Personality and Psychopathology Research. New York: Springer.

Moos, R. H. (1993). *CRI-youth professional manual*. Odessa, FL: Psychological Assessment Resources, Inc.

Moradi, A. R., Taghavi, M. R., Doost, H. T. N., Yule, W., & Dalgleish, T. (1999). Performance of children and adolescents with PTSD on the Stroop colour-naming task. *Psychological Medicine, 29*, 415–419.

Moroz, K. J. (2005). *The effects of psychological trauma on children and adolescents*. Waterbury, VT: Vermont Agency of Human Services.

Morris, B. (2008). Relationship development intervention. Retrieved from http://www.autism-help.org/intervention-relationship-development-1.htm

Morrison, A. P. (1998). A cognitive analysis of auditory hallucinations: Are voices to Schizophrenia what bodily sensations are to panic? *Behavioral and Cognitive Psychotherapy, 26*, 289–302.

Morrison, J. (2007). *Diagnosis made easier: Principles and techniques for mental health clinicians*. New York: Guilford.

Moulds, M. L., & Nixon, R. D. V. (2006). In vivo flooding for anxiety disorders: Proposing its utility in the treatment Posttraumatic Stress Disorder. *Journal of Anxiety Disorders, 20*(4), 498–509.

Mowrer, O. H. (1948). Learning theory and the neurotic paradox. *American Journal of Orthopsychiatry, 18*, 571–610.

Mowrer, O. H. (1960). *Learning theory and behavior*. New York: Wiley.

MTA Cooperative Group. (2004). National Institute of Mental Health multimodal treatment study of ADHD follow-up: Changes in effectiveness and growth after the end of treatment. *Pediatrics, 113*(4), 762–769.

Mufson, L., Weissman, M. M., Moreau, D., & Garfinkel, R. (1999). Efficacy of interpersonal psychotherapy for depressed adolescents. *Archives of General Psychiatry, 56*(6), 573–579.

Mulford, C. F., & Redding, R. E. (2008). Training the parents of juvenile offenders: State of the art and recommendations for service delivery. *Journal of Child and Family Studies, 17*, 629–648.

Mulvihill, D. (2005). The health impact of childhood trauma: An interdisciplinary review, 1997–2003. *Issues in Comprehensive Pediatric Nursing, 28*, 115–136.

Muris, P. (2007). Unique and interactive effects of neuroticism and effortful control on psychopathological symptoms in non-clinical adolescents. *Personality and Individual Differences, 40*, 1409–1419.

Muris, P., & Broeren, S. (2009). Twenty-five years of research on childhood anxiety disorders: Publication trends between 1982 and 2006 and a selective review of the literature. *Journal of Child and Family Studies, 18*, 388–395.

Muris, P., & Meesters, C. (2002). Attachment, behavioral inhibition, and anxiety disorders symptoms in normal adolescents. *Journal of Psychopathology and Behavioral Assessment, 24*, 97–106.

Muris, P., & Merckelbach, H. (2001). The etiology of childhood specific phobia: A multifactorial model. In M. W. Vasey & M. R. Dadds (Eds.), *The developmental psychopathology of anxiety* (pp. 355–385). New York: Oxford University Press.

Muris, P., van Brakel, A. M. L., Arntz, A., & Schouten, E. (2011). Behavioral inhibition as a risk factor for the development of childhood anxiety disorders: A longitudinal study. *Journal of Child and Family Studies, 20*, 157–170.

Murphy, D. A., Pelham, W. E., & Lang, A. R. (1992). Aggression in boys with Attention Deficit–Hyperactivity Disorder: Methylphenidate effects on naturalistically observed aggression, response to provocation in the laboratory, and social information processing. *Journal of Abnormal Child Psychology, 20*, 451–466.

Murphy, S., Russell, L., & Waller, G. (2005). Integrated psychodynamic therapy for bulimia nervosa and binge eating disorder: Theory, practice, and preliminary findings. *European Eating Disorders Review, 13*(6), 383–391.

Myers, S. M., & Johnson, C. P. (2007). Identification and evaluation of children with autism spectrum disorders. *Pediatrics, 120*(5), 1183–1215.

Myths about mental illness. (n.d.). Retrieved from http://www.cmha.ca/mental_health/myths-about-mental-illness

Myths about Posttraumatic Stress Disorder. (2001). PTSD Alliance. Retrieved from http://www.ptsdalliance.org

Myths about suicide. (2011). Centre for Suicide Prevention. Retrieved from http://www.suicideinfo.ca/LinkClick.aspx?fileticket=nIm4k7bARLc%3d&tabid=531

Nadder, T. S., Silberg, J. L., Rutter, M., Maes, H. H., & Eaves, L. J. (2001). Comparison of multiple measures of ADHD symptomatology: A multivariate genetic analysis. *Journal of Child Psychology and Psychiatry, 42*, 475–486.

Nader, K., & Einarsson, E. O. (2010). Memory reconsolidation: An update. *Annals of New York Academy of Science, 1191*, 27–41.

National Alcohol Strategy Working Group. (2007). Reducing alcohol-related harm in Canada: Toward a culture of moderation—Recommendations for a national alcohol strategy. Retrieved from http://www.ccsa.ca/Resource%20Library/ccsa-023876-2007.pdf

National Alliance on Mental Illness. (n.d.). Schizophrenia. Retrieved from https://www.nami.org/getattachment/Learn-More/Mental-Health-Fact-Sheet-Library/Schizophrenia-Fact-Sheet.pdf

National Child Traumatic Stress Network. (n.d.). Narrative exposure therapy for traumatized children and adolescents. National Insutute of Justice. Retrieved from https://www.crimesolutions.gov/default.aspx

National Institute of Mental Health (NIMH). (2008). *Bipolar Disorder*. NIH Publication No. 02-3679. Washington, DC: Author.

National Institute of Mental Health Research Roundtable on Prepubertal Bipolar Disorder. (2001). *Journal of the American Academy of Child and Adolescent Psychiatry, 40*, 871–878.

National Institute of Neurological Disorders and Stroke. (2014). Autism fact sheet. Retrieved from http://www.ninds.nih.gov/disorders/autism/detail_autism.htm

National Institute on Drug Abuse (NIDA). (1997). *Preventing drug abuse among children and adolescents: A research-based guide for parents, educators, and community leaders* (2nd ed.). Bethesda, MD: Author.

National Resource Center on ADHD. (2015). ADHD Science, Information, Resources, Support. Retrieved from http://www.help4adhd.org/index.cfm?varLang=en

Navaneelan, T. (2012). Suicide rates: An overview. Statistics Canada. Retrieved from http://www.statcan.gc.ca/pub/82-624-x/2012001/article/11696-eng.htm

Neil, J. (2006). What is locus of control? Psychology class tutorial. Retrieved from http://wilderdom.com/psychology/loc/LocusOfControlWhatIs.html

Neill, A. S. (1926). *The problem child*. London: Herbert Jenkins.

Nelson, J. R. (1996). Designing schools to meet the needs of students who exhibit disruptive behavior. *Journal of Emotional and Behavioral Disorders, 4*(3), 147–161.

Neufeld, G., & Maté, G. (2004). *Hold on to your kids: Why parents need to matter more*. Published by Ballantine Books, © 2006.

Neumark-Sztainer, D., Story, M., Hannan, P. J., Perry, C., & Irving, L. M. (2002). Weight-related concerns and behaviors among overweight and non overweight adolescents: Implications for preventing weight-related disorders. *Archives of Pediatrics and Adolescent Medicine, 156,* 171–178.

Nevid, D., Rathus, S., & Greene, B. (2010). *Abnormal psychology in a changing world* (8th ed.) Toronto: Pearson.

Nevo, G. A., & Manassis, K. (2009). Outcomes for treated anxious children: A critical review of long-term-follow-up studies. *Depression and Anxiety, 26,* 650–660.

Newmark, S. (2010). There is so much more we can do to help children with ADHD. Retrieved from http://adhdwithoutdrugs.info

Ngan, V. (2014). Compulsive skin picking. Retrieved from http://dermnetnz.org/systemic/skin-picking.html

Nicholson, R., & Rapoport, J. (2000). Childhood Onset Schizophrenia: What can it teach us? In J. L. Rapoport (Ed.), *Childhood onset of "adult" psychopathology* (pp. 167–192). Washington, DC: American Psychiatric Publications Inc.

Nigg, J. T., & Hinshaw, S. P. (1998). Parent personality traits and psychopathology associated with antisocial behaviors in childhood Attention-Deficit Hyperactivity Disorder. *Journal of Child Psychology and Psychiatry, 39,* 145–160.

Nigg, J. T., and Huang-Pollock, C. L. (2003). An early-onset model of the role of executive functions and intelligence in Conduct Disorder/delinquency. In B. B. Lahey, T. E. Moffitt, & A. Caspi (Eds.), *Causes of Conduct Disorder and juvenile delinquency* (pp. 227–253). New York: Guilford.

Nissen, L. B. (1994). Strength-based bill of rights for teens in the juvenile justice system. Retrieved from http://www.cyc-net.org/Journals/rcy/rcy-15-3.html

Nock, M. K., Cha, C. B., & Dour, H. J. (2011). Disorders of impulse-control and self-harm. In D. H. Barlow (Ed.), *Oxford handbook of clinical psychology* (pp. 504–529). New York: Oxford University.

Nock, M. K., Kazdin, A. E., Hiripi, E., & Kessler, R. C. (2007). Lifetime prevalence, correlates, and persistence of Oppositional Defiant Disorder: Results from the National Comorbidity Survey Replication. *Journal of Child Psychology and Psychiatry, 48*(7), 703–713.

Noll, J. G., Trickett, P. K., Susman, E. J., & Putnam, F. W. (2006). Sleep disturbances and childhood sexual abuse. *Journal of Pediatric Psychology, 31,* 469–480.

Norris, F. H., Baker, C. K., Murphy, A. D., & Kaniasty, K. (2005). Social support mobilization and deterioration after Mexico's 1999 flood: Effects of context, gender and time. *American Journal of Community Psychology, 36,* 15–28.

Norris, S. (2006). *Potential causes of Autism Spectrum Disorders.* Parliament of Canada Science and Technology Division. Retrieved from http://www.parl.gc.ca/Content/LOP/ResearchPublications/prb0587-e.htm

Norris, S., Paré, J.-R., & Starky, S. (2006). Childhood autism in Canada: Some issues relating to behavioral intervention. Parliament of Canada. Retrieved from http://www.parl.gc.ca/Content/LOP/ResearchPublications/prb0593-e.htm

Norton, J. (1982). *Expressed emotion, affective style, voice tone and communication deviance as predictors of offspring Schizophrenia spectrum disorders.* Unpublished doctoral dissertation, University of California, Los Angeles.

Nottelmann, E. D., & Jensen, P. S. (1995). Comorbidity of disorders in children and adolescents: Developmental perspectives. In T. H. Ollendick & R. J. Prinz (Eds.), *Advances in clinical child psychology* (Vol. 17, pp. 109–155). New York: Plenum Press.

Nutt, D. J., Fone, K., Asherson, P., et al. (2007). Evidence-based guidelines for management of Attention-Deficit/Hyperactivity Disorder in adolescents in transition to adult services and in adults: Recommendations from the British Association for Psychopharmacology. *Journal of Psychopharmacology, 21,* 10–41.

O'Conner, T. G., Neiderhiser, J., Reiss, D., Hetherington, E., & Plomin, R. (1998). Genetic contributions to continuity, change, and co-occurrence of antisocial and depressive symptoms in adolescence. *Journal of Child Psychology and Psychiatry, 39,* 323–336.

O'Connor, R. C. (2011). The integrated motivational–volitional model of suicidal behavior. *Crisis, 32,* 295–298.

O'Connor, R. C., & Nock, M. K. (2014). The psychology of suicidal behavior. *Lancet Psychiatry, 1,* 73–85.

O'Connor, R. C., Smyth, R., Ferguson, E., Ryan, C., & Williams, J. M. G. (2013). Psychological processes and repeat suicidal behavior: A four-year prospective study. *Journal of Consulting and Clinical Psychology, 81,* 1137–1143.

O'Hanlon, T., & Rowan, B. (1998). *Solution-oriented therapy for chronic and severe mental illness.* New York: Wiley.

Olson, M., Seikkula, J., & Ziedonis, D. (2014). The key elements of dialogic practice in open dialogue: Fidelity criteria. Retrieved from http://umassmed.edu/psychiatry/globalinitiatives/opendialogue

Olsson, M. (2009). DSM diagnosis of Conduct Disorder (CD)—A review. *Nordic Journal of Psychiatry, 63*(2), 102–112. Published by World Psychiatric Association, © 2009.

Oppositional Defiant and Conduct Disorders. (n.d.). Retrieved from http://vcoy.virginia.gov/pdf/OppositionalDefiant_ConductDisorders0513docx.pdf

Overstreet, S., & Burch, B. (n.d.). Mental health status of women and children following Hurricane Katrina. Retrieved from http://tulane.edu/nccrow/upload/NCCROWreport08-chapter7.pdf

Oyserman, D. (2004). Depression during the school-age years. In P. Allen-Meares & M. W. Fraser (Eds.), *Intervention with children and adolescents: An interdisciplinary perspective* (pp. 264–281). Boston: Pearson.

Ozer, E. J., Best, S. R., Lipsey, T. L., & Weiss, D. S. (2003). Predictors of Posttraumatic Stress Disorder and symptoms in adults: A meta-analysis. *Psychological Bulletin, 129,* 52–73.

Ozonoff, S., Young, G. S., Carter, A., Messinger, D., Yirmiya, N., Zwaigenbaum, L., & Stone, W. L. (2011). Recurrence risk for Autism Spectrum Disorders: A baby siblings research consortium study. *Pediatrics, 128*(3), e488–e495.

Palumbo, J. (2011). Executive disorders and self-deficits. In A. Gitterman & N. Heller (Eds.), *Mental health and social problems: A social work perspective.* New York: Routledge, © 2011.

Pan, L. A., Hassel, S., Segreti, A. M., Nau, S. A., Brent, D. A., & Phillips, M. L. (2013). Differential patterns of activity and functional connectivity in emotion processing neural circuitry to angry and happy faces in adolescents with and without suicide attempt. *Psychological Medicine, 43,* 2129–2142.

Papolos, D. (2003). Bipolar Disorder and comorbid disorders: The case for a dimensional nosology. In B. Geller & M. P. DelBello (Eds.), *Bipolar Disorder in childhood and early adolescence* (pp. 76–106). New York: Guilford.

Parsons, T. D., & Rizzo, A. A. (2008). Affective outcomes of virtual reality exposure therapy for anxiety and specific phobias: A meta-analysis. *Journal of Behavior Therapy and Experimental Psychiatry, 39,* 250–261.

Paris, J. (2013). *The intelligent clinician's guide to the DSM-5.* New York: Oxford University Press, © 2015.

Patel, S. D., Le-Niculescu, H., Koller, D. L., Green, S. D., Lahiri, D. K., McMahon, F. J., Nurnberger, J., I. Jr., & Niculescu, A. B., III. (2010). Coming to grips with complex disorders: Genetic risk prediction in Bipolar Disorder using panels of genes identified through convergent functional genomics. *American Journal of Medical Genetics, Part B, Neuropsychiatric Genetics, 153B,* 850–877.

Patterson, G. R. (1992). Developmental changes in antisocial behavior. In R. DeV. Peters, R. J. McMahon, & V. L. Quinsey (Eds.), *Aggression and violence throughout the life span* (pp. 52–82). Newbury Park, CA: Sage.

Patterson, G. E., Chamberlain, P., & Reid, J. B. (1982). A comparative evaluation of a parent-training program. *Behavior Therapy, 13,* 638–650.

Patterson, G. R., Reid, J. B., & Dishion, T. J. (1992). *Antisocial boys.* Eugene, OR: Castalia.

Patterson, T. L., & Leeuwenkamp, O. R. (2008). Adjunctive psychosocial therapies for the treatment of Schizophrenia. *Schizophrenia Research, 100,* 108–119.

Patton, G. C., Selzer, R., Coffey, C., Carlin, J. B., & Wolfe, R. (1999). Onset of adolescent eating disorders: Population based cohort study over 3 years. *British Medical Journal, 318,* 765–768.

Pavlov, I. (1926). *Conditioned reflexes.* London: Oxford University Press.

Pearson, P. (2006 September 4). Fear is shaping our children. Copyright © 2006 by USA Today. Used by permission of USA Today. Retrieved from http://usatoday30.usatoday.com/printedition/news/20060905/oplede15.art.htm

Peeples, L. (2012, May 24). Autism's rising rates increasingly blamed on toxic chemicals. *Huffington Post.* Retrieved from http://www.huffingtonpost.com/2012/05/24/autism-toxic-chemicals-children-environment-risk-factors_n_1543316.html

Peleg-Popko, O., & Dar, R. (2003). Ritual behavior in children and mothers' perceptions of family patterns. *Journal of Anxiety Disorders, 17,* 667–681.

Pelham, W. E., & Fabiano, G. A. (2008). Evidence-based psychosocial treatment for Attention Deficit/Hyperactivity Disorder. *Journal of Clinical Child and Adolescent Psychology, 37*(1), 184–214.

Penadés, R., Catalán, R., Salamero, M., Boget, T., Puig, O., Guarch, J., & Gastó, C. (2006). Cognitive Remediation Therapy for outpatients with chronic Schizophrenia: A controlled and randomized study. *Schizophrenia Research, 87,* 323–331.

Penn, M. & Savage, S. (2004). Walking the Talk with Family and Youth Involvement. Powerpoint presentation. Technical Assistance Partnership for Child and Family Mental Health, © 2004. http://www.tapartnership.org/specialmeetings/Regional04/Regional04.asp

Perisse, D., Amiet, C., Thone, M. V., Gourfinkel, A. I., Bodeau, N., Guinchat, V., Barthelemy, C., & Cohen, D. (2010). Risk factors of acute behavioral regression in psychiatrically hospitalized adolescents with autism. *Journal of the Canadian Academy of Child and Adolescent Psychiatry, 19*(2), 100–108.

Perry, B. D. (1994). Neurobiological sequelae of childhood trauma: Post-Traumatic Stress Disorders in children. In M. Murberg (Ed.), *Catecholamines in Post-Traumatic Stress Disorder: Emerging concepts* (pp. 253–276). Washington, DC: American Psychiatric Press.

Perry, B. D. (2001). The neuroarcheology of childhood maltreatment: The neurodevelopmental costs of adverse childhood events. In K. Franey, R. Geffner, & R. Falconer (Eds.), *The cost of maltreatment: Who pays? We all do.* San Diego, CA: Family Violence and Sexual Assault Institute.

Perry, B. D. (2004). Understanding traumatized and maltreated children: The core concepts. Published by The Child Trauma Academy. Retrieved from http://www.lfcc.on.ca/Perry_Core_Concepts_Violence_and_Childhood.pdf

Perry, B. D. (2005). *Maltreatment and the developing child: How early childhood experience shapes child and culture.* London, ON: The Margaret McCain Lecture Series.

Perry, B. D. (2006). The Neurosequential Model of Therapeutics: Applying principles of neuroscience to clinical work with traumatized and maltreated children. In Nancy Boyd Webb (Ed.), *Working with traumatized youth in child welfare* (pp. 27–52). New York: Guilford, © 2008.

Perry, B. D. (2008). Preface, in Malchiodi, C. A., *Creative interventions with traumatized children.* New York: Guilford.

Perry, B. D. (2009). Examining child maltreatment through a neurodevelopmental lens: Clinical applications of the Neurosequential Model of Therapeutics. *Journal of Loss and Trauma, 14,* 240–255. Retrieved from http://childtrauma.org/wpcontent/uploads/2013/09/TraumaLoss_BDP_Final_7_09.pdf

Perry, B. D. (2012). *Don't try this at home.* Retrieved from http://attachmentdisorderhealing.com/developmental-trauma-3

Perry, B. D. (2014). Helping traumatized children: A brief overview for caregivers. Retrieved from https://childtrauma.org/wp-content/uploads/2014/01/Helping_Traumatized_Children_Caregivers_Perry1.pdf

Perry, B. D., Colwell, K., & Schick, S. (2002). Child neglect. In D. Levinson (Ed.), *Encyclopedia of Crime and Punishment, Vol. 1.* Thousand Oaks: Sage Publications. Retrieved from http://www.childtrauma.org

Perry, B. D., & Hambrick, E. (2008). The Neurosequential Model of Therapeutics. *Reclaiming Children and Youth, 17*(3), 38–43.

Perry, B. D., Pollard, R. A., Blakley, T. L., Baker, W. L., & Vigilante, D. (1995). Childhood trauma, the neurobiology of adaptation and use-dependent development of the brain: How states become traits. *Infant Mental Health Journal, 16,* 271–291.

Pervanidou, P. (2008). Biology of Post-Traumatic Stress Disorder in childhood and adolescence. *Journal of Neuroendocrinology, 20,* 632–638.

Phobias and Panic Disorders. (2015). Canadian Mental Health Association: Mental Health for All. Retrieved from: http://www.cmha.ca/mental_health/phobias-and-panic-disorder

Pike, K., Walsh, B., Vitousek, K., Wilson, G., & Bauer, J. (2003). Cognitive behavior therapy in the posthospitalization treatment of Anorexia Nervosa. *The American Journal of Psychiatry, 160,* 2046–2049.

Pike, K. M., & Borovoy, A. (2004). The rise of eating disorders in Japan: Issues of culture and limitations of the model of "Westernization." *Culture Medicine and Psychiatry, 28*(4), 493–531.

Pinhas, L., Toner, B. B., Ali, A., Garfinkel, P. E., & Stuckless, N. (1999). The effects of the ideal of female beauty on mood and body satisfaction. *International Journal of Eating Disorders, 25,* 223–226.

Pinto, R. (2009). Comorbid mood and substance use disorders in relation to youth suicide. Unpublished thesis. McGill University,

Montreal. Retrieved from http://digitool.library.mcgill.ca/webclient/StreamGate?folder_id=0&dvs=1416165839610~452

Plomin, R., Owen, M. J., & McGuffin, P. (1994). The genetic basis of complex human behaviors. *Science, 264*, 1733–1739.

Pogarell, O., Hamann, C., Popperl, G., Juckel, G., Chouker, M., Zaudig, M., Riedel, M., Moller, H. J., Hegerl, U., & Tatsch, K. (2003). Elevated brain serotonin transporter availability in patients with Obsessive-Compulsive Disorder. *Biological Psychiatry, 54*, 1406–1413.

Polanczyk, G., de Lima, M. S., Horta, B. L., Biederman, J., & Rohde, L. A. (2007). The worldwide prevalence of ADHD: A systematic review and metaregression analysis. *American Journal of Psychiatry, 164*, 942–948.

Pompili, M., Serafini, G., Innamorati, M., Moller-Leimkuhler, A. M., Giupponi, G., Girardi, P., et al. (2010). The hypothalamic–pituitary–adrenal axis and serotonin abnormalities: A selective overview for the implications of suicide prevention. *European Archives of Psychiatry and Clinical Neuroscience, 260*(8), 583–600.

Poole, N. (2012). Essentials of trauma-informed care. The Canadian Network of Substance Abuse and Allied Professionals. Retrieved from http://bccewh.bc.ca/wp-content/uploads/2014/05/PT-Trauma-informed-Care-2012-01-en.pdf

Popper, C. W., Gammon, G. D., West, S. A., & Bailey, C. E. (2003). Disorders usually first diagnosed in infancy, childhood or adolescence. In R. E. Hales & S. C. Yodofsky (Eds.), *Textbook of clinical psychiatry* (4th ed.). Washington, DC: American Psychiatric Publishing.

Posner, M. (2011, November 9). B.C. doctor agrees to stop using Amazonian plant to treat addictions. *The Globe and Mail*. Retrieved from http://www.theglobeandmail.com/life/health-and-fitness/bc-doctor-agrees-to-stop-using-amazonian-plant-to-treat-addictions/article4250579

Post-Traumatic Stress Disorder. (n.d.). U.S. Department of Health and Human Services National Institutes of Health NIH Publication No. 08-6388. Retrieved from http://www.nimh.nih.gov/health/publications/post-traumatic-stress-disorder-ptsd/complete-index.shtml

Poulakis, Z., & Wertheim, E. H. (1993). Relationships among dysfunctional cognitions, depressive symptoms, and bulimic tendencies. *Cognitive Therapy and Research, 17*, 549–559.

Poulin, C. (2006). *Harm reduction policies and programs for youth*. Ottawa: Canadian Centre on Substance Abuse.

Powell, N. R., Lochman, J. E., & Boxmeyer, C. L. (2007). The prevention of conduct problems. *International Review of Psychiatry, 19*(6), 597–605.

Powers, M. B., & Emmelkamp, P. M. G. (2008). Virtual reality exposure therapy for anxiety disorders: A meta-analysis. *Journal of Anxiety Disorders, 22*(3), 561–569.

Powers, M. B., Halpern, J. M., Ferenschak, M. P., Gillihan, S. J., & Foa, E. B. (2010). A meta-analytic review of prolonged exposure for Posttraumatic Stress Disorder. *Clinical Psychology Review, 30*(6), 635–641. Retrieved from http://dx.doi.org/10.1016/J.Cpr.2010.04.007

Poznanski, E. O., & Mokros, H. B. (1994). Phenomenology and epidemiology of mood disorders in children and adolescents. In W. M. Reynolds & H. F. Johnston (Eds.), *Handbook of depression in children and adolescents* (pp. 19–40). New York: Plenum Press.

Preventing and treating eating disorders in children and youth. (2005). Children's Mental Health Policy Research Program, University of British Columbia. Retrieved from http://childhealthpolicy.ca/wp-content/themes/chpc/pdf/RR-10-05-summary.pdf

Preventing Schizophrenia: Tactics and risk reduction strategies. (2014). Retrieved from http://schizophrenia.com/prev1.htm#

Prochaska, J. O., DiClemente, C. C., & Norcross, J. C. (1992). In search of how people change. *American Psychologist, 47*, 1102–1104.

Prochaska, J. O., Norcross, J., & DiClemente, C. (1995). *Changing for good: A revolutionary six-stage program for overcoming bad habits and moving your life positively forward*. New York: Avon Books.

Program policy framework for early intervention in psychosis. (2004). Copyright by the Queen's Printer for Ontario, © 2004. Retrieved from http://www.health.gov.on.ca/en/common/ministry/publications/reports/mentalhealth/psychosis.pdf

Psycho-education. (2014). National Eating Disorder Information Centre. Retrieved from http://nedic.ca/psycho-education

Public Health Agency of Canada. (2002). *A report on mental illnesses in Canada*. Copyright © 2009 by the Public Health Agency of Canada. Used by permission of the Public Health Agency of Canada. Retrieved from http://www.phac-aspc.gc.ca/publicat/miic-mmac/chap_7-eng.php

Public Health Agency of Canada. (2009). The health of Canadian children. In *Report: The state of public health in Canada: 2009*. Retrieved from http://www.phac-aspc.gc.ca/cphorsphc-respcacsp/2009/fr-rc/cphorsphc-respcacsp06-eng.php

Purdon, C., Rowa, K., & Antony, M. M. (2005). Thought suppression and its effects on thought frequency, appraisal and mood state in individuals with Obsessive-Compulsive Disorder. *Behaviour Research and Therapy, 43*, 93–108.

Putnam, F. W. (2006). The impact of trauma on child development. *Juvenile and Family Court Journal, 57*(1), 1–11. Retrieved from http://www.nctsnet.org/nctsn_assets/pdfs/edu_materials/Winter%2006_Putnam.pdf

Quay, H. C. (1993). The psychobiology of undersocialized aggressive Conduct Disorder: A theoretical perspective. *Development and Psychopathology, 5*, 165–180.

Quick facts: Myths about Conduct Disorder. (n.d.). Child Mind Institute. Retrieved from http://www.childmind.org/en/myths-about-conduct-disorder

Quick facts: Myths about Oppositional Defiant Disorder. (n.d.). Child Mind Institute. Retrieved from http://www.childmind.org/en/myths-about-ODD

Rachman, S. (1997). A cognitive theory of obsessions. *Behavior Research and Therapy, 35*, 793–802.

Rafalovich, A. (2001). The conceptual history of Attention Deficit Hyperactivity Disorder: Idiocy, imbecility, encephalitis and the child deviant, 1877–1929. *Deviant Behavior: An Interdisciplinary Journal, 22*, 93–115.

Raine, A. (2002). Annotation: The role of prefrontal deficits, low autonomic arousal, and early health factors in the development of antisocial and aggressive behavior in children. *Journal of Child Psychology and Psychiatry, 43*, 417–434.

Raine, A., Lencz, T., Bihrle, S., LaCasse, L., & Colletti, P. (2000). Reduced prefrontal gray matter volume and reduced autonomic activity in antisocial personality disorder. *Archives of General Psychiatry, 57*, 119–27.

Rajindrajith, S., Devanarayana, N. M., & Perera, B. J. C. (2012). Rumination syndrome in children and adolescents: A school survey assessing prevalence and symptomatology. *BMC Gastroenterology*,

12(163). Retrieved from http://www.biomedcentral.com/1471-230X/12/163

Ranahan, P. (2010). Mental health literacy: A conceptual framework for future inquiry into child and youth care professionals' practice with suicidal adolescents. *Child and Youth Care Forum, 39*, 11–25.

Rapee, R. M. (1997). Potential role of childrearing practices in the development of anxiety and depression. *Clinical Psychology Review, 17*, 47–67.

Raphael's story. (n.d.). Making the Connection: Trauma and Substance Abuse. The National Child Traumatic Stress Network. Retrieved from http://www.nctsn.org/sites/default/files/assets/pdfs/SAToolkit_1.pdf

Rapoport, J., Chavez, A., Greenstein, D., Addington, A., & Gogtay, N. (2009). Autism Spectrum Disorders and childhood-onset Schizophrenia: Clinical and biological contributions to a relationship revisited. *Journal of American Academy of Child and Adolescent Psychiatry, 48*(1), 10–18.

Rapoport, J. L., Addington, A. M., Frangou, S., & Psych, M. R. (2005). The neurodevelopmental model of Schizophrenia: Update 2005. *Molecular Psychiatry, 10*, 434–449.

Rapoport, J. L., Giedd, J. N., Blumenthal, J., et al. (1999). Progressive cortical change during adolescence in childhood-onset Schizophrenia: A longitudinal magnetic resonance imaging study. *Archives of General Psychiatry, 56*, 649–654.

Ray, S. (2012). Cocaine, appetitive memory and neural connectivity. *Journal of Clinical Toxicology,* Suppl. 7(003). Retrieved from http://www.omicsonline.org/cocaine-appetitive-memory-and-neural-connectivity-2161-0495.S7-003.pdf

Read, J. (2001). *The relationship between child abuse and Schizophrenia: Causal, contributory or coincidental?* Paper presented at Royal Australian and New Zealand College of Psychiatrists 36th Annual Congress, Canberra, May 2001.

Read, J., & Argyle, N. (1999). Hallucinations, delusions, and thought disorder among adult psychiatric inpatients with a history of child abuse. *Psychiatric Services, 50*, 1467–1472.

Read, J., Perry, B. P., Moskowitz, A., & Connolli, J. (2001). The contribution of early traumatic events to Schizophrenia in some patients: A traumagenic neurodevelopmental model. *Psychiatry, 64*(4), 319–345. Published by Guilford Press. © 2001.

Reamer, F. D., & Siegel, G. H. (2008). *Teens in crisis: How the industry serving struggling teens helps and hurts our kids.* New York: Columbia University.

Rechichi, J. A., & Baglivio, M. (2011). A sourcebook of delinquency interventions. Florida Department of Juvenile Justice. Retrieved from http://www.djj.state.fl.us/docs/contracting/dt-itn-trans-app-3-sourcebook.pdf?sfvrsn=0

Redl, F. (1966). *When we deal with children.* Glencoe, IL: Free Press.

Redl, F., & Wineman, D. (1952). *Controls from within: Techniques for the treatment of the aggressive child.* Glencoe, IL: Free Press.

Reebye, P., & Stalker, A. (2007). *Understanding regulation disorders of sensory processing in children: Management strategies for parents and professionals.* London: Jessica Kingsley.

Reese, L. E., Vera, E. M., Simon, T. R., & Ikeda, R. M. (2000). The role of families and care givers as risk and protective factors in preventing youth violence. *Clinical Child and Family Psychological Review, 3*, 61–77.

Reif, A., Rosler, M., Freitag, C. M., Schneider, M., Eujen, A., Kissling, C., . . . Retz, W. (2007). Nature and nurture predispose to violent behavior: Serotonergic genes and adverse childhood environment. *Neuropsychopharmacology, 32*, 2375–2383.

Reinblatt, S. P., & Riddle, M. A. (2007). The pharmacological management of childhood anxiety disorders: A review. *Psychopharmacology, 191*(1), 67–86.

Reivich, K. (1996). The prevention of depressive symptoms in adolescents. PhD diss., University of Pennsylvania (UMI 9627995).

Rey, Y., Marin, C. E., & Silverman, W. K. (2011). Failures in cognitive-behavior therapy for children. *Journal of Clinical Psychology, 67*(11), 1140–1150. Copyright © by John Wiley & Sons. Used by permission of John Wiley & Sons vis CCC.

Richards, A. (2004). Anxiety and the resolution of ambiguity. In J. Yiend (Ed.), *Cognition, emotion, and psychopathology: Theoretical, empirical and clinical directions* (pp. 130–148). Cambridge: Cambridge University Press.

Riggs, S. R., & Alario, A. (1989). Adolescent substance use instructor's guide. In C. Dubé, M. Goldstein, D. Lewis, E. Myers, & W. Zwick (Eds.), *Project ADEPT: Curriculum for Primary Care Physician Training* (pp. 1–57). Providence, RI: Brown University.

Risk and protective factors. (2015). Addiction Services. Retrieved from http://www.cha.nshealth.ca/addiction/index.asp

Roberts, M. C., Lazicki-Puddy, T. A., Puddy, R. W., & Johnson, R. J. (2003). The outcomes of psychotherapy with adolescents: A practitioner-friendly research review. *Journal of Clinical Psychology/In Session, 59*(11), 1177–1191.

Robinson, R. T., Smith, S. W., & Brownell, M. T. (1999). Cognitive behavior modification of hyperactivity-impulsivity and aggression: A meta-analysis of school-based studies. *Journal of Educational Psychology, 91*(2), 195–203.

Robinson, S., Goddard, L., Dritchel, B., Wisley, M., & Howlin, P. (2009). Executive functions in children with Autism Spectrum Disorders. *Brain and Cognition, 7*(1), 362–368. Retrieved from http://dmrocke.ucdavis.edu/executive.pdf

Rogers, B., Stratton, P., Victor, J., Kennedy, B., & Andres, M. (1992). Chronic regurgitation among persons with mental retardation: A need for combined medical and interdisciplinary strategies. *American Journal of Mental Retardation, 96*(5), 522–527.

Rohde, P. (2005). Cognitive-behavioral treatment for depression in adolescents. *Journal of Indian Association for Child and Adolescent Mental Health, 1*(1).

Roosa, M. W., Gensheimer, L. K., Short, J. L., Ayers, T. S., & Shell, R. (1989). A preventive intervention for children in alcoholic families: Results of a pilot study. *Family Relations, 38*, 295–300.

Root, E. E. (2009). *Kids caught in the psychiatric maelstrom.* Santa Barbara, CA: Praeger.

Rosen, J. (1947). The treatment of schizophrenic psychosis by direct analytic therapy. *Psychiatric Quarterly, 21*(1), 3–37.

Roth, S., Newman, E., Pelcovitz, D., Van der Kolk, B. A., & Mandel, F. S. (1997). Complex PTSD in victims exposed to sexual and physical abuse: Results from the DSM-IV field trial for Posttraumatic Stress Disorder. *Journal of Traumatic Stress, 10*(4), 539–555.

Rowe, D. C., Almeida, D. M., & Jacobson, K. C. (1999). School context and genetic influences on aggression in adolescence. *Psychological Science, 10*, 277–280.

Rowling, L. & Weist, M. D. (2004). Promoting the growth, improvement and sustainability of school mental health programs worldwide. *International Journal of Mental Health Promotion, 6*(2) 3–11.

Royal Commission on Aboriginal Peoples. (2010). *Choosing life: Special report on suicide among Aboriginal people*. Ottawa: Minister of Supply and Services Canada.

Rubin, K. H., Burgess, K. B., & Hastings, P. D. (2002). Stability and social-behavioral consequences of toddlers' inhibited temperament and parenting. *Child Development, 73*, 483–495.

Rudolph, S. M., & Epstein, M. H. (2000). Empowering children and families through strength-based assessment. *Reclaiming Children and Youth, 8*(4), 207–209. Copyright © by Reclaiming Children and Youth Journal. Used by permission of Reclaiming Children and Youth Journal. Retrieved from http://www.cyc-net.org/Journals/rcy/rcy-8-4.html

RUPP Anxiety Study Group. (2001). Fluvoxamine for the treatment of anxiety disorders in children and adolescents. *New England Journal of Medicine, 344*, 1279–1285.

Rushton, J. L., Forcier, M., & Schectman, R. M. (2003). Epidemiology of depressive symptoms in the National Longitudinal Study of Adolescent Health. *Journal of the American Academy of Child and Adolescent Psychiatry, 41*, 199–205.

Rustin, M. (2003). Research in the consulting room. *Journal of Child Psychotherapy, 29*, 137–145.

Saavedra, L. M., Silverman, W. K., Morgan-Lopez, A. A., & Kurtines, W. M. (2010). Cognitive behavioral treatment for childhood anxiety disorders: Long-term effects on anxiety and secondary disorders in young adulthood. *Journal of Child Psychology and Psychiatry, 51*, 924–934.

Safren, S. A., Sprich, S., Mimiaga, M. J., Surman, C., Knouse, L., . . . Otto, M. W. (2010). Cognitive behavioral therapy vs relaxation with educational support for medication-treated adults with ADHD and persistent symptoms: A randomized control trial. *Journal of the American Medical Association, 304*, 875–880.

Sagestrano, L. M., Paikoff, R. L., Holmbeck, G. N., & Fendrich, M. (2003). A longitudinal examination of familial risk factors for depression among inner-city African American adolescents. *Journal of Family Psychology, 17*, 108–120.

Saleebey, D. (2006). *Strengths perspective in social work practice* (4th ed.). Boston: Allyn & Bacon.

Salomonsson, B. (2011). Psychoanalytic conceptualizations of the internal object in an ADHD child. *Journal of Infant, Child, and Adolescent Psychotherapy, 10*, 87–102.

Saltzman, A. (2015). Children and adolescents. Retrieved from http://www.stillquietplace.com/children-adolescents

Samenov, S. E. (2004). *Inside the criminal mind*. New York: Crown Publishers.

Samuels, S., & Sikorsky, S. (1998). *Clinical evaluation of school-aged children: A structured approach to the diagnosis of child and adolescent mental disorders*. Sarasota, FL: Professional Resource Press.

Sandler, I. N., West, S. G., Baca, L., Pillow, D. R., Gersten, J. C., Rogosch, F., . . . Ramirez, R. (1992). Linking empirically based theory and evaluation: The family bereavement program. *American Journal of Community Psychology, 20*, 491–521.

Sassaroli, S., Gallucci, M., & Ruggiero, G. M. (2008). Low perception of control as a cognitive factor of eating disorders: Its independent effects on measures of eating disorders and its interactive effects with perfectionism and self-esteem. *Journal of Behavior Therapy and Experimental Psychiatry, 39*(4), 467–488.

Scanlon, D. (2006). Learning disabilities and attention deficits. In K. M. Thies & J. F. Travers (Eds.), *Handbook of human development for health care professionals*. Sudbury, MA: Jones and Bartlett Publishers.

Scarlett, W. G., Ponte, I. C., & Singh, J. P. (2009). *Approaches to behavior and classroom management: Integrating discipline and care*. London: Copyright © 2009 by Sage Publications. Used by permission of Sage Publications via CCC.

Schachar, R., & Tannock, R. (2002). Syndromes of hyperactivity and attention deficit. In M. Rutter & E. Taylor (Eds.), *Child and Adolescent Psychiatry* (4th ed., pp. 399–418). Oxford: Blackwell.

Schaeffer, C. M., & Borduin, C. M. (2005). Long-term follow-up to a randomized clinical trial of multisystemic therapy with serious and violent juvenile offenders. *Journal of Consulting and Clinical Psychology, 73*(3), 445–453.

Scheeringa, M. S., Zeanah, C. H., & Cohen, J. A. (2011). PTSD in children and adolescents: Toward an empirically based algorithm. *Depression and anxiety, 28*(9), 770–782.

Scheeringa, M. S., Zeanah, C. H., Myers, L., & Putnam, F. W. (2005). Predictive validity in a prospective follow-up of PTSD in preschool children. *Journal of the American Academy of Child and Adolescent Psychiatry, 44*, 899–906.

Scher, C. D., Ingram, R. E., & Segal, Z. E. (2005). Cognitive reactivity and vulnerability: Empirical evidence of construct activation and cognitive diatheses in unipolar depression. *Clinical Psychology Review, 25*, 487–510.

Schieve, L. A., Tian, L. H., Baio, J., Rankin, K., Rosenberg, D., Wiggins, L., . . . Devine, O. (2014). Population attributable fractions for three perinatal risk factors for Autism Spectrum Disorders, 2002 and 2008 Autism and Developmental Disabilities Monitoring Network. *Annals of Epidemiology, 24*(4), 260–266.

Schiraldi, G. (2000). *The Post-Traumatic Stress Disorder sourcebook: A guide to healing, recovery and growth*. Los Angeles: Lowell House.

Schizophrenia facts. (2015). Retrieved from http://www.medicinenet.com/script/main/art.asp?articlekey=41430

Schmid, M., Petermann, F., & Fegert, J. M. (2013). Developmental trauma disorder: Pros and cons of including formal criteria in the psychiatric diagnostic systems. *BMC Psychiatry, 13*, 1–12. Published by BioMed Central, © 2013. Used by permission of BioMed Central.

Schmidt, U., Lee, S., Beecham, J., Perkins, S., Treasure, J. L., & Yi, I. (2007). A randomized controlled trial of family therapy and cognitive behavior therapy guided self-care for adolescents with Bulimia Nervosa and related conditions. *American Journal of Psychiatry, 164*, 591–598.

Schnurr, P. P. (2007). The rocks and hard places in psychotherapy outcome research. *Journal of Traumatic Stress, 20*(5), 779–792.

Schore, A. N. (2013). Relational trauma, brain development and disassociation. In J. D. Ford & C. A. Courtois (Eds.), *Treating complex trauma and stess disorders in children and adolescents: Scientific foundations and therapeutic models*. Published by the Guilford Press, New York, © 2013.

Schottenbauer, M. A., Glass, C. R., Arnkoff, D. B., & Hafter Gray, S. (2008). Contributions of psychodynamic approaches to treatment of PTSD and trauma: A review of the empirical treatment and psychopathology literature. *Psychiatry: Interpersonal and Biological Processes, 71*(1), 3–34.

Schroeder, C. S., & Gordon, B. N. (2002). *Assessment and treatment of childhood problems: A clinician's guide*. New York: Guilford.

Schwartz, C., Waddell, C., Harrison, E., Garland, O., Nightingale, L., & Dixon, J. (2007, fall). Addressing attention problems in children. *Children's Mental Health Research Quarterly*. Vancouver, BC: Children's Health Policy Centre, Faculty of Health Sciences. Published by Simon Fraser University, © 2007. Retrieved from http://childhealthpolicy.ca/wp-content/uploads/2012/12/RQ-4-07-Fall.pdf

Scott, S. (2012). Developmental psychopathology and classification in childhood and adolescence. In M. G. Gelder, N. C. Andreasen, J. J. Lopez-Ibor, & J. R. Geddes (Eds.), *New Oxford textbook of psychiatry* (2nd ed., Vol. 2, pp. 1589–1594). New York: Oxford University Press.

Screening for concurrent substance use and mental health problems in youth. (2009). Centre for Addiction and Mental Health. Retrieved from http://www.knowledgex.camh.net/amhspecialists/Screening_assessment/screening/screen_CD_youth/Documents/youth_screening_tools.pdf0

Searight, H. R., Rottnek, R., & Abby, S. L. (2001). Conduct disorder: Diagnosis and treatment in primary care. *American Family Physician*, 63(8), 1579–1588.

Seida, J. C., Schouten, J. R., Mousavi, S. S., Hamm, M., Beaith, A., Vandermeer, B., et al. (2012). First and second generation antipsychotics for children and young adults. *Comparative Effectiveness Review*, 39. Retrieved from http://www.effectivehealthcare.ahrq.gov/ehc/products/147/835/CER39_Antipsychotics-Children-Young-Adults_20120221.pdf

Seide, M. (2015). Dismantling the common myths of eating disorders. Retrieved from http://www.anad.org/dismantling-the-common-myths-of-eating-disorders

Seligman, L., & Reichenberg, L. W. (2012). *Selecting effective treatments: A comprehensive systematic guide to treating mental disorders* (4th ed.). Hoboken, NJ: Wiley.

Seligman, M. E. P. (1974). Depression and learned helplessness. In R. J. Friedman & M. M. Katz (Eds.), *The psychology of depression: Contemporary theory and research* (pp. 83–113). Washington, DC: Winston.

Sensky, T., Turkington, T., Kingdon, D., Scott, J. L., Scott, J., Siddle, R., . . . Barnes, T. R. (2000). A randomized, controlled trial of cognitive-behavioral therapy for persistent positive symptoms in Schizophrenia resistant to medication. *Archives of General Psychiatry*, 57, 165–173.

Sestir, M. A., & Bartolow, B. (2007). Theoretical explanations of aggression and violence. In T. Gannon, T. Ward, A. R. Beech, & D. Fisher (Eds.), *Aggressive offenders' cognition: Theory, research, and practice* (pp. 157–178). Chichester, UK: Wiley.

Shafii, T., Rivara, F. P., Wang, J., & Jurkovich, G. J. (2009). Screening adolescent patients admitted to the Trauma Service for high-risk behaviors: Who is responsible? *Journal of Trauma*, 67(6), 1288–1292.

Shakya, Y. B., Khanlou, N., & Gonsalves, T. (n.d.). Determinants of mental health for newcomer youth: Policy and service implications. The Provincial Centre of Excellence for Child and Youth Mental Health at CHEO. Retrieved from http://accessalliance.ca/sites/accessalliance/files/documents/Determinants_of_Mental_Health_for_Newcomer_Youth(Cdn_Issues).pdf

Shamir-Essakow, G., Ungerer, J. A., & Rapee, R. M. (2005). Attachment, behavioral inhibition, and anxiety in preschool children. *Journal of Abnormal Child Psychology*, 33, 131–143.

Shapiro, F. S., & Lentz, F. F. (1991). Vocational-technical programs: Follow-up of students with learning disabilities. *Exceptional Children*, 58, 47–59.

Shapka, J. D., & Keating, D. P. (2005). Structure and change in self-concept during adolescence. *Canadian Journal of Behavioral Science*, 37, 83–96.

Sharpe, C. (2001). Therapeutic child care: Psychodynamic aspects of residential child care. Retrieved from http://www.goodenoughcaring.com/writings/therapeutic-child-care-psychodynamic-aspects-of-residential-child-care

Sharpe, C. (2006). Residential child care and the psychodynamic approach; Is it time to try again? *Scottish Journal of Residential Child Care*, 5(1), 46–56.

Shear, M. K., Cloitre, M., Pine, D., & Ross, J. (2005, January 1). Anxiety disorders in women: Setting a research agenda. Anxiety Disorders Association of America, © 2005. Retrieved from http://www.adaa.org/sites/default/files/ADAA_Womens_R1.pdf

Shenton, M. E., Dickey, C. C., Frumin, M., & McCarley, R. W. (2001). A review of MRI findings in Schizophrenia. *Schizophrenia Research*, 49, 1–52.

Sherman, C. (2015). How cognitive behavior therapy can stop negativity: Cognitive-behavioral therapy helps reverse the negativity that torments adults with ADD—and prevents them from reaching goals. *ADDitude: Strategies and support for ADHD and LD*. Retrieved from http://www.additudemag.com/adhd/article/912.html

Shochet, I. M., Dadds, M. R., Holland, D., Whitefield, K., Harnett, P., & Osgarby, S. M. (2001). The efficacy of a universal school-based program to prevent adolescent depression. *Journal of Clinical Child Psychology*, 30, 303–315.

Shwarz, A. (2013, December 15). The selling of Attention Deficit Disorder. *The New York Times*. Retrieved from http://www.nytimes.com/2013/12/15/health/the-selling-of-attention-deficit-disorder.html

Sigafoos, J., Arthur-Kelly, M., & Butterfield, N. (2006). *Enhancing everyday communication for children with disabilities*. Baltimore, MD: Paul H. Brookes.

Sikström, S., & Söderlund, G. B. W. (2007). Stimulus-dependent dopamine release in Attention-Deficit/Hyperactivity Disorder. *Psychological Review*, 114(4), 1047–1075.

Silberg, J. L, Maes, H., & Eaves, L. J. (2010). Genetic and environmental influences on the transmission of parental depression to children's depression and conduct disturbance: An extended children of twins study. *Journal of Child Psychology and Psychiatry*, 51(6), 734–744.

Silberg, J., Rutter, M., Neale, M., & Eaves, L. (2001). Genetic moderation of environmental risk for depression and anxiety in adolescent girls. *British Journal of Psychiatry*, 179, 116–121.

Silva, R. R., Gallagher, R., & Minami, B. A. (2006). Cognitive-behavioral treatments for anxiety disorders in children and adolescents. *Primary Psychiatry*, 13(5), 68–76.

Silverman, W. K., & Kurtines, W. M. (1996). *Anxiety and phobic disorders: A pragmatic approach*. New York: Plenum Press.

Silverman, W., Pina, A., & Viswesvaran, C. (2008). Evidence-based psychosocial treatments for phobic and anxiety disorders in children and adolescents. *Journal of Clinical Child and Adolescent Psychology*, 37(1), 105–130.

Simonoff, E. (2001). Genetic influences on Conduct Disorder. In J. Hill & B. Maughan (Eds.), *Conduct Disorders in childhood and adolescence*. New York: Cambridge University Press.

Sisask, M., & Värnik, A. (2012). Media roles in suicide prevention: A systematic review. *International Journal of Environmental Research and Public Health, 9*, 123–138.

Skinner, B. F. (1953). *Science and human behavior*. New York: Macmillan.

Skott-Myhre, H. (2014, March). The question of boundaries and encounters. *CYC-Online* (181). Retrieved from http://www.cyc-net.org/cyc-online/mar2014.pdf

Slater, E., & Slater, P. (1944). A heuristic theory of neurosis. In J. Shields & I. Gottesman (Eds.), *Man, mind and heredity: Selected papers of Eliot Slater on psychiatry and genetics* (pp. 216–227). Baltimore, MD: Johns Hopkins University Press.

Smalley, S. L., McGough, J. J., Del'Homme, M., NewDelman, J., Gordon, E., Kim, T., et al. (2000). Familial clustering of symptoms and disruptive behaviors in multiplex families with Attention-deficit/Hyperactivity Disorder. *Journal of the American Academy of Child and Adolescent Psychiatry, 39*(9), 1135–1143.

Smith, B., Barkley, R., & Shapiro, C. (2006). Attention-Deficit/Hyperactivity Disorder: Treatment of childhood disorders. In E. J. Mash & R. A. Barkley (Eds.), *Treatment of childhood disorders* (3rd ed., pp. 65–136). New York: Guilford.

Smith, B. H., Waschbusch, D. A., Willoughby, M. T., & Evans, S. (2000). The efficacy, safety, and practicality of treatments for adolescents with Attention-Deficit/Hyperactivity Disorder. *Clinical Child and Family Psychology Review, 3*, 243–267.

Smith, L., Nathan, P., Juniper, U., Kingsep, P., & Lim, L. (2003). *Cognitive behavioral therapy for psychotic symptoms: A therapists' manual*. Perth, Australia: Centre for Clinical Interventions.

Smith, M., & Segal, J. (2015). Understanding Schizophrenia: Symptoms, types, causes, and early warning signs. Copyright © by Help-Guide.Org. Used by permission of HelpGuide.Org. Retrieved from http://www.helpguide.org/articles/schizophrenia/schizophrenia-signs-types-and-causes.htm

Smith, W. (2011). *Youth leaving foster care: A relationship-based approach to practice*. New York: Oxford University Press.

Smolak, L., & Murnen, S. K. (2002). A meta-analytic examination of the relationship between child sexual abuse and eating disorders. *International Journal of Eating Disorders, 31*, 136–150.

Smoller, J. W., Block, S. R., & Young, M. M. (2009). Genetics of anxiety disorders: The complex road from DSM to DNA. *Depression and Anxiety, 26*, 965–975.

Snodgrass, J. (1984). William Healy (1869–1963): Pioneer child psychiatrist and criminologist. *Journal of the History of the Behavioral Sciences, 20*, 331–339.

Snyder, R., Turgay, A., Aman, M., Binder, C., Fisman, S., Carroll, A., & Risperidone Conduct Study Group. (2002). Effects of risperidone on conduct and disruptive behavior disorders in children with subaverage IQs. *Journal of American Academic Child and Adolescent Psychiatry, 41*, 1026–1036.

Solanto, M. V. (2002). Dopamine dysfunction in AD/HD: Integrating clinical and basic neuroscience research. *Behavioural Brain Research, 130*, 65–71.

Sonuga-Barke, E. (2002). Psychological heterogeneity in AD/HD: A dual pathway model of behavior and cognition. *Behavioural Brain Research, 130*, 29–36.

Sonuga-Barke, E. (2005). Causal models of Attention-Deficit/Hyperactivity Disorder: From common simple deficits to multiple developmental pathways. *Biological Psychiatry, 57*, 1231–1238.

Spiwak, R., Elias, B., Bolton, J. M., Martens, P. J., & Sareen, J. (2012). Suicide policy in Canada: Lessons from history. *Canadian Journal of Public Health, 103*(5), e338–e341.

Sprinson, J. S., & Berrick, K. (2010). *Unconditional care: Relationship-based, behavioral intervention with vulnerable children and families*. New York: Oxford University Press.

Squeglia, L. M., Jacobus, J., & Tapert, S. F. (2009). The influence of substance use on adolescent brain development. *Clinical EEG Neuoroscience, 40*(1), 33–35.

Stanger, C., & Budney, A. J. (2011). Contingency management approaches for adolescent substance use disorders. *Child and Adolescent Psychiatry Clinics of North America, 19*(3), 547–562.

Stark, K. D., Laurent, J., Livingston, R., Boswell, J., & Swearer, S. M. (1999). Implications of research for the treatment of depressive disorders during childhood. *Applied and Preventive Psychology, 8*, 79–102.

Stark, K. D., Sander, J., Hauser, M., Simpson, J., Schnoebelen, S., Glenn, R., & Molnar, J. (2006). Depressive disorders during childhood and adolescence. In E. J. Mash & R. A. Barkley (Eds.), *Treatment of childhood disorders* (pp. 336–407). New York: Guilford.

Statistics Canada. (2001). A profile of disability in Canada. Ottawa: Author.

Statistics Canada. (2003). *Canadian Community Health Survey: Mental health and well-being*. Retrieved from http://www.statcan.gc.ca/pub/82-617-x/index-eng.htm

Statistics Canada. (2007). Mortality, summary list of causes, 2004. Ottawa: Author. Retrieved from http://www.statcan.gc.ca/pub/84f0209x/2004000/4079090-eng.htm

Statistics Canada. (2009). *Canadian Community Health Survey*. Ottawa, Ontario: Statistics Canada. Retrieved from http://www.phac-aspc.gc.ca/cphorsphc-respcacsp/2011/cphorsphc-respcacsp-06-eng.php

Statistics Canada. (2010). Current smoking. Retrieved from http://www.statcan.gc.ca/pub/82-229-x/2009001/deter/cos-eng.htm

Statistics Canada. (2012). Mortality, Summary List of Causes 2009. Retrieved from http://www.statcan.gc.ca/pub/84f0209x/84f0209x2009000-eng.pdf

Statistics Canada. (2013). *Canadian Community Health Survey: Mental health*. Retrieved from http://www23.statcan.gc.ca/imdb/p2SV.pl?Function=getSurvey&SDDS=5015

Steele, R. G., Elkin, T. D., & Roberts, M. C. (Eds.). (2008). *Handbook of evidence-based therapies for children and adolescents*. New York: Springer.

Steele, R. G., & Roberts, M. C. (Eds). (2005). *Handbook of mental health services for children, adolescents, and families*. New York: Kluwer Academic/Plenum Publishers.

Stein, M. B., Jang, K. L., Taylor, S., Vernon, P. A., & Livesley, W. J. (2002). Genetic and environmental influences on trauma exposure and Posttraumatic Stress Disorder symptoms: A twin study. *American Journal of Psychiatry, 159*, 1675–1681.

Stein, P., & Kendall, J. (2004). *Psychological trauma and the developing brain*. Binghampton, NY: Haworth Maltreatment and Trauma Press.

Stice, E. (2001). A prospective test of the dual-pathway model of bulimic pathology: Mediating effects of dieting and negative affect. *Journal of Abnormal Psychology, 110*(1), 124–135.

Stice, E. (2002). Risk and maintenance factors for eating pathology: A meta-analytic review. *Psychopharmacology Bulletin, 128*, 825–848.

Stice, E., Cameron, R., Killen, J. D., Hayward, C., & Taylor, C. B. (1999). Naturalistic weight reduction efforts prospectively predict growth in relative weight and onset of obesity among female adolescents. *Journal of Consulting and Clinical Psychology, 67*, 967–974.

Stock, L., Shearer, M., & Meester, C. (2004). Power card strategy. Retrieved from http://meesterc.files.wordpress.com/2009/11/48-power-card-strategy.pdf

Stockburger, J., Betsabeth, P., de Leeuw, S., & Greenwood, M. (2005). *Youth voices on the prevention and intervention of youth substance abuse.* Prince George, BC: Centre of Excellence for Children and Adolescents with Special Needs. University of Northern British Columbia.

Stockburger, J., Parsa-Pajouh, B., de Leewu, S., & Greenwood, M. (2005). Youth voices on the prevention and intervention of youth substance abuse. Centre of Excellence for Children and Adolescents with Special Needs, the UNBC (University of Northern British Columbia) Task Force on Substance Abuse. Retrieved from http://www.unbc.ca/assets/centreca/english/piysa.pdf

Stoddard, F., Usher, C., & Abrams, A. (2006). Psychopharmacology in pediatric critical care. *Child and Adolescent Psychiatry Clinics of North America, 15*, 611–655.

Stopa, L., & Clark, D. M. (2000). Social phobia and interpretation of social events. *Behavior Research and Therapy, 38*, 273–283.

Straub, R. E., Jiang, Y., MacLean, C. J., Ma, Y., Webb, B. T., Myakishev, M. V., . . . Kendler, K. S. (2002). Genetic variation in the 6p22.3 gene DTNBP1, the human ortholog of the mouse dysbindin gene, is associated with Schizophrenia. *American Journal of Human Genetics, 71*, 337–348.

Straus, M. (2007). *Adolescent girls in crisis: Intervention and hope.* New York: Norton.

Strauss, G. P., Frank, M. J., Waltz, J. A., Kasanova, Z., Herbener, E. S., & Gold, J. M. (2011). Deficits in positive reinforcement learning and uncertainty-driven exploration are associated with distinct aspects of negative symptoms in Schizophrenia. *Biological Psychiatry, 69*(5), 424–431.

Strawn, J. R., Keeshin, B. R., DelBello, M. P., Geracioti, T. D., Jr., & Putnam, F. W. (2010). Psychopharmacologic treatment of Post-traumatic Stress Disorder in children and adolescents: A review. *Journal of Clinical Psychiatry, 71*(7), 932–941.

Strecker, E. A. (1929). Behavior problems in encephalitis. *Archives of Neurology and Psychiatry, 21*, 137–144.

Street children. (n.d.). Youth Advocacy Program International. Washington, DC. Retrieved from http://www.yapi.org/street/#

Striegel-Moore, R. H., Seeley, J. R., & Lewinsohn, P. M. (2003). Psychosocial adjustment in young adulthood of women who experience an eating disorder during adolescence. *American Academy of Child and Adolescent Psychiatry, 42*, 587–593.

Strober, M. (1997). Bipolar illness. In M. C. Mouren-Simeoni, M. Bouvard, & R. G. Klein (Eds.), *Childhood depressions: Facts and perspectives.* Paris: Expansion Scientifique Française.

Strober, M. (2004). Managing the chronic, treatment resistant patient with Anorexia Nervosa. *International Journal of Eating Disorders, 36*, 245–255.

Strober, M., Freeman, R., Lampert, C., Diamond, J., & Kaye, W. (2000). Controlled family study of Anorexia Nervosa and Bulimia Nervosa: Evidence of shared liability and transmission of partial syndromes. *American Journal of Psychiatry, 157*, 393–401.

Stuart, C. (2009a). *Foundations of child and youth care practice.* Toronto: Kendall-Hunt.

Stuart, C. (2009b). Show me the evidence. [Editorial]. *Relational Child and Youth Care Practice, 22*(1), 3.

Stuart, C. (2013). *Foundations of child and youth care practice.* Toronto: Kendall-Hunt.

Stuart, C., & Carty, W. (2006). *The role of competence in outcomes for children and youth: An approach for mental health.* Toronto: Ryerson University.

Stuart, C., & Sanders, L. (2008). The role of child and youth care practitioners in evidence-based practice in group care: Executive summary. *Ontario Association of Children's Aid Societies, 52*(4), pp. 7–11. Retrieved from http://www.oacas.org/pubs/oacas/journal/2008Fall/practice.html

Substance Abuse and Mental Health Services Administration (SAMHSA). (2008). *Understanding the links between adolescent trauma and substance abuse.* Boston: U.S. Department of Health and Human Services (HHS).

Suicide. (2013). Canadian Mental Health Association. Retrieved from http://www.cmha.bc.ca/get-informed/mental-health-information/suicide

Sullivan, P. (2002). Course and outcome of Anorexia Nervosa and Bulimia Nervosa. In C. G. Fairburn & K. D. Brownell (Eds.), *Eating disorders and obesity* (pp. 226–232). New York: Guilford.

Swanson, J., Arnold, L. E., Kraemer, H., Hechtman, L., Molina, B., Hinshaw, S., . . . MTA Cooperative Group. (2008). Evidence, interpretation, and qualification from multiple repots of long-term outcomes in the Multimodal Treatment Study of Children with ADHD (MTA), Part I: Executive summary. *Journal of Attention Disorders, 12*(1), 4–14.

Swanson, J. M., McBurnett, K., Christian, D. L., & Wigal, T. (1995). Stimulant medication and treatment of children with ADHD. In T. H. Ollendick & R. J. Prinz (Eds.), *Advances in clinical child psychology* (Vol. 17, pp. 365–322). New York: Plenum.

Sypeck, M. F., Gray, J. J., & Ahrens A. H. (2004). No longer just a pretty face: Fashion magazines' depictions of ideal female beauty from 1959 to 1999. *International Journal of Eating Disorders, 36*, 342–347.

Szalavitz, M., & Perry, P. (2010). *Born for love: Why empathy is so essential and endangered.* New York: Harper.

Szeszko, P. R., Christian, C., MacMaster, F., Lencz, T., Mirza, Y., Taormina, S. P., et al. (2008). Gray matter structural alterations in psychotropic drug-naive pediatric Obsessive-Compulsive Disorder: An optimized voxel-based morphometry study. *American Journal of Psychiatry, 165*, 1299–1307.

Talbot, C., Poole, N., Nathoo, T., Unsworth, R., & Smylie, D. (2011). Coalescing on women and substance use: linking research, practice and policy. The British Columbia Centre of Excellence for Women's Health. Retrieved from http://www.coalescing-vc.org/virtualLearning/section1/connecting-substance-use

Tandon, R., Keshavan, M. S., & Nasrallah, H. A. (2008). Schizophrenia: "Just the facts": What we know in 2008. Part 1: Overview. *Schizophrenia Research, 100*, 4–19.

Taylor, J., Iacono, W. G., & McGue, M. (2000). Evidence for a genetic etiology of early onset delinquency. *Journal of Abnormal Psychology, 109*, 634–643.

Teen depression: Myths and facts. (2015). Used by permission of University Health System. Retrieved from http://www.universityhealthsystem.com/myths

Teicher, M., Ito, Y., Glod, C., Scheffer, F., & Gelbard, H. (1996). Neurophysiological mechanisms of stress response in children. In C. Pfeffer (Ed.), *Severe stress and mental disturbance in children* (pp. 59–84). Washington, DC: American Psychiatric Press.

Thapar, A., Harrington, R., & McGuffin, P. (2001). Examining the comorbidity of ADHD-related behaviors and conduct problems using a twin study design. *British Journal of Psychiatry, 179*, 224–229.

Thapar, A., Langley, K., Owen, M. J., & O'Donovan, M. C. (2007). Advances in genetic findings on Attention Deficit Hyperactivity Disorder. *Psychological Medicine, 37*, 1681–1692.

Thapar, A. K., & Thapar, A. (2003). Attention-Deficit Hyperactivity Disorder. *British Journal of General Practice, 53*, 225–230.

Therapist Aid. (2012). Therapy worksheets related to suicide and self-harm for all demographics. Retrieved from http://www.therapistaid.com/therapy-worksheets/suicide/none

Thompson, J. K., Coovert, M. D., & Stormer, S. (1999). Body image, social comparison and eating disturbance: A covariance structure modeling investigation. *International Journal of Eating Disorders, 26*, 43–53.

Tienari, P. (1991). Interaction between genetic vulnerability and family environment. *Acta Psychiatrica Scandinavica, 84*, 460–465.

Tienari, P., Wynne, L. C., Sorri, A., Lahti, I., Laksy, K., Moring, J., Naarala, M., Nieminen, P., & Wahlberg, K-E. (2004). Genotype-environment interaction in Schizophrenia-Spectrum Disorder: Long-term follow-up study of Finnish adoptees. *British Journal of Psychiatry, 184*, 216–222.

Tienari, P., Wynne, L. C., Sorri, A., et al. (2004). Genotype environment interaction in Schizophrenia spectrum disorder: Long-term follow-up study of Finnish adoptees. *British Journal of Psychiatry, 184*, 216–222.

Tillfors, M. (2004). Why do some individuals develop Social Phobia? A review with emphasis on the neurobiological influences. *Nordic Journal of Psychiatry, 58*, 267–276.

Tillman, R., Geller, B., Craney, J. L., Bolhofner, K., Williams, M., & Zimerman, B. (2004). Relationship of parent and child informants to prevalence of mania symptoms in children with a prepubertal and early adolescent Bipolar Disorder phenotype. *American Journal of Psychiatry, 161*, 1278–1284.

Tishby, O., Raitchik, I., & Shefler, G. (2005). Changes in interepersonal conflicts among adolescents during psychodynamic therapy. *Psychotherapy Research, 17*(3), 297–304.

Top 11 myths about mental illness. (2014). Retrieved from http://www.mendthemind.ca/stigma/top-11-myths-about-mental-illness

Toplak, M. E., Connors, L., Shuster, J., Knezevic, B., & Parks, S. (2008). Review of cognitive, cognitive-behavioral, and neural-based interventions for Attention-Deficit/Hyperactivity Disorder (ADHD). *Clinical Psychology Review, 28*, 801–823.

Torres, A. (2003). Is fever suppression involved in the etiology of autism and neurodevelopmental disorders? *BMC Pediatrics, 3*(9). PMID: 12952554

Toupin, J., Déry, M., Pauzé, R., Mercier, H., & Fortin, L. (2000). Cognitive and familial contributions to Conduct Disorder in children. *Journal of Child Psychology and Psychiatry, 41*, 333–344.

Tozzi, F., Sullivan, P. F., Fear, J. L., McKenzie, J., & Bulik, C. M. (2003). Causes and recovery in Anorexia Nervosa: The patient's perspective. *International Journal of Eating Disorders, 33*(20), 143–154.

Trauma-focused interventions for youth in the juvenile justice system. (2004). The National Child Traumatic Stress Network. Retrieved from http://www.nctsn.org/products/trauma-focused-interventions-youth-juvenile-justice-system-2004

Trends in drug use among youth. (2013). Canadian Centre on Substance Abuse. Retrieved from http://www.ccsa.ca/Eng/topics/Children-and-Youth/Pages/default.aspx

Trieschman, A. E., Whittaker, J. K., & Brendtro, L. K. (1969). *The other 23 hours: Child care work with emotionally disturbed children in a therapeutic milieu.* New York: Aldine.

Trocmé, N. (2010). *Canadian incidence study of reported child abuse and neglect 2008: Major findings.* Ottawa: Public Health Agency of Canada.

True, W. R., Rice, J., Eisen, S. A., et al. (1993). A twin study of genetic and environmental contributions to liability for posttraumatic stress symptoms. *Archives of General Psychiatry, 50*, 257–264.

Trunzo, A. C. (2006). *Engagement, parenting skills, and parent–child relations as mediators of the relationship between parental self-efficacy and treatment outcomes for children with conduct problems.* Doctoral dissertation. Pittsburgh, PA: University of Pittsburgh.

Trzepacz, P. T., & Baker, R. W. (1993). *The psychiatric mental status examination.* Oxford: Oxford University Press.

Turner, R. W., Ward, M. F., & Turner, D. J. (1979). Behavioral treatment for depression: An evaluation of therapeutic components. *Journal of Clinical Psychology, 35*, 165–175.

Twenge, J. M., Gentile, B., DeWall, C. N., Ma, D., Lacefield, K., & Schutz, D. (2010). Birth cohort increases in psychopathology among young Americans, 1938–2007: A cross-temporal meta-analysis of the MMPI. *Clinical Psychology Review, 30*, 145–154.

Ungar, M. (2001). The social construction of resilience among "problem" youth in out-of-home placement: A study of health-enhancing deviance. *Child and Youth Care Forum, 30*(3), 137–154.

Ungar, M. (2008). A brief overview of resilience: How does the concept help us understand children's positive development under stress? Unpublished paper: Discussion paper for the Learning Partnership. Retrieved from http://www.tlpresources.ca/policyresearch_conference_NDRY_2008/Michae_Ungarl_English.pdf

Ungar, M. (Ed.). (2012). *The social ecology of resilience: A handbook.* New York: Springer.

Unger, R. (2014). Questions and answers about recovery. Blog: Recovery from "Schizophrenia" and other "Psychotic Disorders." Copyright © by Ron Unger. Used by permisison of Ron Unger. Retrieved from http://recoveryfromschizophrenia.org/questions-and-answers-about-recovery

University child/adolescent counselor says process of mindfulness may help children focus in the classroom. (2013). Retrieved from http://www.k-state.edu/media/newsreleases/aug13/mindful8613.html

Van Ameringen, M., Mancini, C., & Farvolden, P. (2003). The impact of anxiety disorders on educational achievement. *Journal of Anxiety Disorders, 17*, 561–571.

Van Ameringen, M., Mancini, C., Patterson, B., & Boyle, M. H. (2008). Post-Traumatic Stress Disorder in Canada. *CNS Neuroscience and Therapeutics, 14*(3), 171–181.

van Brakel, A. M. L., Muris, P., Bogels, S. M., & Thornassen, C. (2006). A multifactorial model for the etiology of anxiety in non-clinical adolescents: Main and interactive effects of behavioral inhibition, attachment, and parental rearing. *Journal of Child and Family Studies, 15*, 569–579.

van der Bruggen, C. O., Stams, G. J. J. M., & Bögels, S. M. (2008). The relation between child and parent anxiety and parental control: A meta-analytic review. *Journal of Child Psychology and Psychiatry, 49*, 1257–1269.

van der Kolk, B. (2005). Developmental trauma disorder: Toward a rational diagnosis for children with complex trauma histories. *Psychiatric Annals, 35*(5), 401–408.

Van der Oord, S., Prins, P. J., Oosterlaan, J., et al. (2008). Treatment of Attention Deficit Hyperactivity Disorder in children: Predictors of treatment outcome. *European Child and Adolescent Psychiatry, 17*, 73–81.

Vander Wal, J. S., Gibbons, J. L., & Pilar Grazioso, M. (2008). The sociocultural model of eating disorder development: Application to a Guatemalan sample. *Eating Behaviors, 9*, 277–284.

Van Heeringen, K. (2010). Functional brain imaging in suicidal patients. *Psychiatria Danubina, 22*(Suppl. 1), 161.

Van Heeringen, K., Van den Abbeele, D., Vervaet, M., Soenen, L., & Audenaert, K. (2010). The functional neuroanatomy of mental pain in depression. *Psychiatry Research: Neuroimaging, 181*, 141–144.

Vartanian, L. R., Herman, C. P., & Polivy, J. (2005). Implicit and explicit attitudes toward fatness and thinness: The role of the internalization of societal standards. *Body Image, 2*, 373–381.

Vasey, M. W., & Dadds, M. R. (Eds.) (2001). *The developmental psychopathology of anxiety*. London: Oxford University Press.

Vasey, M. W., & MacLeod, C. (2001). Information-processing factors in childhood anxiety: A review and developmental perspective. In M. W. Vasey & M. R. Dadds (Eds.), *The developmental psychopathology of anxiety* (pp. 253–277). New York: Oxford University Press.

Velleman, R., Templeton, L., & Copello, A. (2005). The role of the family in preventing and intervening with substance use and misuse: A comprehensive review of family interventions with a focus on young people. *Drug and Alcohol Review, 24*(2), 93–109.

Vitiello, B., Severe, J. B., Greenhill, L. L., Arnold, L. E., Abikoff, H. B., Bukstein, O. G., . . . Cantwell, D. P. (2001). Methylphenidate dosage for children with ADHD over time under controlled conditions: Lessons from the MTA. *Journal of the American Academy of Child and Adolescent Psychiatry, 40*, 188–196.

Vitiello, B., & Swedo, S. (2004). Antidepressant medications in children. *New England Journal of Medicine, 350*(15), 1489–1491.

Vitousek, K. M. (2002). Cognitive-behavioral therapy for Anorexia Nervosa. In C. G. Fairburn & K. D. Brownell (Eds.), *Eating disorders and obesity: A comprehensive handbook* (2nd ed., pp. 308–313). New York: Guilford.

Volkmar, F. R., Klin, A., & Schultz, R. T. (2005). Pervasive developmental disorders. In B. J. Sadock & V. A. Sadock (Eds.), *Kaplan and Sadock's comprehensive handbook of psychiatry* (pp. 3164–3182). Philadelphia, PA: Lippincott Williams & Wilkins.

Volkmar, F. R., Klin, A., Schultz, R. T., & State, M. W. (2009). Pervasive developmental disorders. In B. J. Sadock, V. A. Sadock, & P. Ruiz (Eds.), *Kaplan and Sadock's comprehensive handbook of psychiatry* (9th ed., Vol. 2, pp. 3540–3559). Philadelphia, PA: Lippincott Williams & Wilkins.

Volkow, N. D., Baler, R. D., & Goldstein, R. Z. (2011). Addiction: Pulling at the neural threads of social behaviors. *Neuron, 69*(4), 599–602. Copyright © by Elsevier Ltd. Used by permission of Elsevier Ltd. via Rightslink Service of CCC.

Vukic, A., Gregory, D., Martin-Misener, R. M., & Etowa, J. (2011). Aboriginal and Western conceptions of mental health and illness. *Pimatisiwin: A Journal of Aboriginal and Indigenous Community Health, 9*(1), 65–85. Published by Native Counselling Services of Alberta, © 2011.

Waddell, C., Godderis, R., Hua, J., McEwan, K., & Wong, W. (2004). *Preventing and treating anxiety disorders in children and youth: A research report prepared for the British Columbia Ministry of Children and Family Development*. Children's Mental Health Policy Research Program. Vancouver: University of British Columbia.

Waddell, C., Hua, J. M., Godderis, R., & McEwan, K. (2004). *Preventing and treating depression in children and youth: A research report prepared for the British Columbia Ministry of Children and Family Development*. Children's Mental Health Policy Research Program. Vancouver: University of British Columbia.

Waddell, C., McEwan, K., Shepherd, C. A., Offord, D. R., & Hua, J. M. (2005). A public health strategy to improve the mental health of Canadian children. *Canadian Journal of Psychiatry, 50*(4), 226–233.

Wagner, K. D., Ambrosini, P., Rynn, M., Wohlberg, C., Yang, R., Greenbaum, M. S., . . . Deas, D. (2003). Efficacy of sertraline in the treatment of children and adolescents with Major Depressive Disorder: Two randomized controlled trials. *Journal of the American Medical Association, 290*, 1033–1041.

Wagner, M. (1990). *The school programs and school performance of secondary students classified as learning disabled: Findings from the National Longitudinal Transition Study of special education students*. Menlo Park, CA: SRI International.

Walker, E., Cudeck, R., Mednick, S., & Schulsinger, F. (1981). Effects of parental absence and institutionalization on the development of clinical symptoms in high-risk children. *Acta Psychiatrica Scandinavica, 63*, 95–109.

Walker, E., Kestler, L., Bollini, A., & Hochman, K. M. (2004). Schizophrenia: Etiology and course. *Annual Review of Psychology, 55*, 401–430.

Walker, E., & Tessner, K. (2008). Schizophrenia. *Perspectives on Psychological Science, 3*(1), 30–37.

Walker, E. F., & Diforio, D. (1997). Schizophrenia: A neural diathesis-stress model. *Psychological Review, 104*, 667–685.

Walker, H., Colvin, G., & Ramsey, E. (1995). *Antisocial behavior in public school: Strategies and best practices*. Pacific Grove, CA: Brooks/Cole.

Walker, R. (2009). Translating neurodevelopment to practice: How to go from fMRI to a home visit. *Journal of Loss and Trauma 14*(4), 356–265.

Wallinius, M., Johansson, P., Larden, M., & Dernevik, M. (2011). Self-serving cognitive distortions and antisocial behavior among adults and adolescents. *Criminal Justice and Behavior, 38*, 286–301.

Walsh, B., Kaplan, A., Attia, E., Olmsted, M., Parides, M., Carter, J., . . . Rocket, W. (2006). Fluoxetine after weight restoration in Anorexia Nervosa: A randomized controlled trial. *Journal of the American Medical Association, 295*, 2605–2612.

Walsh, B. T., Fairburn, C. G., Mickley, D., Sysko, R., & Parides, M. K. (2004). Treatment of Bulimia Nervosa in a primary care setting. *American Journal of Psychiatry, 161*, 556–561.

deficithyperactivity-disorder-and-substance-use-disorders-adolescents

Wilens, T. E., Newcorn, J. H., Kratochvil, C. J., Gao, H., Thomason, C. K., Rogers, A. K., . . . Levine, L. R. (2006). Long-term atomoxetine treatment in adolescents with Attention-Deficit/Hyperactivity Disorder. *Journal of Pediatrics, 149*(1), 112–119.

Willcutt, E. G., Pennington, B. F., & DeFries, J. C. (2000). A twin study of the etiology of the comorbidity between reading disability and Attention-Deficit/Hyperactivity Disorder. *American Journal of Medical Genetics (Neuropsychiatric Genetics), 96*, 296–301.

Wilmshurst, L. (2004a). *Child and adolescent psychopathology: A casebook.* Thousand Oaks, CA: Sage Publications.

Wilmshurst, L. (2004b). *Essentials of child and adolescent psychopathology.* Hoboken, NJ: Wiley.

Wilson, G. T., Grilo, M. C., & Vitousek, K. M. (2007). Psychological treatment of eating disorders. *American Psychologist, 62*, 199–216.

Wilson, J. P. (2008). Culture, trauma, and the treatment of posttraumatic syndromes: A global perspective. In A. J. Marsella, J. Johnson, P. Watson, & J. Gryczynski (Eds.), *Ethnocultural perspectives on disaster and trauma: Foundations, issues, and applications* (pp. 351–378). New York: Springer SBM.

Wilson, J. P., & Tang, C. (Eds.). (2007). *Cross-cultural assessment of PTSD and related stress disorders.* New York: Springer SBM.

Winkel, B. (2009). Holistic treatment for substance abuse. Retrieved from http://www.treatmentsolutions.com/holistic-treatment-for-substance-abuse

Wing, L., & Shah, A. (2000). Catatonia in Autistic Spectrum Disorders. *The British Journal of Psychiatry, 176*, 357–362.

Winters, K. C. (2008). Adolescent brain development and substance abuse. The Mentor Foundation. Retrieved from http://www.mentorfoundation.org/uploads/Adolescent_Brain_Booklet.pdf

Winters, K. C. (2011). Commentary on O'Brien: Substance Use Disorder in the DSM-V when applied to adolescents. *Addiction, 106*(5), 882–897.

Winters, K. C., & Kaminer, Y. (2008). Screening and assessing adolescent Substance Use Disorders in a clinical population. *Journal of American Academy Child Psychiatry, 47*(7), 740–744.

Winzer, M. (2005). *Children with exceptionalities in Canadian classrooms* (7th ed.). Toronto: Published by Pearson Canada, © 2004.

Wise, R. A. (2004). Dopamine, learning and motivation. *Nature Reviews Neuroscience, 5*, 483–494.

Witkiewitz, K., & Marlatt, G. A. (2008). Why and how do substance abuse treatments work? Investigating mediated change. *Addiction, 103*(4), 649–650.

Wolchik, S. A., West, S. G., Westover, S., et al. (1993). The children of divorce parenting intervention: Outcome evaluation of an empirically based program. *American Journal of Community Psychology, 21*, 293–331.

Wolfe, D. A., & McGee, R. (1991). Assessment of emotional status among maltreated children. In R. Starr & D. A. Wolfe (Eds.), *The effects of child abuse and neglect: Issues and research* (pp. 257–277). New York: Guilford.

Wolff, J. C., & Ollendick, T. H. (2006). The comorbidity of conduct problems and depression in childhood and adolescence. *Clinical Child and Family Psychology Review, 9*(3/4), 201–220.

Wolpe, J. (1962). Isolation of a conditioning procedure as the crucial psychotherapeutic factor. *Journal of Nervous and Mental Disease, 134*, 316–329.

Wolpert, M., Fuggle, P., Cottrell, D., Fonagy, P., Phillips, J., Pilling, S., Stein, S., & Target, M. (2006). *Drawing on the evidence: Advice for mental health professionals working with children and adolescents.* London: CAMHS Publications.

Wong, C., & Kasari, C. (2012). Play and joint attention of children with autism in the preschool special education classroom. *Journal of Autism and Developmental Disorders, 42*, 2152–2161.

Wood, J. J., McLeod, B. D., Sigman, M., Hwang, W., & Chu, B. C. (2003). Parenting and childhood anxiety: Theory, empirical findings, and future directions. *Journal of Child Psychology and Psychiatry, 44*, 134–151.

Woodbury, L. (2008). Neurosequential Model of Therapeutics (NMT): Struggling teens. Retrieved from http://www.strugglingteens.com/artman/publish/NMT-EI_080505.shtml

Woodside, D. B., Bulik, C. M., Halmi, K. A., Fichter, M. M., Kaplan, A., Berrettini, W. H., . . . Kaye, W. H. (2002). Personality, perfectionism, and attitudes toward eating in parents of children with eating disorders. *International Journal of Eating Disorders, 31*, 290–299.

Woodward, L., Taylor, E., & Dowdney, L. (1998). The parenting and family functioning of children with hyperactivity. *Journal of Child Psychology and Psychiatry, 39*, 161–169.

Woody, G. E., Poole, S. A., Subramaniam, G., Dugosh, K., Bogenschutz, M., Abbott, P., . . . Fudala, P. (2008). Extended vs. short-term buprenorphine-naloxone for treatment of opioid-addicted youth: A randomized trial. *Journal of the American Medical Association, 300*(17), 2003–2011.

World Health Organization. (2001a). *Mental health resources in the world: Initial results of Project Atlas.* Geneva: WHO.

World Health Organization. (2001b). *Mental health: a state of well-being.* Geneva: WHO. http://www.who.int/features/factfiles/mental_health/en/. Copyright © 2014 by the World Health Organization. Used by permission of the World Health Organization.

World Health Organization. (2002). *World report on violence and health.* Geneva: WHO. Retrieved from http://whqlibdoc.who.int/hq/2002/9241545615.pdf

World Health Organization. (2003). *Caring for children and adolescents with mental disorders: Setting WHO directions.* Geneva: WHO. Retrieved from http://www.who.int/mental_health/media/en/785.pdf

Working definition of family-driven care. (2008). Retrieved from http://www.tapartnership.org/docs/workingDefinitionFamilyDrivenCare_200801.pdf

Wykes, T., Newton, E., Landau, S., Rice, C., Thompson, N., & Frangu, S. (2007). Cognitive remediation therapy (CRT) for young early onset patients with Schizophrenia: An exploratory randomized controlled trial. *Schizophrenia Research, 94*(1), 221–230.

Yang, C. K., & Hahn, H. M. (2002). Co-sleeping in young Korean children. *Journal of Developmental and Behavioral Pediatrics, 23*, 151–157.

Yates, T. M., Carlson, E. A., & Egeland, B. (2008). A prospective study of child maltreatment and self-injurious behavior in a community sample. *Development and Psychopathology, 20*, 651–672.

Yen, C. F., Wu, H. Y., Yen, J. Y., & Ko, C. H. (2004). Effects of brief cognitive-behavioral interventions on confidence to resist the urges to use heroin and methamphetamine in relapse-related situations. *Journal of Nervous and Mental Disease, 192*, 788–791.

Youth substance use prevention and early intervention. (2015). Conrad Hilton Foundation. Retrieved from http://www.hiltonfoundation.org/substance-use-prevention

Zabarenko, L. (2011). *Teaming creativity, psychoanalysis and neuroscience: The bridge to nowhere?* Presented at Creativity Study Group, January, Washington, DC.

Zahn, T., Jacobsen, L., Gordon, C., McKenna, K., Frazier, J., & Rapoport, J. (1997). Autonomic nervous system markers of psychopathology in childhood-onset Schizophrenia. *Archives of General Psychiatry, 54*, 904–912.

Ziegler, D. (2002). *Traumatic experience and the brain: A handbook for understanding and treating those traumatized as children.* Jasper, OR: Acacia Publishing, ©2002.

Zilboorg, G., & Henry, G. W. (1941). *A history of medical psychology.* New York: Norton.

Zisser, A., & Eyberg, S. M. (2010). Treating oppositional behavior in children using parent–child interaction therapy. In A. E. Kazdin & J. R. Weisz (Eds.), *Evidence-based psychotherapies for children and adolescents* (pp. 179–193). New York: Guilford.

Zoja, L. (2000). *Drugs, addiction and initiation: The modern search for ritual* (M. E. Romano & R. Mercurio, Trans.). Einsiedeln, Switzerland: Daimon Verlag.

Zou, L., Chen, W., Shao, S., Sun, Z., Zhong, R., Shi, J., & Song, R. (2012). Genetic variant in KIAA0319, but not in DYX1C1, is associated with risk of dyslexia: An integrated meta-analysis. *American Journal of Medical Genetics, Part B: Neuropsychiatric Genetics, 159*, 970–976.

Zubin, J., & Spring, B. (1977). Vulnerability: A new view of Schizophrenia. *Journal of Abnormal Psychology, 86*, 103–126.

Index

Note: Page numbers followed by *f*, *t*, or *b* represent figures, tables, or boxes respectively.

Walsh, B. W. (2006). *Treating self-injury: A practical guide*. Published by The Guilford Press, © 2006.

Wang, L., Huang, Y., Chiang, Y., Hsiao, C., Shang, Z., & Chen, C. (2011). Clinical symptoms and performance on the continuous performance test in children with Attention Deficit Hyperactivity Disorder between subtypes: A natural follow-up study for 6 months. *BMC Psychiatry, 11*, 65.

Warren, S. L., Huston, L., Egeland, B., & Sroufe, L.A. (1997). Child and adolescent anxiety disorders and early attachment. *Journal of the American Academy of Child and Adolescent Psychiatry, 36*(5), 637–644.

Waschbusch, D. A. (2002). A meta-analytic examination of comorbid hyperactive-impulsive-attention problems and conduct problems. *Psychological Bulletin, 128*(1), 118–150.

Watts-English, T., Fortson, B. L., Gibler, N., Hooper, S. R., & De Bellis, M. D. (2006). The psychobiology of maltreatment in childhood. *Journal of Social Issues, 62*, 717–736.

Weatherburn, D. (2008). Dilemmas in harm minimization. *Addiction, 104*, 335–339.

Weber, D., & Reynolds, C. (2004). Clinical perspectives on neurobiological effects of psychological trauma. *Neuropsychology Review, 14*(2), 115–129.

Wedig, M. M., & Nock, M. K. (2007). Parental expressed emotion and adolescent self-injury. *Journal of the American Academy of Child and Adolescent Psychiatry, 46*(9), 1171–1178. doi: 10.1097/chi.0b013e3180ca9aaf

Weems, C. F. (2009). Developmental psychopathology, positive psychology, and knowledge development in child and youth care: Editorial hopes and aspirations for the Forum. *Child and Youth Care Forum, 38*, 1–4.

Weems, C. F., Silverman, W. K., & La Greca, A. M. (2000). What do youth referred for anxiety problems worry about? Worry and its relation to anxiety and anxiety disorders in children and adolescents. *Journal of Abnormal Child Psychology, 28*, 63–72.

Weersing, V. R. (2004, October). The psychotherapy manual: A tool for many tasks. In D. Shaffer (Chair), *Issues in the conduct and interpretation of studies of adolescent depression*. Invited plenary session conducted at the annual meeting of the American Academy of Child and Adolescent Psychiatry, Washington, DC.

Weersing, V. R., Gonzalez, A., Campo, J. V., & Lucas, A. N. (2008). Brief behavioral therapy for pediatric anxiety and depression: Piloting an integrated treatment approach. *Cognitive and Behavioral Practice, 15*, 126–139.

Weins, T. (2006). Attention-Deficit/Hyperactivity Disorder and Substance Use Disorders in adolescents. *Psychiatric Times*. [Editorial]. Retrieved from http://www.psychiatrictimes.com/articles/attention-deficithyperactivity-disorder-and-substance-use-disorders-adolescents#sthash.h90pEpt9.dpuf

Weiss, E. L., Longhurst, J. G., & Mazure, C. M. (1999). Childhood sexual abuse as a risk factor for depression in women: Psychosocial and neurobiological correlates. *American Journal of Psychiatry, 156*, 816–828.

Weissmann, M. M. (2006). A brief history of interpersonal psychotherapy. *Psychiatric Annals, 36*(8), 553–557.

Weissman, M. M., Klerman, G. L., & Paykel, E. S. (1971). Clinical evaluation of hostility in depression. *American Journal of Psychiatry, 128*(3), 261–266.

Weisstaub, N. V., Zhou, M., Lira, A., Lambe, E., Gonzalez-Maeso, J., Hornung, J. P., . . . Gingrich, J. A. (2006). Cortical 5-HT2A receptor signaling modulates anxiety-like behaviors in mice. *Science, 313*, 536–540.

Weisz, J. R. (2004). *Psychotherapy for children and adolescents: Evidence-based treatments and case examples*. New York: Cambridge University Press.

Weller, E. B., & Weller, R. A. (2000). Trauma and the development of eating disorders. Medscape. Retrieved from http://www.medscape.org/viewarticle/420318

Wermter, A.K., Kamp-Becker, I., Hesse, P., Schulte-Körne, G., Strauch, K., & Remschmidt, H. (2010). Evidence for the involvement of genetic variation in the oxytocin receptor gene (OXTR) in the etiology of autistic disorders on high-functioning level. *American Journal of Medical Genetics, Part B: Neuropsychiatric Genetics, 153B*, 629–639.

Werry Centre. (2008). The NGO child and youth mental health and addictions workforce: A current perspective. Auckland, New Zealand: The Werry Centre for Child and Adolescent Mental Health Workforce Development. Retrieved from http://www.werrycentre.org.nz/sites/default/files/NGO_Report_-_Executive_Summary_ONLY.pdf

West, S. G., Sandler, I., Pillow, D. R., Baca, L., & Gersten, J. C. (1991). The use of structural equation modeling in generative research: Toward the design of a preventative intervention for bereaved children. *American Journal of Community Psychology, 19*, 459–480.

Westra, H. A., & Stewart, S. H. (2002). As-needed use of benzodiazepines in managing clinical anxiety: Incidence and implications. *Current Pharmaceutical Design, 8*, 59–74.

Wethington, H. R., Hahn, R. A., Fuqua-Whitley, D. S., Sipe, T. A., Crosby, A. E., Johnson, R. L., . . . Task Force on Community Preventive Services. (2008). The effectiveness of interventions to reduce psychological harm from traumatic events among children and adolescents: A systematic review. *American Journal of Preventative Medicine, 35*(3), 287–313.

What is resilience? (n.d.). Resilience Research Centre. Copyright © by Resilience Research Centre. Used by permission of Resilience Research Centre. Retrieved from http://www.resilienceproject.org/about-the-rrc/resilience/14-what-is-resilience

Whiffen, V. E., & Clark, S. E. (1997). Does victimization account for sex differences in depressive symptoms? *British Journal of Clinical Psychology, 36*, 185–193.

White, H. R., Bates, M. E., & Johnson, V. (1990). Social reinforcement and alcohol consumption. In W. M. Cox (Ed.), *Why people drink: Parameters of alcohol as a reinforcer*. New York: Gardner Press.

White, J. (2014). Practice guidelines for working with children and youth at risk for suicide in community mental health settings. Published by the Ministry of Children and Family Development (MCFD), Province of British Columbia, © 2014.

White, W. L., Dennis, M. L., & Godley, M. D. (2002). Adolescent substance abuse disorders: From acute treatment to recovery management. *Reclaiming Children and Youth, 11*(3), 172–175.

Wicks-Nelson, R., & Israel, A. C. (2006). *Behavior disorders of childhood* (6th ed.). Englewood Cliffs, NJ: Prentice-Hall.

Wilens, T. (2006). Attention-Deficit/Hyperactivity Disorder and Substance Use Disorders in adolescents. *Psychiatric Times*. Retrieved from http://www.psychiatrictimes.com/articles/attention-

Fluoxetine, 286
Freud, Sigmund
   structural model, 29–30
   theory of human personality, 30
   topographic model, 28–29
FRIENDS program, 266
Fruth, Uta, 128
Functional impairment, 261

G

GABA (gamma-aminobutyric acid), 28*b*, 244, 253
GAD. *See* Generalized Anxiety Disorder (GAD)
Gambling Disorder, 388
Garfat, Thom, 51
Gender Dysphoria, diagnostic criteria for, 10–11, 11*b*
Generalization process, 245
Generalized Amnesia, 71
Generalized Anxiety Disorder (GAD), 230–231, 250, 259–260
Genes, 27, 27*f*
Genetics, 27
   and ADHD, 161
   and anxiety disorders, 242–243
   and disruptive behaviour disorders, 197–198
   and feeding and eating disorders, 324
   and MDD, 285
   and neurodevelopmental disorders, 124–125
   and Schizophrenia, 359
   and substance-related disorders, 399
   and suicide, 430
   and trauma- and stressor-related disorders, 82–83
Genetic theory, 393
Gentle teaching, 142
Guetzloe, Eleanor
   on resiliency, 46–47

H

Hallucinations, 349, 374
   interpretation of, 362
Harm-reduction model, 393–394
Healy, William, 199
Heredity, 27
   and ADHD, 161
   and anxiety disorders, 242–243
   and disruptive behaviour disorders, 197–198
   and feeding and eating disorders, 324
   and MDD, 285
   and neurodevelopmental disorders, 124–125
   and Schizophrenia, 359
   and substance-related disorders, 399
   and suicide, 430
   and trauma- and stressor-related disorders, 82–83
Hippocrates, and abnormal behaviour, 24

Historical trauma. *See* Intergenerational/historical trauma
Hoarding Disorder, 232, 261
Holding therapy, 142
Hold On to Your Kids (Maté), 237
Holistic model, 40
Homosexuality, 11
Hormones, 84, 244
Horney, Karen
   on infant–parent relationships, 30–31
Hyperactivity, 149, 150, 152*b*
Hyper-arousal and dissociative continuum, 102
Hypomanic Episode, 279

I

Id, as mind component, 29
Impairment, as indicator of abnormality, 6
Impulsivity, 149, 150, 152*b*
Inattention, 149, 150, 151–152*b*
Indirect self-harm, 330
The Individual Delinquent (Healy), 199
Individual psychodynamic psychotherapy
   for ADHD, 176
   for anxiety disorders, 265
   for disruptive behaviour disorders, 216
   for feeding and eating disorders, 340–341
   for mood disturbances, 304–305
   for neurodevelopmental disorders, 137–139
   for psychotic disorders, 378–379
   for substance-related disorders, 415–417
   for trauma- and stressor-related disorders, 103–104
Infant–parent relationships, 30–31
Insecure attachment relationships, 248
Integrative approach, 41
Intellectual Disability (ID)/Intellectual Developmental Disorder, 115–116
   CYC approach to, 119–121
Intense world theory, 127
Interactionist pathway model, 203
Intergenerational/historical trauma, 89
Intermittent Explosive Disorder, 186, 188
Internal locus of control, 235
Internal working model, 38, 206
Interpersonal therapy (IPT), 296, 300
Interpersonal therapy for adolescents (IPTA), 305
Interpretation bias, 247
Interventions, 49–60, 95
   ADHD
      alternative healing, 178–179
      behavioural and cognitive-behavioural techniques for CYCPs, 174
      family support interventions, 176–177
      medications, 174–176
      prevention programs, 177–178
      psychoeducation and individual counselling, 176
      relational CYC practice, 179

anxiety disorders
   alternative healing, 267
   behavioural and cognitive-behavioural techniques for CYCPs, 263–264
   CYC, techniques for, 266*b*
   family support, 266
   medications, 265
   prevention programs, 266–267
   psychoeducation and individual counselling, 265
   relational CYC practice, 267–268
   defined, 51
disruptive behaviour disorders
   alternative healing, 219–220
   behavioural and cognitive-behavioural techniques for CYCPs, 215–216
   CYC, techniques for, 218*b*
   family support, 216–218
   medications, 216
   prevention programs, 218–219
   psychoeducation and individual counselling, 216
   relational CYC practice, 220
feeding and eating disorders, 339–340
   alternative healing/medicine, 343
   behavioural and cognitive-behavioural techniques for CYCPs, 340
   CYC, techniques for, 342
   family support interventions, 341
   medications, 340
   prevention programs, 341–343
   psychoeducation and individual counselling, 340–341
   relational CYC practice, 343
mood disturbances
   alternative healing, 307
   behavioural and cognitive-behavioural techniques for CYCPs, 302–304
   CYC, techniques for, 306*b*
   family support interventions, 305–306
   medications, 304
   prevention programs, 306–308
   psychoeducation and individual counselling, 304–305
   relational CYC practice, 307–308
neurodevelopmental disorders
   alternative healing, 142
   behavioural and cognitive-behavioural techniques for CYCPs, 135–137
   family support, 139–140
   medications, 137
   prevention programs, 141–142
   psychoeducation and individual counselling, 137–139
   relational CYC practice, 142–143
psychotic disorders, 376–377
   alternative healing, 380
   behavioural and cognitive-behavioural techniques for CYCPs, 377

S